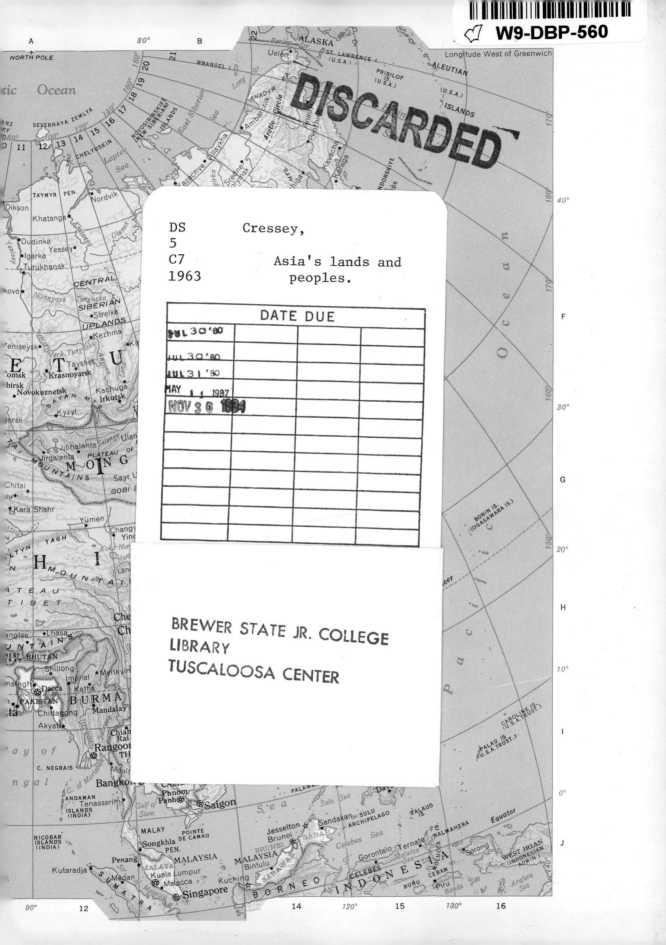

OTHER BOOKS ON ASIA *by George B. Cressey*

China's Geographic Foundations, New York: McGraw-Hill (1934).
    Also published in French: Paris (1939), Chinese: Chengtu (1945) and Shanghai (1947), and Japanese: Tokyo (1940)

Asia's Lands and Peoples, New York: McGraw-Hill (1944 and 1951).
    Also published in Spanish: Buenos Aires (1946), Chinese: Shanghai (1946), and Japanese: Tokyo

The Basis of Soviet Strength, New York: McGraw-Hill (1945).
    Also published in Dutch: Utrecht (1949)

How Strong Is Russia? Syracuse, N.Y.: Syracuse University Press (1954)

Land of the 500 Million: A Geography of China, New York: McGraw-Hill (1955)

Crossroads: Land and Life in Southwest Asia, Philadelphia: Lippincott (1960)

Soviet Potentials: A Geographic Appraisal, Syracuse, N.Y.: Syracuse University Press (1962)

THIRD EDITION

McGRAW-HILL BOOK COMPANY, INC.
New York, Toronto, London

ASIA'S LANDS AND PEOPLES

A Geography of One-third of the Earth and Two-thirds of Its People

George B. Cressey

Maxwell Professor of Geography
Syracuse University

ASIA'S LANDS AND PEOPLES

Title page photograph: Eliya Lake, Nuwara Eliya, Ceylon.
(*Courtesy Trans World Airlines, Inc.*)

PREFACE

ONE-THIRD OF THE EARTH AND TWO-THIRDS OF ITS PEOPLE

Two billion people live in Asia. This book is a study of where they live and how, and of the man-land relations which characterize the largest and most diverse of all continents. These pages contain thousands of detailed facts concerning climate, minerals, food, and livelihood; through them run five main ideas which form the theme of this study.

First and foremost is the concept that people are the most important factor in geography. It is people who give character to the landscape, rather than mountains, rivers, or deserts. In most of Asia people live close to one another and to the earth and have developed a mature way of life. While some sections of the continent appear overcrowded and poor, conditions may improve in the future, for it is evident that man has nowhere applied his skill to the utmost. Human ingenuity remains Asia's greatest unmeasured resource.

Second, the continent is so large and varied that it must be understood in terms of its major realms and individual geographic regions. What is true in one part of a country may not apply elsewhere. Great areas are too mountainous, or too cold, or too dry, or too infertile to be very attractive as a home for man. This book makes an effort to describe specific areas as a basis for an understanding of the whole. Generalizations can be valid only when based on an adequate comprehension of detail.

In the third place, the good things of the earth are unevenly distributed. Some areas are bountifully supplied with good soil, favorable climate, and useful minerals; others appear to be lacking in assets which man can use. This book attempts to weigh potentials for development and to evaluate restrictions on land use. Nature does not determine success or failure, but she does reward those who act wisely and penalizes those who fail to understand their environment. Geography is interested in all the spatial items which give personality to the face of the earth; this volume is an inventory of "how much of what is where."

Fourth, the nations of Asia are in the midst of dramatic change, but these developments should be evaluated in terms of geographic potentials. The Soviet Union transformed its economic life in the period between the First and Second World Wars, and China hopes to duplicate this development during the second half of the century. Japan's progress has been spectacular, the more so since her natural resources are modest. India and Pakistan face complex problems of nationhood and livelihood but are finding solutions. The Southeast Asian realm has great assets, but independence has brought growing pains. Southwest Asia suddenly finds new wealth in her petroleum.

Finally, Asia's hemispheric location and the sheer bulk of her numbers assure her of a growing place in world affairs, but it does not appear likely that her geographic assets will enable her to match North America or Europe

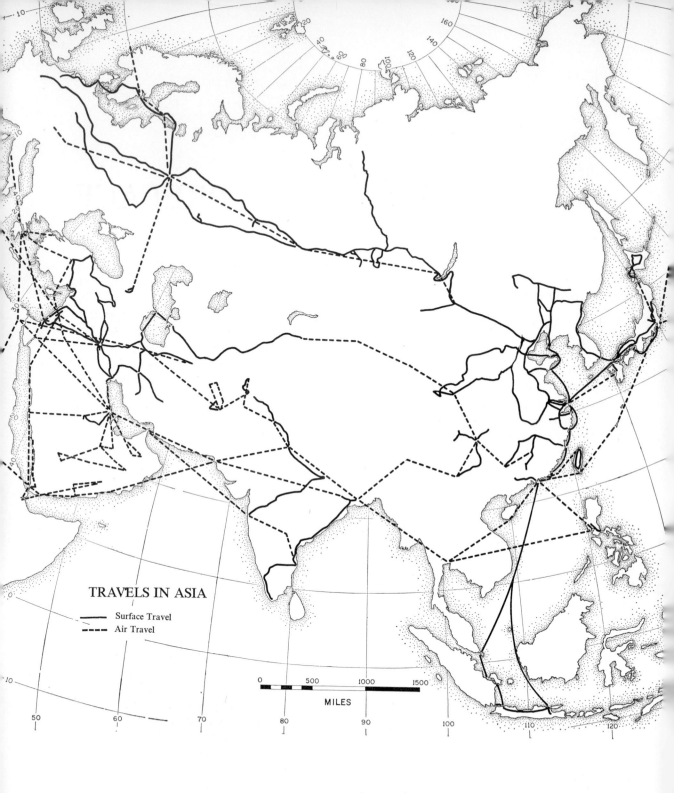

TRAVELS IN ASIA

———— Surface Travel
------ Air Travel

0   500   1000   1500

MILES

viii   PREFACE

in per capita welfare. In terms of present-day geostrategy, the limitations of her isolating mountains, insufficient arable land, scattered mineral assets, and inadequate food supply appear impressive. Anything like continental coherence seems to lie well in the future.

Asia's Lands and Peoples first appeared in 1944. The third edition has been completely reorganized and largely rewritten. The opening paragraph of the first edition still holds true: "This volume is a preface to world citizenship. These chapters may not be required reading for everyone, but it seems essential that many people understand many of the ideas presented here. It is not necessary to compare the relative importance of Asia with other continents, but it is obvious that one-third of the earth and two-thirds of its people command attention."

ACKNOWLEDGMENTS

Hundreds of people have helped to write this book. The words are those of the author, but the ideas have come from countless sources. I am indebted to scores of scholars for their writings, to students and colleagues who have sharpened my ideas, to the many agencies who have supplied photographs, to those who have provided guidance and hospitality in far places during a lifetime of study, and to my most honest critic, Marion C. Cressey.

I am under special obligation to Syracuse University for financial and academic assistance spread over three decades, and to institutions overseas who have aided my field studies. The sketches at the opening of each chapter are the work of Theodore M. Oberlander, who has also worked on many of the maps. Cartographic assistance has also been provided by numerous graduate students at Syracuse, including Edward W. Soja. The manuscript was typed by Mrs. William Bassett.

If the accompanying map of travel and residence seems impressive, one has only to note the many gaps and areas of superficial understanding. To the writer it serves as a reminder of his inadequacies. Readers are at least entitled to know where an author has been. These travels represent nine visits to Asia, a decade of residence, and nearly a half million miles of travel.

GEORGE B. CRESSEY

CONTENTS

MAPS

TABLES

CLIMATIC GRAPHS

THE CONTINENT OF ASIA

No continent has more people than Asia, or higher mountains and wider plains, or more cultural diversity and dramatic change. These are the themes of this volume. This is a study of man-land relations and of the potentials for progress. Asia covers one-third of all the land on earth, and here live two-thirds of all mankind.

"Asia hath a Temperate aire very healthfull, sweete and pleasant. Yet shee enjoyeth not this temperature alike in all parts; for the right and the left climes are . . . malignant and intolerable, in regard of the extremity of heate and cold, which they are subject unto. The delicacies of this Countrie are so great, that they are become a Proverbe. The Soile is so noble for her fertility, diversitie of Fruicts, abundance of Pastures and the multitude of commodities, which are carryed out of her, that she excelleth casely all other Countries. Heere groweth abundance of Fruicts, Spices, Mettalls, Pearles and precious Stones. . . . Wee must note also the ingenious spirits, riches and power of her people." (*Gerardi Mercatoris: Atlas, Amsterdam, 1638, 401*)

Street scene in Tokyo. (*Courtesy American President Lines*)

1 Two Billion People

Population Patterns / Two Square Miles / Ethnic Groups / Political Patterns / References on Asia as a Whole

POPULATION PATTERNS

Two out of every three people on earth live in Asia, and nearly five of every six babies are born here. This is clearly the most human of all continents. More people have lived in Asia than anywhere else, billions in all. Some areas are nearly empty, but where the earth is good, there men throng.

Asia is the home of the world's oldest cultures, and here have developed ideas which have influenced all the world. Southwest Asia has contributed three monotheistic religions; the people of India have found a rich philosophical base; the Chinese have a mature and empirical civilization; Japan amazes the world with its industry; and the Soviet Union challenges other nations with a new and dynamic society. The people of Asia have learned to live intimately with their environment and with one another. This is a continent where man bears the impress of nature and where countless generations have given the landscape a human stamp.

Asia is by far the largest of the continents, for it includes one-third of all the land on earth. Asia's great size at once suggests that there are marked differences from place to place; that what is true in one area is probably not true elsewhere. One of the first questions in geography is thus "Where?" Few generalizations can be valid unless related to specific regions.

Man and land are the essential elements in any geographic study, and only as the two are put together does the face of the earth take on an integrated personality. One function of geography is to present an analysis of the manifold interrelations which give meaning and personality to places. Unfortunately, Asia is very diverse.[1]

Asia has 2 billion people. Where do they live, and how can they be fed? Here are the most interesting of all geographic questions, more significant than the pattern of mountains or winds or minerals, although clearly related to these aspects of the physical environment.

If a geographer were limited to a single map, it should be one of population distribution. Such a map immediately states a fact and raises a question. Why are some parts of Asia densely crowded while others not far away remain nearly empty? How is it possible for thousands of people to support themselves in a few square miles along the Ganges while other areas in India sustain but dozens? The accompanying maps of rural and urban population are thus the most significant in the entire book. Asia has a few places where people are many, and many places where people are few.

Two large areas of concentrated population stand out clearly, both peripheral in their continental relations: One is China; the other is India. Parts of Japan and Indonesia are as crowded, and many countries also have areas of concentration. Among other congested areas are East Pakistan, Korea, and North Viet Nam. In every case irregularity is obvious. Even in Java, where the scale of the map suggests that

[1] The author once received a letter from a student in a six-week summer course in which an earlier edition of this book had been used. The letter read: "I am about to fail this course and I want you to know why. Asia is too big."

A Chinese girl from Penang adjusts her Malay friend's earrings. (*Courtesy Federation of Malaya*)

the whole island is thickly populated, actually, crowded fertile plains contrast sharply with empty mountainsides.

The statistical density of population for the land area of the world is about 60 per square mile. For Asia the figure rises to 100; China as a whole averages 200; eastern China approaches 1,000 people in a single square mile. Such averages have little practical meaning since they include unproductive mountains and wasteland. More significant figures relate people to cultivated areas, and on this basis many sections of southern and eastern Asia support over 2,000 people in each square mile of crop land. In the congested residential areas of Shanghai, Calcutta, and Tokyo the density exceeds 100,000 in each square mile. Where Asia is crowded, it is crowded indeed.

The sparsely settled parts of Asia are much more extensive than the congested areas. Large parts of the interior are too dry or too cold or too rugged to be attractive for settlement. Deserts and rough terrain occupy millions of square miles. While the Yangtze delta is so

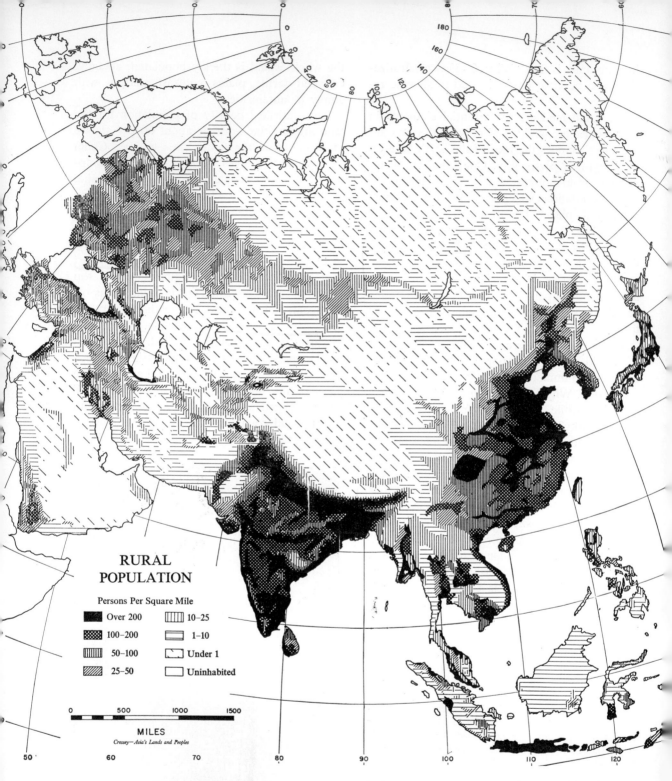

RURAL POPULATION

Persons Per Square Mile

■ Over 200	‖‖ 10–25
▨ 100–200	≡ 1–10
▥ 50–100	⬚ Under 1
⧄ 25–50	☐ Uninhabited

```
0        500       1000      1500
|---------|---------|---------|
              MILES
```
Cressey—Asia's Lands and Peoples

Two people out of every three on earth live in Asia. No map in this volume is so important as this, for it presents the most challenging of all geographic questions: "Where do people live, and why?"

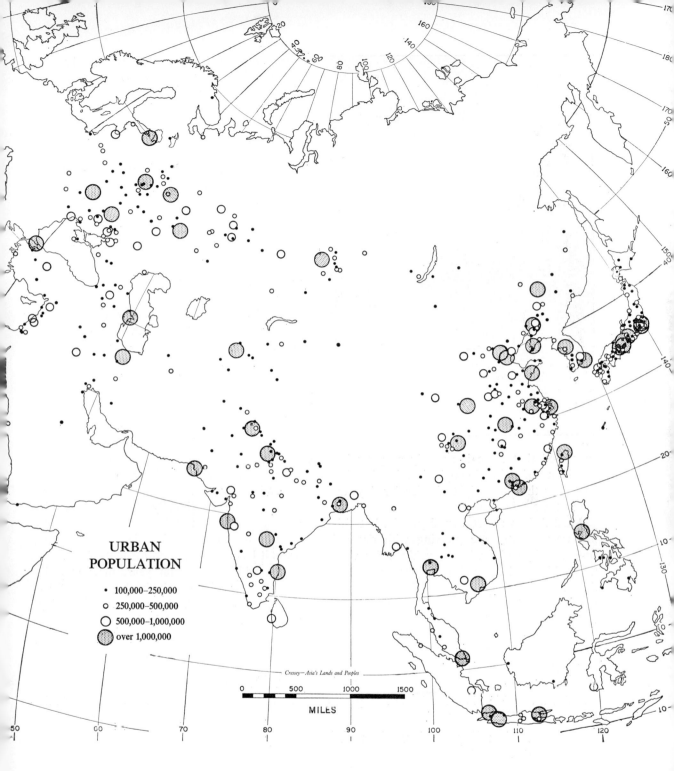

URBAN POPULATION

- • 100,000–250,000
- ○ 250,000–500,000
- ◯ 500,000–1,000,000
- ⬤ over 1,000,000

Cressey—Asia's Lands and Peoples

0   500   1000   1500

MILES

Asia is more urbanized than is sometimes realized; four dozen metropolitan cities count more than a million people, and scores of others are quite in tune with the world.

Here are two Chinese children on the streets of Shanghai. (*Palmer, courtesy American President Lines*)

congested that there is scarcely a spot where one is out of sight of people, interior Arabia is so empty that one might wander for days and see not a single nomad.

Most Asians are still rural people, but cities in every country are growing with dramatic speed. Tokyo vies with New York for world leadership, and three dozen cities count more than 1 million people. Most of these metropolitan centers have a central business district which is completely Westernized, and a few even have residential streets which might pass as European or American. A transect from their urban core into the surrounding countryside shows not merely a gradation in land use, but also a transition in time, for one may pass

from the twentieth century to the Middle Ages in 10 miles.

Are some parts of Asia overcrowded, and do others have room for a vast increase? No simple answer can be given, for the problem of overpopulation is not a numerical matter but one of technology and of standards of living. It may well be that some areas of sparse population are quite unable to support their present inhabitants adequately, while certain congested areas have unrealized potentials of soil and water which might provide an acceptable livelihood for twice their population if development capital were available.

Nature provides an array of conditions; it is man's ingenuity which develops them. The future of Asia is conditioned not so much by its physical geography as by its people. The solution also involves time; it does little good to raise productivity by 1 or 2 per cent a year if the population grows at the same rate.

In some countries the birth rate is high, even 35 and 40 per thousand. In several of these areas people continually suffer malnutrition and ill health, and endemic disease limits the span of life to only a few decades. In certain areas it has been common for half of all babies to die within their first year, their mortality helping to produce high death rates of 30 or more per thousand. As a result of the high mortality the effects of high fertility are canceled out, and until the middle of the century population growth was slow to moderate.

The explosive increase in current Asian population is associated with a sudden lowering of the death rate. Public health, safe drinking

Asian Population Growth [1]
(in millions)

[1] United Nations Department of Social Affairs: *Population Bulletin*, no. 1, December, 1951.

	1650	1750	1850	1950
Asia	257	437	656	1,272
World	470	694	1,094	2,406

This is a Kurd from northern Iraq. (*Jack Percival, courtesy Iraq Petroleum Company*)

water, and better sanitation have materially lengthened life expectancy. Interest in birth control has scarcely begun. Where the birth rate continues around 35 and the death rate drops from 30 to 20 or even 15, populations increase alarmingly. This is the situation in China.

Too many people in Asia are poor, and the rest of the world cannot live in peace—or in good conscience—if the gap between them does not narrow. In some countries, notably in India, there are also great contrasts between the very poor and the very rich. On the basis of United Nations data, at least a dozen countries have per capita incomes under $150 per year, including most of the nations along the rim of the continent from Saudi Arabia to Korea.

It is difficult to know whether or not the gap between Asia and the West is narrowing. Many parts of Asia are making spectacular progress, at least in overall material productivity. While the gross national product grows, national prosperity is not always translated into individual welfare. It would be revealing to plot changes in prosperity year by year on a detailed map of Asia; economic generalizations need to be seen regionally. Unfortunately no such map is available.

TWO SQUARE MILES

Out of the 18 million square miles in Asia, the selection of only two as samples seems scarcely appropriate; and since the continent has 2 billion people, any generalization about population problems from such small areas is impossible. It may nevertheless be helpful to begin our analysis with two separate square miles in order to emphasize that the people of Asia are individuals and that they live in specific environments.

Per Capita Income in Asia [1]

[1] United Nations data for Gross National Product, converted to United States dollars at official rates, divided by population; subject to uncertainties.

Country	Per capita income	Country	Per capita income
Burma	$ 51	Korea	$110
Ceylon	123	Lebanon	260
China-Taiwan	165	Malaya	233
India	63	Pakistan	50
Indonesia	49	Philippines	117
Iran	193	Syria	132
Iraq	120	Thailand	93
Israel	770	Turkey	161
Japan	300		

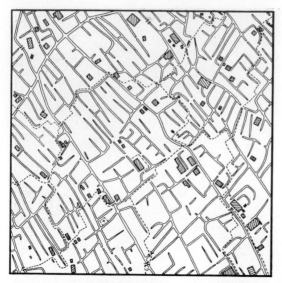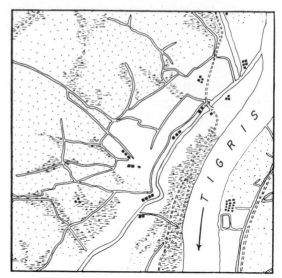

Each map covers 1 square mile, that to the left from the Yangtze delta south of Shang-hai, the other along the Tigris south of Baghdad. While the former supports 2,000 people, the latter numbers only a few hundred. Canals are shown in double lines; trails and roads are dashed; and farmsteads are in solid black or are shaded.

One of these square miles lies in the Yangtze delta near Shanghai; the other is along the Tigris south of Baghdad. The first supports 2,000 people; the second barely counts 100. Although both areas are alluvial and both have been inhabited for centuries, they are very different. Whereas the former receives 45 inches of rain, the latter has only 5; both have an agricultural regime which calls for irrigation. Both have been studied by the author.

Twenty miles south of Shanghai lies the Fenghsien area,[2] with a micropattern of tiny fields and canals. The area lies close to sea level, so that the canals are kept filled by water from the Yangtze. The district is entirely agricultural, and its inhabitants derive all their income from farming. Canals, ponds, house clusters, and grave mounds occupy almost one-third of the 640 acres. Since there are no wheeled vehicles, flagstone trails take the place of roads; canal boats carry the necessary goods. Very little material change has taken place for centuries.

[2] George B. Cressey: "The Fenghsien Landscape," *Geog. Rév.*, XXVI (1936), 396–413.

A house-to-house census in one square mile totaled more than 2,000 people; from the number of children in evidence, we may judge that the population is clearly on the increase. This is a relatively prosperous area; the houses are well built, and the people are adequately nourished. Famine is rare, for plentiful irrigation water assures crops even in dry years. Fields are green the year around.

The Fenghsien landscape has a very human aspect; one can never escape human beings. All trace of the original delta surface has been modified by canals and field patterns. From early till late, men, women, and children are busy in the fields; otherwise they could not eat. Fortunately, two successive crops may be raised each year—rice or cotton in summer and wheat or broad beans in winter. The many water bodies provide fish to supplement the diet.

The surrounding Yangtze delta is a relatively homogeneous area, and each square mile has about the same pattern of irrigated agriculture and dispersed population. Farm clusters are evenly spread, and market villages are spaced about 10 miles apart, although only a few times

Asia has many faces. This is an Arabian emir at Yabrin. (*Courtesy Arabian American Oil Company*)

a year do most farmers visit these commercial or temple centers. People have few wants and little cash with which to buy them. A population-dot map for 10 or 100 square miles would show little distinctive pattern or irregularity.

In contrast, settlement in central Iraq is highly localized, since cultivation in this arid land is limited to ribbons of irrigation supplied by canals from the Tigris. Kut lies 100 miles downstream from Baghdad, and the square mile to be considered lies nearby on the west bank of the river.

Like Fenghsien, Kut lies in a region of waterways, but unlike those in the Chinese area, the canals carry water only when the Tigris is in flood. Since summers are rainless, the landscape alternates between brown and green. Whereas Fenghsien is imperceptibly flat and barely above sea level, the area around Kut has a slight gradient away from the natural levees along the Tigris. Both areas are pro-

tected by dikes; otherwise high tides in China or seasonal floods in Iraq would cause widespread inundation. Since the Kut area slopes away from the river, surplus water cannot drain off; as a result there are many saline basins, especially along the lower ends of the canals. Two-thirds of this square mile near Kut in Iraq is unirrigated desert, and empty. Donkeys carry farm produce and people, for roads are poor and wheeled vehicles uncommon. Camels are found beyond the cultivated fields. Canals are too shallow and their volume too variable for boats.

The Kut area produces dates, vegetables, and some barley. Near the Tigris, palm trees occupy a belt a few hundred yards wide. The few houses are built close to the river and the main canal; in part so that they may be accessible, in part that they may occupy the natural levees and thus be relatively safe from floods. Only a half dozen house clusters appear in this Iraq area, in contrast to the dozens of

This West Pakistan village elder lives between Rawalpindi and Lahore. (*William Simmons, courtesy Ford Foundation*)

ETHNIC GROUPS AND
LANGUAGE FAMILIES

The largest of the continents is also ethnically the most diverse. Even with much simplification, 68 nationalities are recognized in the *Great Soviet World Atlas*. The major linguistic families, as named, are based on Kroeber.

farm units in the Chinese square mile. Although the Kut area has only one-twentieth of the population of the Fenghsien area, people appear poorer.

Many of the soils in Iraq have become salinized through careless irrigation and inadequate drainage. Centuries of cultivation have altered the natural character of the soils in both countries, but painstaking fertilization has maintained Chinese productivity. With care, each area might support more people.

Both in China and in Iraq the pressing problem is more food, and adequate food in turn depends on better management of soil and water. Intensive cultivation is increasing the food supply, but it grows no faster than the number of mouths which need to be fed. Here is the problem everywhere in Asia: Can the food supply increase faster than the population?

ETHNIC GROUPS

People present the most interesting aspect of geography and usually the most complex.

Where do they live and who are they? Hundreds of ethnic types are present in Asia, many of them so mixed that classification becomes difficult. Nowhere is there a pure "race." The accompanying map lists 68 ethnic groups, based on nationalities, as defined in the *Great Soviet World Atlas,* but this number represents a great simplification. Many areas have two or three or even a dozen different peoples living side by side, so that maps indicate only the dominant racial group.

Mongoloid people of various types occupy most of eastern Asia—notably the Chinese, Mongols, Tibetans, and Koreans. Much of northern Siberia has Tungus or early Mongol types. Yellow skin and straight hair characterize Mongoloid people. This is the most numerous block in the world, comprising about a billion people. The Japanese are a Mongol-Malay mixture.

Slavic types predominate in the Soviet Union; they are represented by the Great Russians, Little Russians or Ukrainians, and the White or Byelorussians. Slavs occupy most of the western U.S.S.R. and extend eastward in a

KEY TO MAP ON FACING PAGE

1. Ainu	24. Ceylonese	47. Georgian, Azerbaijani, Avar
2. Japanese	25. Maratha	48. Other Trans-Caucasians (Ossetian,
3. Korean	26. Hindustani	Abkhasian, Kumiki, etc.)
4. Chinese	27. Rajput	49. Ukrainian
5. Mongol	28. Gujarat	50. Great Russian
6. Tibetan	29. Sindhi	51. Moldavian, Magyar
7. Uuigur	30. Punjabi	52. Pole
8. Dungan	31. Kashmirian	53. White Russian
9. Nosu	32. Beluchi	54. Lithuanian, Latvian, Esthonian
10. Thai	33. Afghan	55. Volga-German
11. Mon	34. Tajik	56. Mordovian, Udmurt, Chuvash, Bashkir
12. Annamite	35. Kirghiz	57. Finn, Karelian, Saami (Lapp)
13. Cambodian	36. Kalmyk	58. Komi (Ziryan), Nansi (Vogul)
14. Malayan, Javanese	37. Uzbek	59. Nenetse (Gold), Dolgan
15. Dyak	38. Kazakh	60. Khante (Ostiyak), Kyeti, Syelkupe
16. Aeta	39. Karakalpak	61. Oriot, Khakasian, Buriat-Mongol
17. Burmese	40. Turkmen	62. Evenki
18. Bengalese, Aosami	41. Persian	63. Eveni (Lamut)
19. Nepalese	42. Arab	64. Yakut
20. Bihar	43. Qashqai, Luri	65. Odul (Yukagir), Luoravetlan (Chukchi)
21. Mundan	44. Kurd	66. Nimilan (Koryak)
22. Uriya	45. Turk	67. Hebrew
23. Dravidian	46. Armenian, Persian-Turk	68. Nonai (Goldi), Ude, Nivkhi (Gilyak)

Kuhgalu tribesmen inhabit the Zagros Mountains of western Iran. (*Raymond Wilson, courtesy Iranian Oil Participants*)

Asia has at least ten language families, as defined by Kroeber in his *Anthropology*. These are the Ural-Altaic family, present across northern and central Asia: the Indo-European group, which occurs in the central Soviet Union and India; the Sinitic, centered in China; the Semitic, in Southwest Asia; the Malayo-Polynesian languages in the islands of Southeast Asia; the Dravidian in southern India; the relics of Mon Khmer and Annamese in Cambodia and Viet Nam; Korean; and Japanese.

POLITICAL PATTERNS

Asia has witnessed many great empires, for tides of conquest have repeatedly spread far beyond the original homelands. Chinese, Mongols, Moguls, Persians, Turks, and Arabs have

wedge which continues across Asia to the Pacific, roughly along the line of the Trans-Siberian Railway.

Aryan people occupy a belt which reaches from the Caucasus across Iran to central India, with over a dozen representatives. The total population numbers almost a half billion. Although most of these people are Caucasians, by no means do all have fair skins.

Turkic types are present from Turkey to western China, more of them living in central Asia than in Turkey.

Malay peoples, sometimes known as the brown race, are found in Indonesia and the Philippines and in spots along the adjacent mainland. Among the other large ethnic groups are the Semites, both Arabs and Jews, centered in Southwest Asia, and the Dravidians of South India.

In addition to its diversity of nationalities,

This is a Japanese woman gardener near Tokyo. (*Courtesy British Overseas Airways Corporation*)

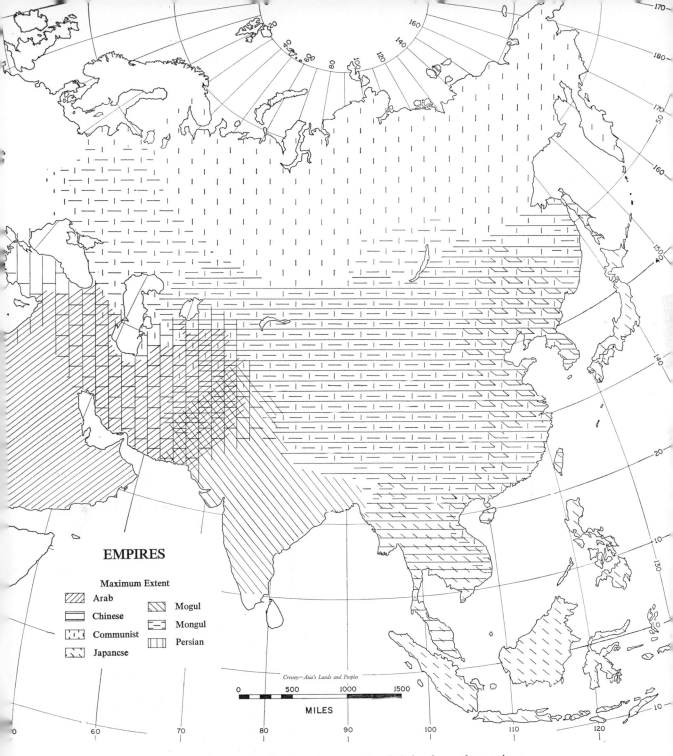

EMPIRES

Maximum Extent

Arab	Mogul
Chinese	Mongul
Communist	Persian
Japanese	

Cressey—Asia's Lands and Peoples

```
0      500     1000     1500
```

MILES

The people of many empires have spread across large parts of Asia, from the ancient Persians to the present-day Communists, but none have ever ruled the entire continent. Barrier of topography and climate divide Asia into fractions, so that pan-Asian unity appears unlikely.

all built empires. So, too, has twentieth-century Communism. Outside powers such as the British, Dutch, and Japanese have tried to conquer at least the marginal areas of Asia. While the United States never held a foreign concession in China or elsewhere, it has had military bases and alliances from the Persian Gulf to the Pacific.

Asia is apparently too large and complex for any single empire, and no imperial power has been able to command even its own outer domain for more than a few centuries. No one has ever been able to unite more than half of the continent.

At the beginning of the twentieth century Asia had but ten sovereign political units; by midcentury the number had doubled. What once were colonies had become independent nations; only traces of European power remained, as at British Hong Kong and Aden, or

✳ *Asian Countries* [1]

Country and cities	Square miles	Population
Aden Colony	125	200,600
* Aden		80,000
Aden Protectorates	112,000	750,000
Afghanistan	ca. 250,000	13,799,037
* Kabul		310,000
Bahrein	231	143,135
* Manama		61,837
Bhutan	19,305	670,000
Brunei	2,226	83,877
* Brunei		10,619
Burma	261,789	20,662,000
* Rangoon		737,079
Cambodia	66,606	4,952,000
* Pnompenh		355,180
Ceylon	25,332	9,651,000
* Colombo		426,127
China (Communist)	3,691,502	582,602,417
Shanghai		6,204,417
* Peking		2,768,149
Tientsin		2,693,831
Mukden		2,299,900
Chungking		1,772,500
Canton		1,598,900
Wuhan		1,427,300
Nanking		1,091,600
Harbin		1,163,000
China (Nationalist)	13,952	10,947,000
* Taipei		854,061
Gaza Strip	125	337,000
Hong Kong	398	3,128,044
* Victoria		1,004,917
India	1,261,602	437,073,429
Bombay		4,146,491
Calcutta		2,926,498
Madras		1,725,216
Hyderabad		1,252,337
Ahmedebad		1,149,852
* Delhi		914,790

* Capital cities.
[1] *Britannica Book of the Year* (1962).

Portuguese Macao, or American Okinawa. New names and new boundaries have changed the map. More than two dozen Asian states cast votes in the United Nations.

Four nations in Asia rank as world powers: the Soviet Union, China, India, and Japan. Each has had its satellite states, though Japan now stands alone. Other countries, such as Pakistan and Indonesia, carry weight because of their size and numbers. At the other ex-

treme, some nations are weak and scarcely viable, as Laos, Bhutan, or Jordan. Asia has a number of independent nations, each of which contains a population of less than a million; only sixteen states count as many as 10 million people. Some countries are wealthy, for example, those around the Persian Gulf with their fabulous oil royalties; others are too poor to support proper governmental machinery. Most of Asia is relatively undeveloped, and large

Country and cities	Square miles	Population
Indonesia	575,893	92,600,000
* Jakarta		2,081,200
Surabaya		1,135,300
Iran	636,293	20,678,000
* Tehran		1,512,082
Iraq	171,599	7,085,000
* Baghdad (Metro-politan)		1,306,604
Israel	7,993	2,173,923
* Jerusalem		166,301
Japan	142,727	93,418,027
* Tokyo		8,310,027
Osaka		3,011,563
Nagoya		1,591,935
Yokohama		1,375,710
Kyoto		1,284,818
Kobe		1,113,977
Jordan	37,297	1,724,868
* Amman		133,201
Korea, North	47,862	8,252,000
* Pyongyang		500,000
Korea, South	38,031	24,994,117
* Seoul		2,444,883
Kuwait	6,000	206,473
* Kuwait		104,551
Laos	91,428	2,277,300
* Vientiane		10,500
Lebanon	4,015	1,783,000
* Beirut		400,000
Malaya	50,700	6,909,000
* Kuala Lumpur		316,230
Masqat	82,000	560,000
* Masqat		5,500
Mongolia	591,119	1,075,000
* Ulan Bator		170,000
Nepal	54,362	9,180,000
* Katmandu		105,247
Neutral Zone (Iraq–Saudi Arabia)	ca. 1,100	

Country and cities	Square miles	Population
Neutral Zone (Kuwait–Saudi Arabia)	ca. 1,100	
North Borneo	29,388	454,328
* Jesselton		50,000
Pakistan	364,373	93,812,000
Karachi		1,916,000
Lahore		1,297,000
* Rawalpindi		343,000
Philippines	115,707	27,455,799
* Manila		1,145,723
Qatar	8,500	45,000
* Doha		30,000
Sarawak	48,250	744,391
* Kuching		50,000
Saudi Arabia	872,722	6,036,000
* Riyadh		150,000
Sikkim	2,744	161,080
* Gangtok		7,000
Singapore	225	1,687,300
* Singapore		953,500
Soviet Union	8,649,489	208,826,500
* Moscow		5,045,905
Leningrad		2,899,955
Kiev		1,104,334
Syria	71,227	4,821,929
* Damascus		232,960
Thailand	198,455	25,519,965
* Bangkok		1,597,000
Trucial States	32,278	83,000
Turkey	301,380	27,809,331
Istanbul		1,459,528
* Ankara		646,151
Viet Nam, North	60,156	15,916,955
* Hanoi		643,576
Viet Nam, South	65,958	14,052,209
* Saigon		1,400,000
Yemen	75,290	5,000,000
* Sanaa		60,000
Total by countries	19,140,854	1,875,380,896

Burma is the home of this college student. (*Horace Bristol, courtesy International Co-operation Administration*)

Almost every Asian nation has a seaport and is thus in touch with ocean trade; only Mongolia, Afghanistan, Laos, Nepal, Bhutan, and Sikkim are completely landlocked. Others, like Jordan and Iraq, barely have a window on the sea. Countries like Lebanon, Ceylon, Malaya, and the Philippines are sea-minded, as are the island areas of Hong Kong, Bahrein, and Singapore. At the other extreme are the land-oriented powers, such as the Soviet Union, China, and India. Probably no more than 2 or 3 per cent of the people in these continental-minded nations have ever seen salt water or a maritime vessel.

From the standpoint of physical geography, the prospects of Asian unity or confederation appear poor. As we shall point out later in this volume, Asia as a whole is a fractionalized continent. Towering mountains and broad deserts isolate an inhospitable core, and divide the margins of the great land mass into isolated pockets. Little cultural contact other than Buddhism has taken place between India and China, and extensive overland trade is unlikely. Few commercial ties have ever linked India with the Soviet Union. In place of having a centripetal focus in the interior as does North America, Asia may be described as centrifugal —oriented outward, with more contact by sea than by land.

While Asia has played a minor role in twentieth-century affairs, the sheer bulk of its prospective population will make its voice heard increasingly during the twenty-first century. Whether rich or poor, a continent which is doubling its population in three or four decades carries political weight in the international scene.

areas appear to lack significant resource potentials. The political result is unbalanced and presumably unstable.

Boundary problems and contested areas are found from the Mediterranean to the Pacific. Fully half of the frontier mileage has shifted during the twentieth century, and not all the present boundaries are finally accepted on both sides of the line. Thus Syria wishes the return of Iskenderun from Turkey. Yemen claims part of the Aden Protectorate. Iran proclaims her rights to Kuwait and Bahrein. Israel and her Arab neighbors have long been in disagreement. Afghanistan has designs on West Pakistan. China and India disagree about the south slopes of the Himalaya, and China claims all islands in the South China Sea south to 4°N. Japan hopes for the return of her old outer islands, both to the north and south. The Philippines claim an interest in North Borneo.

References on Asia

The following references and those for the several countries were compiled largely from the annual *Bibliographie Géographique Internationale* and monthly *Current Geographic Publications*. Only the more recent and accessible items are listed. Extensive bibliographies may also be found in earlier editions of *Asia's Lands and Peoples*. The *Journal of Asian Studies* publishes a comprehensive annual bibliography.

In addition to the standard texts and references listed below, several series are of special value: the volumes on economic development of the International Bank (Washington), the encyclopedic studies on social conditions of the Human Relations Area Files (New Haven), and the superlative Geographical Handbook Series of the British Admiralty (Southampton). Many excellent descriptive articles are available in the *National Geographic Magazine*.

The outstanding French volumes are those in the series entitled *Géographie universelle*, Paris: Librairie Armand Colin (1928–1932), with the following volumes devoted to parts of Asia: *Asie occidentale*, by Raoul Blanchard; *Haute Asie*, by Fernand Grenard; *Asie des moussons*, by Jules Sion, Part 1, "Généralités—Chine—Japon"; Part 2, "Inde—Indochine—Insulinde"; and *Etats de la Baltique, Russie* by P. Camena D'Almeida. The chief German series is in the *Klute Handbuch der geographischen Wissenschaft*, Potsdam Akademische Verlagsgesellschaft Athenaion (1931–1938), with two volumes entitled *Nordasien, Zentral-und Ostasien* by Konrad Bouterwek and others, and *Vorderund Sudasien* by Ulrich Frey and others.

The United Nations Economic Commission for Asia and the Far East (Bangkok) publishes a variety of bulletins.

References of special value are indicated by an asterisk (*).

Air Ministry, Meteorological Office: *Tables of Temperature, Relative Humidity and Precipitation for the World,* Part 5, "Asia," London: H.M. Stationery Office (1958).

Dobby, E. H. G.: *Monsoon Asia,* Chicago: Quadrangle Books (1961).

East, W. Gordon, and O. H. K. Spate (eds.): *The Changing Map of Asia,* 3d ed., London: Methuen (1958).

*Ginsburg, Norton (ed.): *The Pattern of Asia,* Englewood Cliffs, N.J.: Prentice-Hall (1958).

Gourou, Pierre: *L'Asie,* Paris: Hachette (1953).

Kendrew, W. G.: *The Climates of the Continents,* New York: Oxford (1937).

Lyde, Lionel W.: *The Continent of Asia,* London: Macmillan (1933).

Murphey, Rhoads: "New Capitals of Asia," *Econ. Development and Cultural Change,* V (1957), 216–243.

*Spencer, J. E.: *Asia, East by South: A Cultural Geography,* New York: Wiley (1954).

*Stamp, L. Dudley: *Asia: A Regional and Economic Geography,* 10th ed., London: Methuen (1959).

Thompson, Warren S.: *Population and Progress in the Far East,* Chicago: The University of Chicago Press (1959).

Trewartha, Glenn T.: "Climate as Related to the Jet Stream in the Orient," *Erdkunde,* XII (1958), 205–214.

2 Asian Landscapes

The Pattern of Eurasia / Surface Configuration / Climatic Conditions / Natural Vegetation / Mineral Resources

THE PATTERN OF EURASIA

What and where is Asia? Is the huge land mass of Eurasia one continent or two? The common practice is to slice the Union of Soviet Socialist Republics into two parts along an arbitrary line, different on many maps, and assign one part to Europe, the other to Asia.

This so-called continental boundary in the general vicinity of the Ural Mountains follows few significant divisions of topography, drainage, climate, soils, land use, culture, or history. As usually drawn it does not consistently follow either the crest of the Urals or any political subdivision. Even the crest of the Urals

supplies no more of a continental boundary than the Appalachians. Would anyone divide the United States into two continents?

But if it is difficult to divide the Soviet Union into separate continents, is that country to be classed as European or Asiatic? The old and largely untrue saying, "Scratch a Russian and find a Tartar," reflects certain Mongol relations, but the Russians quite properly resent any exclusion from European classification to which they are clearly related in nationality and culture. Soviet geographers recognize the arbitrary nature of any boundary, but it is their judgment that the limits of "Asia" should be placed at the eastern base of the Urals, leaving

18

all the mountains in "Europe," and at the northern base of the Caucasus, placing them in Asia.

The names Asia and Europe appear to have originated in the Aegean Sea, where the term sunrise, *Asu,* came to be applied to Turkey and Asia, and sunset, *Ereb,* to Greece and Europe. Thus arose the division into the Orient and the Occident. Europeans have looked eastward to Asia; hence the egocentric usage of Near East and Far East. These directional terms have no significance to the people of Asia itself, nor to Americans. Accordingly they are not used in this volume.

Nature provides infinite gradation, but since our minds are finite, we find it desirable to establish categories and areas. The geography of Asia reveals endless variation. Every square mile is unique; when geographers set up regions, they are making an arbitrary attempt to define phenomena of understandable dimensions.

The largest geographic unit is the continent, but one may well question how much unity exists in an area so large and diverse as Asia. The next category is the realm, a large area with relative coherence in a few aspects. Then come, in order of size and detail, geographic provinces and regions. Even the smallest areas lack complete uniformity, but valid generalization is usually possible. Seldom do political frontiers correspond with boundaries set by geographic conditions.

Geography uses many criteria for regionalization. Regions may be distinguished by climate or land form or vegetation; where these are combined, the regions may be termed physical areas. Cultural areas may include all or several human features, such as language or economic activities or geopolitics. Regions which are termed geographic have presumably some similarity in overall relationships.

The single mass of Eurasia has at least six major realms, not two. These six divisions recognize great cultural contrasts as well as differences in physical geography. Several of these subcontinents are more populous and more important economically or historically than some of the other continents. One of these realms is the Soviet Union, as large as all of North America; another is East Asia: China and Japan; Southeastern Asia is a third; India and Pakistan, sometimes known as a subcontinent, form a fourth; and Southwest Asia or Swasia, the so-called Near or Middle East, forms the fifth. The Atlantic, Baltic, and Mediterranean peninsulas in the west, commonly known as Europe, form the sixth major realm. Europe is thus defined as western peninsular Eurasia, maritime and Atlantic in climate and accessibility.

This book deals with the first five of these realms. It is impossible to understand Asia without including Siberia and Soviet Middle Asia, and these lands cannot be understood without reference to the balance of the U.S.S.R. The division next to Western Europe thus lies along the Soviet frontier rather than near the Urals. The term Asia has become fixed in our vocabulary, but it is not a unit area to be described in a few simple generalizations.

These five Asiatic realms are not merely physical areas; they have distinct political or cultural characteristics as well. Thus the Soviet realm has very little in common with the Indian realm, or with the Chinese-Japanese realm, or with Southwestern Asia, upon each of which it borders. When one enters the Soviet Union, he is in a different world. The same is true of each major division of the continent.

SURFACE CONFIGURATION

Asia is unique among the continents in its mountain core and radiating ranges. Nowhere between the Aegean and the China Sea is it possible to travel from southern to northern Asia without crossing rugged mountains. Most passes are a mile or more in height except toward either end. A complex of ranges isolates the various coastal lowlands and breaks up the continent into separate units. Asia has little physical coherence.

The configuration of Asia is determined by

Few ranges on earth exceed the Himalaya in grandeur, and none top them in elevation. This is a view from Sandakphu near the border between Nepal and China. (*Ewing Galloway*)

its geologic structure and history. Within the continent are several great structural units. In the southwest are the peninsulas of Arabia and India, underlain by an ancient complex of highly altered pre-Cambrian rocks. These areas are now locally veneered with young sediments. Northern Eurasia has two similar areas of ancient rocks: one is the Fenno-Scandian Shield around the Baltic Sea; the other is a block northeast of Lake Baikal known as Angaraland. Other such massive areas exist in China; all are composed of ancient metamorphosed rocks.

Between these resistant blocks is a succession of east-west folded ranges. During much of the Paleozoic and Mesozoic eras, these were the site of a great sea known as Tethys, longer and wider than the present Mediterranean.

Sediments accumulated in this geosyncline, and mountain building then compressed and deformed the rocks at the close of the Mesozoic and especially in the Cenozoic era. The Himalaya form one of these ranges and are among the youngest mountains on earth. Similar mountains extend from Turkey to Japan.

The classification of land forms needs clarification, and before considering the various mountain ranges, we should define a few terms. Slope and relief are the two basic elements in surface configuration; they are the angular degree of the surface and the vertical difference between the highest and lowest points within a given area.

Plains and plateaus are both essentially flat, or have gently rolling forms with slopes to 5 degrees. Depositional plains, as, for example, the Hwang delta, are commonly flatter than erosional plains, such as those in central Manchuria. The difference between a plain and a plateau consists in the amount and character of relief. Whereas plains have little or no relief, say tens or a few hundreds of feet at the most, plateaus are uplifted plains that are intersected by deep valleys so that the area as a whole has noticeable relief. While this may amount to hundreds or thousands of feet, the essential feature is undissected flat or rolling land cut by steep-sided valleys or bordered by escarpments. One may travel across the rolling surface of southern India and not know whether it is a plain or plateau until he finds a canyon. The term plateau can be used only in a regional sense, for 90 per cent of its surface may be a plain. Some so-called plateau areas encircled by mountains are really upland or highland basins, such as we find over much of Turkey. A true plateau must be dissected, and this requires canyons or fault escarpments. The term is often used, however, for high tablelands like Mongolia. Plains are near their base level, whereas plateaus are not; either may be at low or high elevations. Many areas called plateaus by geologists were once exactly so described; but they have now been so dissected that only hills remain.

Hills and mountains are slope lands and may be classed as gentle, say 4 to 10 degrees, or steep, if over 10 degrees. The distinction be-

The barren foothills of the Zagros Mountains in Iran reflect the aridity which characterizes so much of Southwest Asia. This view is near the Dez Plateau. (*Lackenbach, courtesy Development and Resources Corporation*)

tween hills and mountains is not in the degree of slope but in the amount of local relief. Thus hills, as in Szechwan, are measured in hundreds of feet whereas mountains are measured in thousands. These figures do not refer to elevation above sea level, which does not enter into the definition, but to the difference between summits and valley bottoms. Some hills, such as badlands, have steep slopes; some mountains have gentle slopes. Not all high mountains necessarily have steep slopes.

Land forms are one thing; elevation above sea level is another. Most of the lower Si River Basin west of Canton is within a few hundred feet of sea level, while interior Tibet is notably high; the former is actually hilly, while the latter is a featureless plain. Three types of elevation deserve standard names: lowlands, from sea level to 1,000 or 2,000 feet; uplands, to a mile or so; and highlands, which lie roughly above a mile. The terms basin and valley are used in their hydrographic sense without reference to land form.

From Turkey eastward to China there is a double series of mountain ranges, draped like festoon loops, alternately merging to a nucleus or knot and diverging to enclose a high plateau of intermontane basin. The following description is in terms of topographic continuity rather than structural unity, but for the most part the mountains are geologically young and hence rugged. In Turkey the series includes the Pontus Mountains along the Black Sea and the Taurus Mountains bordering the Mediterranean. Between them is the upland basin of Anatolia. Eastward these ranges merge into the Armenian nucleus. Parallel to this system on the north is the alpine range of the Caucasus, which extends westward into Crimea and continues to the east of the Caspian in the low Kopet Dagh. Iran and Afghanistan hold a second upland basin, similar to Anatolia. Its eastern part is set off as the Seistan Basin. To the north are the Elburz, Khorasan, and Hindu Kush Mountains; on the west and south are the Zagros, Fars, and Makran Mountains.

This twin series again unites to form a nu-cleus in the Pamirs. This is the "roof of the world," a highland over 12,000 feet, with mountains, deep canyons, and rolling plateaus. Mountain chains radiate from this center like the arms of an octopus. To the west are the Hindu Kush; southward are the Sulaiman and their extension which continues westward into the Makran. Northwest of the Pamirs are the Alai Mountains; to the northeast are the Tien Shan. To the east are four major ranges, among the greatest in Asia. These are the Himalaya, the Karakoram, the Astin Tagh, and the Kunlun. These surround the great highland of Tibet with its plains and lesser ranges. In eastern Tibet there is a third nucleus, formed where the Kunlun and the Himalaya approach each other.

East of Tibet the double arrangement is less clear. Part of the Himalaya chain apparently turns into southeastern Asia and may be followed topographically into the Indonesian arc. Other low mountains, such as the Nan Ling, extend across southern China and turn northeast along the coast. The Kunlun continue into China as the Chin Ling Mountains and account for the major geographic division of China into the North and the South. The Szechwan Basin and Yunnan Plateau may be thought of as an enclosed area somewhat comparable to Iran and Anatolia. The easternmost Astin Tagh is known as the Nan Ling or Nan Shan; other mountains continue along the border of Mongolia east and north as far as the Khingan Range.

Northeastern Asia has an independent sequence. The Altai is a narrow range that projects into Mongolia from Siberia, where it joins the Sayan Mountains on the east. The Yablonovi Mountains extend northeast from Lake Baikal and merge with the Stanovoi Mountains. In the extreme northeast are the Verkhoyansk, Cherski, and Kamchatka Mountains.

In addition to these mountain systems, several other topographic units need to be added. The plateaus of Anatolia, Iran, and Tibet have already been listed. Other plateau or related areas are Arabia, the Deccan of peninsular India, Mongolia, and the Central Siberian

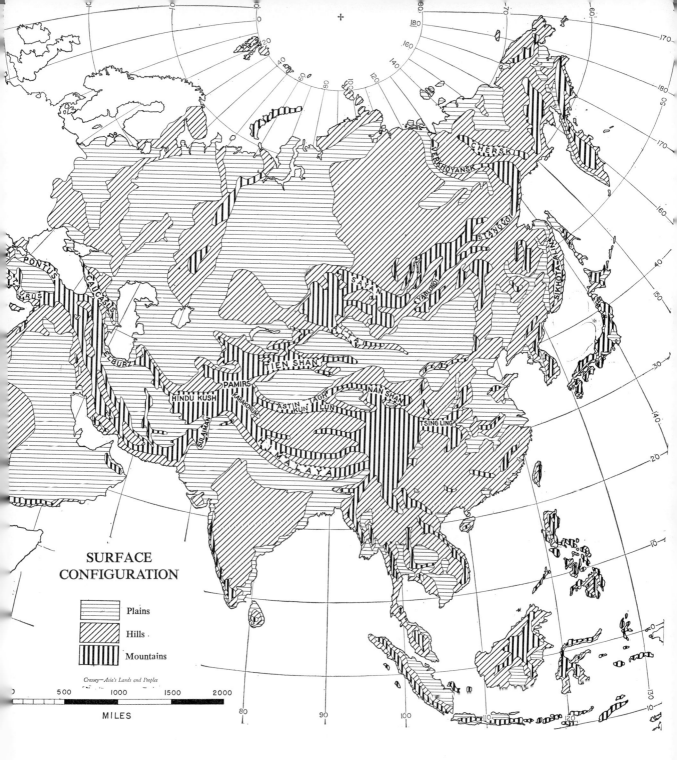

SURFACE
CONFIGURATION

	Plains
	Hills
	Mountains

Cressey—Asia's Lands and Peoples

500   1000   1500   2000

MILES

Asia is a mountain-hearted continent. Great ranges fan out at both ends of the Tibetan highlands and block easy communications from north to south or from east to west. There are only limited areas of level land, and much of this is too cold or too dry for agriculture.

Platform. Two of these plateaus, the Arabian and the Indian, are bounded on the west by bold escarpments. A comparable situation exists along the eastern and southeastern margins of Mongolia. In the middle of Asia are three lowlands: the Tarim and Dzungarian Basins of western China and the Turan Basin east of the Caspian Sea.

The principal plains are found in the great river valleys and in interior areas of limited rain. There are thus such divisions as the Arabian and Syrian deserts, the Kara Kum and Kizil Kum in Soviet Middle Asia, the Takla-makan Desert in western China, the Gobi in Mongolia, and the Thar Desert in northwest India and West Pakistan.

No single valley predominates, as in North or South America; instead a series of rivers radiate from the interior. Along the Arctic Coast are three great rivers: the Ob, Yenisei, and Lena, each among the dozen longest in the world; and five smaller rivers, the Dvina, Pechora, Yana, Indigirka, and Kolyma. Pacific drainage accounts for four major rivers, again among the dozen longest: the Amur, Hwang or Yellow, Yangtze, and Mekong. Smaller streams are the Liao, Hai, Hwai, Min, Si, Red, and Chao Phraya (or Menam) Rivers. The Indian Ocean receives three rivers, large in volume but of lesser length—the Brahmaputra, Ganges, and Indus; plus smaller streams such as the Salween, Sitang, Irrawaddy, Mahanadi, Tapti, Narbada, Tigris, and Euphrates. The Black Sea receives the Dniester, Dnieper, and Don Rivers.

Six million square miles are without drainage to the ocean. Scant rainfall combined with excessive evaporation does not supply enough water to fill the interior basins to overflowing. During an earlier period of greater humidity, the Aral Sea expanded and overflowed to the enlarged Caspian, which in turn drained into the Black Sea. Five important rivers drain into inland seas: the Volga and the Ural to the Caspian, the Amu Darya and Syr Darya to the Aral Sea, and the Ili to Lake Balkhash. In all this vast area, evaporation greatly exceeds the total precipitation. (See p. 41.)

CLIMATIC CONDITIONS

The continentality of Asia is best revealed in its climate. The maritime coastal areas present striking contrasts to the land-dominated interior where the seasons are accentuated. The mountain pattern adds to these contrasts. Interior Asia is nearly 2,000 miles from any ocean.

Other continents have their maximum extent from north to south, and are more exposed to the prevailing westerlies or to the easterly trade winds. Eurasia stretches east and west for nearly halfway around the earth. It has the lowest recorded temperatures for any inhabited place, and some of the highest. Winters in the interior are much colder than at corresponding latitudes in North America, and rainfall also shows very great extremes. Almost every known climate occurs in Asia, from the equatorial rainy type of Malaya to the ice-field climate of Novaya Zemlya.

The usual but overly simplified explanation of Asiatic climate is that in summer the over-heated interior warms the overlying air, causing it to expand, rise, and overflow aloft, and thus creating low pressure on the surface, which draws in air from the surrounding relatively cooler oceans. In winter excessive radiation over the continent chills the air and develops a stationary high-pressure area from which winds blow outward to the regions of low pressure over the oceans, where there is still a reservoir of warmth from the preceding summer.

These to-and-fro winds are alternately moist in summer and dry in winter and account for the seasonal distribution of rainfall. Where mountains rise in the path of incoming winds, exceptionally heavy precipitation results; in their lee are deserts. This is the seasonal monsoon, best developed in India, less conspicuous in China, and present elsewhere only as a tendency.

Unfortunately, this simple explanation is not entirely correct, and the climatic regime of Asia becomes more and more involved when it is

Some of the varied environments of Asia are presented in these habitat groups of the American Museum of Natural History. This is the Banting group from southern Burma. (*American Museum of Natural History*)

examined in detail. Thus the Himalaya are so high that they block winds from central Asia, and the Indian winter monsoon is an almost entirely separate circulation. In fact, the monsoon is a very complex phenomenon, though it may seem simple in outline. One basic factor is the relative location of Asia and Australia on either side of the equator. Each continent develops alternating high and low pressure, with descending or inblowing winds, but at opposite seasons.

There is also the shift in latitude of the northeast and southeast trade-wind belts with the seasonal tilt of the earth's axis. In the Southern Hemisphere the trade winds blow toward the equatorial low-pressure or doldrum belt, but from the south*east,* steadily deflected to their left according to Ferrel's law. When the thermal equator shifts north of the geographic equator in spring, as the sun moves into the

Northern Hemisphere, these southern trade winds cross the geographic equator and are deflected to their right, as are all winds in the Northern Hemisphere, and become the south*west* trades. The rainy monsoon of India thus reaches Bombay from the southwest, a deflected Southern Hemisphere trade wind.

In summer the combination of winds from the Australian high toward the Asian low, merged with the southern trade winds, brings a southerly circulation. This involves the importation into South and East Asia of hot, humid air from the Indian Ocean and South China Sea. Any dry air masses originating over Australia become moist en route. On the other hand, winter monsoon winds over the southern two-thirds of Asia come from northerly directions, a combination of the northeast trade winds and the outblowing circulation from the interior Asiatic high. They are thus relatively cool and dry as they pass over China and India.

In India the wet summer monsoon from the ocean is much more powerful than the weaker winter circulation, since India is protected from central Asian air by the Tibetan highlands. In China the situation is reversed, for dry winter winds out of Siberia are stronger than the summer maritime circulation. Everywhere in southern and eastern Asia wet summers stand in contrast to dry winters. So striking is the contrast that it divides life into two periods—dramatically in India, less so elsewhere. Since most of Monsoon Asia is densely populated and has critical food problems, and since agriculture is dependent on the rain, any variation in the time or duration of the monsoon has a major effect on prosperity or famine. Drought and/or flood bring distress to millions every decade.

Much of southwestern Asia has a Mediterranean rather than a monsoon climate. Both areas have wet and dry periods but in a climate of the Mediterranean type rain falls during the winter months when the path of cyclonic storms which normally cross Europe shifts southward, while the summers are dry because of stationary high pressure and descending air.

Not enough is known of air-mass movements over Asia to enable us to present a complete picture, but air of polar, tropical, and equatorial origin may be identified far into the interior. Polar maritime air masses move from

Large Siberian tigers inhabit the well-forested mountains along the Amur valley in the Maritime Province of the U.S.S.R. (*American Museum of Natural History*)

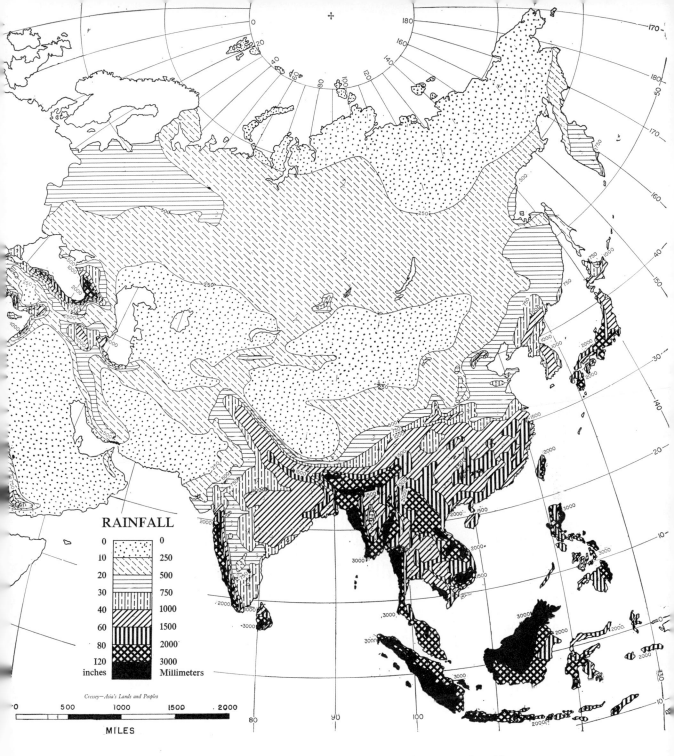

RAINFALL

inches	Millimeters
0	0
10	250
20	500
30	750
40	1000
60	1500
80	2000
120	3000

Cressey—Asia's Lands and Peoples

MILES
0   500   1000   1500   2000

Rainfall varies from 400 inches to 1 inch, according to winds and topography. The heaviest precipitation occurs on mountain slopes in the path of prevailing winds or where air is rising as in the doldrums; the driest areas are in the lee of mountain barriers or in areas of descending air.

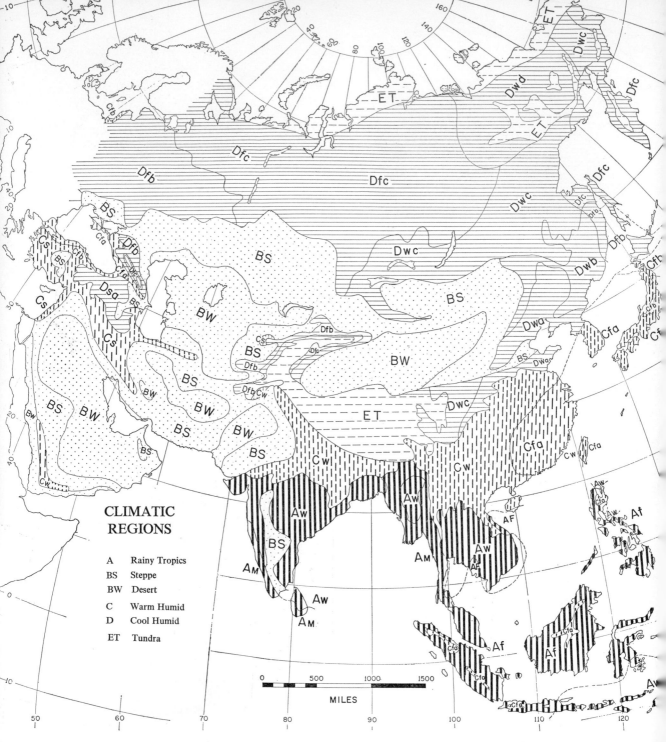

CLIMATIC REGIONS

A   Rainy Tropics
BS   Steppe
BW   Desert
C   Warm Humid
D   Cool Humid
ET   Tundra

Almost every known climate occurs in Asia. The following Koeppen symbols define the major regions. *A* climates have rain and high temperatures the year around. *B* represents dry climates, modified by *S* for steppe or *W* for desert (*Wüste*). *C* and *D* are rainy temperate climates, *C* with long hot summers and mild winters and *D* with short

Novaya Zemlya as far as southern China, and tropical air at times penetrates to Lake Baikal. These several air masses, some maritime in origin, others continental, vary with the season. Frontal action where they meet is a common cause of rain. Sounding balloons show that the upper air is everywhere moving from the west.

Migrating cyclonic and anticyclonic storms are more important in Asia than is sometimes realized. These moving lows and highs are fewer and smaller than those which cross the Atlantic and enter Europe. Many die out in the interior. They bring with them, however, the bulk of the rainfall that falls in Siberia. As their paths approach the Pacific, both highs and lows become larger and more numerous, so that China and Japan have alternations of weather several times a month. In eastern Asia the southeast quadrant of a cyclonic storm draws in moist winds from the South China Sea, which occupies a position as a source of moisture similar to that of the Gulf of Mexico for eastern North America. Much of the eastern United States and much of eastern China would be a semidesert if it were not for these tropical seas to the south in each continent. In winter weak cyclonic storms cross Palestine, Iran, and northern India, but during most of the year the main path is well to the north; and in summer it is even near the Arctic Circle.

Typhoons are important sources of rainfall in the southeast during the summer and fall, at times resulting in serious destruction. They develop in the South and East China Seas and over the Bay of Bengal, and are similar to the hurricanes of the Gulf of Mexico.

The influence of the Indian Ocean is limited to the lands south of the Himalaya and east of the Indus valley. Pacific moisture seldom penetrates beyond western Manchuria or occasionally to Lake Baikal. The cold Arctic Ocean contributes little precipitation and that only along a fringe of the continent in the north; it is, however, a source area for cold invading air masses. Despite the great distance to the Atlantic, that ocean supplies such rain or snow as falls on one-third of Asia. Even 4,000 miles east of the Atlantic most rain originates in that ocean.

Several million square miles are essentially without ocean-derived moisture; any precipitation is obtained by local evaporation from rivers, swamps, salt lakes, or vegetation. Since some of these areas appear to be growing drier, more moisture is blown out than comes in. As Lyde has said, "This is continentality at its fiercest."

The seasonal extremes of temperature increase from the equator toward the northeastern interior. Near Singapore and Colombo the averages of the warmest and coldest months differ by scarcely a degree. Along the Tropic of Cancer the figure rises to 20°F. Western Siberia shows an annual range of 45°F. Peking and the Aral Sea both have seasonal differences of 60°F. Around Lake Baikal the figure exceeds 75°F. At the Asiatic cold pole in the vicinity of Verkhoyansk, the July average is higher by 119°F than that for January. Thus average annual temperatures mean little and scarcely form a basis for mapping climatic regions.

Although no scheme of climatic regions is entirely satisfactory, the most widely used is that of Wladimir Koeppen. Five major types are recognized, all of them present in Asia. Tropical rainy climates with no winters form the *A* group. *B* is the designation for dry climates. Temperate rainy climates with mild winters, where the coldest months average between 27 and 65°F, are classed as *C*; or *D* if

summers and severe winters. *E* stands for polar climates, divided into *ET* for tundra and *EF* for permanent frost or snow fields.

These major groups are modified as follows: *a*, hot summers, with the warmest month over 72°F; *b*, cool summers, with four months above 50°F; *c*, cool, short summers, one to three months above 50°F; *d*, coldest month below −36°F; *f*, no dry season; *s*, dry summer; *w*, dry winter.

the winters are boreal with the coldest month below 27°F and the warmest above 50°F. Polar climates with no warm season are designated *E*.

Various modifications are introduced to indicate the season of rainfall or distribution of warmth. Thus *EF*, frost or ice cap, has no month above freezing, whereas *ET*, tundra, has temperatures up to 50°F in its warmest month. *BS*, steppe, is less dry than *BW*, *wüste* or desert, according to the ratios between temperature, rainfall, and season. Various lower-case letters are used to modify *A*, *C*, and *D* climates: *f*, *feucht* or moist, indicates rainfall every month or at least enough at other times to tide over a dry period; *w* refers to a dry winter and *s* to a dry summer; *a* indicates hot summers; *b*, cool summers with four months above 50°F; *c*, cool, short summers with less than four months above 50°F; and *d* indicates a climate where the coldest month is below −36°F. *B* climates are modified by *k*, *kalt* or cold, where annual temperatures are below 65°F, and *h*, *heiss* or hot, where they exceed 65°F.

Tropical *A* climates characterize the peninsulas of India and Southeast Asia as well as the adjoining islands. This is a monsoon area with every month above 65°F. Coastal areas are *Af*, some interiors *Aw*. Though such areas are near the equator, temperatures seldom exceed 90°F.

B climates cover millions of square miles in the interior, with *BS* grassland surrounding large areas of *BW* desert. Summer temperatures are everywhere high, but winters are cold in Mongolia, Sinkiang, and Soviet Middle Asia in contrast to the year-round heat of Arabia, interior Iran, and the Thar Desert of Pakistan.

Temperate *C* climates are present in China, Japan, northern India, and parts of Southwest Asia. All of these except the last have summer monsoon rain and winter drought, *Cw*, but in southern Japan and the Yangtze valley the symbol is *Cfa*.

The most characteristic climate of northern Asia is the cool temperate *D* type, present in Manchuria and Turkey and also throughout most of the U.S.S.R., except in Soviet Middle Asia and beyond the Arctic Circle. Where Atlantic influences penetrate the continent in the west and bring year-round rain and mild summers, the symbol is *Dfb*. The northern area is *Dfc*, moist but with short summers. Eastern Siberia has only summer rain and is *Dwc* or *Dwd*, according to temperature.

Polar *E* climates occur in three situations: The ice cap of Novaya Zemlya is *EF*; most of the lowland Arctic coast is covered with tundra and has an *ET* climate; while higher mountains in both northeastern Siberia and in Tibet are also *ET*, or *EB* where especially arid.

NATURAL VEGETATION

Natural vegetation is the best single summary of the physical environment, for it reflects temperature, rainfall, drainage, elevation, and soil. Parts of Asia have been cultivated so long that no trace of the undisturbed cover remains, and in many areas studies of ecological botany are incomplete. The general distribution shows many resemblances to the Koeppen map of climatic regions.

Land Use in Asia [1]
(in million hectares)

	Total area	Arable land incl. fallow and orchards	Permanent pasture and meadows	Forest and wood-lands
China	976.1	109.4	178.0	76.6
U.S.S.R.	2,240.3	221.4	369.7	880.3
Other Asia	1,739.0	325.0	258.0	442.0
All Asia	4,955.4	655.8	805.7	1,398.9

[1] United Nations, Food and Agricultural Organization: *Production Yearbook*, 1960.

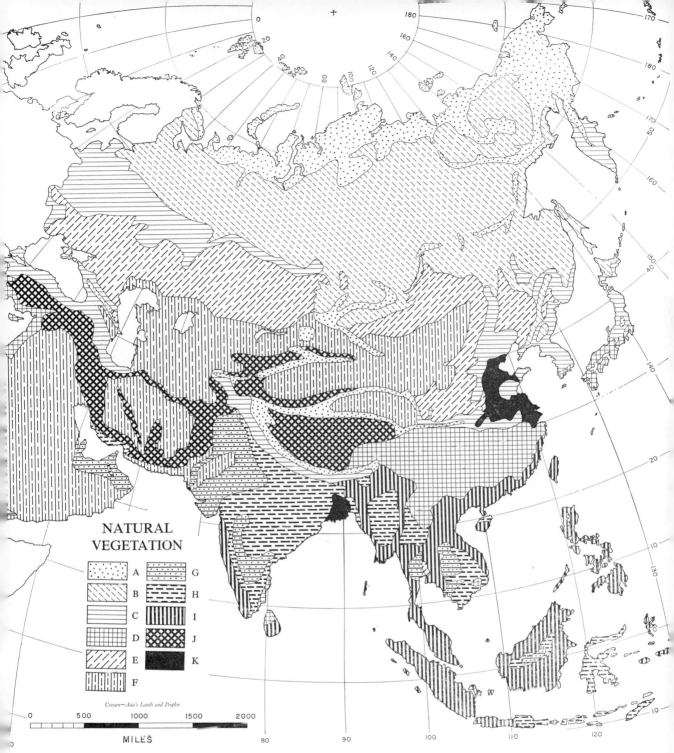

NATURAL VEGETATION

⠿	A	—	G
⫽	B	▦	H
☰	C	▥	I
▦	D	▨	J
⫽	E	■	K
▦	F		

Cresser—*Asia's Lands and Peoples*

```
0        500      1000      1500      2000
|--------|--------|--------|--------|
              MILES
```

The distribution of original vegetation is one of the best guides to land usability, but in the long-settled areas of Asia little unmodified cover remains. Underlying this pattern are the maps of land form and climate. (*Data from Great Soviet World Atlas, Buck, Champion, and elsewhere*)

    A. Tundra and alpine   *B.* Taiga   *C.* Mixed evergreen and deciduous (mid-latitude)
D. Mixed evergreen and deciduous (subtropical)   *E.* Grasslands and brush   *F.* Desert
    G. Scrub woodland   *H.* Mixed evergreen and deciduous (tropical)   *I.* Rain forest
    J. Undifferentiated mountain vegetation   *K.* Original vegetation unknown

The rare giant panda lives in the high snow mountains of western China between Szechwan and Tibet, where bamboo has become adjusted to a rigorous environment. (*American Museum of Natural History*)

A belt of tundra extends along the entire Arctic coastal plain and inland along higher elevations between the valleys. The subsoil is permanently frozen, and plant growth is limited to less than three months. Swamps and lakes are very numerous, many of them associated with Pleistocene glaciation. Mosses, lichens, brush, and dwarf trees form the vegetation. The mountain flora of the Himalaya, Tien Shan, and other high areas is a specialized subtype.

Temperate coniferous forests cover millions of square miles in regions where the summers are short and the winters continentally cold. This is the Siberian taiga, a boreal forest of conifers such as larch, fir, and pine, with some deciduous whitewoods such as birch and aspen. Commercial timber is limited to the southern portions. The soils are acid podsols.

Splendid mid-latitude forests of mixed conifers and deciduous trees occur where milder climate prevails, both in the extreme east and west. Brown forest soils are the prevailing type.

Subtropical mixed forests once covered southern China and Japan and still remain in the mountains. They include broad-leaf evergreen trees, pine, fir, oak, and bamboo. Soils are yellow to red.

Prairie, steppe, and semidesert vegetation corresponds roughly to the distribution of cool *BS* climate. Dry grasses and low brush reflect the aridity and provide pasturage for nomads. Where the temperature is low and evaporation moderate, excellent grasslands may develop, even with as much as 12 inches of rainfall. These regions have exceptionally fertile chernozem soil.

Deserts, *F*, are not necessarily lifeless, but plants are so scattered that bare ground is exposed between them.

Savanna and tropical scrub woodland is a result of seasonal rainfall, high temperatures, and excessive evaporation. It is found in the drier parts of India and is the proper jungle. Laterite is the end product of soil leaching on level areas.

Tropical deciduous forests are characteristic of the moist monsoon lands of southern Asia which have 40 to 80 inches of rain. Teak is one of the best-known trees.

Regions of heaviest rainfall are covered by a dense green forest, composed of a great variety of hardwoods, often 200 feet high. Mangrove coastal swamps are a special type. Soils are seriously leached and invariably infertile.

Undifferentiated mountain vegetation occurs on the high barren plains of Tibet and other highlands; in places a specialized tundra.

In the deltas of the Hwang and Yangtze, which appear to have been occupied by man almost since the time of their formation, natural vegetation never had an opportunity to develop. Similar conditions may have prevailed in parts of the Ganges delta.

MINERAL RESOURCES

Asia, the largest of the continents, is not necessarily also the richest. Although preliminary geological surveys have covered most countries, it is too early to make continent-wide generalizations. Vast reserves are known to exist, but they are not always of the right quality, or in the proper location or combina-

Production Data [1]

	China	Japan	India	U.S.S.R.	U.S.	World
Population (in millions)	582.6	93.4	434.8	208.8	179.3	2,983.0
Coal (in million metric tons)	420.0	0.7	53.0	375.0	392.0	1,988.0
Petroleum (in thousand metric tons)	3,700.0	526.0	449.0	147,859.0	347,975.0	1,056,000.0
Steel (in million tons)	18.5	22.1	3.3	65.3	90.1	345.5
Wheat (in million metric tons)	31.3	1.5	10.3	63.7	36 8	243.4
Rice (in million metric tons)	85.0	16.1	51.4	0.2	2.5	239.7
Electricity (in billion kilowatt hours)	42.0	115.0	20.0	292.0	841.0	2,294.0
Railway traffic (in million ton kilometers)	265.0	54.0	69.0	1,504.0	835.0	

[1] United Nations: *Statistical Yearbook*, 1961.

tion, or accessible to markets. India has great deposits of iron but little coal; China has coal but limited iron; Japan has industrial needs but lacks adequate ore; the Soviet Union has a wide variety of minerals but there are several limitations.

Even before the days of Marco Polo who brought back tales of the riches of far Cathay, Europe had been impressed with the mineral wealth of the Orient. Damascus steel blades, the gold of Ophir, Chinese bronze and jade, Indian diamonds, and Burmese rubies helped to create an aura of wealth.

Probably Asia leads the world in reserves of oil, tin, manganese, tungsten, antimony, and mica. It may also be true that the continent has more coal than North America and that her iron deposits are of top rank. Asia may someday dominate in the production of hydroelectricity. Chromium and aluminum appear to rank high. Such generalizations mean little until plotted on a map or weighed in terms of their cost-benefit ratio or measured in per capita amounts.

The word *ore* has an economic definition, in that it refers to a rock which contains something desirable which may be extracted at a profit. The interior of South India contains high-grade iron deposits, but they are remote from coal or a market and are at present unworkable. Low-grade iron ore is mined profitably in the Philippines and in Malaya for shipment to Japan because it is close to tidewater. Difficult-to-work tin deposits are worthwhile in southwest China with its cheap labor whenever the international need for tin is great enough. Some areas have deeply buried coal which is too expensive to mine under present conditions of technology but may someday prove valuable. Large-scale mining operations require a combination of many geographic factors.

Among the countries of Asia, the Soviet Union stands far in the lead in its mineral wealth. Coal and iron are present in abundance and in many localities. Oil is more than adequate. Probably no country on earth has an array of industrial minerals so nearly complete, though several ores are of low grade. But the U.S.S.R. is a country of great distances, and frequently commodities are in the wrong place.

China ranks next, with abundant coal and such uncommon metals as antimony and tin. Unfortunately, her supplies of iron, copper, and oil appear to be modest. Probably China has enough resources to develop spectacular industrialization in a few centers, but there is no present prospect that she can equal Western Europe in per capita terms.

India's mineral reserves present a problem. Her iron ore is exceptionally rich and abundant, and she is outstanding in manganese, but coal and oil are quite limited. Hydroelectric possibilities are complicated by the seasonal character of the rainfall and stream flow. The future of heavy industry appears problematical.

Japan has become a great industrial state, but largely on the basis of imported raw materials. For their size, the islands contain a surprising variety of mineral deposits, but they do not have enough of any of them. Japan is self-sufficient in steam coal but lacks coking coal. Her supplies of iron and oil are especially inadequate; copper is her best metal.

No other area has yet achieved industrial importance. Southwest Asia has fabulous reserves of oil, but Turkey, the only nation with much coal or the metals, has almost no oil. The countries of Southeast Asia lack good coal but do have oil plus rich reserves of many metallic minerals. It will be interesting to see whether these raw materials move to Japan and China in crude form, or whether the development of enough local purchasing power will warrant their smelting and fabrication within the realm.

Asia is so large and its various parts so inaccessible to one another that the presence of rich deposits and large-scale heavy industry in one area may have little or no direct economic effect elsewhere. On the other hand, a powerful China might sway a less-developed India, or an industrialized Soviet Union could exert political influence over Southwest Asia.

3 The Realms of Asia

Physical Realms / Political Realms / Geostrategy in Asia

PHYSICAL REALMS

One of the most useful subdivisions of Asia is that which recognizes the overall pattern of physical geography. Five realms stand out. Mountain Asia forms the core of the continent, diverse and overlapping the other realms. To the south and east lies Monsoon Asia, with its regime of summer rainfall. Arid Asia occupies millions of square miles in the interior, including much of the southwest, which receives a little Mediterranean-style winter rain. Boreal Asia covers the north, an area with too short a summer for normal cultivation. Toward the west, largely in the Soviet agricultural triangle but also near the Mediterranean, lies Atlantic Asia, an agricultural area of year-round precipitation derived from the Atlantic ocean.

Mountain Asia

The continent of Asia contains the world's grandest mountains. A hundred peaks rise higher than the loftiest summits in any other continent, most of them at least a mile above the highest elevations in North America. A series of great ranges lie in the center, radiating from the Pamirs: the Himalaya, Karakoram, Hindu Kush, Kunlun, Astin Tagh, and Tien Shan. Beyond these extend a score of mountains with peaks in excess of 12,000 feet, such as the Elburz, Caucasus, Taurus, and Zagros in the west; and the Altai, Chin Ling, Sayan,

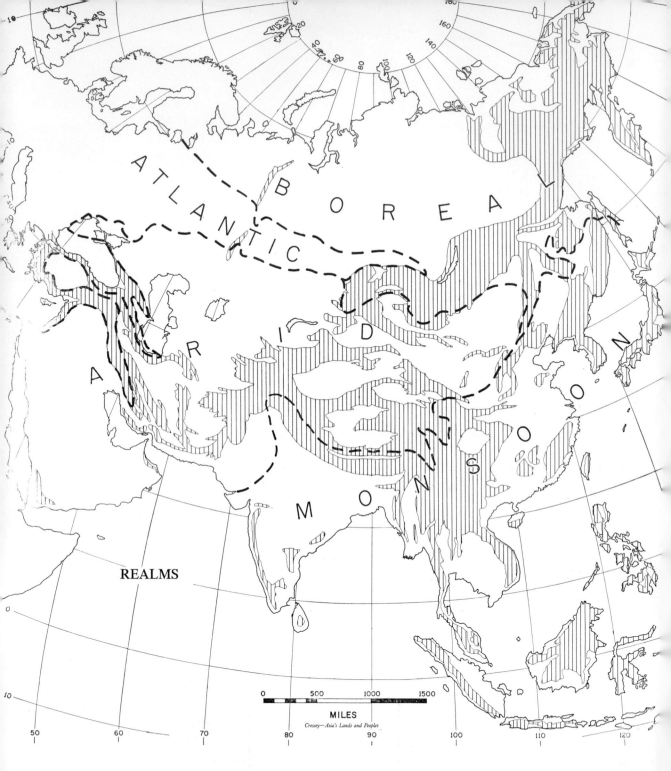

Five major geographic realms characterize the continent: Mountain Asia, largely in the interior (shaded); Monsoon Asia on the south and east; Arid Asia in the west and the interior; Boreal Asia in the north; and Atlantic Asia in the west.

Cherski, and Kamchatka ranges to the north and east. In addition to isolated peaks, uplifted by folding or faulting or by volcanic action, great plateaus are in the process of dissection into tabular mountains, cut by canyons over a mile in depth.

All these mountains present a vertical zonation of climate, vegetation, and human occupancy. Heavy precipitation and rich vegetation on windward slopes are balanced by aridity and desert flora on their lee sides. Tongues of glacial ice push down from snowy summits into wooded valleys. Within a few miles, horizontally, one may thus find several of the major climatic realms of Asia. The south face of the Himalaya have monsoon conditions on their lower slopes, while their upper elevations are boreal; not far away arid climates characterize the north face.

Many of these mountains are geologically young and therefore high and rugged. Such precipitous topography restricts land use and travel, interrupts normal wind patterns, provides contrasting life environments, and effectively isolates the several Asian cultures.

The Himalaya are the greatest of these ranges, towering and impressive when seen from the plains of India though not so bold when viewed from high Tibet. As Dhyrenfurth has said, "He who has once looked on these incomparable mounts . . . must dream of them to the end of his days." The name is from Sanskrit and means "the abode of snow." The highest peak is known to the Tibetans as Chomolungma, Goddess Mother of the World, and to Westerners as Mount Everest. The mountain is a three-sided pyramid, a matterhorn, flanked by knifelike ridges and stupendous precipices. No more fitting glimpse of the summit can be quoted than these paragraphs written by its first conqueror, Sir Edmund Hillary.[1]

After an hour's steady going we reached the foot of the most formidable looking problem on the ridge—a rock step some forty feet high. We had known of the existence of this step from

[1] In John Hunt: *The Conquest of Everest,* New York: Dutton (1954), 204–205. Quoted by permission.

aerial photographs and had also seen it through our binoculars from Thyangboche. We realized that at this altitude it might well spell the difference between success and failure. The rock itself, smooth and almost holdless, might have been an interesting Sunday afternoon problem to a group of expert rock climbers in the Lake District, but here it was a barrier beyond our feeble strength to overcome. I could see no way of turning it on the steep rock bluff on the west, but fortunately another possibility of tackling it still remained. On its east side was another great cornice and running up the full forty feet of the step was a narrow crack between the cornice and the rock. Leaving Tenzing to belay me as best he could, I jammed my way into this crack, then kicking backwards with my crampons I sank their spikes deep into the frozen snow behind me and levered myself off the ground. Taking advantage of every little rock hold and all the force of knee, shoulder, and arms I could muster, I literally cramponed backwards up the crack, with a fervent prayer that the cornice would remain attached to the rock. Despite the considerable effort involved, my progress although slow was steady, and as Tenzing paid out the rope I inched my way upward until I could finally reach over the top of the rock and drag myself out of the crack into a wide ledge. For a few moments I lay regaining my breath and for the first time really felt the fierce determination that nothing now could stop our reaching the top.

The ridge continued as before. Giant cornices on the right, steep rock slopes on the left. I went on cutting steps on the narrow strip of snow. The ridge curved away to the right and we had no idea where the top was. As I cut around the back of one hump, another higher one would swing into view. Time was passing and the ridge seemed never-ending. In one place where the angle of the ridge had eased off, I tried cramponing without cutting steps, hoping this would save time, but I quickly realized that our margin of safety on these steep slopes at this altitude was too small, so I went on step cutting. I was beginning to tire a little now. I had been cutting steps continuously for two hours, and Tenzing, too was moving very slowly. As I chipped steps around still another corner, I wondered rather dully just how long we could keep it up. Our original zest had now quite gone and it was turning more into a grim struggle. I then realized that the ridge ahead, instead

Great ranges cross Asia from west to east and from south to north, isolating each realm from the others. These porters are carrying cakes of cheese over the 18,400-foot Gangja La Pass in Nepal. (*Courtesy United Nations*)

of still monotonously rising, now dropped sharply away, and far below I could see the North Col and the Rongbuk Glacier. I looked upward to see a narrow snow ridge running up to a snowy summit. A few more whacks of the ice ax in the firm snow and we stood on top.

Monsoon Asia

Monsoon Asia extends in a crescent from the valley of the Indus in West Pakistan to that of the Amur in the eastern Soviet Union. While the seasonal monsoon circulation is best developed in India, the alternation of summer rain and winter drought continues across eastern China and Japan. Inland, monsoon rain-

fall extends as far as the high mountain barriers; moisture from the Indian Ocean occasionally penetrates Tibet, and Pacific-derived rain may at times reach to Lake Baikal.

In political terms, Monsoon Asia includes India, Pakistan, Ceylon, Burma, Thailand, Laos, Cambodia, Viet Nam, Malaya, Indonesia, the Philippines, eastern China, Korea, and Japan. The total area measures 5.6 million square miles. Here are some of the world's oldest cultures and some of its most pressing problems. Everywhere there is rapid change, at times reaching a revolutionary tempo.

Climatic conditions range from continental to maritime and from equatorial to mid-latitude; it is the summer rainfall regime that gives unity to the way of life. In Koeppen's terms, Monsoon Asia includes *Aw, Cw,* and *Dw* types, all with wet summers but progressively cooler winters toward the northeast.

This is humid and warm Asia. Except where topography creates rain shadows, rainfall generally exceeds 50 inches a year, and on exposed mountain slopes it may be double and quadruple that amount. Summer temperatures are high, and so is the humidity. The combination of abundant moisture and warm growing season makes this an ideal area for rice, grown wherever climate and soil permit. Few places on earth are used more intensively. The importance of Monsoon Asia becomes apparent when it is recognized that the realm contains roughly half of the world's population, and that here lies nearly one-third of the world's farm land.

Between most of these countries are barriers of mountains or seas, the former of greater effectiveness in creating isolation. Monsoon Asia thus lacks internal coherence. China and India share many aspects of physical geography, but their historic trade and political relations have been negligible. Even the islands and peninsulas of Southeast Asia have known little about one another; the people of the Philippines are much more in tune with distant America than with nearby Malaya.

The arrival of the monsoon in India has been vividly described by James W. Best.[2]

Officially the rains are due on the fifteenth of June. That year they never broke until the first of July, and the heat was awful. I had not felt a spot of rain since my arrival in India the previous November. Every day one would see dust storms in the distance; leaden clouds with dark pencil lines leading to the earth looking like cascades of rain; nothing but shadows. With the gathering of clouds, the heat became yet more oppressive; it was bottled up; the air was stagnant. . . . We slept in the open, of course. The

[2] James W. Best: *Forest Life in India.* Quoted by permission. (Taken from Anderson: *Splendour of Earth,* London: George Philip & Son (1954), 55–56.)

sheets were so hot and the pillows so soaked in our perspiration that we had to turn them two or three times in the night. Even in the morning the ground was hot to the bare feet. The clouds grew bigger and darker in hue as we watched them anxiously, hoping for the long-delayed rain.

I remember on the first of July walking from the railway station back to the rest-house, and passing over the causeway that spanned the small *nala.* How absurdly large it looked in that sun-scorched land of withered grasses and leaves! It was a mockery to suppose that water ever flowed along that course, or ever would.

At midday the sun went out and the heat became almost worse. But there was a change. There was something new in the midday wind. It was still a scorching blast, it still made the window-panes of the rest-house unbearably hot, but there was a damp feeling of softness in the air, a perspiring greasy feeling. We heard thunder, but that was nothing new. Thunder had mocked us loudly for the last week. . . .

The higher hills were covered with cloud and a strong wind blew from them towards us. It was heavily charged with moisture and there was the rank smell of rain on parched earth. One or two large drops flicked the dust in front of the rest-house. There was the roar of close thunder, and suddenly the rain came down in bucket-loads. Never before had I seen such a downpour. It continued till nearly sundown, and in the great stillness of the evening, when the fury of the storm had passed away, we went towards the railway station. We only got half-way; the causeway had disappeared under a raging torrent of dark muddy water.

In the space of a few hours the country had changed from a land scorched and arid with a shade temperature of over 120° Fahr. to one of flowing rivers and floods and a temperature of about 70° Fahr.

That night we dined in the verandah listening to an orchestra of frogs that croaked and squeaked their joy in the marsh below us. Heaven knows that we wanted the rain, but our prayers could have been nothing to those of the frogs. . . .

Arid Asia

Only Antarctica is drier than Asia. Based on various definitions of steppe and desert conditions, dry lands in the continent measure from 6.5 to 9.8 million square miles. This means that one-third of Asia is arid, parts of it among the most rainless areas on earth. This aridity is the result of many factors. In interior Asia high mountains so effectually block moisture-bearing winds from the ocean that only negligible rainfall from the Indian Ocean crosses the Himalaya into Sinkiang. Elsewhere, deserts lie in areas of semipermanent high pressure, where dry air steadily descends from aloft, somewhat warmed by adiabatic compression, and is so low in humidity that rain is unlikely. Where these air masses move equatorward, as they do over Arabia, they are generally warmed during their advance southward; this rise in temperature increases their evaporative capacity and reduces the possibility of precipitation.

It is well to remember that desert conditions may be seasonal. If India were as dry throughout the year as during the winter monsoon, most of the peninsula would resemble Arabia. A similar situation prevails in North China. Even in year-round deserts, as in Iran, the degree of aridity varies with the temperature.

The impact of Asian deserts on ancient empires and trade routes is obvious, as are the present-day restrictions on land use. As populations expand in nearby favored areas and as technology enables man to intrude into desert borderlands, these dry lands will play a changing role. It seems probable, however, that for centuries to come Asian geography will be characterized by vast areas of aridity. The following paragraphs, adapted and abridged from an article by the author,[3] present various definitions and measurements of Desert Asia; some are climatic, ecologic, geomorphic, hydrologic, or pedalogic; others are geographic.

No deserts are completely rainless, but the annual amount may be only an inch or two, and years may pass between chance showers. To report that Yarkand in Sinkiang averages ½ inch a year may merely mean that once or twice during a decade there were sharp rains. With

[3] George B. Cressey: "The Deserts of Asia," *Jour. of Asian Studies*, XIX (1960), 389–402.

5 inches of precipitation and low temperatures, northern Mongolia has a fair grass cover, whereas the same rainfall in Arabia results in a barren surface. Areas with less than 8 inches of rain total 4,881,000 square miles, and the area with 8 to 16 inches amounts to 4,982,000 square miles, a total of 9,863,000 square miles.

Rainfall alone is not an adequate criterion for a desert. One of the best climatic evaluations of desert lands is based on the effective balance between precipitation and solar energy. Climatic deserts may be defined as areas where evaporation greatly exceeds precipitation through much of the year. Three moisture groups may be distinguished: an extremely arid group of areas, 422,000 square miles in all, where at least twelve months may elapse without rain; an arid category covering 3,173,000 square miles; and a semiarid group of 2,942,000 square miles. This gives a total desert area, climatically defined, of 6,537,000 square miles. In the first category, vegetation is essentially absent or very sparse; in the second, rainfall is quite inadequate for agriculture without irrigation; and in the semiarid category a few crops can be grown with dry-farming techniques.

Another measure of a desert is the kind and amount of plant life. Few deserts are completely lifeless, but all show a specialized adjustment to aridity. The apparent wide spacing of desert grasses or brush may be due to competition below ground where the far-reaching roots occupy all the intervening areas. To the botanist deserts are characterized by the appearance of wide areas of bare ground between the scanty natural vegetation so that there is a discontinuous plant cover. The encircling steppe is thus a zone with a nearly continuous vegetative cover. Essentially barren lands in Asia occupy 1,105,000 square miles, while desert floras cover 3,574,000 square miles. In the slightly more humid margins there are 2,333,000 square miles of steppe. Asian dry lands, as defined by vegetation, thus total 7,012,000 square miles.

In geological terms, deserts are areas where unique types of weathering plus erosion by

RIVERS

≡ Interior Drainage

0   500   1000   1500
MILES
Cressey—Asia's Lands and Peoples

Eight of the fifteen longest rivers in the world are in Asia, but 5 million square miles in the interior are without drainage to the sea. Such rain as falls ends in salt lakes and is lost by evaporation. As Lyde has said, "This is continentality at its fiercest."

Aridity dominates the heart of Asia, together with much of the southwest. Shifting sand dunes cover a million square miles. (*Courtesy Arabian American Oil Company*)

wind and intermittent streams have given the landscape a distinctive stamp. Many desert rivers which rise in distant snow-covered mountains lose water and wither as they cross the dry lowlands; their sediments thus accumulate in great alluvial fans or waste-filled basins, and the debris never reaches the ocean. Whereas running water can move detritus only downslope, wind may cause sand dunes to migrate uphill. Fine silt particles may be lifted high into the air and transported great distances; where such silts are trapped by the scanty steppe vegetation that encircles a desert basin, loess accumulates.

One obvious mark of the desert is the presence of loose sand, whether concentrated into dunes or present as an irregular sheet. Such sand areas occupy at least 962,000 square miles in Asia. Active sand dunes cover 30 per cent of Arabia, 5 per cent of Iran and Afghanistan, 2 or 3 per cent of Iraq, Jordan, Syria, and Israel, perhaps 25 per cent of West Pakistan, nearly 30 per cent of Sinkiang, and possibly 5 per cent of Mongolia.

In humid lands all surface runoff flows onward to the sea. If there are depressions, they are filled to overflowing with freshwater lakes. In hydrographic terms, deserts may be defined as areas where little or no runoff ever reaches the ocean, and where topographic depressions contain salt lakes or intermittent playas. In such arid basins, drainage is inward or centripetal, rather than outward or centrifugal as in humid lands. If Asia were more humid, a series of great freshwater lakes would appear, each overflowing into the next lower basin. For example, Lake Balkhash and the Aral Sea would enlarge and empty into a Caspian Sea almost twice its present size, with its level raised until it in turn overflowed to the Black Sea. The total extent of interior drainage in Asia measures 4,786,000 square miles; at the same time areas which slope outward but are so dry that they contribute nothing to the ocean add an additional 1,558,000 square miles. If deserts might be defined in this hydrographic fashion, their area in Asia totals 6,344,000 square miles.

Desert soils are unique in their lack of leaching and eluviation and in the limited accumulation of nitrogen, in contrast to steppe grassland soils, which are rich. Soluble salts are seldom present to excess except toward the center of saline basins or where careless irrigation practices have concentrated. Pedologic deserts, as they reflect the environment, are widespread.

All the preceding criteria have their bearing on the geographic definition of a desert, for geography is concerned with the totality of aridity. A geographic definition of a desert thus centers around land usability: They are areas where human life is difficult without special techniques for securing water. What one culture regards as desolation, another may find usable through new methods. Old maps label western Manchuria as the "Eastern Gobi," but most of it is now cultivated. Engineering works may divert irrigation water from the Hwang Ho and thus change the map of land utilization around the Ordos Desert. Measurements of the larger Asian deserts give a total of 3,454,000 square miles, plus a steppe area of 987,000 square miles, but since many smaller areas are omitted, the total for geographic deserts may well exceed 5,500,000 square miles.

Scattered across all deserts are oases, large and small, which form steppingstones along caravan routes. Mildred Cable and Francesca French have graphically described some of those which they visited in the western Gobi on the ancient cart road to Sinkiang.[4]

GATES OF SAND. This was the very last oasis which tireless Chinese industry had been able to wrest from the ruthless and encroaching Mongolian sands. Beyond this we knew there would be no well, but only pits dug deep in the sand, at the bottom of which some dark brown water might have oozed up and collected. There would be nothing to burn save branches broken from dead tamarisk bushes, and we must carry all we should need with us. How should we ever

[4] Mildred Cable and Francesca French: *The Gobi Desert*, New York: Macmillan (1944), 109–114. Quoted by permission.

find our way across this chartless ocean of sand? The camel driver was not afraid. He jerked the halter, which told the camel to kneel, and bade the riders take their seats. "By day we shall pick up signs," he said. "Others have gone before us, and no caravan can move without leaving some trace behind. If I miss the way, my camels will find it. At night we have the stars and they can never mislead us. Have no fear, rest your heart. There will be a road.". . .

INEXHAUSTIBLE SPRING HALT. At last the eight stages of bitter water were over. With inevitable delay for frontier permits, these stages had dragged out to thirteen days of unquenchable thirst in a stony, shadeless wilderness. At dawn I caught the outline of a soft waving mass against the pale sky. It was a tree, with branches moving gently in the morning breeze, and it seemed to me to be the loveliest tree in the whole world. Something within me relaxed, for I knew that the worst of the desert stages were now over.

Seized with a strange excitement I walked straight to the tree and found that it overhung a little sunken pond. Was this also acrid water? Experience insisted that it might be, but a woman filling her water-pot read my thought and smiled up at me. "Our water here is clean and sweet," she said. "Take a drink and try it. This is the stage of Inexhaustible Spring, and when the wayfarer tastes this sweet draught he will drink until all the pain of his parched throat and cracked lips is softened and fades away."

"How is it that after so many brackish springs the water here is pure and sweet?" I asked.

The woman lifted her head toward the line of distant snow-hills: "It all comes from the Barkul Range," she said, "and flows direct from the hills to our hamlet. This is the mouth of the karez which carries it here. Blessed be Allah who sends the snow and the rain," she added.

Boreal Asia

Northern Asia is cold, but the natural vegetation and agricultural possibilities are a measure of the brief duration of the frost-free period rather than of absolute low winter temperatures. Even those parts of Boreal Asia which record the lowest winter extremes may experience summer temperatures in the upper 80s F. Winters are severe and long, leaving but two or three months with averages above freezing. Even in summer the sun never rises very high in the sky.

The extremely low temperatures recorded in Siberia occur in interior valleys, remote from any moderating maritime influence, where air drainage develops layers of cold heavy air in sheltered, windless basins. An example of this cold in northeastern Siberia is found in the following description by Alexander Polovtsoff.[5]

[5] Alexander Polovtsoff: *Wyna: Adventures in Eastern Siberia.* Quoted by permission. Taken from Anderson: *Splendour of Earth,* London: George Philip & Son (1954), 31–32.

The next day it was −70°C (−94°F), which was perfectly unbearable. When I came out of the house, such clouds of steam escaped with me through the door that it looked as if the vestibule was on fire behind my back. I felt the cold so acutely in my nose and throat that I did not dare to breathe, and expected that if I inhaled the air freely I would share the fate of the cock who had escaped on the previous day from the priest's hen-coop and fallen down stone dead after having flown for about fifteen yards. In my ears I heard all the time a sound as of a trickle of corn, produced by the freezing of one's own breath into hoar-frost; this music was locally called "star-whisper" and only occurred when the thermometer was below −60°C (−75°F).

Wide contrasts characterize Asia's physical realms. Arctic conditions dominate northern Siberia, where reindeer provide the conventional transport for much of the year. (*Courtesy Soviet Embassy, Washington*)

The hard snow of the road did not rustle, but cracked. All the trees were covered with a white layer, so thick that even a bit of straw was as big as a finger, and the woods seemed to be clothed with white foliage. The dogs's nostrils emitted such dense steam that they were like fire-breathing dragons and smoke curled up from their coats. Out of my sleeves rose whiffs of vapour which looked as if I had hidden a lighted cigarette in them, like a naughty schoolboy. The air was absolutely quiet and the smoke rose up out of the chimneys in straight columns, widening out at the top from the accumulation of consecutive puffs. The sky was greenish-blue and the glare of the snow was unbearable. The stillness was complete, nothing stirred, even the dogs did not bark.

Two vegetation zones extend from west to east across Boreal Asia. The first is the treeless tundra which lies along the Arctic Coast and extends southward at increasing elevations in the mountains. The larger zone is that of the taiga, a trackless coniferous area which makes up the world's largest forest. Agriculture is impossible in the former and feasible only to a limited extent in the latter. These limitations are due to both climate and soil, for acid soils cause low fertility. As a result, the population is both sparse and spotty. Hunters, fishermen, lumbermen, miners, and townspeople form the few groups. Cities reflect the needs of government, regional commerce, or the exploitation of resources for the outside world; no part of the area feeds itself.

For the most part the taiga is an untouched wilderness, over which one may fly for hours without seeing a trace of man's occupancy. Not even the desert is so trackless or empty. In all Boreal Asia the occupied or utilized area amounts to only a fraction of 1 per cent.

This is a land of great rivers: The Ob, Yenisei, Lena, each of them among the dozen largest in the world, form the natural avenues of travel and settlement. Conditions along the Lena are described by J. Stadling.[6]

On the 1st of June, we started on our way

[6] J. Stadling: *Through Siberia,* London: Constable. Quoted by permission.

down the gigantic Lena on the small steamer Synok. . . .

It is impossible to convey by words and figures any idea of the gigantic proportions of this superb river. Every second it empties into the ocean 10,000 tons of water, which through its myriad tributaries, it receives from an area of one million square miles, or about five times the size of Great Britain and Ireland. . . .

Having passed the mouth of the Vilui, . . . the country is utterly wild and desolate. The trees become smaller, the woods thinner. North of the Vilui the pine is no more seen. Near the polar circle the spruce ceases, and yet a little farther north the beech, until finally only the hardy Siberian larch remains and continues all the way to within a few miles of the Lena delta.

On the shores of the river were heaped masses of driftwood, and here and there, even though we were at the end of June, lay colossal blocks of ice.

Atlantic Asia

The western fringe of Asia is under the influence of the Atlantic Ocean, both in climate and in culture. A parade of cyclonic storms brings moisture and moderating temperature well into the continent, where not blocked by mountain barriers. Some of this influence is present near the Mediterranean, but the major penetration is across the Soviet Union.

Between the boreal forests and the arid interior lies a temperate wedge of humid agricultural land, the fertile triangle of the Soviet Union. To the east the triangular-shaped realm tapers to limits near Lake Baikal; to the west it widens to take in southern Scandinavia and France. This wedge represents the extreme penetration of moisture from the Atlantic Ocean. To the north is a land of short summers, to the south, an area of drought, neither attractive for agriculture. Winter temperatures are low, as in Boreal Asia, but the growing season extends through four or five months; unlike Arid Asia the region has enough rainfall for crops.

In its natural state Atlantic Asia was about evenly divided between a mixed deciduous and coniferous forest in the north and grasslands in the south; both are now cleared and plowed.

The broad deltas of eastern and southern Asia provide the base for a rice culture which supports a billion people. This is a view in the Philippines. (*D. C. Canlas, from International Cooperation Administration*)

The term steppe has been defined by L. S. Berg, the Russian botanist and geographer.[7]

The name "steppe" is given to an area which is more or less level, unforested, not flooded by high water in spring, well drained, and covered throughout the entire vegetative season with a more or less dense herbaceous vegetation growing on chernozem soils. Outside the steppe zone, steppes are found also in the forest steppe and in the semidesert, and also in some places in the mountains.

Writing in 1901, while Siberia was still relatively undeveloped, Richard Penrose, Jr., de-scribed the country east of the Urals as he saw it along the Trans-Siberian Railway.[8]

We continued eastward over unbroken steppes for over 1,000 miles in the governments of Tobolsk and Tomsk and the Kirgiz country, across the valleys of the Tobol, Ishim, Irtish and Obi rivers, whose courses meandering toward the north are marked by long lines of trees intersecting the plains. As far as the eye can reach are seen scattered fields of grains, separated by grasslands brilliant with wild flowers, and dotted by droves of cattle with their Kirgiz herdsmen; while occasionally caravans and emigrant wagons pass slowly along the country roads. Whole train loads of butter from the dairies of the Obi Valley are shipped thence by sea to England.

The steppe regions contain numerous prosperous rural communities, and a number of towns of considerable size, with population of from ten to sixty thousand people.

[7] L. S. Berg: *Natural Regions of the USSR,* New York: Macmillan (1950), 90. Quoted by permission.

[8] Helen B. Fairbanks and Charles P. Berkey: *Life and Letters of R. A. F. Penrose, Jr.,* New York: Geological Society of America (1952), 246–247. Quoted by permission.

POLITICAL REALMS

One goal of political geography is to organize the world into significant units and to weigh their relative assets and liabilities. Since geography is focused on place, various political theories have naturally examined strength in terms of location or position. The American Admiral Alfred Mahan has stressed sea power and control of the World ocean. Sir Halford Mackinder, a British geographer, has emphasized the ultimate victory of land power as represented in his Asiatic Heartland. Nicholas Spykman, the American political scientist, has found the key to Asia in its Rimland. Any interpretation of Asian geopolitics must appreciate the continent's complexity and the rapid change in its culture.

Asia, though the largest of the continents, is but one part of the round world, and its place in international affairs must be seen on a globe. Only here can true relations be realized. Although Asia is enormously large, the Pacific is five times larger. Actually, the real ocean between Asia and North America is not the Pacific but the Arctic Mediterranean. Americans too often look *westward* from San Francisco toward Shanghai, whereas Chicago is almost as close to Shanghai *northward*. The direct route from Washington to Delhi crosses Greenland.

Many strategists have long been concerned with sea power, in the belief that victory in war depends on command of the seas. They have believed that in the long run it is better to be the attacker outside a castle, no matter how long or hard the siege, than to be on the inside with dwindling supplies. An illustration is Britain's victory over Germany. To this thesis Mackinder found one exception: one impregnable fortress fully immune to any sea-based attack. Such a fortress he found in what he termed the Asiatic Pivot or Heartland. As he defined it, this was an area behind the encircling mountains, deserts, and frozen seas, all of it with interior or Arctic drainage. Since this Asiatic Heartland was readily accessible only on the west, we may understand the importance of the gateway plains of Eastern Europe. Hence Mackinder's famous statement concerning the importance of the tricontinental area of Asia, Europe, and Africa, which he termed the World Island.

Who rules East Europe commands the Heartland,
Who rules the Heartland commands the World Island,
Who rules the World Island commands the World.

In contrast to this emphasis on the interior, Nicholas Spykman has stressed the importance of the periphery of Asia, with its access to the high seas, in the following formula:

Who controls the Rimland rules Eurasia,
Who rules Eurasia rules the world.

What Mackinder apparently failed to realize is that the vast spaces of Soviet Asia, Iran, Mongolia, and interior China offer little in the way of potential food supply or large-scale natural resources, and that they present major problems in unity and accessibility. They thus fail to provide an attractive home for large numbers of people.

The problems of Asia are complex and rapidly changing; factors which were significant in the days of Genghis Khan now have a different importance. Changing cultures place different values on geographic constants. To the Mongol nomads of the thirteenth century, grasslands were the prize; to the Chinese of today, coal and iron are of paramount importance; the seas which once isolated Japan now provide a highway. Civilization and prosperity in the twentieth century develop through stimulating contacts and trade. Some of these cultural assets are best found near the oceans, which today link people and goods from all the world. Access to the sea takes on a new meaning.

India was once self-contained, and its chief neighbors were in the northwest; today it is world-conscious. The absence of good harbors may have been unimportant in earlier centuries but can now be partly overcome by artificial construction. Beirut, Baghdad, and Bangkok were once off the main track and hard to reach; today they are major airports on the direct lines from Europe to eastern Asia. The Trans-China railway from the Pacific to Sinkiang has revolutionized the accessibility and politics of this distant province. The Arctic Ocean was once thought unnavigable, but icebreakers bring many ships to Soviet ports each summer.

Geopolitical realms can represent relations only in terms of momentary factors. The supposed security of Mackinder's Heartland has been altered by the airplane. Mere size is no guarantee of security or importance. The discovery of vast oil reserves around the Persian Gulf suddenly makes the area a political magnet. Physical realities may be more or less constant, but man's technology gives them new meanings.

With these reservations in mind, it may be helpful to identify the major political realms of Asia. In place of Mackinder's hydrographic Heartland we may recognize a Coreland of mountains and deserts; difficult of access and unattractive in its material assets but of some historic significance as an age-old contest area for the countries on its periphery.

This Coreland may be defined as lying north of the Himalaya and Hindu Kush, east of the Caspian, south of the Siberian mountains and forests, and west of the Chinese lowlands in Manchuria and Kansu. All of it is relatively inaccessible, for this is continentality at its extreme. In political terms, the Coreland includes the deserts and mountains of Soviet Middle Asia, southwestern Siberia, Mongolia, Sinkiang, and Tibet.

This central Coreland, being remote from ocean-derived moisture, is characterized by aridity; by nature this is a desert or steppe; only scattered oases offer dependable crops. The realm is partly rimmed by high mountains, is without attractive agricultural possibilities, and has a low population density. So far as known, its mineral assets are modest.

Yet the Coreland has had a dynamic history. Mongol horsemen once overran China and spread far into Europe. Afghan tribesmen

have several times burst into India. Turkic people, with an original Central Asiatic homeland, now occupy Turkey and western China. As Meinig has pointed out,[9]

The Mongol era of the thirteenth century provides the outstanding functional illustration of this quality of the core of Eurasia, when the horsemen based upon the fertile valleys of Mongolia thrust outward in nearly every direction, pushing deep in Muscovy nearly to Novgorod; into Silesia, Moravia, and Hungary; southwestward to the Turkish Mediterranean, Syria, and the Persian Gulf; over the ranges into the Punjab and Upper Ganges; and finally overrunning the whole of China to the southern seas. Never before or since has the positional advantage of this nuclear area been utilized so sharply and comprehensively.

The Asian Coreland has been both explosive and magnetic. Outside powers have often found strategic attractions here. Czarist conquests acquired the states of Bukhara and Khiva only a century ago. Both Mongolia and Sinkiang have been contest areas for Russia and China within the twentieth century. India watches Tibetan developments with concern. During the 1930s the German airline Lufthansa sent camel caravans loaded with gasoline tins across the Gobi Desert in the hope of developing a trans-Asian air route. Both Britain and America once maintained consulates in Sinkiang, even though there was little for them to do except to watch.

Most of the Coreland is now ruled by outside nationalities, as it has been through the past. The Mongolian People's Republic is a sovereign state but is under Soviet tutelage. Minority peoples inhabit western China and the southern Soviet Union. It seems unlikely that the Coreland will again dominate Asia.

The southern and eastern periphery of Asia is quite different. Here the orientation is outward rather than inward. Chinese junks and Arab dhows replace camel caravans. Along the shores of the eastern Mediterranean and the Indian and Pacific Oceans are dozens of mod-

[9] Donald W. Meinig: "Heartland and Rimland in Eurasian History," *Western Political Quarterly*, IX (1956), 557–558. Quoted by permission.

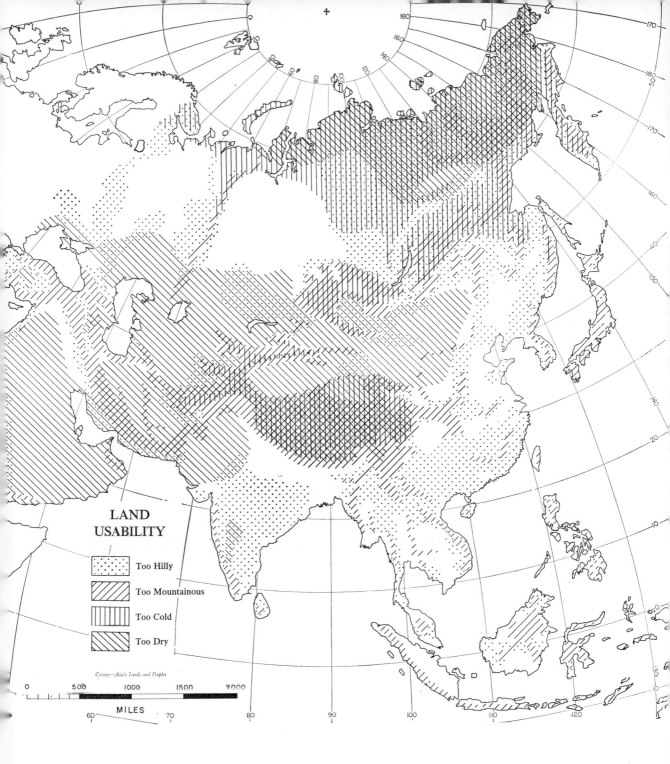

LAND
USABILITY

- ∷ Too Hilly
- ⫽ Too Mountainous
- ‖ Too Cold
- ⟍ Too Dry

Cressey—Asia's Lands and Peoples

0   500   1000   1500   2000

MILES

Large parts of Asia are unproductive and unattractive as a home for man. Too much is too hilly or too mountainous, too cold or even too hot, or too dry or too wet.

ern seaports. Each is a focal point for foreign trade, especially where there is a productive hinterland and rail connection. These scattered ports, rather than a continuous land-sea frontier, characterize the fringe of Asia. Mere proximity to the sea does not ensure maritime consciousness, especially if harbors are lacking and fishing is poor.

This discontinuous peripheral zone is here termed the Fringeland. It has no precise limits, but may be thought of as the zone within one or two hundred miles of each port—wider with good transport, less where communications are poor. In reality, fingerlike extensions follow navigable rivers and major railways. Siberia has a somewhat exceptional character, which is in part due to the closed nature of the Arctic

Ocean. While the Fringeland is discontinuous along many coasts, the port zones overlap in Japan and the Philippines, so that all these island groups are included; this overlapping only partly exists among the larger Indonesian islands. Port zones overlap along the South China coast with its many harbors, but there are gaps in India. During the twentieth century this Fringeland has been the most dynamic part of Asia. Western-oriented trade and education have penetrated here, and here the standard of living is highest. The Fringeland is also a contest zone between European and traditional ideas, so that it has been the scene of political unrest, economic movements, and social confusion. Since distances around the periphery of Asia are great, there is little cultural coherence,

The Tien An Men, or Gate of Heavenly Peace, stands at the entrance to the old Forbidden City in Peking and provides the setting for elaborate Communist parades. The building was begun in 1417, but the present structure was erected in 1651. (*Eastfoto*)

Asia has three great centers of geopolitical power: the Soviet Union, China, and India.
This is a view of the Kremlin, with its churches and palaces. The Moscow River flows
in the foreground. (*Courtesy KLM, the Royal Dutch Airline*)

and only access to the sea and a new way of life give a semblance of unity.

As an extension of the Fringeland, one might mention what was formerly colonial Asia, much of which radiated inland from these seaports. This still includes survivals such as Aden, Timor, and Hong Kong; and the treaty-related states of Kuwait and Bahrein. Okinawa is another quasicolonial area. Even though parts of colonial Asia were hundreds of miles from a seaport, Fringeland influences have left their impress.

Between the Coreland and the Fringeland lies the bulk of Asia, termed by Mackinder the Inner Crescent. Though it might be convenient to use such an all-inclusive title, the area in question is too diverse to treat as a unit. What have Iraq and Thailand in common, or Iraq

and the Yenisei valley? Each is underdeveloped and each is land-minded, but the state of political culture is very different. Some other approach is desirable.

Three centers of strength appear to dominate the margins of Asia, with intervening contest areas. One power realm is clearly China, for centuries the undisputed leader in the East. Another is the Indian peninsula, which is a power even though not always united. The third is Russia, the twentieth-century giant which increasingly looks east and south. Japan attempted to operate in this top category but could not hold the pace.

These three areas of strength meet in the central Coreland and in the encircling Fringeland; between each realm lie intermediate contest zones, three in number. Southwest Asia includes a series of small states, none of them viable against global pressures; all Southeast Asia is in cultural dispute between India and China and may well be the scene of political contest; Japan and Korea are increasingly caught between Chinese and Soviet pressure on the one hand and American on the other. While Japan had a moment of expansionist grandeur during the Second World War, it seems unlikely that she can seize power again.

Each of the three great power zones—China, India, and the western Soviet Union—have developed relatively good internal accessibility. India has had a closely spaced railroad net for many decades, and in eastern China and southern Siberia communications are developing rapidly. The western Soviet Union has good communication facilities, and only northern Siberia lacks widespread rail and road services. In contrast, several of the intervening contest zones lack both internal and interconnecting transport services.

In terms of political potentials, present-day Asia thus has three major and three minor areas. The chief centers of power are the Indian, Chinese, and Soviet realms. Between them are the transitional contest areas of the Southwest, the Southeast, and Japan-Korea. In the center is the Coreland. Linking the peripheral coastal areas is the Fringeland, with its relics of colonial rule but without unity. Since these represent dynamic situations, an increase in power within one realm leads to pressures along its borders. During the second quarter of the present century Russia was the most dynamic realm; during the third quarter it may well be China. Her development promises ill for her neighbors if they lag behind.

Another obvious regionalization of Asia relates to its mid-twentieth-century political coloration. The Communist bloc includes the Union of Soviet Socialist Republics, the People's Republic of China, the Mongolian People's Republic, North Korea, and North Viet Nam. In the realm allied with the West, through groupings such as the Central Treaty Organization or the South East Asia Treaty Organization, are

Turkey, Iran, Pakistan, Thailand, the Philippines, the Republic of China, Japan, and South Korea. This leaves, first, an uncommitted group in the Southwest: the Arab States of Syria, Iraq, Jordan, and Saudi Arabia; Israel; and Afghanistan; second, another group in South Asia composed of India, Ceylon, and Nepal; and, third, the uncommitted nations of the Southeast: Burma, Malaya, Indonesia, South Viet Nam, Laos, and Cambodia.

Schemes for Pan-Asian unity have so far failed. During the period between the First and Second World Wars, Japan initiated a number of cultural, financial, and political programs, but they did not meet with much approval. Whether Communist ideology will achieve greater success remains to be seen. It may well be that the physical and cultural diversities of the continent are so basic that Asia will remain fractionalized. In place of the centripetal coherence of Europe and the Americas, Asia appears to have a centrifugal orientation. Each Asian realm has its own focus center, and extrarealm interests tend to be outward by sea rather than inward by land. It will be interesting to see whether future trans-Coreland railways and airlines will reverse this external orientation and produce an all-Asian community.

America's location in relation to Asia has some similarities to her position with respect to Europe. The United States faces both continents across an ocean, and approaches the mainland of each through the territory of an important island nation: the United Kingdom and Japan, respectively. Since any threat to either insular power would compromise our access to the mainland, America has a concern in their welfare, even though the major centers of resource and trade lie on the continent. Here is a basic problem in American foreign policy.

GEOSTRATEGY IN ASIA

Since geography is concerned with the totality of place, it deals with all of those factors—

The Red Fort in Delhi is a symbol of ancient India's imperial power under the Mogul dynasty. History, population, and location ensure India's place in South Asia.

some physical, some cultural—which bear on the personality and potential of areas. Geography thus lists and weighs the items which make some places and some nations stronger than others.

This is the field of geostrategy: the broad application of geographic principles to international affairs as well as to domestic evaluation. In part it involves economic geography; in part, as applied to states, it is geopolitical. Obviously Asia as a whole is characterized by vast area and great distances, by high mountains and broad deserts, by ancient cultures and dense populations. What should be equally obvious is that these items must be seen in terms of their distribution.

One major function of this volume is to give meaning to the map, to clothe it with personality.

Geostrategy includes many components. Among them are: (1) location, (2) size and shape, (3) land forms, (4) climate, (5) soil, (6) accessibility, (7) boundaries, (8) relation to the ocean, (9) raw materials, and (10) people. The following paragraphs may serve as a checklist, to be applied to each country in Asia. Though physical characteristics may appear impressive, it should be emphasized that people and ideas may be more meaningful than mountains and metals. Nature may be static, but man is dynamic.

Location is the prime question in all geography: not "where" in terms of latitude and longitude, but "where" in terms of good land and markets and world highways. Shanghai does not owe its importance to latitude but to the hinterland of the Yangtze valley. The mouths of the great Siberian rivers lack good harbors, but the productivity of the interior is forcing port developments. Position is inescapably important in political policy and economic orientation. Asia has been off-center for the modern North Atlantic world, but it is central for those who live there.

Inner Asia represents the climax of continentality. Yet few nations have achieved cultural or any other progress without external contacts. Coastal wartime China may have wished that she did not have such an exposed shoreline, but the peacetime assets greatly outweigh the military liabilities. Japan has an excellent position in the western Pacific but lacks a secure home base. Her defeat was difficult during the Second World War because of her temporarily enlarged size and the central position of Japan within this empire. The significance of location can change. Rome was once the center of the civilized world; but the Mediterranean is now a minor body of water. Interior Asia is increasing its population, and remote cities have become accessible through air travel.

The importance of size was dramatically demonstrated during the Second World War, when both the Soviet Union and China were able to retreat and thereby gain time for further resistance, whereas smaller countries lacked defense in depth. But mere size is not enough. No large army could withdraw into Mongolia or northern Siberia and survive, for there are inadequate productive potentials. Too great an area may be a handicap unless well united. The Heartland castle of Inner Asia, though large and remote, is devoid of the possibilities for major economic strength. No country anywhere can have sufficient size to be immune to air attack or to furnish an adequate base for world conquest. The air age has brought close for both "inaccessible countries" and continental cores. Even a combination of neighboring nations, such as the Soviet Union and China, could not be secure on the basis of size alone.

Form or shape is a further factor in the strength of a nation. Although China appears compact on the map, her population distribution is concentrated in a few fertile valleys while vast areas remain nearly empty. The true size of the country is apparent only in terms of habitability and productivity. Mackinder's Heartland has a satisfactory gross shape, but the distribution of good land and people and communications is so eccentric that the region lacks coherence.

Land form is the third element in geostrategy. Here Asia suffers, for rugged ranges isolate its various realms. The Himalaya provide the interior with security from invasion on the south, but they also block trade. Asia has great areas of level land, as in Siberia or Mongolia, but most plains are separated from their neighboring lowlands by imposing mountains, and many are dry or cold. Six-sevenths of Japan is hilly or mountainous, and even India has many areas too hilly to cultivate.

Climate is another of the components in overall geographic evaluation. Here is the obvious basis for agriculture. Unfortunately, great sections of Asia are too cold, too dry, or too wet to be very productive. It is not likely that climatic advantages will ever lead the United Nations to locate its capital in Singapore or in Yakutsk. Nor will exceptionally energetic people live in these areas. Maps of climatic energy give lower rank to most of Asia than to Europe or North America. The long period of winter inactivity in the northern interior is certainly a disadvantage.

Along with climate goes its by-product, the soil. Where the soil permits, agriculture has been intensive; without many fertile areas Asia could not have fed its billions. Unfortunately, great areas are infertile because of excessive leaching, or the accumulation of salt, or too much acidity, or inadequate humus. One should visualize the map of soils in terms of their productivity and color. Nature has two great pigments, iron and carbon, respectively red and black. Where soils are stained reddish or yellowish by iron rust, their fertility is usually low. Where they are black with humus, they are commonly high in organic matter.

Accessibility is of great importance in modern economy. Anything beyond subsistence livelihood requires trade and communication. Vast areas in Asia lie more than 10 miles from a railway, navigable river, or automobile road. Elsewhere travel is by camels or mules, carts, or canal boats. Three large areas with good transportation stand out clearly: the western Soviet Union and India, both well supplied with a network of railways, and China, where many of the lines represent automobile roads or navigable rivers. Unfortunately, these three areas are poorly connected with one another. Only one road links Burma and India, and but one road leads from Burma to China. A single railway and only two roads connect Pakistan with Southwestern Asia. Only three railways and a few desert roads link China and the U.S.S.R.

Much of interior Asia is inaccessible in terms of modern communications. Mongolia and Tibet present major travel difficulties, and journeying in Soviet Middle Asia is only slightly less arduous. Northern Siberia has little more than its rivers, icebound for much of the year. The coherence and strength of a continent are necessarily dependent, in large part, upon its accessibility.

International boundaries frequently present problems; here is the seventh component of geostrategy. No boundaries are good without good will on either side, but some natural limits are better than others. Deserts, mountains, and icebound seas form natural obstacles to ground travel but not to the airplane. If such barriers keep armies from trespassing, they equally keep out goods, people, and ideas. No civilization can progress without stimulating contacts. Almost every frontier in Asia has experienced change within the past century, and many boundaries are still poorly defined or are in dispute.

The ocean is the cheapest and most international highway; without free access to it, a nation suffers. Oceans, no longer barriers, have become roads. Countries without access to the high seas include Afghanistan, Nepal, and Mongolia. Several others, such as Jordan and Iraq, barely have a coast line. In contrast, Japan and Malaya are sea-oriented. The Soviet Union has a long border next to the Arctic Ocean, but it is frozen for much of the year. Throughout history the Russian bear has sought warm water, an outlet to the unfrozen seas. Under any form of government, Russia will inevitably continue its quest for access to the open Atlantic, the Mediterranean, the Persian gulf, and the Yellow Sea.

Raw materials, both mineral and agricultural, are vital in our modern world. Other nations in other times have achieved conspicuous success through art or philosophy, but in the twentieth century national greatness rests, perhaps too much, on coal, oil, iron, copper, and aluminum. Lord Curzon remarked that, during the First World War, the Allies "floated to victory on a sea of oil." During the Second World War they flew to victory on a cloud of gasoline.

Nature has distributed the good things of the earth unevenly. Although the Soviet Union is exceptionally rich in many of these resources, and although China has coal in abundance and India large amounts of iron ore, no nation is fully self-sufficient in mineral resources. The twenty-first century will presumably witness tremendous industrial developments in Asia based on the development of her mineral wealth.

No other factor of geography begins to compare with people. Nationality, skills, religion, population density, and even patriotism are of geographic concern. Nature may lay down a variety of restrictions to settlement, but man still has a choice. Under some cultures, countries may reclaim part of the desert or tunnel through mountains or drain swamps. A nation's greatest assets are its people, not primarily their number but their quality. The last item in this list is thus, appropriately, humanity. Man is well advised to work in recognition of nature's assets and handicaps, but the decision to do so rests with him. Asia's manpower is her greatest asset, but until people are properly fed and housed they are also her greatest liability. Problems of the man-land ratio and of overpopulation are paramount in any consideration of geostrategy.

THE BEAST ASIAN REALM

Eastern Asia contains nearly a billion people. Everywhere they confront the basic problems of existence—an exploding population and meager agricultural resources. The Chinese have developed a rich culture whose roots go deep into the earth; the maritime-minded Japanese have made the transition to a great industrial state; and divided Korea faces problems of livelihood.

"Almost every foot of land is made to contribute material for food, fuel or fabric. Everything which can be made edible serves as food for man or domestic animals. Whatever cannot be eaten or worn is used for fuel. The wastes of the body, of fuel and of fabric worn beyond other use are taken back to the field; before doing so they are housed against waste from weather, compounded with intelligence and forethought and patiently labored with through one, three or even six months, to bring them into the most efficient form to serve as manure for the soil or as feed for the crop. It seems to be a golden rule with these industrial classes, or if not golden, then an inviolable one, that whenever an extra hour or day of labor can promise even a little larger return then that shall be given, and neither a rainy day nor the hottest sunshine shall be permitted to cancel the obligation or defer its execution." (*F. H. King: Farmers of Forty Centuries, Madison: Democrat Printing Co., 1911, 13. Quoted by permission*)

Fields and mountains in Hokkaido.
(*Courtesy John H. Thompson*)

4 China's Cultural Patterns

The Chinese Landscape / Population Problems / Political Framework / Communist Developments / Historical Backgrounds / References on China

THE CHINESE LANDSCAPE

China presents a unique phenomenon. Other lands are older and others more beautiful, but nowhere else have so many people lived so close to nature and with such cultural continuity as in China. The landscape everywhere reflects the intensity of man's occupancy. The culture of the ages has so permeated all levels of society that even the simple farmer quotes Confucius. No land on earth is so mature in its man-land relations.

The Chinese landscape is vast in time as well as in area and in numbers. More human beings have lived on this good earth than on any similar area in the world—at least 10 billion in all. Almost everywhere man long ago utilized the resources of nature up to the limit of the tools at his command. The present is thus the product of a long and very rich heritage. The problems of the twentieth century arise from the sudden impact of the Western world upon China and the reorientation of her pattern of life. Only those who understand China's history and geography in their entirety can properly evaluate the events of the present. We are not witnessing a typical period in her history, for the previous maturity of her social adjustments has been upset by the sudden discovery of a different world order.

The roots of the Chinese go deep into the earth. The carefully tilled gardens, the hand-plucked harvest, and the earthen homes all tell the story of man's intimate association with nature. On every hand a substantial peasantry labors industriously to wrest a meager livelihood from the tiny fields. Innumerable groups of farm buildings, half hidden in clumps of bamboo or willow, suggest the intensity of man's quest for food, and the ever-present grave mounds serve as reminders of the heritage of this venerable land.

The most significant element in the Chinese landscape is thus not the soil or vegetation or climate, but the people. Everywhere there are human beings. In this old, old land, one can scarcely find a spot unmodified by man and his activities. Whereas life has been profoundly influenced by the environment, it is equally true that man has reshaped and modified nature and given it a human stamp. The Chinese landscape is a biophysical unity, knit together as

Chinese culture reaches its apex in Peking, where the empire commanded the finest in architects, scholars, and craftsmen. This is part of the former Summer Palace. (*Green, from Publisher's Photo Service*)

intimately as a tree and the soil from which it grows. So deeply is man rooted in the earth that there is but one all-inclusive unity—not man and nature as separate phenomena but linked together in a single organic whole. The cheerful peasants at work in the fields are as much a part of nature as the hills themselves. So, too, the carefully tended rice fields are an inescapable element in the human panorama.

No mere photographic portrayal of China can reveal all the varied ties that bind man and the soil together. Crisscross through the

Communist China Data [1]

Area (mainland)	3,691,502 square miles	
Population	582,602,417 [2]	660,000,000 (1960 est.)
Shanghai	6,204,417	6,977,000
Hong Kong (British)		3,128,044 (1961 census)
Peking (capital)	2,768,149	4,148,000
Tientsin	2,693,831	3,278,000
Mukden (Shenyang)	2,299,900	2,423,000
Chungking	1,772,500	2,165,000
Canton	1,598,900	1,867,000
Wuhan (Hankow, Hanyang, and Wuchang)	1,427,300	2,226,000
Harbin	1,163,000	1,595,000
Nanking	1,091,600	1,455,000
Tsingtao	916,800	1,144,000
Chengtu	856,700	1,135,000
Changchun (Hsinking)	855,200	
Sian	787,300	1,368,000
Dairen-Port Arthur (Luta)	766,400	1,590,000
Taiyuan	720,700	1,053,000
Kunming	698,900	
Hangchow	696,600	
Tangshan	693,300	
Tsinan	680,100	
Fushun	678,600	1,019,000
Changsha	650,600	
Lungki (Changchow)	594,700	
Wusih	581,500	
Foochow (Minhow)	553,000	
Anshan	548,900	
Penki	499,000	
Elementary school pupils	97,000,000	
Higher education students	810,000	
Grain	180,000,000 metric tons (1960)	
Cotton	2,400,000 metric tons (1959)	
Coal	425,000,000 metric tons (1960)	
Steel	18,500,000 metric tons (1960)	

[1] *Britannica Book of the Year*, 1962. (1958 estimate unless otherwise noted.)
[2] All population figures in this column are from 1953 census.

Floods have always presented serious problems, especially along the Hwai River. This is the Futseling dam, one of many reservoir developments on the tributaries designed for flood control and hydroelectricity. (*China Photo Service*)

visible scene run innumerable threads of relationship. The landscape is a mosaic of many diverse elements, some dependent upon the vagaries of a none-too-certain rainfall, some conditioned by the limitations of the soil, still others molded by the force of tradition. All these are linked together into a synthetic, animated picture. It is the task of geography to describe and understand these relationships, to draw information from widely scattered sources, and to give it a new significance as applied to the understanding of specific areas. This living panorama forms the cultural landscape.

China is not only rich in her culture; she is diverse in her physical environment. Rainfall varies from 1 inch a year in the desert to 100 inches along the coastal mountains. Extensive forests stand in contrast to denuded hillsides. Few large countries have such a high percentage of hilly or otherwise uncultivable land. Roughly half of China exceeds a mile in elevation. Only through prodigious effort and painstaking care have the Chinese been able to support so large a population.

This topographic diversity has divided China into many regions, each with its personality. The Chinese of the various provinces differ in physical appearance, in language, and in psychology. For example, the development of the "almond eye" characterizes 36 per cent of the people around Canton, 23 per cent near Shanghai, and only 11 to 21 per cent in the north.

Rice is eaten daily in the south, but is an occasional luxury elsewhere. Shanghai is a cosmopolitan city, but one need go only a few hundred yards beyond its borders to find a primitive countryside.

Despite these contrasts, China has a distinct homogeneity. Dialects may differ, but the written language is the same. The degree of modernization may vary, but everywhere there is a coherent way of life, in large measure the heritage of Confucius and the sages. It is this pattern of living, of getting along with each other and with nature, that makes the Chinese people so genuine.

China's 3¾ million square miles present wide contrasts in physical and cultural environments. In climatic terms, and thus in natural vegetation and soils, eastern China is a rough equivalent of eastern North America; both areas lie to the leeward of a great continent. But in complexity of topography, eastern Asia is much more hilly. Whereas both the United States and the Soviet Union extend from east to west, China stretches from north to south. The distance from the far south in Hainan to the northernmost bend of the Amur River is 2,500 miles. Thus agricultural possibilities and means of livelihood vary notably.

If China were superimposed on North America, it would reach from Puerto Rico to southern Hudson Bay, and from the Atlantic to the Pacific. Canton and Hong Kong lie within the tropics in the latitude of Havana. Shanghai is on the parallel of Savannah; Chungking corresponds to San Antonio; Tientsin and Peking are in the latitude of Washington; Mukden parallels Albany and Harbin, Montreal. The northern part of Manchuria is but 13 degrees from the Arctic Circle, while the southern island of Hainan is 18 degrees from the equator. The more important areas of China are somewhat farther south than the most populous parts of the United States.

The physical features which characterize the geography of China grow out of the vast size of Asia, with its pronounced seasonal climates and its complex mountain pattern.

Considered as a whole, China has much less level land than the United States, especially in the south and west, where on a clear day one is never out of sight of hills or mountains. The plateau of Tibet averages 3 miles in elevation, with numerous peaks up to 5 miles high. In Sinkiang the oasis of Turfan descends to 928 feet below sea level. Temperatures also show broad extremes. All of these set the stage for wide cultural contrasts.

POPULATION PROBLEMS

No one can travel across China without being aware of the pressure of people on the arable land. Even in remote and inhospitable areas, where one may journey for miles without seeing a house, on every bit of good land one finds that painstaking farmers have crowded the soil to its maximum capacity. Centuries of famine and invasion and political strife and population increase have pushed the Chinese into every corner that will support life. Essentially no more good land remains unused, even in the far interior.

Though a glance at the population map will show how unevenly these people are distributed, the answer to overcrowding does not lie in redistribution. The sparsely settled areas merely have less population-supporting capacity, but they are effectively as crowded as the others. The dense areas are dense because conditions of livelihood are more attractive. China's population map is at the same time a map of agricultural productivity; change the legend and one would almost pass for the other.

China, which is not considered an urban land, has a dozen cities with a million or more people, and as many others with a population of between a half million and one million.

The size of China's population has long been in dispute. Traditional references once described China as the "Land of the Four Hundred Million." Estimates from various sources during the first half of the present century amounted to 440,000,000 (1900), 485,508,-838 (1926), 472,580,216 (1938), and 483,-

869,687 (1950)—none of them based on actual counts.

In 1953 the Peking government conducted a detailed census, the first ever held in China. The total proved to be unexpectedly high, 601,938,035, but this included 11,743,320 overseas Chinese plus 7,592,298 on Taiwan, giving a Mainland total of 582,602,417. These figures present sober problems of food supply and livelihood. The above data do not include Hong Kong with over 3 million or Macao with a half million people.

On the basis of the best available evidence it appears that from 75 to 80 per cent of the population are farmers.

Whatever the exact data, China has a vast population. If it were suddenly possible to introduce modern sanitation, check infant mortality, eliminate famines, and reduce the death rate to Western standards without lowering the birth rate, a tremendous increase in population would occur within a generation. Without a great increase in food supplies, large sections of the population already at subsistence levels might then be driven into desperate economic straits.

Something of this sort has already taken place, for the 1953 census figures indicate a birth rate of 37 per thousand and a death rate of 17 per thousand, hence a net increase of 2 per cent a year. If data of the above magnitude are correct, China's population will surpass a billion people well before the end of the century.

Population densities are often misleading unless properly interpreted. For the world as a whole the average is about 60 people per square mile. The United States closely paral-

Railway construction has opened many areas in the west, once accessible only by river boat or mule cart. This track-laying operation is along the desert line which links Paotow and Lanchow, where drifting sand creates maintenance problems. (*Li Feng, from Eastfoto*)

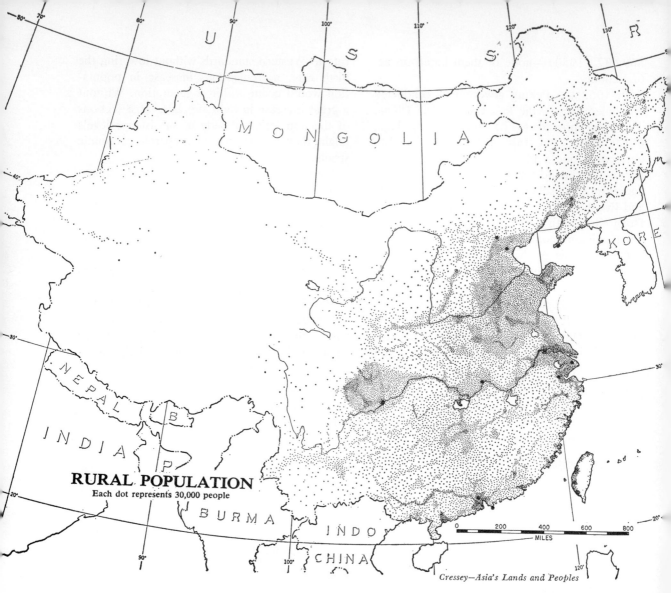

RURAL POPULATION
Each dot represents 30,000 people

Cressey—Asia's Lands and Peoples

Four-fifths of China's population live on farms or in villages of less than 25,000 people. Their distribution reflects the pattern of climate and soil; everywhere man uses the land to the limit of his technology. (*Based on provincial maps by Charles Y. Hu*)

lels this average with 55. Within Asia the Soviet Union has 30, China 200, India 350, and Japan 700 people for each square mile of total area.

China's figure, which is about the average for Ohio and Illinois, does not appear to represent undue crowding. On the other hand, in the eastern and more crowded part of the country, the average density is tripled. Only when specific areas are considered does a significant picture emerge. We thus realize that the Yellow Plain has about 1,000 people per square mile of cropland. This adds up to an average of one-third of an acre of cultivated land per capita.

Overpopulation is not a matter of absolute numbers alone, but rather a matter of balance between available income and mouths to be fed. Lower Manhattan Island in New York City can support a million people within a square mile

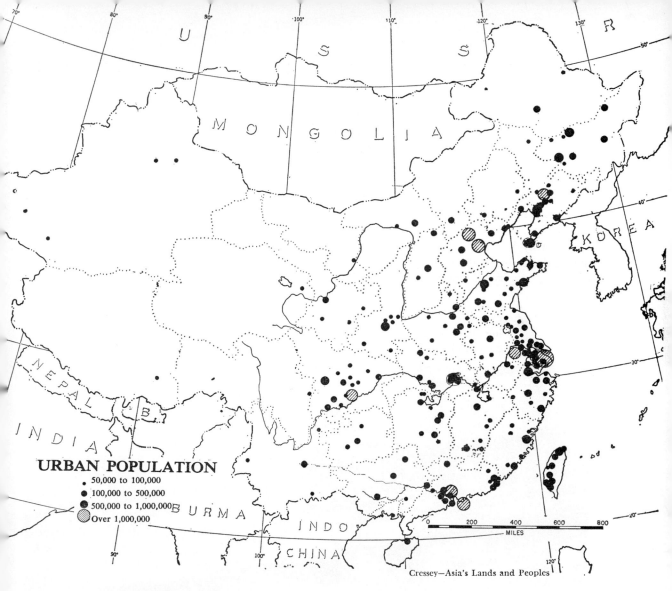

URBAN POPULATION

- . 50,000 to 100,000
- ● 100,000 to 500,000
- ⬤ 500,000 to 1,000,000
- ◉ Over 1,000,000

Cressey—Asia's Lands and Peoples

China has more than 200 cities whose population exceeds 50,000; the total number of towns is more than 1,000. All these urban centers have been in the midst of dramatic transformation since the mid-1930s.

without economic distress, whereas, under existing types of utilization, parts of Inner Mongolia or Tibet may be overcrowded with an average of only two people per square mile. China's basic problem is not one of numbers but of livelihood. So long as millions of people periodically suffer from starvation or live on the edge of want, China unquestionably will have a population problem. Unfortunately, it does not appear that available soil and minerals can

adequately increase the present standards of living for so many people.

China has certainly been overpopulated in the past. Whether this situation must continue depends on the possibility that technological changes can provide increased income. The Malthusian checks of starvation, disease, and war have operated cruelly over the centuries. Flood and drought have caught people without any reserve of food or money. Perhaps 100 million have died of famine or malnutrition in the past century.

When confronted with this problem, the official Communist answer is that under Marxian economics, a rise in population automatically brings an increase in prosperity. In view of the many jobs to be done in reconstructing the country, Communists actually contend that China today is "underpopulated."

No more important problem confronts the new China. Too many people now live on a dangerously low standard. The greatness of a nation depends not upon its total numbers, but upon the quality of the people's life. China's

rich culture rests upon weak material foundations. The cultivation of marginal land and increased crop yields will help for a while. Industrialization offers other possibilities, of uncertain value. In terms of the present and near future it appears clear that China has too many people.

Within the total population are many races other than the Han people or Chinese proper. Nearly 20 million "aborigines" live in the southwest, a mixture of Miao, Thai, Monkhmer, Lolos, and many others. Mongol, Turkish, and Tungan people each number about 2 million. More than a million Manchus and

China is so full of people that many families have spilled over onto the water, spending their lives on boats. This scene is in Shanghai but might be duplicated in every coastal city. (*Courtesy Northwest Airlines*)

POLITICAL DIVISIONS

≡ Autonomous districts	• Cities under one million
‖ Disputed boundary areas	■ Cities over one million
▨ Special municipalities	— Provincial capitals

Cressey—Asia's Lands and Peoples

0 200 400 600 800
MILES

Traditional China included eighteen provinces south of the Great Wall, plus the outer areas of Manchuria, now divided into three provinces; Mongolia, now limited to an enlarged Inner Mongolia; Sinkiang; and Tibet, now reduced by the creation of Tsinghai. The word "autonomous" refers to areas with large ethnic minorities.

a million Koreans live in the northeastern provinces. Large numbers of Chinese live overseas, especially in Thailand, Malaysia, the Indochina states, the Philippines, and Indonesia. The total is at least 7 million, or possibly 12 million, if all categories of citizenship and racial mixtures are included.

POLITICAL FRAMEWORK

Under the Manchu dynasty, China was divided into eighteen provinces and four dependencies or territories, the latter being Manchuria, Mongolia, Sinkiang, and Tibet. It is thus customary for the Chinese to refer to the tradi-

Political regions	Pronunciation	Capital city	Area, square miles	Population, 1953 census
The People's Republic of China (Communist)				
Provinces				
Anhwei	*on whay*	Hofei (Luchow)	54,305	30,343,637
Chekiang	*jer jiang*	Hangchow	39,621	22,865,747
Fukien	*fu jien*	Foochow (Minhow)	45,539	13,142,721
Heilungkiang	*hay loong jiang*	Harbin	109,009	11,897,309
Honan	*hoe nan*	Lungki (Changchow)	63,744	44,214,594
Hopei	*hoe bay*	Tientsin	54,482	35,984,644
Hunan	*hu nan*	Changsha	79,042	33,226,954
Hupei	*hu bay*	Wuhan	71,936	27,789,693
Jehol [2]	*ji hoe*	Chengteh	69,473	5,160,822
Kansu	*gan soo*	Lanchow (Kaolan)	151,121	12,928,102
Kiangsi	*jiang see*	Nanchang	66,783	16,772,865
Kiangsu	*jiang su*	Nanking	42,455	41,252,192
Kirin	*gee lin*	Changchun	46,127	11,290,073
Kwangsi [3]	*gwong see*	Nanning	84,505	19,560,822
Kwangtung	*gwang doong*	Canton (Kwangchow)	84,443	34,770,059
Kweichow	*gwei joe*	Kweiyang	65,696	15,037,310
Liaoning	*leao ning*	Mukden (Shenyang)		18,545,147
Shansi	*shan see*	Taiyuan (Yangku)	60,378	14,314,485
Shantung	*shan doong*	Tsinan	54,544	48,876,548
Shensi	*shen see*	Sian (Changan)	72,533	15,881,281
Sikang [4]	*see kang*	Yaan	174,287	3,381,064
Szechwan	*ssu chuan*	Chengtu	117,197	62,303,999
Tsinghai	*ching hai*	Sining	257,553	1,676,534
Yunnan	*yoon nan*	Kunming	162,300	17,472,737
Autonomous Regions				
Tibet		Lhasa	349,149	1,273,969
Inner Mongolia		Huehot (Kweisui)		6,100,104
Sinkiang-Uighur	*hsin geeong*	Urumchi (Tihwa)	660,805	4,873,608
Municipalities				
Shanghai	*shang hai*		345	6,204,417
Peking	*bay king*		270	2,768,149
All Communist China		Peking	3,643,884	582,602,417
The Republic of China (Nationalist)				1957 census
Taiwan		Taipei	13,952	9,409,886
All China			3,657,836	592,012,303

[1] Data from *Statesman's Yearbook*, 1961.
[2] Since 1955, divided between Hopei, Liaoning, and Inner Mongolia.
[3] Since 1957, the Chuang Autonomous District.
[4] Since 1955, part of Szechwan.

tional part of their country south of the Great Wall as the "Eighteen Provinces." These are sometimes referred to as "China proper," but the term seems improper since the balance of the country is equally Chinese.

Since many provincial and city names are based on the combination of basic Chinese characters, it may be appropriate to list a few geographical terms as follows: north—*pei,* south—*nan,* east—*tung,* west—*si,* mountain—*shan,* sea—*hai,* lake—*hu,* river—*ho* or *kiang.*

Eighteen provinces make up historic China. Around the capital at Peking is Hopei, the province north of the river with reference to the Hwang Ho. Just to the south is Honan, south of the river. On either side are Shantung and Shansi, respectively east and west of the mountains. Northwest China inside the Great Wall also includes Shensi and Kansu.

Provinces of the Yangtze valley, reading up river, begin with Kiangsu and Kiangsi, in which the first character is that of the Yangtze Kiang. Alongside is Anhwei. Just as northern China has two provinces on either side of the Hwang Ho, so central China has two provinces north and south of the Mid-Yangtze lakes, the Chinese name for which is *hu;* thus Hupei and Hunan. Farther west and beyond the Yangtze gorges is Szechwan, the province of the four rivers, *chwan* being another name for river.

Two provinces along the southeastern coast are Chekiang and Fukien. Southernmost China has a pair of provinces, Kwangtung and Kwangsi, the eastern and western areas. Farther inland are Kweichow and Yunnan, the latter meaning south of the clouds (referring to cloudy Szechwan).

The nineteenth province was created in 1878 when Sinkiang was raised from territorial status. Under Communist rule, Sinkiang is known as the Uighur Autonomous Region.

The use of the term "autonomous" in Communist terminology, both Chinese and Soviet, reflects the presence of people who differ from the ethnic majority. Thus several of the provinces now contain subdivisions, usually "autonomous districts," which indicate their population makeup, as in Kwangsi, where much of the area is administered as the Chuang Autonomous District.

Manchuria was divided into three large provinces in 1903: Liaoning, Kirin, and Heilungkiang. The first name refers to the main river of southern Manchuria, the Liao; the third province has the same name as that of its river, known to Westerners as the Amur and to the Chinese as the Black Dragon River.

Mongolia traditionally has been made up of two parts: Inner Mongolia next to the Great Wall and thus closer to Peking, and Outer Mongolia. Outer Mongolia proclaimed its independence in 1913, and since 1945 has been recognized by China as the Mongolian People's Republic, an independent state with its capital at Ulan Bator, formerly Urga. In 1912 Inner Mongolia was divided into four provinces: Ningsia, Suiyuan, Chahar, and Jehol. In 1947 most of the area, plus western Manchuria, was consolidated to form the Inner Mongolian Autonomous Region.

Tibet is also made up of two sections, Nearer Tibet and Farther Tibet, so named with respect to their distance from Peking. The former is divided into two provinces, Tsinghai and Sikang. The latter is now the Tibetan Autonomous Region.

To these must be added Taiwan (Formosa), returned from Japan in 1945 and the seat of the Nationalist government of the Republic of China.

If to the original 18 provinces are added the 10 provinces carved out of the former territories by the Nationalist government, the number would rise to 28, plus Taiwan. The Communist government has combined several provinces and has created new autonomous regions, thus reducing the Mainland provincial total to 22.

Mainland China, namely the area controlled by the People's Republic of China under the Communists, measures 3,657,836 square miles. The Nationalist government in turn controls Taiwan, with an area of 13,952 square miles. In comparison, the Soviet Union covers 8,650,-

Modern industry has revolutionized urban life in scores of cities. This is a flax mill in Harbin. (*Eastfoto*)

069 square miles; Canada accounts for 3,851,-809 square miles; and the fifty United States cover 3,615,210 square miles. America thus stands fourth in area.

COMMUNIST DEVELOPMENTS

Few scholars from the free world have been able to travel widely in Communist China, and critical field studies are lacking. It is clear that while the People's Republic has made spectacular progress in some directions, the attempts at planning have involved serious mistakes and have suffered repeated setbacks. Part of the government's errors have undoubtedly arisen from the inadequacy of its own statistical data.

Communist China has set for itself the goal of becoming a full-fledged Marxist state, and in some particulars, communal living, for example, the country claims to be ahead of the Soviet Union. A succession of five-year plans have set audacious goals and have brought dramatic changes. Industry has outrun agriculture. One notable advance is that for the first time in decades, all the Mainland is under the effective control of the central government.

China now has a planned economy, and one geographic result has been to give increased attention to the interior. This, in part, represents security lessons learned during the war with Japan. It may also reflect the new orientation toward the Soviet Union, which has been a source of economic assistance. Another equally important factor is the increased desire to give balanced attention to the country as a whole.

If one might fly over China today in order to compare the landscape with pre-Communist conditions, several changes would appear. In the wheat lands of the north and especially along the margins of Mongolia, fields have been merged into state or collective farms, and mechanized agriculture has been increased. In the terraced rice areas of the south, the change in land management has brought little modification in field patterns. A few hillsides have been reforested.

Industrial changes are obvious. Cities have grown tremendously, especially in the interior, and new street patterns everywhere cut through the old maze of lanes. Thousands of miles of new railways have opened the west. Many rivers are bordered by improved dike systems, and flood-control works have reduced the areas subject to inundation. For the most part, however, China is too big to be changed in a few decades.

Agriculture remains China's number one occupation and problem. To feed the growing population, the production of grains should increase by 5 million tons per year, while to raise the standard of living the harvest should increase even more. The few opportunities for adding to the cultivated acreage lie in submarginal dry areas or in the full use of land which occasionally lies fallow. Emphasis has thus been placed on better seeds, chemical fertilizers, and farm management. Agricultural communes were designed for these ends, but their operation had to be modified. In its initial

China has three major centers of steel industry, the mills at Anshan in southern Manchuria, the developments near Wuhan on the Yangtze, and the operations at Paotow along the Mongolian bend of the Hwang Ho. This is a new power plant at Paotow. (*Eastfoto*)

The Sanmen dam on the Hwang Ho is China's first great hydroelectric development, with a planned capacity of a million kilowatts. Since the Hwang or Yellow is one of the world's muddiest rivers, the reservoir will rapidly accumulate silt. (*Courtesy China Reconstructs*)

drive for national development, the government gave a too low priority to agriculture, and the combination of poor management and climatic distress produced recurrent food shortages. The problem is made the more difficult since agricultural products form the main basis for China's export trade, so that to purchase essential imports of machinery, petroleum, and rubber it has been necessary to export much needed foodstuffs.

Industrial development has been the major goal of the Communist regime, and the achievements in heavy industry have been spectacular. Communist planning always lays more stress on steel than on grain. China has already become one of the world's major producers of coal and steel. In overall industrial capacity, China has overtaken India and is catching up with Japan. Intensive geological studies have greatly enlarged the known mineral reserves, although the economic feasibility of their development is another matter. Light industry and consumers' items have received less attention.

The political orientation of China toward the Communist bloc and away from her traditional relations with Europe and America has brought major changes in trade. Shanghai is no longer one of the world's great seaports, and China occupies only a minor place in international commerce. At the same time, the new China desires to exert more influence throughout Asia, thus reasserting the country's historic imperialism. It is interesting to note that China has become an important source of economic assistance for several underdeveloped countries in Asia and Africa. America's support of Nationalist China and the consequent inability of the Peking government to occupy Taiwan have made the United States the country's number-one enemy.

Some of the most startling and sober developments under the Communists concern population problems. The growth in numbers has already been discussed; it is the apparent welcome of the increase by the government which raises questions. The problem is not so much that mere numbers will engulf the world, though they may well lead to expansionist moves into Southeast Asia, but that the rest of mankind cannot live in normality if China is to experience chronic malnutrition and distress.

HISTORICAL BACKGROUNDS

The human history of China begins with Sinanthropus pekinensis, the Peking man, discovered near Peking in 1928. Sinanthropus lived in the early Pleistocene era and is roughly contemporaneous with Pithecanthropus in Java. Many features connect the Peking man with present-day Mongoloids. So far as is known, the Chinese have always lived in China; suggested theories about a central Asian nomadic ancestry have little foundation.

The earliest written records date from 1200 B.C.; earlier dates may be fictitious. The Shang dynasty is supposed to have covered the period from 1523 to 1027 B.C., the Chou dynasty from 1027 to 250 B.C. The first nationwide dynasty was the Han, 206 B.C. to A.D. 220. Later came the Tang, 618 to 906, the Sung, 960 to 1279, the Yuan or Mongol, 1260 to 1368, the Ming, 1368 to 1644, and the Ching or Manchu, 1644 to 1911. Most of these half dozen dynasties have been times of stability and progress; between them have been intervals of chaos and confusion. It is unfortunate that we of the Occident should be learning of China during one of these transition intervals, unrepresentative of the country at its best.

As Latourette has pointed out: [1]

[1] Kenneth Scott Latourette: *The Chinese: Their History and Culture,* New York: Macmillan (1934), II, 21. Quoted by permission.

Seldom has any large group of mankind been so prosperous and so nearly contented as were the Chinese under this governmental machinery when it was dominated by the ablest of the monarchs of the Han, the Tang, the Sung, the Ming, and the Ching. It was due largely to their government, moreover, that the Chinese achieved and maintained so remarkable a cultural unity and displayed such skill—all the more notable because they were partly unconscious of it—in assimilating invaders. When one recalls how Western Europe, no larger than China proper and with no more serious internal barriers of geography, failed, both to its great profit and infinite distress, to win either political or cultural unity, the achievement of the Chinese becomes little short of phenomenal.

Following the Revolution of 1911, which overthrew the Manchus, the Nationalist government was established in 1928. The capital was moved from Peking to Nanking, and during the Japanese invasion was temporarily located at Chungking. The first phase of the war with Japan, and of the Second World War, began with the Japanese capture of Mukden on September 18, 1931. During the war with Japan China's assets proved to be an unsuspected patriotism and defense in depth. With plenty of room in which to retire, China sold space in order to buy time.

After the defeat of Japan and the withdrawal of the Nationalist government to Taiwan, the People's Republic of China was established in Peking under Communist direction in 1949. Two rival Chinas thus came into being, each claiming sovereignty over the entire country, one backed by the United States, the other aided by the Soviet Union.

China's history is a by-product of her geography. Eastern Asia has been almost an oasis, largely self-sufficient and isolated from the rest of mankind. Until the era of modern travel, the most perfect barriers surrounded China on all sides. Towering plateaus, arid deserts, tropical forests, and the widest of the oceans all helped to preserve the unity of China. Nowhere nearby was there an equal neighbor, except India, which was months of travel away.

Japan was merely a backward disciple. It is but natural that the Chinese thought of themselves as living in the "Middle Kingdom."

The most dangerous of these frontiers was in the north, where the Mongols gave the Chinese more trouble than all other "barbarians" put together. Hence the Great Wall was built, linked together out of earlier parts by the Emperor Chin Shih about 220 B.C. Unfortunately, this rampart failed to achieve the desired result. In times of greater rainfall, the Chinese farmers were unwilling to stay on their side of the fence and pushed cultivation into the grasslands to the north, while, during decades of drought, the wandering Mongol shepherds sought pasturage in the more humid lands within the wall.

Only a few medieval travelers reached China from Europe, notably Marco Polo and the Jesuit missionaries. Only occasional Chinese pilgrims went westward, but even in 128 B.C. the explorer Chang Chien crossed the Pamirs and reached Bokhara in what is now Soviet Middle Asia. The first Chinese to visit India was Fa Hsien in A.D. 413; like other pilgrims in quest of Buddhism he traveled via Sinkiang. Most of this contact with the West was overland, but a few Arab vessels came to Canton and Hangchow, even as early as 300, and Marco Polo returned to Europe by sea.

Insofar as China had a front door, it was the Jade Gate at the Tibetan end of the Great Wall, named from the caravans that brought jade from the Kunlun Mountains. Out through it passed other caravans carrying silk and porcelains, some of which were transported as far as Roman Britain. China thus faced toward Inner Asia, and Japan was a backdoor neighbor of only incidental concern. With the arrival of Europeans by sea and the development of Canton, Shanghai, and Tientsin a century ago, these seaports became the new front doors of China. Instead of being a barrier, the ocean is now a highway, and the Jade Gate has faded into poetic memory. Through the new coastal cities has flowed a tide of ideas which have altered the superficial life of many Chinese. But large countries do not easily change their cultural momentum or orientation, and the reconstruction of a nation as big and numerous and ancient as China has created major problems. In a sense, the alliance with the Soviet Union has represented a reorientation toward the interior.

China's international boundaries have never remained fixed for more than a few centuries at a time. Chinese dynasties have variously included areas west of the Pamirs, on the south slopes of the Himalaya, much of Southeast Asia, along the left bank of the Amur River, as well as Korea, Taiwan, and the Ryukyu Islands. Most of these outer areas formerly sent tribute to the emperor and were regarded as part of greater China; they are today listed by the Chinese as "lost territories." The areas "stolen" by Russia, Great Britain, France, Japan, and Mongolia since 1689 total 3 million square miles. Since India's government is the successor to colonial Britain, India claims the south slope of the eastern Himalaya up to the British-determined McMahon line, once part of China. Several other boundaries are in dispute.

The twentieth century has been a difficult period in which to gauge China's prospects. The first decade was associated with the decline of the Manchu dynasty, and the second was filled with revolution and civil war. Only in the 1930s were there relative peace and progress. The Second World War brought further distress and ushered in a period of Communist domination. Stability during the second half of the century waited on a solution of the problem of Taiwan.

Whatever may be the course of Chinese foreign relations, it appears safe to forecast that China will remain Chinese. Nationalism is so vigorous that it appears here to stay. Neither imperialistic penetration from Europe nor conquest by Japan was successful; it does not seem likely that Soviet influence will do more.

Although China is vast and diverse, many factors of coherence have contributed to her unity, at least to the established areas of traditional China east of Tibet and Mongolia. Effective physical boundaries block out alien cultures; internal resources make economic subsistence possible and render international trade of secondary importance. The uniformity of the written language and the historical awareness of traditional unity add to the centripetal character of the political geography.

China has always been the dominant nation in eastern Asia, and she will probably continue to dominate. Any appraisal of prospects during the second half of the twentieth century must recognize her hemispheric location and the growing tide of nationalistic confidence.

Special problems remain in British Hong Kong, ceded in 1842, and the adjoining leased territory of Kowloon, and in Portuguese Macao. Irredentist sentiment may someday call for the return of Outer Mongolia, the Japanese Ryukyu Islands known to the Chinese as the Liukius, and other areas once subject to China.

Present-day China faces a bewildering array of needs, many of which can be satisfied most rapidly with foreign economic assistance. The requirements for transport, industry, and public technological ability greatly exceed the capital and skill available within the country. Unless China is prepared to spend decades in lifting herself by her own bootstraps, outside aid is desirable. Given a few decades of peace and an appropriate measure of international cooperation, China may be expected to show a spectacular renaissance, comparable to that of the Soviet Union under its five-year plans or of the United States following the Civil War. Geographic factors point to China's leadership in eastern Asia and to her place as one of the major world powers.

References on China

An extensive bibliography may be found in an earlier volume by the author: *Land of the 500 Million.*

See also the references listed under Asia in Chapter 1, many of which deal in detail with East Asia and China. References of special value are indicated by an asterisk (*).

Alexander, John W.: "The Prewar Population of China: Distribution and Density," *Annals, Assn. Amer. Geogs.,* XXXVIII (1948), 1–5.

Borchert, John R.: "A New Map of the Climates of China," *Annals, Assn. Amer. Geogs.,* XXXVII (1947), 169–176.

Boxer, Baruch: *Ocean Shipping in the Evolution of Hong Kong,* Chicago: Dept. of Geography Research Paper no. 72 (1961).

*Buck, J. Lossing: *Land Utilization in China,* 3 vols., Chicago: The University of Chicago Press (1937).

*Cable, Mildred, and Francesca French: *China: Her Life and Her People,* London: University of London Press (1949).

Cable, Mildred, and Francesca French: *The Gobi Desert,* New York: Macmillan (1944).

Cable, Mildred, and Francesca French: "A New Era in the Gobi," *Geog. Jour.,* C (1942), 193–205,

Cable, Mildred, and Francesca French: "Urumchi: Capital of Chinese Turkestan," *Geog. Mag.,* XVI (1944), 445–451.

Cameron, Nigel: "Tibetan Herdsmen in China," *Geog. Mag.,* XXXIII (1961), 692–705.

Chang, Chi-Yi: "Land Utilization and Settlement Possibilities in Sinkiang," *Geog. Rev.,* XXXIX (1949), 57–75.

Chang, Jen-Hu: "Air Mass Maps in China Proper and Manchuria," *Geography,* XLII (1957), 142–148.

Chang, Jen-Hu: "The Climate of China According to the New Thornthwaite Classification," *Annals, Assn. Amer. Geogs.*, XLV (1955), 393–403.

Chang, Kuei-Sheng: "The Changing Railroad Pattern of Mainland China," *Geog. Rev.*, II (1961), 534–548.

Chang, Sen-Dou: "Some Aspects of the Urban Geography of the Chinese Hsien Capital," *Annals, Assn. Amer. Geogs.*, LI (1961), 23–45.

Cressey, George B.: "The Ordos Desert of Inner Mongolia," *Jour. of the Scientific Laboratories,* Denison University, XXVIII (1933), 155–248.

Cressey, George B.: *China's Geographic Foundations,* New York: McGraw-Hill (1934).

*Cressey, George B.: *Land of the 500 Million,* New York: McGraw-Hill (1955).

Cressey, George B.: "The Land Forms of Chekiang," *Annals, Assn. Amer. Geogs.*, XXVIII (1938), 259–276.

Davis, S. G.: *Hong Kong in Its Geographical Setting,* London: Collins (1949).

Davis, S. G.: *The Geology of Hong Kong,* Hong Kong: Govt. Printer (1952).

*Dickerman, Nelson: "Mineral Resources of China," Washington: *Foreign Mineral Survey,* II, no. 7 (1948).

Durand, John D.: "The Population Statistics of China, A.D. 2–1953," *Population Studies,* XIII (1960), 209–256.

Erroll, F. J.: "Industrial Progress in China," *Geog. Mag.*, XXXI (1958), 265–276.

Erselcuk, Muzaffer: "The Iron and Steel Industry in China," *Econ. Geog.*, XXXII (1956), 347–371.

Gherzi, E.: *Climatological Atlas of East Asia,* Shanghai (1944).

Gherzi, E.: *The Meteorology of China,* 2 vols., Macao (1951).

Ginsburg, Norton S.: "Ching-Tao: Development and Land Utilization," *Econ. Geog.*, XXIV (1948), 181–200.

Ginsburg, Norton S.: "Chang-chun," *Econ. Geog.*, XXIII (1947), 290–307.

Ginsburg, Norton S.: "China's Railroad Network," *Geog. Rev.*, XLI (1951), 470–474.

Ginsburg, Norton S.: "China's Changing Political Geography," *Geog. Rev.*, XLII (1952), 102–117.

Gould, Sidney H. (ed.): *Sciences in Communist China,* Washington: Amer. Assn. Adv. Science (1961).

Hanson-Lowe, J.: "Notes on the Climate of the South Chinese-Tibetan Borderland," *Geog. Rev.*, XXXI (1941), 444–453.

Hanson-Lowe, J.: "Notes on the Pleistocene Glaciation of the South Chinese-Tibetan Borderland," *Geog. Rev.*, XXXVII (1947), 70–93.

Herman, Theodore: "Group Values toward the National Space: The Case of China," *Geog. Rev.*, XLIX (1959), 164–182.

Hu, Chang-Tu: *China: Its People, Its Society, Its Culture,* New Haven: Human Relations Area Files (1960).

Hughes, R. H.: "Hong Kong: An Urban Study," *Geog. Jour.*, CXVII (1951), 1–23.

Jackson, W. A. Douglas: *Russo-Chinese Borderlands,* Princeton: Van Nostrand (1962).

Jones, Fred O.: "Tukiangyien: China's Ancient Irrigation System," *Geog. Rev.*, XLIV (1954), 543–559.

Juan, V. C.: "Mineral Resources of China," *Econ. Geol.*, XLI (1946), 399–474.

*King, F. H.: *Farmers of Forty Centuries,* New York: Harcourt Brace & World (1926).

Laai, Yi-Faai, Franz Michael, and John C. Sherman: "The Use of Maps in Social Research: A Case Study in South China," *Geog. Rev.*, LII (1962), 92–111.

Lattimore, Owen: *Pivot of Asia: Sinkiang and the Inner Asian Frontiers of China and Russia,* Boston: Little, Brown (1950).

Lattimore, Owen: *Inner Asian Frontiers of China,* New York: Amer. Geog. Soc. (1951).

Lattimore, Owen: "The New Political Geography of Inner Asia," *Geog. Jour.,* CXIX (1953), 17–32.

Lee, Shu-Tan: "Delimitation of the Geographic Regions of China," *Annals, Assn. Amer. Geogs.,* XXXVII (1947), 155–168.

Mallory, Walter H.: *China: Land of Famine,* New York: Amer. Geog. Soc. (1928).

Moyer, Raymond T.: "Agricultural Practices in Semi-arid North China," *Scientific Monthly,* LV (1942), 301–316.

Murphey, Rhoads: *Shanghai, Key to Modern China,* Cambridge, Mass.: Harvard University Press (1953).

Orchard, John E.: "Industrialization in Japan, China Mainland, and India: Some World Implications," *Annals, Assn. Amer. Geogs.,* L (1960), 193–215.

Rodgers, Allan: "The Manchurian Iron and Steel Industry and Its Resource Base," *Geog. Rev.,* XXXVIII (1948), 41–54.

*Shabad, Theodore: *China's Changing Map: A Political and Economic Geography of the Chinese People's Republic,* New York: Praeger (1956).

Shabad, Theodore: "The Population of China's Cities," *Geog. Rev.,* XXXXIX (1959), 32–42.

*Shen, T. H.: *Agricultural Resources of China,* Ithaca, N.Y.: Cornell University Press (1951).

Spencer, Joseph E.: "Chinese Place Names and the Appreciation of Geographic Realities," *Geog. Rev.,* XXXI (1941), 79–94.

Spencer, Joseph E.: "The Houses of the Chinese," *Geog. Rev.,* XXXVII (1947), 254–273.

Spencer, Joseph E.: "Salt in China," *Geog. Rev.,* XXV (1935), 353–366.

Spencer, Joseph E.: "On Regionalism in China," *Jour. Geog.,* XLVI (1947), 123–136.

Spencer, Joseph E.: "Kweichou: An Internal Chinese Colony," *Pacific Affairs,* XIII (1940), 162–172.

*Todd, O. J.: "The Yellow River Problem," *Transactions,* Amer. Soc. of Civil Engineers, CV (1940), 346–453.

Todd, O. J.: "The Yellow River Reharnessed," *Geog. Rev.,* XXXIX (1949), 38–59.

*Trewartha, Glenn T.: "Chinese Cities: Origins and Functions," *Annals, Assn. Amer. Geogs.,* XLII (1952), 69–93.

*Trewartha, Glenn T.: "Chinese Cities: Numbers and Distribution," *Annals, Assn. Amer. Geogs.,* XLI (1952), 331–347.

Trewartha, Glenn T.: "New Maps of China's Population," *Geog. Rev.,* XLVII (1957), 234–239.

Wang, Chi-Wu: *The Forests of China: With a Survey of Grassland and Desert Vegetation,* Cambridge, Mass.: Harvard University Press (1961).

Wang, Kung-Ping: "Mineral Resources of China, with Special Reference to the Nonferrous Metals," *Geog. Rev.,* XXXIV (1944), 621–635.

Wiens, Herold: *China's March into the Tropics,* Hamden, Conn.: Shoe String Press (1954).

Wiens, Herold: "Riverine and Coastal Junks in China's Commerce," *Econ. Geog.,* XXXI (1955), 248–264.

*Wiens, Herold: "China," in Norton Ginsburg: *The Pattern of Asia,* Englewood Cliffs, N.J.: Prentice-Hall (1958).

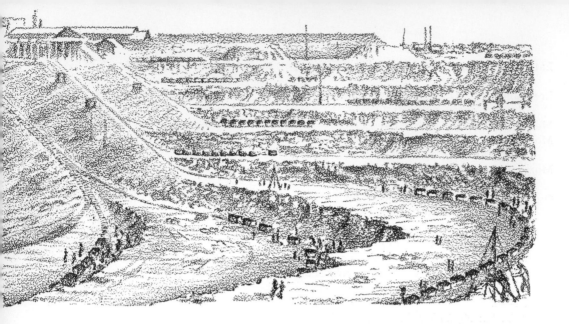

5 China's Physical Foundations

Geological Background / Land Forms / Climatic Contrasts / Natural Vegetation / Types of Soil / Mineral Resources

GEOLOGICAL BACKGROUND

Since the Chinese are very dependent upon the earth, an appreciation of land forms and the underlying geology is necessary to an understanding of the people's use of their physical environment. Land usability grows out of the geological structure and history.

Beneath all the hills and plains of China lies a massive foundation of crystalline rocks which date back to the earliest geological times. In most areas these ancient formations are deeply buried; here and there they are exposed at the surface. Three old land masses composed of these hard rocks form buttresses between which

the younger sedimentary formations accumulated and were subsequently folded. These shields or massifs are Tibetia in the west, Gobia in the north, and Cathaysia in the southeast. In each area a complex of granites and metamorphic formations have tended to remain above sea level during most of earth history.

Later on, repeated marine invasions spread between these old lands, leaving thousands of feet of limestones, sandstones, and shales, which form a nearly continuous record of earth history. Extensive coal beds were formed when swamps covered wide areas, especially in the north. Later, continental formations veneered parts of Mongolia and the northwest, while at the same time lava flows spread wide over the southeast.

The structure of eastern Asia is complex. Near the Pacific the major trend of folding and faulting is parallel to the coast, roughly from northeast to southwest. Toward the interior of China there are several east–west zones, and farther inland are great mountain chains of uncertain relationships.

From Hong Kong northeast to Ningpo and southern Korea are remnants of the old subcontinent of Cathaysia. This structure continues, *en échelon,* from Shantung and Liaotung through the Sikhote-Alin of Siberia to the mouth of the Amur River. To the west and parallel to these uplands are a series of basins in the plains of the central Yangtze, the Hwang delta, and Manchuria.

West of these lowlands is another discontinuous ridge or axis, which extends southwest from the Great Khingan Mountains in Manchuria to the Taihang and Luliang anticlines of Shansi, the Gorge Mountains of Szechwan, the eastern edge of the Kweichow Plateau, and into Kwangsi. Although more strongly developed and accompanied by greater igneous intrusions in the north, the system is roughly homogeneous. This is the innermost series of the northeast–southwest Cathaysian system.

This series of parallel zones is continued to the east of China by a line of depressions in the Sea of Japan and the East China Sea; by the elevated arcs of the Japanese Islands, the Ryukyu, and Taiwan; and by the Japan trough and Tuscarora Deep. Thus, in all, there are three major anticlines and three synclines, of which at least those in China have been defined and active since early geological times. Pressures were apparently directed from the Pacific.

Farther inland, this Cathaysian pattern is replaced by four equally spaced east–west structures which lie between the Siberian frontier and the South China Sea. To the north of the Gobi old land are the Tannu-Ola, Khangai, and Kentei Ranges in Outer Mongolia. Another parallel mountain chain, south of the Gobi, is the Taching and Yin Shan of Inner Mongolia.

The third and largest of the east–west mountains is the Chin Ling Range between the Hwang and Yangtze Rivers, an eastward continuation of the Kunlun. The fourth range is that of the low Nan Ling Mountains in southern China.

The highest and most complex of Chinese mountains are those which encircle the borders of Tibet. The Himalayan system, as young as any great mountain chain on earth, is made up of three ranges which end in the east near the Brahmaputra. North of them are the Nyenchen Tangha or Trans-Himalaya. Along the east of the Tibetan Highlands are a series of north–south mountains which continue to the Great Snowy Range facing the Szechwan Basin. Farther north, the highlands are bordered by the Kunlun and Astin Tagh Ranges, while beyond them are the Tien Shan and Altai Ranges.

Destructive earthquakes have been recorded in Kansu, Szechwan, and Yunnan, as well as in the Kunlun, Astin Tagh, Nan Shan, and Altai Ranges. Smaller shocks have also occurred in Shantung. The province of Kansu was intensely shaken in 1920 and 1927. In 1556 an earthquake in central Shensi and the resulting famine are said to have taken 830,000 lives.

No continental glaciation spread over China during the Pleistocene era, for the south was too warm and the far north too dry. Small glaciers developed in a few of the higher mountains. In place of ice, the geological record closes with widespread dust deposits, the famous loess. Deposits of this wind-blown silt exceed 100,000 square miles south of the Great Wall, plus other areas in Sinkiang. Over extensive areas the thickness exceeds 100 feet, so that the original bedrock topography is buried; locally, the thickness may reach 300 feet.

Most loess occurs in the semiarid grasslands inside the Great Wall. The bulk of the material is derived from river and lake deposits of the Hwang River spread out in the Ordos Desert, with lesser amounts as the product of weathering in the Gobi Desert. Local deposits along the Yangtze near Nanking and in Szechwan have their source in river-flood plains. Dust storms

Over 100,000 square miles of northwest China is veneered with the fine wind-blown silt known as loess, easily terraced, but too dry and too porous for rice fields. Accelerated erosion characterizes many areas, as here at 34°55′N and 108°00′E in Shensi. (*Courtesy United States Air Force*)

today indicate that loess accumulation is still under way.

The only area of recent volcanic activity is along the Korean border where there is a large crater lake at the summit of Paitou Shan.

All China's great rivers drain eastward to the Pacific. However, more than a million square miles in Mongolia, Sinkiang, and Tibet are without drainage to the sea; such streams as exist fail to fill their terminal basins or even to reach them, and all moisture disappears by evaporation.

The Heilung Kiang or Amur River, together with its tributary, the Ussuri, forms the northern and eastern boundaries of Manchuria next to Siberia. Its total length is 2,700 miles. The chief tributary within China is the Sungari. Each of these rivers is navigable for river steamers.

The great river of North China is the Hwang Ho or Yellow River, 2,900 miles in length. The chief tributaries are the Fen Ho in Shansi and the Wei Ho, classical river of Chinese history, which flows across Shensi. After the

Hwang enters its delta, the Yellow Plain, the average slope is 10 inches per mile, but the Hwang is so overloaded with loessial silt that extensive deposition follows.

The Yangtze Kiang, 3,430 miles in length, is the sixth longest river in the world and by far the most important waterway in China. Navigation extends to the border of Tibet, 1,630 miles from the sea. The chief tributaries are the Min Kiang in Szechwan, the Han Kiang which gives its name to the city of Hankow, and two large streams from the south, the Siang and Kan. These latter flow through the Tungting and Poyang Lakes, which serve as reservoirs for the surplus flood waters of the Yangtze.

LAND FORMS

Topography sets the stage on which the Chinese drama unfolds. Any piece of level land, no matter how inaccessible, is used as intensively as climate and soil permit. Over much of China, slopes are so steep that normal agriculture is impossible. Extensive plains are found only in the deltas of the Yangtze and Hwang, the rolling lowland of central Manchuria, and the deserts of Mongolia and Sinkiang. Level land may represent no more than one-fifth of the total area, but only half of this is arable.

Diverse mountain structures and erosional history divide Mainland China into a number of topographic units. The largest of these are termed land-form *provinces,* ten in number, the names of which reflect their characteristic elevation, such as lowland, upland, or highland. These in turn are divided into land-form *regions,* more than fifty in all, whose names indicate their characteristic configuration, such as plain, plateau, hill, or mountain.

The Tibetan Highlands are coextensive with a province comprising a rim of lofty mountains and an enclosed plateau-basin, much of it without external drainage. In the far west is the mountain core of the Pamirs, from which radiate several of the great ranges of Asia. The Himalayan system, made up of three ranges, extends in an arc for 1,500 miles. Fifty summits

exceed 25,000 feet in height. Mount Everest, 29,028 feet high, lies on the border between Tibet and Nepal.

Within southern Tibet are a series of mountains and basins. In the south is the valley of the Tsangpo, the local name for the Brahmaputra, in which is the city of Lhasa and the only cultivated part of Tibet. To the north is the Nyenchen Tanglha or Trans-Himalaya Range, which in turn forms the southern boundary of the Chang Tang plains and mountains. This is an area of desert playas and massive mountains, all at elevations of over 16,000 feet. There are many lakes, both fresh and salt, of which the largest is Nam Tso, or Tengri Nor.

Northern Tibet has two great mountain systems, of which the outermost is the Astin Tagh and its eastern extension the Nan Shan. These form a rampart overlooking Sinkiang and Kansu. Parallel and farther south is the Kunlun Range. Both systems have numerous peaks of 20,000 feet elevation. Between them are the enclosed Tsaidam and Koko Nor Basins at elevations of 9,000 and 10,500 feet, respectively. Koko Nor is the largest lake in Tibet; it is known to the Chinese as Tsing Hai, or blue lake.

Eastern Tibet, east of 95°E, is a land of great canyons and intervening high ranges, with a general northwest-to-southeast orientation. This area is known to the Tibetans as Kham, the Land of the Great Canyons. Here flow the Hwang, Yangtze, Mekong, and Salween Rivers. The easternmost mountains, bordering Szechwan and Yunnan, are the Tahsueh Shan or Great Snowy Mountains. This range is sometimes known as the Szechwan Alps. The highest peak is Minya Konka, 24,900 feet, first climbed by a party of Harvard students in 1932.

The Tien Shan Highlands, second of the major land-form provinces, lie in Sinkiang between the Tarim and Dzungarian basins. The Tien Shan or Heavenly Mountains extend into Soviet Middle Asia to join the Pamirs. The range has a length of 1,000 miles in China, with peaks over 20,000 feet high. The northernmost component is the Dzungarian Ala-tau. In the

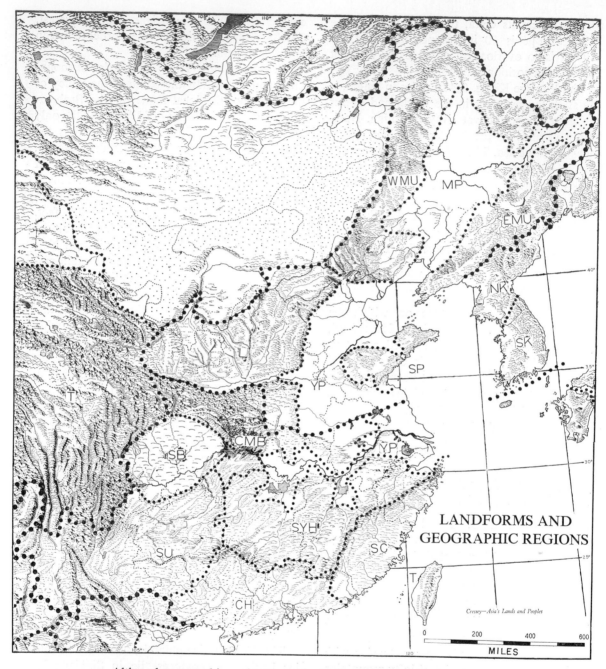

LANDFORMS AND
GEOGRAPHIC REGIONS

Cressey—Asia's Lands and Peoples

0   200   400   600
MILES

Although geographic regions consider both physical and cultural factors, in an old land
like China there is a close correspondence with landforms.

Within China are three major provinces and seventeen regions. North China includes
the Yellow Plain, the Shantung Peninsula, Loessland, the Manchurian Plain, the Eastern
Manchurian Uplands, and the Western Manchurian Uplands. South China is made up
of the Yangtze Plain, the Szechwan Basin, the Central Mountain Belt, the South Yangtze
Hills, the Southeastern Coast, the Canton Hinterland, and the Southwestern Uplands,
plus Taiwan. Outer China includes Inner Mongolia, Sinkiang, and Tibet. (*Base map
by Erwin Raisz, with modifications by Rowland Illick*)

east the main range is the Bogdo Ola; in the southeast are the Kuruk Tagh Hills.

The Mongolian-Sinkiang Uplands form a third province, which covers a half million square miles in northwestern China. The largest region is the Gobi Plain, which occupies a broad, basinlike depression, approached over a mountain rim on every side. Long erosion has worn ancient mountains to a featureless peneplain, subsequently warped to form numerous shallow basins, now filled with younger sediments. These in turn have been partly excavated by wind work. Monotonous desert plains continue for hundreds of miles, often so flat that one may drive an automobile in any direction. Only the southern edge of the Gobi lies inside China. The Ordos Plain is a subdivision which lies within the loop of the Hwang River. The Dzungarian Plain is a lowland corridor from Mongolia into Soviet Middle Asia between the Altai and the Tien Shan. Farther south, the Tarim Basin lies between the Tien Shan and the Astin Tagh; this is the Taklamakan Desert, the driest area in Asia.

The Mongolian Border Uplands lie between the Gobi and the lowland plains of eastern China, and extend in an arc from Kansu to northwestern Heilungkiang; they comprise the fourth land-form province. The northernmost region, the Great Khingan Mountains, is the upturned edge of the Mongolian Upland. As viewed from the east, these appear as high, dissected mountains; seen from the west, they are merely low hills. Toward the south, the Great Khingan become lower, and there is an easy passage from Manchuria to Mongolia. Most of the

Large areas of western China have mountains which rise above the snow line or would do so were precipitation more abundant. This once-glaciated valley is near Likiang in western Yunnan. (*Courtesy United States Air Force*)

province of Jehol is a hill and mountain land with conspicuously steep, soilless slopes. Elevations reach 5,000 feet. To the west of the Jehol Mountains is a series of low mountains along the southern margin of the Mongolian Uplands. These are collectively known as the Taching and Yin Mountains. Although barren and rocky, their elevations are not great. Since the range is not continuous, there are several gateways to the Gobi. To the west of the Hwang River are the 10,000-foot Holan Mountains, often known as the Ala Shan.

A large part of the Mongolian Border Upland is made up of the Loess Hills, a region where fine silt, blown outward from the Ordos Plain, has formed a veneer over the entire landscape. Two mountain areas rise above the loess, the Liupan Mountains in Kansu and the Shansi Mountains farther east. Two portions of the latter deserve special names, the Taihang next to the Yellow Plain in southern Shansi, and the Wutai farther north. Within the Loess Hills are a series of alluvial basins known as the Shensi-Shansi Plains. The most important of these is drained by the Wei River and dominated by the historic city of Sian. The second is that along the Fen River in Shansi, where there are areas of alluvium around Taiyuan. The plains of the Wei and Fen lie in a crescentic structural graben, which reappears farther north to form the plain around the city of Tatung.

The Eastern Highlands form the fifth landform province, extending from Shantung to eastern Heilungkiang. In the latter and in Kirin are the East Manchurian Hills, a rounded and forested region with only pioneer agricultural settlement. The highest portion of this region, along the Korean frontier, has the name of the Changpai Shan or Long White Mountains. The Little Khingan Hills lie south of the Amur River and may be placed either in this province or with the preceding one. The Shantung Hills were formerly an island in the Yellow Sea but are now half surrounded by the encroaching delta of the Hwang River. An important corridor north of Tsingtao divides the region into

two subdivisions and provides an avenue for the railway to Tsinan. The highest point is the sacred peak of Tai Shan, 5,056 feet, made famous by Confucius.

The Eastern Lowlands, the sixth province, include by far the larger part of China's level land which has adequate rainfall for agricultural settlement. In the far north, the Amur-Ussuri Plains, mostly within Siberia, provide flat land along the respective rivers. There are considerable areas of swamp, and part of the area is underlain by permanently frozen subsoil. The Manchurian Plain, largely the product of erosion, covers 140,000 square miles in the provinces of Heilungkiang, Liaoning, and Kirin. The northern portion is drained by the Sungari River; in the south flows the Liao River. The Manchurian Plain is surrounded by hills with only three lowland gateways. One of these is to the northwest along the narrow valley of the Sungari. The second is a broad saddle in the southern Great Khingan near the upper sources of the Liao, leading to Mongolia. The third and most important is the narrow coastal plain at Shanhaikwan where the Jehol Mountains border the Gulf of Chihli (Po Hai). This point, where the Great Wall reaches the sea, has been the scene of repeated Manchu invasions.

The Yellow Plain is the largest alluvial landform region in eastern China, covering 125,000 square miles. This remarkably flat plain is the compound delta of the Hwang and other streams that flow out of the encircling hills. Widespread floods have resulted from the breaking of the dikes. On account of poor drainage and the high water table, extensive areas have saline or alkaline soils. The entire region is below 500 feet elevation. Peking lies at the northern margin of the plain in close proximity to two important gateways through the Great Wall, the Nankow and Kupeikow Passes, and not far from the equally important corridor at Shanhaikwan. Other important cities are Tientsin, Tsinan, and Kaifeng.

The Yangtze Delta Plain merges imperceptibility with the Yellow Plain in northern

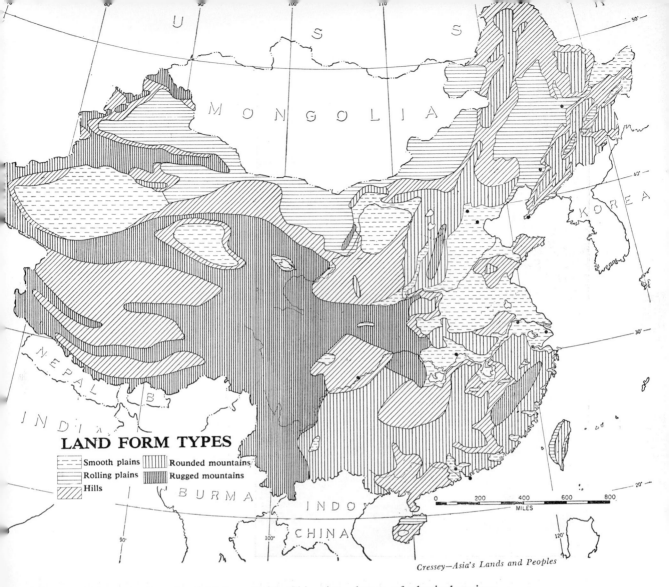

LAND FORM TYPES

Smooth plains	Rounded mountains
Rolling plains	Rugged mountains
Hills	

Cressey—*Asia's Lands and Peoples*

Geologic structure and erosional history divide China into dozens of physical regions. Hills and mountains cover 50 per cent of the country; dissected plateaus account for 20 per cent; and land which is approximately level totals some 30 per cent, half of it alluvial plains, half erosional basins.

Kiangsu. Important climatic, soil, and crop boundaries mark the transition along the line of the Hwai River. Unlike the waterless delta of the Hwang, the lower Yangtze Plain is cut by innumerable canals. Shanghai, Hangchow, and Nanking are the principal cities. The Mid-Yangtze Lake Plains surround the numerous lakes, chief of which are the Poyang and Tungting. Whereas the delta is flat, this region is studded with low rocky hills. Northwest of

Hankow is a nearly enclosed alluvial area drained by the Han River and termed the Han Plain.

The Central Uplands, the seventh province, are a spur of the Tibetan Highlands which continue the Kunlun structures eastward to the vicinity of Nanking. Elevations decrease from 20,000 feet in the west to a few hundred feet in the east, where the Central Uplands disappear beneath coastal alluvium. The Chin Ling

LAND FORMS 85

The Chin Ling Mountains mark the major boundary between North and South China. This canyon is in southern Shensi. (*Bailey Willis, courtesy Carnegie Corporation*)

Range, the greatest mountain system of eastern China, forms a lofty and rugged barrier from Kansu to Honan. South of Sian, peaks reach 12,000 feet in elevation. The Chin Ling have a series of parallel ridges, all tending a little south of east, with canyons whose walls often rise sheer to a height of 1,000 feet above the streams. The eastern extensions of the range are known as the Sung Shan and the Funiu Shan.

The Chin Ling act as a barrier to monsoon rainfall from the south and to dust-laden winds from the north. They thus serve to define the most important geographic boundary of the country. On one side is the dry, brown, dust-blown wheat country of the north; on the other are the green, humid ricelands of the south. These mountains have also been of political significance, for in 1860 they prevented the Taiping rebels from coming north, and in 1875 they similarly limited the southward advance of the Mohammedan rebellion.

The Chin Ling Range lies north of the Han River, whose valley locally widens to a plain. To the south are the slightly lower Tapa Mountains, also with an east–west trend. These join the Gorge Mountains, so named from their development across the Yangtze River above Ichang. The easternmost extension of the Central Uplands is variously known as the Tapieh

Hills or the Hwaiyang Hills. Elevations here are largely under 3,000 feet, and the whole character of the physical landscape is more gentle, with rounded mountains and open valleys.

The Szechwan Lowland is an island province in the heart of western China. Most of it is known as the Red Basin Hills, from the red or purplish color of the underlying sandstones. Hilltops rise to 3,000 or 4,000 feet, with valley bottoms at half these elevations. Chungking dominates this thoroughly hilly region. The Chengtu Plain is a small but intensively utilized alluvial fan along the western margin of the Szechwan Lowland next to the Great Snowy Mountains.

The Southern Uplands, which form the ninth province, include a large area of southern China. Level land is nowhere more than a few square miles in extent, and hills or mountains are always in sight. Flat lands cover less than 15 per cent of the whole region and are largely confined to flood plains. The South Yangtze Hills lie largely within the drainage basin of the Yangtze River. Numerous valleys lead into the area from the Mid-Yangtze Lake Plains. To the east are the Wuyi and Tayu Mountains; on the south are the Nan Ling Mountains. These three ranges form a continuous arc parallel to the coast, with peaks that rise to 6,000 feet. The coasts of Chekiang, Fukien, and eastern Kwangtung form a region which might be termed the southeastern hills and deltas. North of Canton are two famous passes across the Nan Ling. The first is the old imperial highway to Nanchang by way of the Meiling Pass. The second leads to Changsha over the Cheling Pass, and is the route of the Canton-Hankow Railway. The hinterland of Canton is drained by the Tung, Pei, and Si, or the East, North, and West Rivers, which give their names to an area of hills and scattered alluvial basins between the Nan Ling and the sea. These rivers have formed the compound Canton Delta Plain. In western and northern Kwangsi, in Yunnan, and in Kweichow are remarkable areas of almost vertical-sided hills of limestone, representing an advanced stage of solution or karst to-

pography. In southern Kwangtung is the Luichow Peninsula, a rolling plain linked with that in the northern part of Hainan Island. Hainan itself is largely mountainous, with elevations to over a mile.

The Southwestern Uplands, which lie in Kweichow and Yunnan, are the tenth of the land-form provinces. These uplands are a subdued continuation of the Tibetan Highlands, with plateau remnants cut by deep valleys and crossed by rugged mountains. Dissection has been most extensive in the Kweichow Hills, where many rivers flow in valleys 2,000 feet in depth. Elevations in the Yunnan Plateau average 6,000 feet; the Kweichow Hills are about 4,000 feet high. Within the province of Yunnan, plateau characteristics are found east of the Red River and the city of Tali, and south of the Yangtze River. The only part of the region which is level is the Kunming Plain where there are several lake basins. Northwestern Yunnan lies in the Great Snowy Mountains. The southwest is part of the Shan Plateau along the border of Burma. Level land probably amounts to less than 5 per cent of the entire region.

CLIMATIC CONTRASTS

The Chinese live close to nature and are vitally dependent upon the weather. Climatic averages seldom tell the whole story, for rain often comes too early or too late, or in exceptional amounts. Flood and drought are equally serious. In contrast to Honan, which has received 18 inches in a day, a Kwangsi station with a yearly average of 50 inches once dropped to 8 inches for 12 months. Mountains exposed to typhoons from the South China Sea receive as much as 100 inches; the Tarim Basin is nearly rainless. In North China, June is the critical month for summer planting, but a Tientsin June rainfall of over 8 inches in two successive years, three times the average, was preceded and followed by years with $\frac{1}{2}$ inch in the same month. The resulting crop uncertainties are especially serious in a land so crowded.

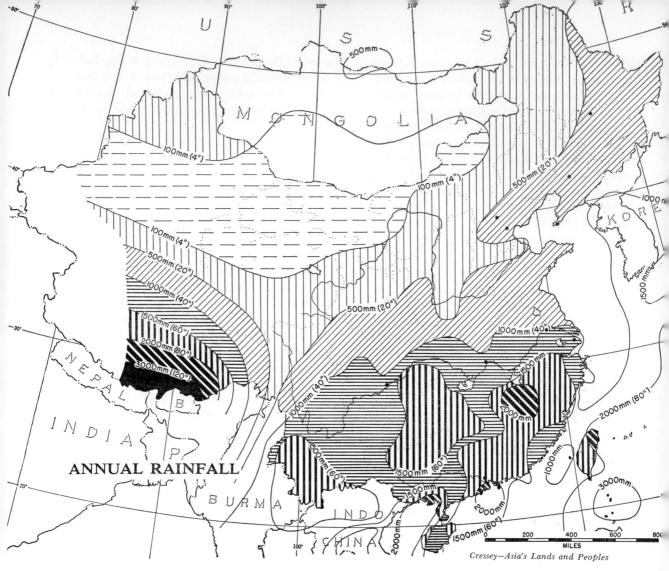

ANNUAL RAINFALL

Cressey—Asia's Lands and Peoples

Precipitation ranges from nearly 100 inches near the southeastern coast to less than 4 inches in the western deserts. Windward and leeward mountain slopes introduce local variations which cannot be shown at this scale. (*E. Gherzi: Climatological Atlas of East Asia*)

China lies on the east coast of the largest continent. As a result of its location, the climate is alternately continental and Asiatic in winter, and maritime or Pacific in summer. On this seasonal to-and-fro circulation are superimposed lesser air-mass movements, cyclonic storms, and typhoons. Unlike India, where the summer monsoon with its inblowing air is the dominant period, in China winter continental winds provide the most powerful circulation.

Thus southern China has unusually cool winters for its latitude.

China's climate is something like that of the eastern United States. The similarity arises from the presence, in both, of a continental hinterland and an ocean to the east and south. In both continents the frequent weather changes are due to the contest between invading air masses which come alternately from polar and tropical latitudes. The differences between

China and America arise from the greater size of Asia, and hence the greater activity of its winter cold-air factory; from the barrier position of the east–west Chin Ling Mountains, the absence of similar east–west mountains across North America, and from the fact that the more populous sections of China lie farther south than the center of population in the United States.

Cold, dry air masses from polar continental sources push into China during all months except July, to a total of twenty-nine a year. Many of these first appear in the Arctic near Novaya Zemlya. After crossing Soviet Middle Asia they enter China via Dzungaria and Mongolia and come to the Wei Valley, where the Chin Ling Mountains protect Szechwan. The air masses are then turned eastward to the Yellow Plain and continue southward along the coast. The advancing wedge of a cold wave is usually less than 1,000 feet thick. This front is stopped by moderate relief, but farther back from the front the thickness of the air mass increases to a mile, so that cold air may overtop peaks such as Tai Shan in Shantung. These successive cold air masses collectively form the winter monsoon.

Cold waves travel from Dzungaria to the southern extremity of China in about a week. Their speed increases with temperature contrasts, which are most pronounced in winter. Across Mongolia the average velocity is but 5 miles per hour; in the Yellow Plain it reaches 30 miles; and over the central Yangtze the wind may blow as much as 60 miles per hour. This force diminishes to 5 miles per hour along the southern coast. A few polar continental cold waves also come into China from eastern Siberia; if they pass over the Sea of Japan en route, they acquire a limited amount of moisture.

In their source areas both air masses are dry, but as the waves advance, evaporation from the ground adds some moisture to the lower layers, so that only modified polar continental air masses reach China. Dust storms rather than rainfall are brought by these winds. Such dust clouds are common throughout North China during winter months. Visibility is notably reduced, and impalpable dust finds its way even into closed rooms.

Precipitation results from cooling the air. This happens most effectively when winds rise against mountain barriers or are lifted by air masses of greater density. Where the front of an advancing cold air mass encounters moist tropical air, the latter is lifted and precipitation results. This wedge action accounts for three-quarters of China's rainfall and operates at all seasons.

Southern tropical air masses invade China throughout the year from both the South China Sea and the Southwestern Uplands. Their number and strength are less than those of air masses from the north. They are often altered in their passage over southern and eastern China so that the air that reaches the Yangtze valley is characteristically known as modified tropical marine or modified tropical continental air. Occasional winter outbursts of polar air reach the equator, but South China is so well protected by the Chin Ling Range that in this area tropical winds are important even in midwinter.

During summer months, most of China is bathed by repeated invasions of hot humid air from the ocean, which push as far as Mongolia. Since these air masses are light, buoyant, and thick, they easily pass over the Southern Uplands, and equally override any cold air masses in their path. As the tropical maritime air rises, it is cooled, and rain falls. Without the lifting and cooling action caused by mountains or a cold front in their path, tropical air masses yield no rain even though their relative humidity is high.

The summer monsoon is thus the time when successive tropical air masses are strong enough to push back the polar air and shift the front to northern China. There is no continuous seasonal monsoon wind; it is rather a tendency. In spite of the obvious correlation between the period of maximum rainfall and the time of the summer monsoon, rain seldom occurs with strong southerly winds. When they blow constantly, drought may even follow. Rain occurs principally when a northerly wind at the surface can underrun and lift the southeast monsoon sufficiently high to cool it and cause condensation.

Cyclonic or anticyclonic storms and typhoons introduce further variability. Numerous highs and lows from Europe cross Siberia and Mongolia to enter northern China on their way to Japan and Alaska. Others, especially in winter, follow a route from Europe south of Tibet into southern China. Still others may originate in the interior, especially in the upper Yangtze valley, by the interaction of opposing warm- and cold-air masses. These cyclonic storms average eighty per year. The cyclones of China have an average diameter along the major axis of 900 miles and are thus considerably smaller than those of the United States, whose corresponding dimension is 1,500 miles. Although the extent of individual storms is limited, they follow various paths, so that almost every part of China feels their effect at one time or another.

The cyclonic storms of China may be grouped into several types according to their paths. One appears from Siberia and moves southeastward across southern Manchuria. Many of these storms are known to come from Europe. Two North China types first appear in the vicinity of the Ordos Desert and move either eastward across southern Manchuria or southward to the mouth of the Yangtze. Three types pass down the Yangtze valley; the more important traverse the provinces just south of the river from Kweichow and Hunan. Two other types come from the eastern seas and the northeast.

When the cyclonic circulation coincides with monsoon air movements, the resulting winds are strong. Thus, counterclockwise winds on the back side of a low reinforce the winter polar invasion, producing unusually strong northwest winds. Since cyclonic storms are fewer and less developed during the summer, and invading tropical air moves more slowly

than polar air masses, the coincidence of southerly summer winds gives lower velocities. Nevertheless, great quantities of moist marine air are drawn into China, and at such times heavy precipitation frequently results. When low pressure areas from Southeast Asia have stagnated over the Han valley, they have brought as much as 14 cubic miles of rain in six days.

The typhoons of the western Pacific originate east of the Philippine Islands in the vicinity of the Marshall and Caroline groups along the equatorial front where tropical air undercuts unstable equatorial air and thus releases the large amounts of energy needed for typhoons. Typhoons move west and then northeast, either striking the southeastern coast of China or recurving toward Japan. When they occasionally recurve northeastward after entering the continent, they travel twice as fast as when moving westward, and after reaching the ocean, their intensity is greatly increased. Since typhoons follow more or less regular paths, it is often possible to predict their movement to a certain extent and to issue appropriate warnings to shipping. The China coast experiences an average of 8.5 typhoons per year.

Though no part of the year is entirely free from typhoons, they are especially abundant during the late summer. Typhoons may visit Kwangtung during May, but by June the track of most storms has moved northward to Taiwan. July and August are the most destructive months along the central coast. By October the increasing pressure of the Siberian high appears to be sufficient to keep typhoons away from the continent.

Typhoons always bring a succession of heavy rain squalls. The wind blows with velocities up to 150 miles per hour and carries the rain horizontally with such violence that severe damage is often done to ships and coastal districts. Pressures against vertical surfaces reach 100 pounds per square foot. Much of the summer rainfall of the southeastern provinces is derived from the fringe of these tropical storms, in contrast to the gentle spring rains which are associated with cyclonic areas.

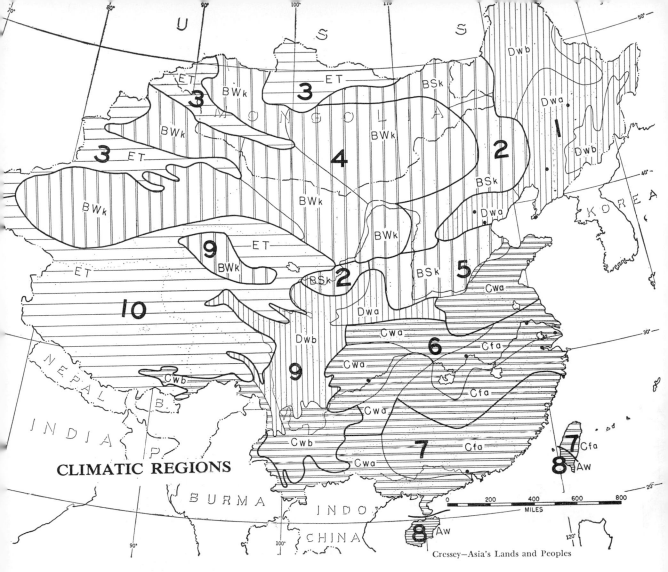

Most of the major Koeppen types of climate are present within China. *A* represents tropical climates; *B* stands for arid and semiarid conditions; *C* and *D* are moderate climates with long or short summers, respectively; *E* climates are present at high elevations. (*A. Lu: Climatological Atlas of China*)

Seasons are well differentiated. Winter temperatures show great contrast with latitude, for the January average in northern Manchuria is −13°F as compared with 68°F in Hainan in the south. During July, temperatures are more uniform, and these extreme locations average 70°F and 84°F, respectively. Summers everywhere have oppressive heat and humidity. Peking regularly experiences temperatures over

100°F and may even be warmer than Shanghai or Canton. The duration of the warm period increases southward, so that in Canton white tropical clothing may be worn for ten months.

Rainfall shows even greater regional contrasts than temperatures; it is the major item differentiating North China and South China. South of the Chin Ling barrier, which lies midway between the Hwang and Yangtze Rivers,

CLIMATIC CONTRASTS   91

rainfall is from 40 to 75 inches; to the north it ranges from 25 inches in the Yellow Plain to less than 10 inches outside the Great Wall. In North China rainfall occurs exclusively during the summer, and winters have bright sunshine; in South China summer is also the wet season, but all months have some rain.

China may be divided into a number of climatic regions. On the Koeppen basis, all South China has a warm, rainy climate with long, hot summers and mild winters, classified as a *C* type. Most of North China falls into the cool, rainy *D* category, with short summers and severe winters. Interior China receives but limited contributions of moisture from the Pacific and depends for its rainfall upon small amounts squeezed from the already dry westerlies. Much of it has a *BS* classification. Central Mongolia and Sinkiang are proper deserts, classed as *BW*.

Most of Mongolia and the northern half of the Yellow Plain are characterized by semiarid or steppe conditions, classified as *BS*. The delta of the Hwang has not usually been thought to belong in this steppe category, since the normal rainfall is approximately 20 inches; but because of the high summer temperatures the precipitation effectiveness is low, and because of the annual variability of rainfall, semidesert conditions may prevail during many years. It is the concentration of a dense population in this area of marginal *BS* climate with alternate drought and flood that has led to frequent famines.

The highlands of Tibet present local variations but for the most part belong to the *ET* or tundra category.

The *C* climates of South China may be further subdivided in terms of summer temperatures, in that most of the south has a hot *a* type, with the warmest month averaging over 72°F in contrast to a cooler *b* type in the Southwestern Uplands. There is a slight tendency toward a winter precipitation minimum, Koeppen *w*, but all months have adequate rainfall. The extreme south never experiences frost.

North China, with its cool *D* climates and the semiarid *BS* type, has a marked drought in winter, *w;* but summer temperatures are generally as high as in South China; hence *a* types are found except in the far north or in the mountains, where cooler *b* and even *c* types prevail.

NATURAL VEGETATION

Few areas in China still preserve the original cover of natural vegetation, and they are, for the most part, localities where climate or topography prevent agricultural operations. Such areas are restricted to the steppe and desert vegetation of Mongolia, Sinkiang, and Tibet, to some of the forest regions and dry grasslands of Manchuria, and to relatively small forested areas in the mountains of central and southern China. Temple groves and ancestral cemeteries also provide souvenirs of unmodified natural vegetation. Villages and farmsteads are usually surrounded by planted trees even in the dry north.

The popular conception of China as a deforested land is only partly correct. The heavier rainfall of South China enables the region to produce large though inadequate amounts of lumber, and there has long been systematic replanting in many districts. The subhumid parts of North China have many planted trees, but in the drier northwest a natural forest cover may never have existed. Too little is known of Tibet and Sinkiang to include them in this review.

Nine types of vegetation may be recognized, ranging from the desert to tropical rain forests: desert flora, steppe grasslands, semiarid brush, dry mountain flora, mixed upland forests, the flora of Szechwan, high-mountain vegetation, subtropical forests, and tropical broad-leaf forests. In addition there are the areas of long-cultivated river alluvium.

Considerable parts of the Gobi, Taklamakan, and other deserts of northern and far western China have dry xerophytic plants. The vegetation mainly comprises shrubs, some short

This pair of photos may well be entitled "From Forest to Desert in a Decade." The scene is in Shansi, where virgin forests once covered the higher slopes in inaccessible areas. Where the timber has been cut, usually at a profit of only a few cents per tree, excessive erosion follows. (*W. C. Lowdermilk, courtesy University of Nanking*)

grass, and many small flowering plants that spring up rapidly following sporadic summer rains, quickly reach maturity, and disappear with the return of the drought. Barren gravels and scattered sand dunes cover no more than 10 per cent of the Gobi and Ordos Deserts but are more widespread in the Taklamakan. Salt-tolerant species, halophytes, and tamarisk occur in scattered areas of saline, alkali, or wet soils in poorly drained localities; similar plants are found along the seacoast from Tientsin to southeast of Shanghai.

The short-grass steppe is found chiefly in Inner Mongolia, although it also occurs in Farther Tibet and Sinkiang. Near the border of the true desert the clumps of grass are a foot or two apart, but along the more humid border of the short-grass steppe the vegetation forms a continuous cover and includes patches of tall grasses. In moist, nonsaline areas there is a rich growth of tall grasses. The tall-grass steppe lies southeastward and eastward from the short-grass steppe of Inner Mongolia, without a sharp boundary. In addition to grasses are many flowering plants and shrubs. Though one may find a few elms and pines on some of the hills, most of the scattered trees of the region were cut long ago. Tall bunch grass, short grasses, and shrubs also occur around Koko Nor.

Semiarid brush and grasses once formed the natural cover over the loess deposits in Shensi and Kansu. Most of these soils have been cultivated or overgrazed for so long that natural ecological associations have been seriously disturbed. Around protected temples magnificent groves of trees thrive fairly well. These trees are sometimes thought to indicate that the Loess Hills were once forested, but we have no valid reason to suppose that forests grew anywhere except above the general level of the loess, on the higher mountains which have more rain. In the valley bottoms farmers have planted groves of poplars. These grow quickly on irrigated lands, and in five or ten years can produce timber for building purposes. Willows have also been planted on the sandy flood plains for stream control, timber, fuel, and material for baskets, and they line the ancient highways of the region. It seems probable that willows formed a natural feature of the landscape in ancient times.

A prominent feature in western China is the difference in vegetation between the exposed sunny side and the shady side of the hills. The northward-facing slopes receive much less insolation; as a consequence the soils are cooler and more moist. Where sunny slopes are covered by short-grass vegetation, corresponding shady slopes have tall grass and brush; where the sunny slopes are covered by tall grass and brush, corresponding shady slopes usually have a forest.

Dry mountain floras, composed of trees and grass, cover much of eastern Tibet and northwestern Kansu. Most of the valley lands and lower mountain slopes are covered by grassy vegetation and a dense cover of brush. In scattered areas at altitudes approaching 10,000 feet, shady slopes are covered by forests of poplar, spruce, and fir. At greater heights, patches of forests are more common on the sunny slopes; the shady slopes and high peaks are too cold for trees of any kind. Above 14,000 feet, and still higher on the southern

slopes, is an alpine vegetation of short grasses, "cushion plants," and small flowers.

Mixed deciduous and coniferous forests were the original cover in the Mongolian Border Uplands. At present the area is a land of eroded grassy hills and barren stony mountains, with occasional forest remnants as reminders of former conditions. Among the trees still standing are oaks, elms, chestnuts, maples, and coniferous types such as pines and junipers. Deciduous trees grow more commonly on the deeper soils of the low hills; pines tend to occupy the thin soils of the eroded mountains. In the valleys, groves of poplars, willows, locusts, and elms have been planted as a source of wood.

Mixed forests also originally dominated the Central Uplands. From remnants in the Chin Ling Range it seems evident that this forest was somewhat more dense than that of the drier Mongolian Border Uplands, and dominantly of deciduous types. In the southern part there are occasional evergreen broad-leaved trees. On the shallow soils of the high mountains and on poor acid soils of the low hills in the south, pines are common. Practically all the original forest has been destroyed, but new growth springs up readily on the better soils. In much of Honan and Anhwei, grass has taken the place of forest and is cut every year for fuel, along with young bushes and trees.

Mixed coniferous and deciduous forests also cover the rolling to mountainous Southwestern Uplands, the mountains surrounding the Szechwan Lowland, and the higher mountain peaks of western Fukien, eastern Kiangsi, and Kweichow. The vegetation owes its character to the heavy rainfall and high humidity. Areas of undisturbed growth are rare, but natural reproduction takes place readily. Spruce, fir, and hemlock are common on the higher mountains and are interspersed with many different deciduous trees on the hilly lands, such as oak, chestnut, and sweet gum. Many temples are surrounded by small areas of forest. Evergreen broad-leaved trees with thick and leathery leaves of dark green color occur in the south.

The Szechwan Lowland is characterized by

pine, bamboo, and cypress. Most of the valley bottoms and a large part of the hills are now used for cultivated crops, and much of the remainder is devoted to planted forests of pine and cypress. On the higher hills many deciduous trees are mixed with the pines. In some places oaks dominate. There are a few species of palms. One of the most noticeable trees of Szechwan is the banyan, which was introduced into the region a long time ago. Banyans are evergreen broad-leaved trees used for ornamentation and shade, and as objects of worship.

High-mountain flora is found in the borderland between Szechwan and the Tibetan Highlands. Along the headwaters of the Min River and beyond the rain-screen mountains of western Szechwan, the tops of the mountains are covered with coniferous forests, while the intermediate slopes are in grass. Still farther northwest, grass grows on the south slopes and forests on the northerly slopes. To the west is a series of deep canyons and high rolling uplands. The gorges are either bare or covered with spruce, fir, and pine, while the smoother parts of the uplands have a thick sod of avena and festuca grasses.

Subtropical evergreen broad-leaved trees, pine, fir, and bamboo characterize much of China south of the Yangtze. Approximately virgin conditions exist only in some of the more remote and thinly settled regions and on sacred mountains. The original cover was probably a mixture of coniferous and deciduous trees, with pines and oaks important on the old red and yellow soils, and broad-leaved ever-

Rich tropical forests cover many mountains in South China. This view is along the Burma Road in western Yunnan. (*Courtesy United States Air Force*)

green trees playing a subordinate role. The latter become dominant on the more fertile brown and gray soils of the region. At the present time parts of these regions are used for regular crops of fir and bamboo, as well as pine and broad-leaved evergreen trees. Most of the lower hills have been cleared again and again by fuel gatherers, and in many places the work of these people has been so intensive that the soil has become severely eroded.

Over a large part of South China it is a common practice to burn the grass and brush of the hills every year. In some areas young trees sprout up from the roots of the old after the land has been burned, but on the poorer soils a continued practice of burning ultimately results in the complete destruction of the forest growth and its replacement by tall, coarse grasses and ferns. Much of central and southern Kwangsi has been almost entirely deforested in this manner. The present vegetation then comprises various grasses whose chief value is as fuel. On some of the strongly acid and deforested red soils of South China, especially in the areas of Kwangtung and Kwangsi, coarse ferns entirely cover the land and are used as fuel.

Many grave plots are partly covered by shade trees, among which sweet gums and camphors are common. Camphors, found frequently also around village sites, are often held in veneration and so protected for centuries. The camphor trees of Kiangsi and Hunan are among the most magnificent trees that exist in China today. The northern limit of the subtropical forest region approximately coincides with the northern limit of palm and citrus trees, not far from the Yangtze.

Tropical semideciduous broad-leaf forests are present along the Southeastern Coast, and in Hainan. Broad-leaved evergreens dominate but are mixed with pines, deciduous trees, and bamboo. On the older red earths and on some of the poor, thin soils of mountain slopes, pine trees are more plentiful. On denuded hills coarse grasses or ferns have monopolized the soil. Some of the grasslands of this region resemble the cogonals of the Philippines and other parts of the tropics. Citrus trees, sugar cane, bananas, and other tropical and subtropical fruits are grown. In many parts of Kwangtung and Kwangsi, crops of trees and bamboo are raised on the hills, especially near navigable rivers. In a few inaccessible mountainous areas near the southeastern and southern coasts there are patches of tropical selva or rain forest. In this type of forest large trees of the evergreen broad-leaved style form a dense canopy of leaves 40 or 50 feet above the forest floor and make a shade so dense that relatively little undergrowth can flourish.

In the cultivated river plains of the Hwang, Hwai, Yangtze, and Si Rivers, the alluvial soils are more or less constantly renewed by sedimentation and have never had a chance to develop a natural vegetation because they have been under continuous cultivation. On the newly forming delta lands in the Tungting and Poyang lakes, and on alluvial soils bordering small lakes of the central basins, there are large areas of reeds. This type of growth was probably characteristic of alluvial lands in the south prior to their cultivation.

TYPES OF SOIL

Well-developed soils are largely a by-product of climate and natural vegetation. Geological parent materials place their initial stamp on immature soils, but as time goes on, the composition, texture, and profile of mature soils take on environmental characteristics that increasingly reflect temperature, rainfall, drainage, and the accumulation of organic matter.

In classifying Chinese soils, we find two great groups. They result from the major physical contrasts between the north and the south, and lie behind the agricultural and cultural differences of these same major regions. To the north of the Hwai River, where rainfall diminishes, soils tend to be rich in lime and soluble plant nutrients, porous and friable, and easily permeated by water. With limited rainfall there is but little opportunity for ground water to leach the soil, and with a grassland cover, humus accumulation is more rapid than beneath a forest growth. In the Yangtze valley and south, many soils are leached, heavy-textured, more or less stiff, and less fertile, except where renewed by flood deposits. Throughout China, soils tend to be low in organic matter, and many are deficient in plant nutrients.

The soils of subhumid North China are chiefly pedocals, or calcium carbonate–accumulating types, hence, the "cal" of their name. Where well developed on the uplands, they include chernozems, chestnut-brown soils, and light-colored desert soils. Lowland soils of mature characteristics include shachiang and saline oils. Young alluvial soils lack a profile, but many are calcareous and some are also saline.

Chernozems occur chiefly in the grasslands of northern Manchuria, Inner Mongolia, and northeastern Tibet. The black upper horizon of these soils derives its color from the decomposed roots of the tall grass vegetation. Lime concretions or soft-lime carbonates occur in a lower horizon. Typical chernozems are not extensive in China, but if present, they are better developed on the shady and moist slopes of hills where the grass cover is more abundant. Elsewhere in more humid areas are modified chernozems, similar to the black prairie soils of the United States, since they are without lime accumulation. Chernozems are among the most fertile soils in the world, but in China they occur in regions where rainfall is barely adequate for agriculture, and where latitude or altitude makes the frost-free season precariously short.

Chestnut-colored soils have an upper horizon which varies from dark to light brown, largely in terms of the humus content. They are found along the drier margins of the chernozems in Inner Mongolia, eastern Tibet, northwestern Manchuria, and Sinkiang. Short grass is the typical vegetation. Although the soil is fertile, rainfall is inadequate for normal crops, so that irrigation or dry-farming techniques are necessary. Since dry climates are notably variable,

deserts expand and contract with the centuries. Colonization of these areas, as in the American dust bowl, is sure to involve occasional disaster. Inner Mongolia is full of evidence of alternating settlement and abandonment. Remnants of three ancient great walls north of the present one reflect the shifting boundary between farmer and pastoralist.

The loessial soils of Shansi, Shensi, Honan, and Kansu require a special classification since they are derived from parent material of high lime content and are subject to constant renewal by wind work. They are low in organic matter but rich in mineral nutrients. In general they represent imperfectly developed light-colored chestnut earths. On more humid mountain slopes chernozems and dark chestnut soils have developed. A considerable part of this area is under cultivation, although serious erosion restricts full land use. In years of adequate and properly distributed rainfall crops are bountiful, but unfortunately good years in this area are not the rule.

Gray and yellow-gray desert soils are common in the short-grass and brush areas of Mongolia and Sinkiang. Evaporation of capillary moisture forms a crust of lime and salts which may partly cement the surface. Where red soils occur, the color reflects the local parent material rather than arid soil-forming processes. Agricultural development is limited to oases whose total extent is insignificant in relation to the whole desert.

Shachiang soils are unique, although apparently similar to some on the Indo-Gangetic Plain and in Texas. They occupy large parts of Shantung, Honan, Anhwei, and Hopei. These soils are poorly drained and have a subsoil horizon of lime and iron-manganese concretions. The lime is not all derived from the leaching of the surface horizon as in proper pedocals, but probably comes from the ground water, whose fluctuating level corresponds to the zone of concretions. Flat topography is a prerequisite, and extensive sections are flooded almost every season. When the dikes of the Hwang, Hwai, or Hai are breached, shallow lakes develop and remain for a year or more. In wet weather the soil is heavy and sticky; in dry weather it becomes very hard. Crop yields are moderate.

Recent calcareous alluvium covers the flood plains of North China and may range in composition from sand to clay. The silty soils are usually the most productive for agriculture. The coarser deposits lie closer to the rivers, and local sand dunes have developed from these deposits. During one flood in Shantung some of the Hwang River deposits were 6 feet thick; farms that had had poor sandy soil were covered with productive silt, and the good soil of other farms was washed away. These alluvial soils lie in the winter wheat and kaoliang area and also produce important amounts of corn, cotton, and tobacco.

Saline and alkaline soils are widespread in North China, even in the Hwang River delta. In their technical classification they belong to solonchak and solonetz types. Evaporation of capillary water from a high water table develops a surface concentration of soluble salts. The wet season is too short to flush out the accumulation of the dry period. Such soils are found from the Yangtze delta to northern Manchuria and northwest to Mongolia and Sinkiang. True alkali soils contain sodium or potassium carbonate and are not very common in China, but concentrations of sodium chloride with some sodium sulphate and sodium bicarbonate are common. Where these soils are too saline for food crops, salt-tolerant plants are harvested for fuel. Even where saline soils have not yet developed, the introduction of irrigation, as along the Mongolian bend of the Hwang River, raises the water table, increases capillary activity and evaporation, and may quickly ruin the soil. Adequate subsoil drainage must be provided to keep the water table at least 5 feet below the surface. Here and elsewhere, irrigation is safe only when the net movement of soil moisture is downward, so that any saline minerals may be moved out with the ground water.

Three other pedocal soils must be listed.

One is the Shantung brown soil, resembling the brown forest soils of Mediterranean Europe. Crops of pears, persimmons, and other fruits supplement the common grains. Purple-brown soils are common in Szechwan and Yunnan, and in parts of Hupei, Kiangsi, and Hunan. These are derived from highly colored Cretaceous and Triassic formations. Rice is the dominant crop, but there is also a diversified production of corn, wheat, sweet potatoes, beans, tobacco, and tung oil. The third type is the rendzina, best developed in Kwangsi and Kweichow but found even in Manchuria. Rendzinas are dark-colored, warm-climate soils with imperfect profiles, which in color and humus somewhat resemble temperate chernozems and chestnut soils. Though now covered with grass in uncultivated areas, they may at one time have had forests. These soils are used not only for rice cultivation but for upland crops such as corn; or they are allowed to produce coarse grass for fuel.

South China has pedalfer or non-lime-accumulating soils, named from their aluminum and iron, "al" and "fe." Upland well-developed varieties include podzol and podzolic soils, and red and yellow earths. On lowlands with poor drainage, various rice-paddy soils are formed, either with or without podzolization. Recent alluvium constitutes still another type. All pedalfers are characterized by their lack of lime.

Podzols are leached forest soils with a thin layer of raw humus over an ash-gray sandy soil and a dense lower horizon. Although originally described from cool forest regions of the Soviet Union, they are now known to occur also, under special conditions, in warm climates. Very few areas of virgin podzols remain in China, except for the occurrences in the mountains from northern Manchuria to Viet Nam.

Where true podzols are absent, the same or related processes may produce podzolic types. Two of these are the brown and gray-brown leached podzolic soils which are widespread in the hills on either side of the lower Yangtze River, with patches throughout the south.

These soils are related to the Shantung brown soils. They are found in a wide variety of environmental conditions, both hot and cool, steep slope and flat land, and moderate to excessive rainfall. Soils of the clay-pan variety occur where the subsoil is especially compact. Rice is the chief crop on the clay pans, where the dense lower horizon is an asset in allowing the fields to be kept flooded. Wheat is a winter crop.

Red and yellow soils are developed in areas of over 40 inches of rainfall and little or no freezing weather. Red soils involve lower humidity and usually higher temperatures than yellow soils. Where derived from limestone, the iron-stained red soils are called "terra rosa." Some of the red soils have been developed from lateritic rocks, which in turn are but fossil red soils, so that the resulting soil is too deficient in plant nutrients to be of much agricultural value. Sheet erosion and gullying are severe where the land has been cleared. The red soils have been used for tea, tung-oil trees, and for producing fuel. Yellow soils are somewhat better agriculturally and can be utilized for the foregoing crops and for rice, but they are largely in forest or wild grass. True laterite like that of India occurs in only a few places in southernmost China.

Rice-paddy soils are a specialized type on the plains and terraced hillsides of the south where irrigation has developed an artificial clay pan. Both podzolic and nonpodzolic types are present.

Recent deposits of noncalcareous alluvium occur in the south as well as the north.

Each of these soils has its characteristic crops, with varying productivity according to climate, fertility, and other factors. Only through intensive use of manures have the Chinese been able to secure so many thousand harvests from the same fields. This is especially true in South China where the original fertility was low and hillside erosion has been severe.

The most important fertilizer is human waste or night soil, carried from the cities to the farms and there either allowed to ferment or composted with earth and waste organic matter. Animal manures are available in only small quantity. Oil-seed cakes remaining after the oil has been extracted from cotton seeds, soybeans, peanuts, and sesame are also used. In areas of canals and ponds, rich bottom mud is spread over the fields. Wheat and rice straw are seldom used in compost piles because of their value for roofing purposes, for making rope and sandals, or for serving as a fuel. Commercial fertilizers are increasingly used, but only near the larger cities or along transport lines.

Since the cities are the chief source of night-soil fertilizer, each one is surrounded, as Thorp has pointed out, by a ring of fertile and more productive soils which extends about as far as a man may go and come in a day with a load. Immediately outside the city wall, vegetable gardeners use enormous quantities of night soil, ashes, and city waste. In places these artificial soils are as black and rich as chernozems. Thorp adds: [1]

In riding by train across the North China Plain just before the time of wheat harvest, one can always tell when the train is approaching a large city by the improved appearance of the wheat crop. As one approaches nearer and nearer any large railway station the wheat plants become more and more luxuriant and the ears larger and more filled with seed.

It should not be inferred that because Chinese agriculture has continued for many centuries, natural soil fertility is high or that permanent productivity is simple. Production is maintained only through great care and the conservation of organic waste. Thousands of square miles have been abandoned because of reduced crop yields or severe erosion. With adequate care, China may continue to use her soils indefinitely, but evidently no large areas of unused good land are awaiting colonization. Increased harvests must come largely from

[1] James Thorp: *Geography of the Soils of China,* Nanking (1936), 423–433.

better farm practices and improved plants rather than from new acreage.

MINERAL RESOURCES

The future material prosperity and political strength of China are closely related to the availability of raw materials for industry and to her skill in developing them. China may remain an agricultural nation and still preserve her classical culture, but unless there is adequate mineral wealth there is not enough good farm land to provide an adequate livelihood for her people.

For two thousand years the Chinese have known something about the common metals and have searched the more accessible parts of their country for the easily smelted ores. Copper, tin, and bronze were used in 1000 B.C.; iron dates from 800 B.C. European travelers during the Middle Ages brought back strange stories about the wealth of Cathay, and Marco Polo was able to report to his fellow Venetians that the Chinese excelled them in the use of coal and iron.

Although geological surveys are far from completion, the general picture is reasonably clear. Major discoveries will probably be confined to remote areas or to resources whose geology is less predictable.

To summarize her resources in a paragraph: China is bountifully supplied with coal and has major reserves of antimony and tungsten. Tin and iron are available in moderate amounts, and there are small quantities of a wide variety of minerals. Copper, sulfur, petroleum, and other essentials appear to be limited. China has the mineral basis for a modest industrialization, but in terms of her total area and population she ranks well down the list of the great powers. Nevertheless, no other area on the Pacific side of Asia is better supplied. When Americans are able to revisit China, they will be amazed at the spectacular development of heavy industry in a few concentrated areas.

An interesting measure of China's industrial progress may be found in the production statistics for coal and iron. In the years prior to the Second World War, China was producing about 200 pounds of coal per capita per year; by 1960 production had risen to 1,200 pounds, despite a major increase in population. Figures for iron are equally suggestive. These amounted to a per capita average of about 3 pounds in China before the war and grew to 50 pounds in 1960.

Coal is China's great source of natural power, and the country ranks among the top three nations in reserves, along with the United States and the Soviet Union. Each country measures its coal in trillions of tons. Although every province has some coal, the major reserves are significantly concentrated. Shansi and Shensi, with at least two-thirds of the total, constitute one of the major coal fields of the world. The only coastal provinces that are well supplied are

China's Mineral Sufficiency

Surplus for export	Adequate for present needs	Apparently deficient
Antimony	Aluminum	Chromium
Bismuth	Asbestos	Copper
Coal	Cement materials	Gold
Fluorite	Gypsum	Lead
Graphite	Iron	Nickel
Magnesite	Manganese	Petroleum
Molybdenum	Mercury	Sulfur
Talc	Phosphate	Zinc
Tin	Salt	
Tungsten		

The open-cut mines at Fushun in southern Manchuria operate on a seam of bituminous coal which is over 400 feet thick. Oil shale overlies the coal. (*Courtesy South Manchuria Railway*)

Shantung, Hopei, and Liaoning. Coal production has developed in the more accessible areas of the northeast rather than in the richest provinces. The total output for all China amounted to 30 million metric tons in normal years between the First and Second World Wars and reached 400 million by 1960. Since China's reserves amount to several thousand tons per capita, coal will be adequate for many centuries.

The leading mines are the great open cuts at Fushun to the east of Mukden, at Fuhsin in Jehol farther west, and the Kailan works north of Tientsin. These and a half dozen other coal mines each have a capacity of over 10 million tons a year. Other important mines are in Hei-

lungkiang, Kirin, Liaoning, and Jehol, all in Manchuria; and in Shantung, Hopei, Anhwei, Honan, Shansi, and in Szechwan, all elsewhere in North China. The only important producer in the south is Pingsiang in Kiangsi.

Petroleum appears to be absent over most of China, and geological factors, such as the presence of igneous and metamorphic rocks, make the discovery of major fields unlikely. The most attractive possibilities are in the far northwest, especially near Yumen in western Kansu, in the Tsaidam Basin of Tsinghai, at Karamai west of Urumchi in Sinkiang, and near Tzekung in Szechwan. Lanchow has a large refinery, supplied by a 548-mile pipeline from the oil fields in western Kansu. Both Shanghai

Pipelines link the oil fields at Karamai in Sinkiang with the Tushantzu refinery. (*Y. F. Li, from Eastfoto*)

and Nanking have refineries for imported crude oil. There is little prospect that China can become self-sufficient in petroleum.

Oil shale is distilled at Fushun in southern Manchuria and elsewhere, but the oil content is low. If further search fails to find adequate oil, China fortunately has large quantities of coal from which to make synthetic gasoline.

The potential water power of China lies largely in the south and west, where there are swift rivers and high rainfall. One of the problems throughout China is that the seasonal character of monsoon rainfall makes large storage works necessary for year-round power. It is estimated that the resources available 95 per cent of the time amount to 22 million kilowatts, whereas those available but 50 per cent of the time, owing to seasonal flow, may total twice as much.

While the Japanese were in Manchuria they constructed the Hsiaofengman dam on the Sungari above the city of Kirin, and the Supung dam on the Yalu along the Korean border, both of them in the half-million-kilowatt category. China's largest hydroelectric center is the Sanmen dam on the Hwang Ho east of Sian, with a capacity of a million kilowatts.

China appears to be only modestly supplied with iron ore. Small deposits are widespread, but only a few occurrences are large and of high quality. While these reserves are low in international terms, China does have enough iron ore to supply several very large steel mills for several decades.

High-grade magnetite ores are mined along the Yangtze River at Tayeh in Hupei, and in Anhwei. Excellent sedimentary hematite occurs in the Hsuanhua district 150 miles northwest of Peking. Large reserves are also present near Paotow on the Hwang Ho farther west. Important deposits occur in Honan, Shansi, Szechwan, and on the island of Hainan.

By far the largest iron-ore developments are those of southern Manchuria, but the metallic content of the ore is low and there are numerous metallurgical problems. The largest deposit is at Anshan.

The total known iron-ore reserves for China amount to billions of metric tons. While such a total is impressive, it is modest for a country of this size and population and places a limit on the long-range future of industrialization. Conspicuous centers of heavy industry have already developed at Anshan, Paotow, Wuhan, and Shanghai, but in total per capita production China does not yet match the major powers. Equally serious is the distance between iron ore and coal suitable for metallurgical coke.

Next to iron, tin is China's most valuable metallic resource. Yunnan is the major producer, and Kwangsi holds second place. At times,

China has held third place in world production, following Malaya and Indonesia. Reserves of metallic tin in Yunnan may be as high as 1,500,000 metric tons, with 100,000 tons for the balance of the country. The chief production is from the Kochiu district in southern Yunnan, where there are both surface placer operations and shaft mines.

Tungsten, derived from the mineral wolfram, is found in southern Kiangsi, and is also produced in small amounts in Hunan, Kwangtung, and Kwangsi. The reserves are very large, and at times China has supplied the major part of the world market.

China, along with Bolivia and Mexico, is one of the world's principal sources of antimony. Total reserves in China have been estimated at 3,800,000 metric tons. Half of this lies in Hunan, especially in the Sikwangshan area. Kwangtung and Kweichow also have significant reserves.

Manganese ore occurs in Kwangsi, Hunan, and Kiangsi. Though production has fluctuated

Szechwan has long been famous for its salt, produced from the brine of wells hundreds of feet deep. These bamboo derricks are at Tzeliutsing. (*Ewing Galloway*)

widely, reserves are adequate for domestic needs.

Copper has been used in China since 660 B.C., but the deposits are small and scattered. Manchuria is a major producer, along with Yunnan. Reserves are of low quality, and China will apparently never be able to supply more than part of the copper needed for its domestic requirements.

Aluminum production is limited to developments in Manchuria, Liaoning, and Hopei, where there are deposits of alunite and aluminous shale. Bauxite ore is present in Shantung and Yunnan.

China has never had a large production of lead or zinc. The oldest mines are those in the Shuikowshan district of Hunan with newer and larger developments in Kirin and Liaoning.

Mercury is obtained in Kweichow and Hunan, production being adequate for domestic needs.

Sulfur production is widespread, despite a limited supply. Leading provinces are Hunan and Shantung, with lesser centers in Shansi, Liaoning, and Szechwan. The prospects for self-sufficiency are poor.

Large amounts of salt are obtained for domestic consumption. Most of China's salt is obtained from the solar evaporation of sea water, largely along the coast north of the Yangtze where the humidity is low. Salt lakes in western Manchuria, Inner Mongolia, and southern Shansi yield a small output, and Szechwan has numerous salt wells. The normal production for the entire country amounts to about 3 million metric tons a year. The leading provinces are Liaoning, Hopei, Shantung, Szechwan, and Kiangsu. Salt may follow coal and iron as China's most valuable mineral resource.

Gold is secured along the borders of Tibet and in northern Manchuria from low-grade stream gravels. Statistics on gold production are quite incomplete but suggest a total of ½ million ounces. Silver production is limited to small amounts obtained as a by-product from lead in Hunan.

There are many other minerals in production: graphite, talc, magnesite, bismuth, mica, fluorite, asbestos, molybdenum, and phosphates.

China's mineral wealth lies in two areas. Coal and iron are in the north, largely in the basin of the Hwang Ho and beyond. Many of the nonferrous metals—tin, antimony, tungsten, and such copper and lead as are present— occur in metalliferous zones south of the Yangtze. Although there is no shortage of suitable coking coal in China as a whole, smelting problems are usually complicated by the distance between metallurgical coke and ore.

The location of future industry will reflect the distribution of raw materials, transport facilities, access to markets, and political considerations of security. The enormous coal deposits of Shansi will undoubtedly attract major industrialization. Hankow and other Yangtze centers are well located as far as transport is concerned. Seaports such as Shanghai are accessible to imported materials and skills but lack local raw materials. The mineralized areas of the far west and the south have important ores but lack adequate coal and are remote from present-day needs. Transport will everywhere be a critical economic factor.

Few areas in the world present the basic industrial needs that China will seek to meet during the remainder of the twentieth century. Many of these problems are involved with the availability of raw materials, the possibility of heavy industry, and ultimately with the geology of the country. The situation is somewhat comparable to the problems of the Soviet Union during the second quarter of the century; but unlike the U.S.S.R., China is only modestly endowed with natural wealth. It is fortunate that coal is superabundant, for it is the key to power and to chemical industry. Before many decades, however, the shortage in metals may be serious.

6 China's Economic Potential

Intensive Land Use / Agricultural Regions / Prospects for Food /
Industrial Prospects / China's Economic Problems

INTENSIVE LAND USE

The Chinese live very close to nature, and since three-quarters of the population is rural, agriculture supplies the bulk of the national livelihood. The problem of an adequate food supply is an old one in China. Even in the thirteenth century Marco Polo spoke of the pressure of man on the land as so great that "no spot on earth is suffered to lie idle that can possibly be cultivated." Fortunately, the productivity of the soil was then such that the three main grain crops, "rice, panicum [wheat?], and millet yield, in their soil, a hundred measures for one."

Fifty years later the Arab traveler, Ibn Batuta, added that "Cathay is the best cultivated country in the world. There is not a spot in the whole extent of it that is not brought under cultivation. The reason is that if any spot is left uncultivated its inhabitants or their neighbors are assessed for the land-tax due thereon." [1]

Marco Polo described how the emperor, knowing the uncertainties of the harvest, developed grain warehouses and regularly sent commissioners to

[1] H. A. R. Gibb: *Ibn Batuta's Travels,* London (1957), 282.

105

. . . ascertain whether any of his subjects have suffered in their crops of corn (grain) from unfavorable weather, from storms of wind, or by locusts, worms, or by any other plague; and in such cases he not only refrains from exacting the usual tribute of that year, but furnishes them from his granaries with so much corn as is necessary for their subsistence, as well as for sowing their land. With this view, in times of great plenty, he causes large purchases to be made of such kinds of grain as are most serviceable to them; which is stored in granaries provided for this purpose in the several provinces, and managed with such care as to ensure its keeping for three or four years without damage.[2]

In describing the Chinese landscape we must keep specific locations in mind; few generalizations are true for the country as a whole. The oases of Sinkiang, the mountain valleys of Tibet, and the steppes of Inner Mongolia, which are all part of China, are very different from the humid and densely settled areas of the east. Even crops in the vicinity of Peking and of Canton have little in common with each other. With all this in mind, certain generalizations are valid. Chinese agriculture is intensive in its use of human labor, aided by relatively few draft animals or machines. Large yields are obtained through painstaking care from microscopic fields. Everywhere industrious people are cultivating the soil; one can hardly escape from this teeming population of farmers.

The density of the rural population closely parallels the productivity of the land. In several places there are over 3,000 people per square mile, and the average density for the whole country in terms of cultivated land is about 2,000 people per square mile. Despite the greatest care, distress and famine have repeatedly resulted from environmental uncertainties or from the hazards of war, banditry, and excessive taxation.

Chinese agriculture has had a long and honored history. For at least forty centuries, farmers have been able to till the same fields—in

[2] Yule-Cordier: *The Book of Sir Marco Polo,* II, 212–213.

places with two harvests a year. Long experience has shown the best crops for different areas, and agricultural practices have endeavored to maintain the fertility of the soil rather than to squander its productivity. As one flies over the agricultural parts of China, he sees a landscape that everywhere reflects the intensity of man's quest for food. Wherever crops can possibly be raised, the land is under full cultivation. River plains are divided into tiny geometric garden plots, and hillside fields wind along the contours. Throughout the country a superabundance of people wrest their living from an undersupply of arable land.

Grains supply 90 per cent of the diet; only a small part of the necessary energy is derived from vegetables, meat, or fruit. The diet of the north is more diversified. In the Hwang River delta wheat, kaoliang (a sorghum), millet, corn, sweet potatoes, and soybeans each supply at least 5 per cent of the total calories. In the hills south of the Yangtze no crop other than rice supplies more than 5 per cent of the food.

In a countryside so densely crowded as China, little land can be spared for pasture. More food can be obtained by the direct consumption of crops than through feeding them to livestock. Pigs and chickens live on the household refuse. Fish are an important part of the diet near the seashore and in the canal areas.

Domestic fuel is also a by-product of agriculture, for rice and wheat straw, corn and kaoliang stalks, and other plants are used in cookstoves. Supplies of firewood or coal are seldom available, but villages near the hills commonly have uncultivated areas from which brush and grass are gathered. In drier areas such as Mongolia, Sinkiang, and Tibet, dried animal dung is widely used for fuel, and this use is often in direct competition with the needs for fertilizer.

Prior to collectivization, Chinese farms were small, averaging 2 or 3 acres, but surveys show that the typical holding was divided into six pieces, each made up of two unfenced fields. These had been subdivided through in-

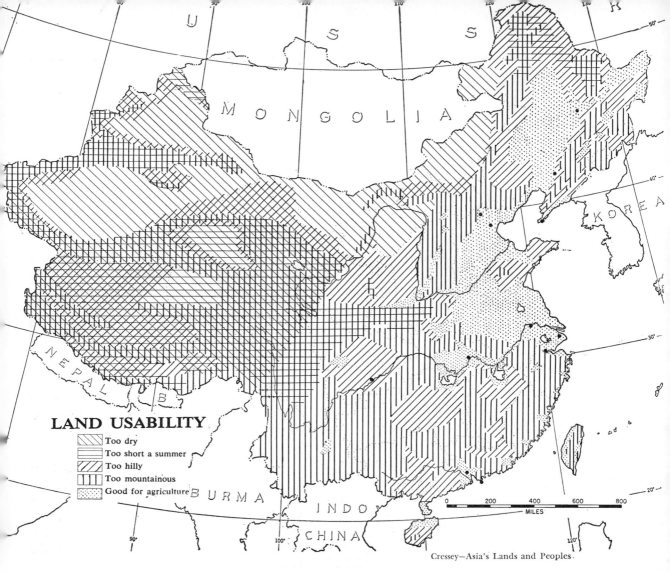

LAND USABILITY

- ◹ Too dry
- ▤ Too short a summer
- ◿ Too hilly
- ▥ Too mountainous
- ⋮ Good for agriculture

0   200   400   600   800
MILES

Cressey—Asia's Lands and Peoples.

China has large areas which receive less than 15 inches of rain, or have a growing season of less than three months free from frost, or have slopes which are too steep for cultivation. The best agricultural land lies in the lowlands of the Sungari, Liao, Hai, Hwang, Hwai, Yangtze, and Si Rivers.

heritance and were scattered over a radius of as much as a mile from the farmstead. Although the subdivision was inefficient, it did provide a sort of crop insurance; for if one lowland plot was too wet, the hillside field might remain productive. Even now that farms have been merged, factors of terrain and irrigation keep many fields small.

Chinese agriculture produces good yields per acre, but such production is a result of laborious and wasteful use of manpower. Excessive care is bestowed upon tiny fields, and production is secured only through concentration on a small per capita area. In terms of national welfare it is not the yield per acre but the yield per person that brings prosperity.

Large amounts of human labor are used in place of machines to produce crops. Pre-Communist studies showed that the man-equivalent required for 1 acre of wheat in China was 26

Every foot of available land is in some productive use. Terraced rice fields follow every valley and climb the slopes, in this aerial scene near Hsintin in Szechwan. (*Courtesy United States Air Transport Command*)

days of labor compared with 1.2 days in the United States. For cotton the comparison was 53 and 14 days; 1 acre of corn in China required 23 days but only 2.5 days in the United States. On the basis of yield per farmer, the China output was only 3,080 pounds a year as compared with 44,000 pounds in the United States. A farmer who produces little cannot expect to have very much of this world's goods.

Chinese agricultural statistics contain many uncertainties. Nationalist government data compiled shortly before the establishment of the Communist regime gave a total cultivated area in Mainland China of 359,300 square miles, or nearly 10 per cent of the total area. Sample field measurements made by J. Lossing Buck indicate that the areas actually cultivated amounted to one-tenth and even one-third more than actually reported for tax purposes.

In 1960 Premier Chou En-lai told Edgar Snow that the land under cultivation amounted to 110 million hectares, or about 424,500 square miles. He added that since 1955 there had been a decrease of about 2 million hectares due to land withdrawn for new highways, reservoirs, urban and industrial developments, railways, and airports.[1] Chinese press dispatches in 1960 refer to 107 million hectares under cultivation.

Allowing for unrecorded areas and developments in recent decades during which some crop land has been added along the Mongolian frontier plus reclamation elsewhere, we can estimate that the total cultivated area may reach 425,000 square miles. This amounts to less than 12 per cent of Mainland China. In comparison, the United States, with one-fourth of China's population, cultivates about 500,000 square miles. Other countries report cultivated land as follows: Japan, 15 per cent; India together with Pakistan, approximately 35 per cent; the Soviet Union, 8 per cent; Great

[1] Edgar Snow: *The Other Side of the River*. New York: Random House (1962), 81.

Britain, 30 per cent; and the United States 14 per cent.

About 8 per cent of China is forested, with percentages ranging up to 23 in Yunnan, 27 in Kirin, 28 in Heilungkiang, and 34 in Szechwan, and down to less than 1 per cent in most of Inner Mongolia.

Pasture lands account for roughly 20 per cent of the entire country, largely semidesert areas in Inner Mongolia, Sinkiang, and Tibet.

More than half of China has negligible productive value. Large areas are so seriously eroded that they have little or no soil or are so dissected that utilization is impractical. Other sections are too dry or too cold or otherwise unproductive. China appears large on the map, but its usability is limited.

The most significant agricultural fact is the amount of cultivated land per person. Such statistics as are available place this at one-third of an acre per capita for farmer and city dweller together. In the United States the comparable figure is eight times as large, namely 2.5 acres per capita. Prior to collectivization the average farm measured only 2 or 3 acres, not all of which was actually in crops since graves, farm buildings, and other nonproductive uses accounted for 7 per cent of the average farm.

Nearly half of the cultivated land is irrigated, in almost all instances for rice. Terraced land amounts to about one-fourth of the cultivated area and is common in both the irrigated ricelands of the south and the dry wheat area of the north. This suggests the great investment of labor that has been necessary to make China productive.

Many crops are grown, and Chinese agriculture differs from that elsewhere less in the varieties of things grown than in the methods used. The most important food grains are rice and wheat, with cotton as the chief textile crop. Other important products are millet, soybeans, the grain sorghum called kaoliang, barley, corn, sweet potatoes, rapeseed, broad beans, and peanuts in decreasing importance of acreage. Distinctive crops are opium poppy, mulberry— whose leaves are fed to the silkworm—tea, oranges, and tobacco. Hay and fodder are notably lacking.

Two-thirds of the cultivated area produces two or more crops a year. Rotation is common.

It seems probable that China leads the world in total agricultural production, taking first place in rice, wheat, sweet potatoes, kaoliang, soybeans, millet, barley, peanuts, and tea.

AGRICULTURAL REGIONS

China is large and diverse; no one can travel more than a few hundred miles without being impressed by marked differences in crops and farm practices. Some of these grow out of custom, as in places where immigrants of centuries ago brought their crops with them; others are related to climate and soil; still other differences reflect markets. Taken together, the various patterns of agriculture form a mosaic that may be grouped into broad regional characteristics.

The most conspicuous boundary is the northern limit of rice cultivation, with its flooded fields, canals, and water buffalo, near latitude 33°N. This line lies midway between the Yangtze and Hwang Rivers, along the crest of the Chin Ling in the west and near the Hwai River in the east. Rice is grown as far north as Manchuria, but this line marks the limit of continuous cultivation. South China is a green, humid, and subtropical riceland, while North China is a dry brown wheatland under the influence of the desert. Wheat extends well into the Yangtze valley as a winter crop, but is not widespread in the south.

Major contrasts appear between the wheat and rice provinces. Since the growing season in North China is five to eight months as against ten months to a year in South China, double cropping is more widespread, and the same land can support more people. Rainfall is over twice as heavy in the south. The gross area of the South is larger, but the presence of extensive plains in the North gives it a greater cultivated area. Nevertheless, the higher productivity of the ricelands enables them to support nearly twice the total population of the wheat-producing section.

Rice and wheat are the outstanding Chinese crops. Winter wheat is a conspicuous crop in the Yangtze valley and almost as far north as the Great Wall, beyond which spring wheat is common. The total wheat acreage exceeds that in rice. Water buffalo go with rice, while oxen, known to the Chinese as yellow cows, are widely used in wheat areas. Pre-Communist farms in the wheat province were twice the size of those in the rice province, but land values per acre in the latter were nearly twice those in the former. The intensity of farming in the South is shown by the 50 per cent greater farm population per square mile of crop area.

Within the wheat province of the north, Buck has described four agricultural regions: the winter wheat–kaoliang region in the Yellow Plain, the winter wheat–millet region in the Loess Hills, the spring wheat region along the Mongolian frontier and into Manchuria, and the Manchurian soybean-kaoliang region. The rice province of the south is similarly divided into the Yangtze rice-wheat region, the Szechwan rice region, the rice-tea region in the hills south of the Yangtze, the double-cropping rice region in the far south, and the Southwestern rice region. Scattered oases in Sinkiang and sheltered valleys in Tibet are to be added.

The winter wheat–kaoliang region is the most important of the wheat regions, and includes one-third of all cropland south of the Great Wall. Its concentrated population of 125 million people covers the Yellow Plain and in addition reaches into the Shantung Hills. The chief provinces are Hopei, Shantung, and Honan. Although the rainfall is only 24 inches, it falls during the hot summer. Most soils are calcareous; some are saline. Irrigation is uncommon and usually limited to vegetable gardens near hand-operated wells. Vegetables are grown in a wide variety. Winter wheat, summer millet, and kaoliang are the chief crops. Corn, cotton, soybeans, and sweet potatoes also cover a considerable area in the summer. Barley is a minor winter crop. Delicious persimmons and hard pears are important fruits. No other agricultural area has so much diversification. Flood and drought present recurrent hazards.

The winter wheat–millet region lies to the west in the Loess Hills, with fertile soils, steep slopes, excessive erosion, and marginal rainfall. The chief plains are along the Fen and Wei Rivers in Shansi and Shensi. More than one-third of the cropland is terraced, not in order to flood the fields but to check erosion on the steep hillsides. Winter wheat, millet, cotton, kaoliang, and corn are the crops. Cotton is grown in the warmer Fen and Wei valleys; kaoliang and wheat are confined to the plains and valleys; millet is grown on the higher and drier hillsides. Kansu is noted for its superior apricots. Double cropping is practiced on one-fifth of the land as compared with two-fifths in the winter wheat–kaoliang region.

The spring wheat region forms a fringe along the Mongolian frontier, lying on either side of the Great Wall. Elevations in this hilly area range from 3,000 to 8,000 feet. The rainfall is so low that normal cultivation is unsafe without irrigation, but available water is limited to the Hwang and to streams from northeastern Tibet. Elsewhere dry-farming techniques must be used. Only five months are free from frost. Considerable areas are used for pasture, and it would be wise if many hillsides now plowed were put back into grass. Instead of being a prospective zone for pioneer settlement, most of the spring wheat region already has more people than it can safely support. The crops are all summer-grown, and include spring wheat, millet, Irish potatoes, oats, kaoliang, barley, corn, rice, and sometimes opium poppy, which is raised on the frontier because of poor transport facilities for more bulky crops. Crop yields per acre are considerably below the national average. Famine is more severe here than elsewhere. Standards of living are low.

The Manchurian soybean-kaoliang region spreads over the Manchurian Plains and the East Manchurian Hills, and is larger than any other agricultural area in China. During the early decades of the twentieth century, this new land was the goal of millions of Chinese immigrants, but by 1950 the population had approached 50 million, and little good land remained except along the cold northern and dry western margins. In the central portion rainfall is adequate for successful agriculture, and soils are fertile. The area of cultivated land per person is the largest in all China, and there is the beginning of mechanized agriculture. Draft animals are more numerous here than elsewhere. The chief crops are kaoliang in the south and soybeans in the north, each covering one-quarter of the total acreage. Other crops are millet, spring wheat, corn, barley, and some rice grown by Koreans along the eastern frontier.

The Yangtze rice-wheat region in the rice province of South China is the smallest of all the agricultural areas, but its economic importance as the hinterland of Shanghai is very great. Most of the region is a low flood plain, intersected by a network of rivers, canals, and lakes, and all of it is intensively utilized. Even the water bodies yield fish, aquatic plants, and fertile bottom mud for fertilizer. The rainfall is abundant and the growing season long. As elsewhere in South China, most of the soils are noncalcareous. Rice is the main crop and in this region supplies four times the total food energy derived from wheat. Winter crops occupy a considerable percentage of land, so that two-thirds of the area is double-cropped. In order to provide better drainage for dry winter crops, the fields are laboriously spaded into ridges a foot or more in height. Winter crops

Tractors are coming into use in North China, where fields are larger and drier. This is a machine and tractor station in Shensi. (*Eastfoto*)

Many attempts have been made to mechanize rice culture. Here simple machines on a commune in Kwangtung are transplanting rice seedlings. Many hillside terraces are too narrow for any mechanization. (*M. L. Lo, from Eastfoto*)

include wheat, barley, rapeseed, and broad beans. Other summer crops are cotton, soybeans, and corn. Mulberry for silkworms is distinctive.

The rice-tea region lies in the South Yangtze Hills in Chekiang, Kiangsi, and Hunan, with only small areas of level land. Cultivated land amounts to only one-fifth of the total area, but three-fourths of it is irrigated and one-third terraced. Rapeseed, wheat, and barley are grown in the winter, followed by rice in the summer. Intertillage is common in Chekiang, with alternate rows of early and late rice. Tea is a hillside crop, as are corn, soybeans, wood oil, and sweet potatoes.

In the Szechwan rice region, the lowlands raise rice in the summer, and wheat, rapeseed, and broad beans in winter. On the hills the crops are sweet potatoes, corn, kaoliang, sugar cane, sesame, soybeans, tobacco, and tung oil. Yields are nearly 10 per cent above the all-China average, and the grain production per capita is also the highest. The crops of this area—one of the most productive in the country—are representative of both north and south. Crops are closely adjusted to the available water, so that the upper dry fields and lower flooded terraces each have their specialized use. Rice is sown in seed beds during April or May and transplanted to the fields early in June; the harvest occurs in September. During the winter, beans may be interplanted with wheat. Szechwan is noted for its crop of delicious oranges.

The double-cropping rice region lies in the hills of subtropical China where there is but limited level land. Only 12 per cent of Kwangtung is cultivated. The growing season continues practically throughout the year, and the rainfall averages 70 inches, the highest in China. Most soils were initially poor but are now so badly eroded that they have passed out of agricultural use. Extensive areas of rolling hills are covered with wild grass, used only for fuel. Over three-fourths of the land is double-cropped between spring and fall, but nine-tenths remains idle in winter. Two successive crops of rice are common, planted in March and August with harvests in June or July and November. Whereas the yield per crop is low, double cropping yields a larger total per acre than anywhere else in China. Rice supplies over three-quarters of the food energy. There are considerable areas of sweet potatoes, sugar cane, tobacco, tea, mulberry, and oranges. Famines are rare.

In the southwestern rice region, dissected topography and mile-high elevations introduce local contrasts. In the few valleys, rice is the summer crop, followed by opium poppy (when grown), broad beans, or wheat. In the mountains the chief crops are corn, barley, and millet, and these form the staple diet of the non-Chinese tribespeople. Excellent fruit is grown. Although this is the second largest of the agricultural regions, next to Manchuria, the proportion in cultivation is the lowest. Nowhere is there so much crowding, for the farm population reaches the incredible density of 3,000 per square mile of cropland.

PROSPECTS FOR FOOD

China needs more food. This need would exist even if the population should remain static, but as the number of mouths to be fed approaches 1 billion the problem of mere subsistence takes on sober dimensions. If the problems of land, climate, and soil appear imposing, we should remember that China's greatest resource lies in human ingenuity. Geography may describe the environment, but the absolute limits on agricultural production depend on skill in developing new crops with larger yields, better fertilizers, and more efficient farm management. Yet most of China is an old land of stabilized agriculture, where the soil is so intensively cultivated that increased yields are difficult to secure without large expenditures for fertilizers, machinery, or reclamation. Few opportunities for pioneering exist, and these are largely in areas of precarious climate or unfavorable terrain. One of China's most pressing problems concerns the relation between expanding population and limited agricultural productivity.

Since the rural-urban ratio is 4 to 1, and most families number six people, it is clear that the average Chinese family grows only enough food for itself and one-and-a-fraction other persons. There is thus no agricultural surplus to feed the expanding urban population. If China should quickly develop an extensive industry, its workers might have to be fed with imported food. This situation is in striking contrast to

Land Use in East Asia [1]

(in thousand hectares)

	Total area	Arable land incl. fallow and orchards	Irri-gated land	Forest and wood-lands
China, Mainland	976,101	109,354	—	76,600
China, Taiwan	3,596	878	481	1,755
Hong Kong	101	13	—	7
Japan	36,966	6,072	2,852	24,998
Korea, total	22,079	4,390	—	15,442
Korea, South	9,693	2,016	1,203	3,742
Mongolia	153,100	—	—	25,000
All East Asia	1,191,943	120,707		143,802

[1] United Nations, Food and Agricultural Organization: *Production Yearbook,* 1960.

that in the United States, where each farm family feeds dozens of city workers and there is a surplus of food.

Here in China, as elsewhere around the world, the best prospects for additional food lie in the further intensification of production in the already developed areas. The same capital investment in the Shanghai delta will probably yield more food than if applied to the development of remote areas in the far west.

Any discussion of increased food supply must include a reference to the length of the frost-free period. While the growing season in the far south lasts for 365 days, in northern Manchuria it is but 150 days and may drop to less than 4 months. Canton normally has 360 continuous frost-free days, Shanghai 300, Peking about 225, and Harbin barely 175 days of agricultural growth. Rainfall in the same cities amounts to 67 inches, 47 inches, 25 inches, and 20 inches.

China has seldom produced enough food for her own needs. Prior to the Second World War she imported normally some 2 million tons of rice, wheat, and sugar. During the early years of Communist rule the elimination of this import was due probably not so much to increased per capita production as to a lower standard of living. Since agricultural products comprise the major items which China produces and might thus export, the country was obliged to ship several million tons of foodstuff annually to the Soviet Union in repayment for technical assistance. China likewise bartered rice for rub-

Cormorants are trained to catch fish in the canals of South China. A ring around the neck prevents the bird from swallowing the fish. This scene is along the Grand Canal. (*Ewing Galloway*)

ber from Ceylon. When crop production fell during the "bitter years" around 1960, large imports of food were again necessary.

Early Communist planning gave inadequate attention to agriculture, concentrating instead on heavy industry. Once collectivization was achieved, the next step was the development of agricultural communes designed to increase the efficiency of food production and further to regiment the farmer. When these failed to meet the problem, major changes took place. State farms have been limited principally to drier areas of new cultivation in the north and west; the use of tractors has been limited in the same way.

The prospects of agricultural expansion prior to the Communist regime were summarized in 1937 by J. Lossing Buck, one of the leading students of land use in China.[3]

Certain facts as regards land in China are now clear. In the first place, no great increase in the amount of farm land can be expected. The removal of graves from farm land, the elimination of land in boundaries by the consolidation of the fragmented holdings, the profitable cultivation of arable lands not now cultivated, and an economic size of farm which would lessen the proportion of area in farmsteads would probably make available an additional ten per cent of the present area in farms.

In the second place, farm land in China is already intensively used. A very large proportion of the land is in crops used directly for human food, an extremely small amount in pasture, and a comparatively small amount in forest or in other fuel crops. Not only is the type of use intensive, but the modification of the physical conditions of the land by irrigation, drainage, terracing, and to a smaller extent by fertilization, also tends to bring about a higher degree of utilization. It is, however, through the still more intensive use of the present farm land of China that the greatest increase in food production is to be expected, not only by modifying the physical conditions themselves, but through improvements in the technique of crop and animal production, independent of the physical factor of the land itself. Perhaps a

[3] J. Lossing Buck: *Land Utilization in China*, Chicago (1937), I, 202–203. Quoted by permission.

25 per cent increase in total production by more intensive methods and by modern techniques would be a conservative estimate of the possible increase economically, in China's agricultural production with the known methods of agricultural production.

Although it scarcely seems possible to increase the acreage of good cropland, there are extensive areas of unused uplands and semi-arid steppe whose future remains problematical. It appears unlikely that these can all be put under profitable cultivation, but they might be used for tree crops as well as for grazing.

The second half of the twentieth century is seeing notable changes in agriculture. Transportation has opened markets for the isolated interior producer, and new skills have improved production. But whether all the needed changes are feasible and adequate is an open question. What China needs in order to take her place as a world power is an increase in her per capita income of several hundred per cent. It does not appear that agriculture holds the key to such a change.

INDUSTRIAL PROSPECTS

The three great geographic assets of China are manpower, coal, and location. Most metals appear to be present in only modest amounts, and the soil is good but so inadequate in view of the population that there is little room for industrial crops or export surplus. Extensive forests might be grown on the hillsides. The country appears to be deficient in petroleum, and where water power is available it is seasonal. Despite such shortages, China can look forward to a far greater industrial future. Certainly no other country in eastern Asia is so well endowed as a nation; per capita possibilities are more modest.

China's millions provide the world's largest source of labor. At present they are inefficient, but there is no reason why two generations of training may not make labor as skilled as elsewhere. Despite a limited diet and a somewhat enervating climate, the sheer bulk of China's manpower is impressive. The new China has an enormous amount of work to do in building roads, controlling rivers, improving agriculture, developing forests, operating factories, and improving housing. The people for the job are available.

The exploitation of the varied mineral resources of China is a matter of metallurgy, economics, and political policy. Their location within China and the competition in world prices are quite as important as geological origin. China has possibly enough of most metals to supply all the industries that can be built for several decades. Coal without iron ore is better than iron without coal, for coal is the key to chemical industries, to cement, and to power. China's coal supply is very great and well distributed, though not all is of metallurgical quality.

Good location is a geographic resource; the possession of material assets is of little value in Antarctica or remote regions. Much of China's economic potential lies in areas accessible to the seacoast, which in turn is at the meeting point of the main sea routes from Europe and from North America. In the triangle between India, Australia, and Siberia, China has no possible rival except Japan, which is dynamic but poor.

Few countries have such regional diversity as China. Here are most of the major climatic types with a resulting variety of agricultural products. Varied topography, soils, and vegetation add to the other advantages of regional contrasts. Such contrasts contribute to national self-sufficiency.

Starting with the early 1930s, China experienced spectacular developments in road building, city rehabilitation, and education, all of which were arrested by the Japanese invasion a decade later. Present-day China faces exceedingly urgent economic needs that touch her entire life. To list some of them alphabetically, they include agriculture, consumer goods, export products, housing and sanitation, hydroelectric power, industry both heavy and light, land reclamation and resettlement, military defense, mining, reforestation, river conservancy, roads and railways, shipping and port facilities, and urban reconstruction.

Some plan is essential. When the Chinese Communists started their five-year programs they ruthlessly postponed the problems of agriculture and consumer goods and started at the bottom with mining, heavy industry, and transportation. China has attempted to duplicate the Soviet program but lacks the mineral wealth and initial tools of the U.S.S.R. China's first economic need is inventory. Few major developments are justified until all the possibilities are clear. China should not plan for heavy industry until the location of available resources is known. Does China have unused land with soil and climate suitable for crops? Is the flow of certain rivers dependable enough to justify large hydroelectric installations? Can the metal of various ores be extracted economically? What population trends may be counted on? What areas, if any, will be strategically safe from invasion during a major war?

Dramatic industrial changes characterized the postwar decades under Communist control. Many developments initiated by the Nationalists were interrupted by the war. It is thus possible to recognize that China has already become one of the world's great industrial states. While per capita production remains low, the sheer bulk of national production is impressive.

By 1960 Mainland China apparently led the world in the output of tungsten and antimony; held second place in the production of salt; ranked third in coal, tin, graphite, magnesite, and talc; took fourth place in iron ore, bismuth, mica, and fluorite; ranked fifth in asbestos; and stood sixth among the nations in the production of steel and mercury. (Data from United States Bureau of Mines.)

In all these industrial resources China holds modest to good reserves. She has, in addition, molybdenum, magnesium, aluminum, gypsum, and phosphate. Her deficiencies appear to lie in copper, lead, zinc, chromium, nickel, sulfur, and petroleum. For the production of these raw materials, several dozen centers of industry

Spectacular industrial developments have enabled China to become a major producer in heavy industry, closely rivaling Japan in overall output, though not in per capita production. These steel rails have been produced at Anshan. (*Courtesy China Pictorial*)

have arisen, some of them resulting in the transformation of sleepy towns into industrial giants. Ten coal mines have capacities in excess of 10 million tons a year. Great steel mills, with giant furnaces, rolling mills, and associated heavy industry have developed at Anshan in southern Manchuria, Wuhan on the Yangtze, Paotow on the middle Hwang where it turns south from Inner Mongolia, and at Shanghai despite its lack of local raw materials. Each of these mills has an annual capacity of several million tons. A dozen other steel mills are rated at over ½ million tons each, notably Peking, Tientsin, Tsingtao, Taiyuan, Chungking, and Penki in Manchuria.

Since the Anshan mills are located next to the ore and only 40 miles from Fushun coal,

their assembly costs are low; unfortunately the iron content of the ore is low, and Fushun coal does not make good coke. With its annual capacity of 5 million tons, Anshan ranks among the dozen largest steel centers on earth. Hankow brings its ore 47 miles up the Yangtze and must reach several hundred miles north or south for coal. Paotow has coal 20 miles distant, and its ore moves 100 miles. Shanghai has no nearby coal or iron, but does supply scrap, along with cheap transport and a local market.

Industrial production has developed in several major regions. South Manchuria leads, thanks to coal and oil shale at Fushun, iron and steel at Anshan, and miscellaneous machine production around Mukden and Dairen. These areas each owed their start to Japanese capital. Northern Manchuria is represented by Harbin and Changchun (or Hsinking), which produce specialized items such as electrical equipment, trucks, and machine tools. These cities secure some of their importance from their proximity to Soviet technical aid and supplies.

In the Yellow Plain the major industries are grouped around Peking and Tientsin-Tangshan, each important for textiles, steel, and light industry.

Northwest China has steel mills at Taiyuan and at Paotow, and a regional center at Lanchow with its rail yards and oil refinery.

Industry in the Yangtze Plain is dominated by Shanghai, by far the largest center for miscellaneous manufacturing in all China. Shanghai's industries include shipbuilding and the production of electrical goods and textiles. Nearby are Hangchow and Nanking. Both Shanghai and Nanking have refineries for imported petroleum.

South China production is centered on Canton and on British Hong Kong, each noted for light industry. Two small centers in the west are Chungking and Kunming, both with small steel mills.

All these will continue to be important. New centers of industry should arise in the Shansi coal basin and in the mineralized belt across south central China. Although the lower Yangtze valley does not have the largest resources, it has superior water transport for both river and ocean steamers, and is fed by numerous rail lines. Here is the largest market, the greatest head start, and the easiest contact with imported materials and skills. Should China, like Japan, desire to import iron ore from the Philippines and Malaya, neither of which has proper coal, the Yangtze provides a good setting for steel mills. The Yangtze valley is also the source of important agricultural exports.

The new China should plan regionally, with balanced attention to the problems of all areas and adequate appreciation of geographic conditions. It should be clear that the possibilities of Sinkiang and of the Southeastern Coast are un-

like, but each has its needs. Only a balanced China can be a strong China.

Notable changes have occurred in the character of China's foreign trade. During the nineteenth century the country was self-sufficient, and importers found it difficult to offer anything in exchange for tea and silk; hence the introduction of opium. Later on, a large market developed for cotton cloth and thread, kerosene, cigarettes, matches, sugar, rice, and manufactured goods. China in turn exported unprocessed agricultural products. Between the First and Second World Wars the country came to weave much of its own cloth and to supply many of its simple factory needs. Owing to the cheapness of labor, these articles were exportable to the markets of Southeastern Asia. Here they successfully competed with products from Japan, where efficiency was higher but where labor costs were also greater.

The China market originally called for consumer goods which could be sold at very low prices. Once China develops its own industrial capacity, the need for cheaper imports will diminish, and what once were imports may become export items. Imports now include mining equipment; smelters and refineries; factories for automobiles, paper, cement, and chemicals; railroad and highway equipment; and electric power plants. In addition there is a need for materials that are largely unobtainable in China, such as gasoline, rubber, copper, and other metals.

If the outside world desires to sell to China, it must buy in return. China will naturally make strenuous efforts to find markets for her goods, and these must be largely the product of her agriculture, mines, and cheap labor. Before the Second World War the chief exports were soybeans and bean cake, raw silk, wool, hides, furs, egg products, tin, antimony, tungsten, and tung oil. Not all of these will regain their former prominence. Manchuria no longer has a monopoly in the world supply of soybeans; silk is partly replaced by synthetic substitutes; and wool and hides of better quality are available elsewhere. China's unique metals will continue to find a ready market. China once supplied the world's tea and might regain some of the market. Artistic items such as embroideries and lace, novelties, and products in which unskilled labor is important may increase. The basic problem is whether China's potential exports can pay for her needed imports.

China's pre-Communist trade was concentrated on a few countries. Japan probably led but was closely followed by the United States. Great Britain was third, followed by Germany and France. A large trade also existed with the areas to which Chinese have emigrated, such as Indochina, Thailand, Malaya, Indonesia, and the Philippine Islands. Taken together they surpassed Great Britain. Pre-Communist trade with the Soviet Union was negligible, and developed only because of political ties.

The new China may well develop a large interest in Southeast Asia. From here will come petroleum, rubber, coconut oil, sugar, hemp, lumber, aluminum, nickel, chromium, manganese, and iron ore. To these areas China might ship cheap manufactured goods, such as textiles, cigarettes, novelties, and articles requiring moderate skill. A modernized China will have all it can do for decades to meet its internal needs and balance its foreign trade. It will increasingly dominate its corner of Asia, but it lacks the iron and associated materials to achieve first rank as an exporter.

CHINA'S ECONOMIC PROBLEMS

In the twentieth-century era of material civilization and international rivalries, a nation's physical features and population provide a significant background for evaluating geostrategy. In the various aspects of her environment China appears well endowed.

Some of the material elements of her domestic geostrategy include (1) favorable location, (2) large size and compact shape, (3) reasonably satisfactory land forms with internal accessibility, (4) an agriculturally productive climate, (5) good soil, (6) accessibility, (7) fairly clear international boundaries, (8) access to the ocean, and (9) diversified minerals and abundant coal. To this material list should be added the most important item of all: (10) a large and industrious population. Few nations are more fortunate in their overall geopolitical picture.

China's location may not be of first rank for world commerce or political leadership, but she is well situated with respect to an Asiatic-Pacific area within which are exceedingly great resources and attractive markets. Her location is both continental and maritime. Two great ocean highways meet along the China coast, one from Europe via Singapore, the other from North America. Overland communications with the Soviet Union and India are long and inadequate but can be improved. China may sometime reassume her traditional leadership in East Asia.

Large size is not synonymous with self-sufficiency, but within the diverse environments of China a wide variety of resources is available. At the same time large size brings problems in communications and the welding together of diverse peoples. China has adequate living room, even though it is not all of the best. If China had not been huge, she might not have survived the Japanese invasion. One of a nation's military assets is defense in depth; without the ability to trade space for time, China could scarcely have held out.

Much of China is too hilly or mountainous, but there are several large plains. Except for the Central Mountain Belt, eastern China has few mountains higher or more rugged than the Appalachians, or hills more difficult of access and utilization than the Appalachian plateaus.

Little attention is sometimes given to the importance of climate. Not only is agriculture intimately related to temperature and rainfall, but human health and energy are also tied up with climatic stimulus. Much of China is too cold or too dry, and famine due to climatic conditions has been recurrent. Nevertheless, soil and climate are reasonably satisfactory.

China's soil is as diverse as her topography

and climate. Fortunately the Chinese farmer has done a remarkable job in conserving its fertility, so that thousands of harvests have been gathered from the same field. Since only about 12 per cent of China is cultivated, we may conclude that only about the same fraction of the land is usable soil.

Poor accessibility has long handicapped China. In the days of the Empire, travel was often by sedan chair or canal boat, and even today many cities are without modern means of access. Fortunately, mail and telegraph services are well developed.

Many international disputes arise from unsatisfactory boundaries. China's frontiers have shifted widely over the centuries. The boundary with India along the Himalaya is in dispute but should be easily defined. Next to Outer Mongolia, the broad Gobi Desert interposes a different environment, and there is no sharply defined natural boundary; a strong China pushes her control to the north of the desert, while a strong Soviet Union pushes its influence to the southern margin in the form of the Mongolian People's Republic. The only part of China across which a foreign power might legitimately wish a transit route is in the far northeast where Manchuria projects into Soviet territory and blocks the normal avenue from Lake Baikal to Vladivostok.

China has a varied coast line. The delta sections are deficient in good harbors, but on the whole there are adequate port possibilities and good access to the hinterland. The coastal Chinese have a long record of maritime interests; native junks reached Ceylon early in the Christian era. Nevertheless, China as a whole has been continent-minded, and one of her problems relates to the orientation of her economic and social interests. Although China has a long coast line, she does not enjoy unrestricted access to the sea. Korea and the Maritime Provinces of the Soviet Union block access to the Sea of Japan. To the east of Shanghai are the Ryukyu Islands, once a Chinese dependency, taken over by the Japanese late in the nineteenth century; it is but natural that China

should consider their retrocession. Taiwan is an obvious barrier to free maritime access.

The mineral picture includes superabundant coal and passable iron ore. China is moderately well equipped for industrialization. The neighboring countries of Southeast Asia are exceptionally rich. A strong China will presumably wish assured access to the South Seas, from which region she will have to draw numerous mineral and agricultural products.

China leads the world in manpower. While the country includes minor differences in race and dialect, no other great nation is so unified in culture. Since in sheer numbers the cultural and industrial contributions are impressive, it is important to recognize the inequalities in distribution and skill.

In addition to these more or less domestic matters, several external aspects of China's geostrategy call for attention: (1) access to the resources and markets of Southeast Asia; (2) possibilities of colonization in the same area; (3) transit corridors: across northern Korea from Manchuria to the Sea of Japan, via northern Vietnam from Yunnan to the South China Sea, and across Burma for a window to the Indian Ocean; and (4) military security through possession of Taiwan and the Liukius. The political status of the Paracel Islands south of Hong Kong is not clear, but their ownership would add to China's security. Several of these point to a southern orientation of foreign policy. Hong Kong and Macao remain political danger spots.

Will China's foreign contacts be oriented northward to the Soviet Union, or toward the Pacific and thence to America and Western Europe, or southward to Southeast Asia? Insofar as this is a question of geographic accessibility, the answer seems clear. For 3,300 miles China faces the sea, with no less than two dozen modern seaports. On her landward side the frontier measures 9,300 miles, of which 6,100 miles border the U.S.S.R. and the Mongolian People's Republic. Across all this land border there are but six railways and a dozen poor automobile roads, of which only half connect with Soviet or Mongolian territory. These interior avenues are totally inadequate to care for any major commerce. China's seaports can handle a thousand times the volume of trade which can move through her internal gateways.

Only modest overland trade appears feasible with China's landward neighbors. Towering mountains block off India, and wide deserts isolate the U.S.S.R. Trade with Southeast Asia and even Korea will largely travel by water. Should China ever develop extensive commerce with the Soviet Union, the bulk of it will of necessity move by ship via Suez and Singapore or through the Arctic rather than overland by rail.

Ideas travel with light baggage; witness China's earlier importation of Buddhism from India and her current interest in Soviet Communism. Trade is another matter, and it seems probable that China's material culture will show increasing ties with lands across the seas.

China has been imperialistic in the past, and may well develop territorial ambitions again. Will these push north or south? Eastern Siberia offers little in the way of additional food supply, and Western Siberia appears too remote for conquest. In between lie 1,000 miles of Mongolian desert. In contrast, the lands of the "South Seas" have surplus food, a wide array of minerals, and very large markets. Already China has 10 million colonists in the South Seas area, and the coming decades may see closer relations in trade and overall interest.

Leadership in any part of the world depends partly upon factors such as those discussed above. China has a large and secure home base and a commanding position in her larger region. Japan's location is as good, but she lacks the security, the resources, and the number of people. Under able leadership, the new China will find that she has the geographic resources with which to meet her geographic needs, provided that her population remains within bounds.

7 Regions of North China

Geographic Regions / The Yellow Plain / The Shantung Hills /
Loessland / The Manchurian Plain / The Eastern Manchurian
Uplands / The Western Manchurian Uplands

GEOGRAPHIC REGIONS

One function of geography is to organize areas into unified and significant regions. The face of the earth may be likened to a mosaic picture made up of a myriad number of fragments. Each bit of colored glass or tile has its own features, but they bear little resemblance to the whole. If your eye is within a few inches of the mosaic, you will discern no pattern; stand back a few feet, and though you will lose the microscopic detail, you will find that the picture takes on meaning.

So too with the earth. Each field or hillside has its unique character, of interest to the individual who lives thereon but of little significance to the state as a whole. Geography is interested in this micropattern chiefly as it reveals the personality of the larger whole. Airplane panoramas convey more meaning than a worm's-eye view, provided they are oriented and interpreted in terms of reality. Thus regional generalizations are valid only as they rest upon demonstrated relations within the smaller mosaic, and the latter acquire significance only as oriented in their larger setting.

122

The function of geography is to give character and meaning to the face of the earth and to differentiate the personality of one region from that of another. This is the geographic landscape, the totality of land and water and air and people in their mutual interrelations. In pioneer lands, where man comes as an exotic intruder, these correlations are imperfectly developed; in mature lands such as China the organic unity of man and the earth is obvious.

Each geographic region is an entity. In some areas the dominant feature is climate, as in a desert; elsewhere a crop or a coastal position is characteristic; still other regions are unified by a mode of livelihood. Though boundaries are seldom precise, a geographer can usually block out major landscape areas which will show characteristic differentiations, one from another.

The task of regional geography is to group the infinite variations which characterize the face of the earth into meaningful units which can be understood within the limits of our finite minds. This chapter is devoted to geographic regions, defined in terms of their total characteristics, both physical and cultural. Their names refer to some dominant feature. For a plain it may be topography; for a coast, location; for a desert, climate; or for another area, political considerations.

China is too large and diverse to fit into any single mold. No common denominator is everywhere present, unless it is a unique way of life and a similar history. Climate, vegetation, and soil differ strikingly from north to south. So, too, do the people. The major geographic division of China is into three geographic provinces: the dry, brown, wheat-growing North; the wet, green, rice-growing South; and the arid nomadic steppes and mountains of Mongolia, Sinkiang, and Tibet, known as Outer China.

"China proper" is an improper name, for in a political sense the claim of the central government to Manchuria is as valid as the claim to the provinces south of the Great Wall. If we desire a term for the traditional area of agricultural settlement and classical history east of Mongolia and Tibet, we might speak of "Agricultural China" in contrast to Outer China to the west. No single criterion of political boundary, rainfall, or elevation separates the two, but the traveler who leaves the settled area of Chinese agriculture for the more arid or more mountainous lands of the nomad is conscious of an abrupt change in culture.

The major division of Agricultural China is twofold: the North and the South. The former lies in the valleys of the Hwang, Liao, and Sungari; the latter is drained by the Yangtze and the Si. Environment, temperament, and history combine to make the differences between North and South so distinct that there are two Chinas, almost as unlike as two nations. Many years ago Marco Polo was so impressed by these contrasts that he gave the two sections separate names. The North he called Cathay; the South he named Manji. Although both parts have many qualities in common, no observer can travel overland from Peking to Canton without finding great differences in the geographic environment.

South China comprises nine major regions, each with its own geographic personality. In general, the rainfall is so abundant that the landscape is always green. Marine climatic influences predominate. Hills and mountains are the principal land forms; level land is limited to deltas and flood plains. Forests cover most uncultivated hillsides. Where the land is in crops, rice is dominant. A snowless climate provides a growing season of nine months to a year. Famine is uncommon. The people are shorter in stature than those of the North, with a more restless temperament and a distinct psychology.

North China is an area of limited and variable rainfall, under the influence of the desert. Only four to six months are free from frost. Level land is much more abundant than in the South. The varied crops include wheat and a variety of dry grains. But for many reasons famine has been recurrent. Other differences from the South are noticeable. Draft animals, two-wheeled carts, and wheelbarrows replace canalboats and sedan chairs. North China speaks a uniform dialect, the kuan hua or Mandarin, in contrast to the variations of the South. Whereas the people of South China have emigrated overseas, those in the North have gone overland to Manchuria.

Chinese culture first emerged in the basin of the Wei and the middle Hwang, in a region of roughly 100,000 square miles. This area of well-watered valleys surrounded by the loess hills was the homeland where rudimentary agriculture developed out of animal husbandry. The management of water may have provided one of the earliest tests of cultural organization.

The boundary between the North and the South lies midway between the Yangtze and the Hwang, near the 33d parallel. In the west the line corresponds with the crest of the Chin Ling Mountains; farther east it follows the Hwai River.

Within the North China province are six geographic regions: the Yellow Plain, the Shantung Peninsula, Loessland, the Manchurian Plain, the Eastern Manchurian Uplands, and the Western Manchurian Uplands.

THE YELLOW PLAIN

The delta of the Hwang Ho or Yellow River forms the heart of North China. No other region has played such a large role in Chinese history, nor has any other given birth to so many people. During the forty centuries of recorded history, billions of people have lived on this good earth. No other spot on earth has nourished so many people. The very dust is alive with their heritage. The Yellow Plain is

Although the Great Wall was designed to keep out the nomadic Mongols, it also marked the boundary between the steppe, Koeppen *BS*, and the agricultural lands to the south, *Dwa*. (*Courtesy Canadian Pacific Railway*)

the most important area of level land in the country, and it includes the essential features of the North China landscape. Few other geographic regions are so clearly defined. It seems appropriate to call it the Yellow Plain, not only because it is the gift of the Hwang Ho or Yellow River, but because of the color of its soil and the imperial yellow of its ancient rulers.

The Yellow Plain covers 125,000 square miles, and has a population of at least 125 million people, one-sixth of China's total. This would be equivalent to two-thirds of the people of the United States living in the area of Kansas and Oklahoma. Parts of five provinces are involved. Two of these take their name from the Hwang Ho: Honan to the south of the river and Hopei to the north. Half of Shantung is included and smaller parts of Anhwei and Kiangsu.

The plain of the Hwang is an enormous alluvial fan and subaerial delta, built into a crescentic embayment once occupied by the Yellow Sea. Other streams have contributed to the growth of the plain, notably those which converge to form the Hai at Tientsin and the Hwai in the south, but the Hwang is dominant. Where these rivers leave the encircling loess-covered mountains they are heavily burdened with sediment. As they enter the plain, their gradient and velocity decrease; hence their transporting power is lessened and deposition occurs.

The deposition of this excess silt raises the bed of the stream. If the river were unrestricted, the channel would repeatedly shift to lower ground on either side. To prevent this periodic flooding of fertile farm land, the Chinese, since at least the first century, have built confining dikes. As a result of continued sedimentation within the dikes, the bed of the river in many places is now above the level of the surrounding countryside and dikes progressively need to be raised. The rivers of the Yellow Plain thus flow on broad ridges rather than in valleys. One may look up from the land at the sails of passing boats. Since bedrock is lacking, dikes are built of local earth and are easily

eroded at times of flood. Once the dikes are breached, the river shifts to lower land on either side. This usually slopes away from the stream, so that it is a major engineering feat to close the gap and persuade the river again to flow on top of a ridge. When breaks occur, flood waters spread to the horizon and disaster follows. Millions of people have drowned or have died of starvation from the resulting crop failures. Many villages are thus built on low mounds, the accumulation of centuries of mud homes.

The Hwang has repeatedly changed its course, first to the north and then to the south of Shantung. More than a dozen old channels are known. In 1853, when Great Britain wished to bring pressure on the Chinese government, she decided to blockade the mouth of the river. After her fleet had anchored off the coast for several months without seeing any native shipping, it was learned that during the previous year the mouth of the river had moved 250 miles farther north. In 1938 the Chinese cut the dikes in the path of the invading Japanese and diverted the Hwang southeast to the Hwai River along channels used in 1289 and 1887, where it continued to flow until 1947, when the dikes were repaired as a contribution of the United Nations.

The flow of the Hwang varies from 10,000 cubic feet per second at low-water stage to 900,-000 cubic feet per second during flood. This variation obviously complicates the problem of building dikes. During freshets the river carries a measured load of up to 40 per cent sand, silt, and clay by weight. After one dike break, 18 inches of sediment was deposited 60 miles south of the river. No part of the Hwang is navigable for steamers; only a few sections are deep enough for launches.

Since the Hwang flows above the level of the Yellow Plain, it receives no tributaries in the lower 400 miles, except where it borders the Shantung Hills. Thus rainfall in adjacent areas accumulates in shallow lakes, remaining until evaporated or until it finds its way to the sea along indistinct drainage lines.

The American-founded Yenching University in the western suburbs of Peking had one of the most attractive campuses in the world, with splendid adaptations of Chinese palace architecture. (*Serge Vargassoff*)

South of the Hwang flows the Hwai, a river without a mouth. The Hwai lost its normal route to the sea after its original bed was usurped by a diversion of the Hwang prior to 1852, when so much sediment accumulated that the old channel was elevated. Thus the Hwai now discharges into a series of shallow fluctuating basins, chiefly the Hungtse Lake. The drainage of the present Hwai system reaches the sea through artificial channels, one directly eastward and the other via the Grand Canal southward into the Yangtze.

The smaller rivers which converge near Tientsin experience floods every six or seven years. At times the flooded area exceeds 10,000 square miles and a million and a half people may be driven from their homes. As is the case with Hwang Ho floods, the waters cannot readily drain back into the rivers or to the sea, and so cover the countryside until they have evaporated.

The climate in the Yellow Plain is as unpredictable as the flow of the rivers. The annual rainfall decreases from 30 inches in the south to 20 inches in the north, but seasonal variations in time and amount are wide. Thus Tientsin with a 20-inch average varies from 10 to 31 inches a year. Winters have only a light snowfall, and the summer rains do not begin until mid-June. When they are a few weeks late, spring planting may be delayed so that fall frosts precede the harvest. Inadequate rainfall brings famine through drought, just as surplus rainfall results in famine from flood.

Strong winter winds from Mongolia lower temperatures to 0°F and bring clear skies but no moisture. Dust storms are common, and there is often a high haze created by the fine dust. Summer temperatures rise to 100°F, with high humidity borne by ocean winds. Peking experiences higher temperatures than Canton. The frost-free period is about 200 days, or as much as 240 days in the south.

Soil is almost the only natural resource. Few minerals occur beneath the plain, except for coal at Kailan in the far north and in Honan in the southwest. The fertility is moderately high and has been maintained through intensive fertilization. Much of the region is underlain by recent calcareous alluvium. Where ground water lies too close to the surface, capillary action brings moisture to the surface; this then evaporates, leaving behind a white coating of salts. Much of North China has moderately alkaline soils.

On account of the repeated flooding and high ground water, many soils belong to the unique shachiang type, already described. Shachiang soils have an extensive development of concretions at the water table.

Wheat, the distinctive crop, does not dominate other crops as does rice in South China. Rice can be grown, but the water supply is usually inadequate, and the soils are too sandy to allow water to stand in the fields. Few other regions in China raise such a variety of crops. The grain sorghum kaoliang and a variety of millets are important summer grains; cotton and hemp are locally significant; corn is surprisingly widespread. Soybeans and many vegetables are widely grown during the summer months, and winter crops include wheat, barley, and soybeans.

About two-thirds of the land is in cultivation, usually without irrigation, which is used for

Modern Peking has scores of Western-style buildings, such as this thirteen-story Nationalities Hotel with 597 suites. (*Fu Chun, from Eastfoto*)

under 10 per cent of the area. At least one-third of the cultivated land bears two crops a year. With a cultivated area of about 85,000 square miles, this means that each square mile of farm land must provide food for 1,500 people. Such data reflect the intensity of man's quest for food.

It is the people who everywhere give character to the plain. No landscape is without their presence, and no square inch of earth lacks the impress of repeated toil. One cannot separate man and the environment; they belong together as intimately as a tree and the soil from which it grows. When harvests are normal, few farmers on earth are more cheerful or contented. But too often the good earth is not good. Repeated famines from drought or flood, heavy taxation, and government mismanagement or civil unrest make it difficult for the people to accumulate a reserve against distress, and they undergo periods of acute suffering. The fact of all facts for the Yellow Plain is excessive population.

This vast plain teems with human activity. Everywhere people are busily at work in the fields. Man's intimacy with nature is vividly portrayed by Count Keyserling.[1]

Never before have such impressive pictures of country life been unfolded before me as on this journey through inner China. Every inch of the soil is in cultivation, carefully manured, well and professionally tilled. . . . The villages, built of clay and surrounded by clay walls, have the effect of natural forms in this landscape: they hardly stand out against the brown background. And wherever I cast my eyes, I see the peasants at work, methodically, thoughtfully, contentedly. It is they who everywhere give life to the wide plain. The blue of their jerkins is as much part of the picture as the green of the tilled fields and the bright yellow of the dried-up river beds. One cannot even imagine this flat land devoid of the enlivening presence of these yellow human beings. And it represents at the same time one great cemetery of immeasurable vastness. There is

[1] Herman Keyserling: *The Travel Diary of a Philosopher,* London: Cape (1925), II, 70–71. Quoted by permission.

hardly a plot of ground which does not carry numerous grave mounds; again and again the plow must piously wend its way between the tombstones. There is no other peasantry in the world which gives such an impression of absolute genuineness and of belonging so much to the soil. Here the whole of life and the whole of death takes place on the inherited ground. Man belongs to the soil, not the soil to the man; it will never let its children go. However much they may increase in number, they remain upon it, wringing from Nature her scanty gifts by ever more assiduous labor; and when they are dead, they return in childlike confidence to what is to them the real womb of their mother. And there they continue to live forevermore. The Chinese peasant, like the prehistoric Greek, believes in the life of what seems dead to us. The soil exhales the spirit of his ancestors; it is they who repay his labor and who punish him for his omissions. Thus, the inherited fields are at the same time his history, his memory, his reminiscences; he can deny it as little as he can deny himself; for he is only part of it.

Numerous cities dot the plain, some mere market towns, others railway junctions and industrial centers. A dozen count 100,000 people or more. The largest and finest city is the ancient capital of Peking or "northern capital," which was known from 1928 to 1949 as Peiping or "northern peace." The city was founded in 920 under the name of Yenching, but the present city pattern dates from Kublai Khan. Over the centuries the court at Peking attracted the finest craftsmen and artists, the leading scholars, merchants, and cooks, and the cream of Chinese society. Their heritage remains, so that Peking, a product of its rich history, still represents the finest in classical Chinese culture. Beautiful temples and palaces and quiet courtyards with a profusion of flowers supply a setting for a quality of life which is China at its best. Peking occupies a logical position for the capital of an invading Mongol or Manchu dynasty, and is equally well situated for purely Chinese rulers who are concerned with relations to the north. Although the immediate site offers no particular advantages, the city

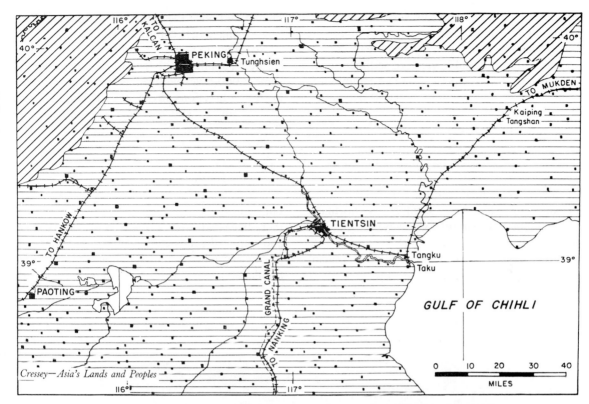

Peking and Tientsin rank second and third in population among Chinese cities. All city maps in this book are on the same scale and use the same symbols for land forms: Plains are shown in horizontal lines, hills by diagonal shading, and mountains by vertical lines. Every small square represents a village.

lies in a corner of the Yellow Plain and commands Nankow Pass, the easiest avenue through the mountains to the Mongolian Plateau, and is not far from the Shanhaikwan gateway to Manchuria.

High walls divide Peking into five parts. The innermost was the Forbidden City of the Emperor; around it was the Imperial City for his Manchu retainers. These two parts are enclosed by the 50-foot walls of the Tatar or Manchu City, within which is also the former walled Legation Quarter. Immediately to the south is the so-called Chinese city, built when Chinese were not permitted to live in the main part of the city. The population of Peking exceeds 4 million. The city has spread far beyond its original walls.

The Yellow Plain lacks a satisfactory sea-

port. Except for the Shantung and Liaotung Peninsulas, the seacoast of North China is a mud flat bordered by shallow water. River mouths all have submerged bars. Tientsin is by far the leading port, but the city lies 30 miles from the sea on the winding Hai River. Farther north is the artificial harbor of Chinwangtao, while in the southeast is the port of Tunghai (Haichow), terminus for the railway to Sinkiang.

Tientsin has grown to be a city of 3 million, not because of its advantageous site but because of the compelling needs of its hinterland. Several small rivers focus on Tientsin, joining to form the navigable Hai. Alternately one or the other of the tributaries is in flood and brings so much sediment that the Hai is choked for months. A sand bar at the mouth formerly forced medium-sized ocean vessels to anchor out of sight of land. The river freezes in winter, but is usually kept open by ice breakers. Although millions of cubic yards of sediment have been dredged from the river and equal amounts from the bar, in a few days of flood deposition the bed has been raised 5½ feet; 9 feet of sediment was once deposited on the bar in 48 hours. Because of the difficulties of creating a river port, modern facilities have been developed on the coast at one side of the mouth of the river, which can care for 10,000-ton ocean-going steamers. Tientsin is normally China's second seaport, gateway to the rich Yellow Plain.

Other large cities of the plain include Tsinan, capital of Shantung; Kaifeng, the capital of Honan and once the capital of China; and Paoting (Tsingyuan), capital of Hopei.

No other region south of the Great Wall is so well supplied with railways, amounting to some 2,000 miles within the area. Lines radiate in four directions from the Peking-Tientsin area; south to Hankow and Canton, west to Paotow and Lanchow, north to Mukden and Siberia, and southeast to Nanking and Shanghai. The difficulty of railway construction across the plain is shown in the latter line; since no rock was available for ballast, brick kilns were built and fired with straw, and the roadbed was then ballasted with broken brick. Cart trails and unpaved roads connect the many towns.

Ancient China's most famous line of communication was the Grand Canal. The canal

The Yellow Plain supports an average of 1,000 people in each square mile. Closely spaced villages reflect the intensity of man's pressure on the land. This aerial view is near Shihchiachwang in western Hopei. (*Courtesy United States Air Force*)

was built to bring tribute rice from the Yangtze valley to the court at Peking. The section across the Yellow Plain was dug in the thirteenth century, a thousand years after the part in the Yangtze Plain. On account of seasonal rainfall, it has been difficult to keep the canal full of water, and many sections have often been out of commission. South of Tientsin the Grand Canal is partly a canalized river which diverts water to the Hai which would otherwise flow directly to the sea.

THE SHANTUNG HILLS

The province of Shantung is about equally divided between lowland and upland. The latter region was once an island in the Yellow Sea but has now been half surrounded by the advancing delta of the Hwang Ho. It does not include that part of Shantung which lies in the Yellow Plain. The peninsula is a region of hills and mountains, with a limited amount of level land. Although the smallest of China's geographic regions, the Shantung Hills have a distinctive role in the country's economy. One source of pride in the region is historical rather than geographical. Confucius lived in Shantung, and the eightieth generation of his descendents still live here, under the name of Kung.

On the sacred mountain of Tai Shan elevations reach 5,056 feet, but summits elsewhere are generally under half of that figure. A structural lowland or graben cuts across the center of the peninsula; this provides a level route from the seaport of Tsingtao to the capital at Tsinan.

Excellent bituminous coal occurs in abundance, with several important mines. Reserves exceed a billion tons.

The geography of the Shantung Peninsula resembles that of the Yellow Plain as to crops and way of life, but with modifications due to unfavorable topography and slightly greater rainfall. Many of the steeper slopes have been denuded of their original soil cover, and forests are uncommon. Settlements lie chiefly in valley bottoms or where valleys open onto the plain.

Spring-sown crops include millet, kaoliang, peanuts, and cotton. Summer crops are soybeans, peanuts, corn, sweet potatoes, and millet. Winter crops are wheat or barley. Shantung is well known for its silk, produced from worms that feed on oak leaves rather than mulberry leaves.

Shantung owes some of its importance to the possession of excellent harbors at Chefoo and Tsingtao. The latter is the rail terminus for a hinterland which includes much of the central Yellow Plain. Tsingtao was once a German outpost, and many buildings with their characteristic red-tiled roofs still betray this bit of history. It has a splendid harbor on Kiaochow Bay. The population exceeds one million.

LOESSLAND

To the west of the Yellow Plain lies a region of hills and mountains whose dominant characteristic is the widespread occurrence of yellow wind-laid silt, known as loess.

Loess is so fine a powder that when rubbed between one's fingers it has no gritty feel. It is thus easily blown by the wind and has been spread over the underlying bedrock as though by a giant flour sifter. The thickness of the loess ranges from nothing on steep mountain slopes to a maximum of some 300 feet. Over wide areas the average is 100 or 200 feet. Similar deposits occur over the Yellow Plain, where they are mixed with stream alluvium, and in Sinkiang, but they do not equal the development in Loessland where the silt covers 119,000 square miles and has a volume estimated at 2,853 cubic miles. The Chinese term for loess is *hwang tu,* yellow earth.

The source of this loess is sometimes thought to lie in Mongolia, derived from wind scour in the Gobi Desert, but its distribution gives no suggestion of such an origin. Instead, the source of the loess appears to lie in the Ordos Desert, outside the Great Wall and within the loop of the Hwang, where repeated deposition by the river has supplied large quantities of lake and river sediments. These are an easy prey to the winter monsoon winds as they blow outward from central Asia. Sand and coarser materials lag behind, but the silt is lifted aloft and comes to rest in the bordering grasslands of slightly greater rainfall. Most of the loess is strongly calcareous.

Loessland occupies the middle valley of the Hwang Ho and the basins of its two major tributaries, the Fen and the Wei. The region includes all of Shansi, much of Shensi and Kansu, and smaller parts of Chahar, Suiyuan, Ningsia, Honan, and Hopei. Loessland has an area of 200,000 square miles and a population of over 50 million. These figures give an average density of 250 inhabitants per square mile, in contrast to 1,000 per square mile for the Yellow Plain.

Mountains and broad plains divide Loessland into numerous subdivisions. Level land is present in central Shansi along the Fen River and continues southwestward up the valley of the Wei. Other basins occur in northern Shansi around Tatung and near Kweisui in Suiyuan. Along the eastern margin rise the Taihang Mountains, which continue opposite Peking as the Western Hills. The highest elevation in eastern Shansi is the sacred peak of Wutai Shan, 9,971 feet high. In western Shansi, midway between the Fen and the Hwang, are the Luliang Mountains.

The adjoining province of Shensi is a structural basin, although topographically it is a dissected plateau, buried in loess. Eastern Kansu is marked by the Liupan Mountains, with another loess-filled basin to the west. The southern limits of Loessland border the towering Chin Ling Mountains, while the northern limits face the desert plains of the Ordos and the Gobi deserts.

Earthquakes have been particularly severe, as for example in 1920 when the great landslides on the loess hills of Kansu caused the loss of 246,000 lives.

In climate, Loessland is intermediate between the aridity of Mongolia and the barely adequate rainfall of the Yellow Plain. Precipitation in most areas is about 15 inches; less next to the desert and considerably more on the highest mountains. A few forests remain in the more inaccessible mountains; in general the original vegetation was a steppe grassland. Almost all rain occurs in summer, with half the total in July and August. Summer temperatures seldom exceed 90°F, but winter winds from Mongolia bring three months with averages below freezing. Wide fluctuations occur from year to year. In some seasons the rainfall is adequate for normal hillside agriculture, but partial crop failure is more commonly the rule. Moisture-conserving techniques of dry farming are necessary. About 175 to 200 days in the year are frost-free.

Cultivated land amounts to about one-sixth of the region, in contrast to two-thirds on the Yellow Plain. In the plains of the Wei and the Fen the intensity of cultivation equals that of the Hwang delta. Millet leads kaoliang as the chief summer grain. Wheat is a winter crop except near the Great Wall where it is planted in the spring. Taken together, these three grains account for three-fourths of the agricultural acreage. Other crops include white potatoes, cotton, tobacco, and considerable amounts of opium. Each of these crops normally requires irrigation. Lanchow grows exceptionally fine apricots.

The great resource of Loessland is its high-grade coal which here forms one of the great concentrations on earth. Reserves may total a trillion tons, but large-scale production is only beginning. A new source of power is available along the Hwang Ho where the Sanmen dam supplies a million kilowatts of electricity. The dam is 394 feet high and ½ mile long; one serious problem may lie in the rapid accumulation of silt in the reservoir.

Iron ore is produced at Hsuanhua, west of Peking, and near Taiyuan and Paotow, each with related steel mills.

Few regions in China have greater population pressure. Unfortunately, some persons in authority have assumed that this and other regions in the northwest might be areas for colonization. On the contrary, the farm population

Many of the hills in Loessland are terraced in order to hold the scanty rainfall and to check erosion; flooded fields are impractical because of the permeability of the loess. This is a view near Wutai Shan in Shansi. (*Bailey Willis, courtesy United States Forest Service*)

per square mile of cultivated land is almost as great as in the Yellow Plain, 1,400 as compared with 1,500, despite a much less favorable environment. In place of offering room for settlement, Loessland may profit by emigration. Irrigation holds local promise but is not possible on a large scale. Saline soils are common where the water table is high.

Some of the earliest traces of Chinese culture are found here, notably around the city of Sian in Shensi, which was the capital of the Han dynasty, 206 B.C. to A.D. 220. Here was found the Nestorian Tablet, erected in 781 to record the early penetration of Christianity. Several million Muslims of Persian and Turkic descent live in Kansu.

The chief cities are each provincial capitals:

Taiyuan (Yangku) in Shansi, Sian (Changan) in Shensi, Lanchow (Kaolan) in Kansu, and Ningsia, capital of the province of the same name. Two other cities command important gateways, Kalgan (Changchiakow) in the north next to Mongolia, and Tungkwan on the Hwang along the route to the Yellow Plain.

Travel is restricted, for the dissected topography makes road construction difficult. Much of the area is linked only by trails. From Sian to Lanchow extends the famous ancient highway which led from Peking westward to Europe, crossing the Liupan Mountains by a 9,000-foot pass. Over this route moved silk and porcelain in early times. Two railways penetrate the area: One in the north extends from Peking to Paotow and around the great loop of the Hwang Ho to Lanchow, and in the south the line from the sea to Sian extends to Lanchow in Kansu and on to Sinkiang to provide a new trans-Asian route. Other lines are in Shansi. None of the rivers are navigable.

THE MANCHURIAN PLAIN

In 1644 Manchu tribesmen invaded the area south of the Great Wall and established the Manchu dynasty which ruled China until 1911. The area from which they came is now known to the Chinese as the three eastern provinces—Liaoning, Kirin, and Heilungkiang—and to foreigners as Manchuria. To these three may be added the province of Jehol, once considered a part of Inner Mongolia. On the west is the Inner Mongolian Autonomous Region.

These northeastern provinces are now overwhelmingly Chinese in race and culture and occupy a significant place in China's national consciousness. We should point out that this area has been an integral part of greater China during most of the past 2,000 years; in fact China once held land north of the Amur River. Chinese merchants and farmers have long lived in southern Manchuria, but under the Manchu dynasty immigration was periodically restricted. With the establishment of the republic in 1911 all regulations on colonization were removed and a great tide of migration followed.

Manchuria has been a cradle of conflict since the end of the nineteenth century. In 1896 an agreement was signed with Russia for the construction of the Chinese Eastern Railway as a short cut for the Trans-Siberian line to Vladivostok, a saving of 300 miles as compared with the route around the Amur River. This agreement was later amended to include a branch southward to Port Arthur. The activities of the Russians in the area provoked the Russo-Japanese War of 1904 to 1905, after which Japan took over the southern part of the line and renamed it the South Manchuria Railway. In 1935 the Soviet Union sold its rights in the Chinese Eastern Railway to Japan, but regained these and other czarist concessions through the Yalta agreement of 1945, which provided for free port facilities in Dairen and a joint Chinese-Soviet naval base at Port Arthur.

In addition to Russian, Japanese, and, later, British railway activity, many Chinese lines have been built, so that the region is better supplied with transportation than any other area in China. The railway total in all Manchuria at the end of the Second World War exceeded 7,000 miles, about as much as in all the rest of the country.

On September 18, 1931, Japanese forces seized the city of Mukden and the next year set up the former Manchu emperor, whom the Chinese had deposed in 1911, as ruler of the kingdom of Manchukuo. It is clear that Japan's primary interest was to make Manchuria a commercial and strategic strongpoint rather than to provide an outlet for surplus population. Despite extensive efforts at colonization, the total number of Japanese on Manchurian farms never exceeded 100,000.

The Manchurian Plain differs from the Yellow Plain in that the latter is of depositional origin and thus amazingly flat, whereas the

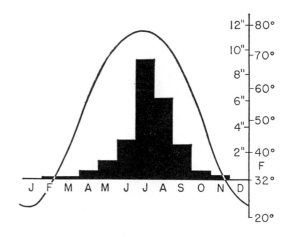

PEKING. Elevation 131 feet, average temperature 53°F, annual precipitation 25 inches. All climatic diagrams in this volume are drawn on the same scale. Since the base line for rainfall corresponds to 32°F, that part of the year which is normally below freezing and receives snow rather than rain may easily be noted.

former is an erosional plain with rolling topography. Two river systems, those of the Liao and the Sungari, divide it into a southern and northern half. From north to south the plain measures 600 miles, from east to west, 400 miles. The area of the region is 140,000 square miles.

Except for three narrow gaps, the Manchurian Plain is everywhere surrounded by mountains. On the east are the Long White Mountains; to the north is the Little Khingan Range; in the west are the Great Khingan; and to the southwest are the mountains of Jehol. Between these uplands are two river corridors to the outside world, those of the Liao and the Sungari.

The valley of the Liao in the south has a 75-mile frontage on the Gulf of Liaotung. A narrow strip of coastal lowland leads to the Yellow Plain at Shanhaikwan where the Great Wall reaches the sea. This coastal avenue of invasion may be likened to the situation of Thermopolae in Greece. In the northeast, the Sungari enters the Amur lowland along a valley where hills close in on either side of the river. To the west, a low portion of the Great Khingan Range gives easy access to Mongolia; in fact on old maps a part of the western and more arid Manchurian Plain is labeled the Eastern Gobi. Within this enclosure, nature has provided a most favorable environment, and man in turn has developed one of the most spectacular pioneer lands of this century.

Manchuria lies in the latitudes of the northern United States and southern Canada. Dairen is on the parallel of Baltimore, Mukden, of Albany, Harbin, of Montreal; and the northern border along the Amur River reaches the latitude of southern Hudson Bay. This suggests similar climatic conditions, but the greater continentality of Asia brings sharper seasonal contrasts. Winters are long and bitterly cold, summers short and hot. Snow begins to fall in the north in late September and in the south a month later; it continues until mid-April in the south and mid-May in the north. Monthly averages are below freezing from November through March. Central Manchuria often has January temperatures of −30°F, while August maxima rise to 95°F. Frequent weather changes

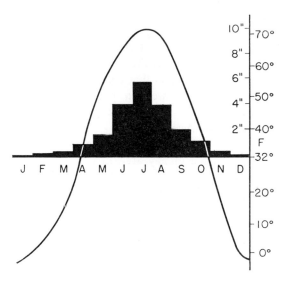

MUKDEN. Elevation 141 feet, average temperature 47°F, annual rainfall 28 inches. Most of Manchuria receives less than 25 inches of precipitation.

HARBIN. Elevation 526 feet, average temperature 38°F, annual precipitation 19 inches. Half of the year has temperatures below freezing.

Harbin lies at the crossing of the Sungari River and the Chinese Eastern Railway. The river is navigable for large river boats. (*Eastfoto*)

are related to the passage of cyclonic storms. Thus winter months characteristically have "three cold and four mild" days in succession. Only 150 to 175 days are frost-free.

Precipitation is seasonal, with light winter snowfall, a dry spring and fall, and concentrated rain in July and August. The amount decreases from 25 inches in the east to 15 inches in the west, so that agriculture becomes precarious in the western plain. Fortunately most rains occur during the growing season from June to August.

Owing to the natural cover of grass, soils are the most fertile of any area in China, with an extensive development of chernozem and chestnut-brown soils. Some saline and alkali soils appear in the drier western areas.

Good empty land has attracted tens of millions of farmers from the overcrowded lands south of the Great Wall, often a million a year. Thus the population of Manchuria rose from 15 million in 1910 to 55 million by 1950. Many of these settlers have gone to the pioneer fringe, either in the dry west or cold north,

where they have plowed new land, formerly the home of the nomad.

Crops resemble those grown elsewhere in North China but are raised in larger fields and with a surplus for export. This is the chief area of mechanized farms, many of them Soviet-style developments. Nowhere else is the yield so large per person; hence living standards are higher. In the north large fields of wheat and soybeans predominate; in the south the crops are more diversified, the most important being kaoliang, millet, soybeans, corn, and wheat. At one time Manchuria grew 60 per cent of the world's soybeans, and their export supplied the basis for considerable prosperity.

A few uncultivated areas remain in the far north where the growing season is too short, or in the extreme west where aridity creates a peril. Another undeveloped area lies in the extreme northeast in the Amur valley along the lower Sungari and Ussuri. This area resembles the Amur lowland of Siberia rather than the Manchurian Plain, in that it has swamp and meadowland and a rigorous climate.

Since the mineral resources of Manchuria have been more intensively developed than those in the rest of China, this is the chief center of heavy industry. Coal reserves are large, amounting to several tens of billions of metric tons, and the annual production is over 100 million tons. Much of it comes from the Fushun deposits, near Mukden, which have the thickest bed of bituminous coal in the world, as much as 394 feet thick. Fuel oil is distilled from associated oil shales, with an annual production of several million tons. At nearby Fuhsin the coal seam is from 180 to 200 feet thick. This is to be China's largest open-cut mine. Coal is also produced at Pehpiao.

Iron ore is available near Anshan, where the steel works, with a capacity of 5 million tons a year, are among the dozen largest in the world. Other steel centers are at Penki and Mukden.

All the cities are of recent growth. The only seaports in the plain are Yingkow at the mouth of the shallow Liao and the new port of Hulutao on the western shore of the Gulf of Liaotung. Most seaborne commerce is handled through Dairen, which will be considered in the next section.

The three metropolitan cities of the Plain, Mukden (Shenyang), Changchun (Hsinking), and Harbin, lie along the main north–south railway. Mukden is near the junction of the lines to Peking and to Korea. It includes an old walled city and a newer commercial area around the railway station. The size of the population—over 2 million—is due to the development of light industry. Not far away are the coal and steel cities of Fushun and Anshan, respectively; the latter with ½ million people. Changchun, known as Hsinking while the capital of Manchukuo, has grown rapidly; its population exceeds 1 million. Changchun is the rail junction for a line eastward to the seaports of northern Korea. Harbin lies at the crossing of the old Chinese Eastern Railway and the Sungari River, and is the junction of the line south to Dairen, 12 hours distant by streamlined express trains. Harbin's population considerably exceeds a million, of whom several tens of thousands are Russians.

The initial urbanization of Mukden and Changchun was due to the Japanese; Harbin was a Russian product. Following the establishment of Communist China, all three cities experienced major industrial growth, since their location made them the immediate beneficiaries of Soviet aid.

THE EASTERN MANCHURIAN UPLANDS

Uplands border the Manchurian Plain on almost all sides. Those on the east, north, and southwest are forested, whereas aridity gives rise to a grass cover in the west. Agricultural settlement has penetrated well into the eastern and southern mountains, but those in the west are still the home of the nomad and resemble Mongolia in their geographic characteristics.

Since the Eastern Manchurian Uplands extend 850 miles from the Liaotung Peninsula northeast nearly to the junction of the Amur and the Ussuri and are some 200 miles wide, conditions naturally differ from place to place. The region covers 120,000 square miles. The south has a mild climate; all level land is intensively utilized; and the forests are magnificent. Parts of the north are still an undeveloped coniferous wilderness.

The Eastern Manchurian Uplands have the finest forests in China, with large reserves of excellent Korean pine, spruce, larch, elm, birch, oak, and fir. Many trees reach a height of 100 feet and have a diameter of 3 feet. Timber is rafted southward along the Yalu River to the port of Antung or westward on the Sungari to Kirin. Fur-bearing animals are trapped in the more mountainous areas.

The rainfall is more abundant than in the Manchurian Plain, with as much as 40 inches in the higher areas, part of which falls as snow. Where the land is sufficiently level for cultivation, agriculture is thus more productive than on the Plain. Soybeans, millet, wheat, and ka- oliang are the crops. Many Koreans have pushed across the border and are engaged in raising rice.

Coal is present along the western margin of the region, and large iron reserves occur in the south and in the east. Prospects are especially favorable in the Tungpientao district near Korea, where there is an important iron and steel industry.

The large Hsiaofengman dam on the Sungari River provides hydroelectric power. Along the Yalu River, adjoining Korea, is an even larger hydroelectric development at Suifenho; both installations generate over a half million kilowatts.

The highest elevations occur in the Long White Mountains or Changpai Shan along the Korean frontier, where the volcanic peak of Paitou Shan with a crater lake rises to 9,000 feet.

The leading city is Dairen—at the southern tip of the Liaotung Peninsula—the major seaport for all northeastern China. When the Russians first came to the area, Port Arthur was their chief base, but the Japanese emphasized Dairen and made it into a splendid port. The population exceeds a million. Antung lies near the mouth of the Yalu, opposite Korea; Kirin is the capital of the province of the same name. The only other center of importance is the coal and steel town of Penki.

THE WESTERN MANCHURIAN UPLANDS

Although the uplands that border the Manchurian Plain on the north, west, and south cover more than 200,000 square miles, their economic importance is slight. Elevations are under a mile, but the local relief is generally less than 1,000 feet. Nowhere is there a dense population.

Along a north–south axis is an area called the Great Khingan Range, known to the Chinese as the Ta Hsingan. Toward the southeast this is largely the upturned edge of the Mongolian Plateau; farther north the region widens and is a hill complex. The Little Khingan Range lies roughly at right angles and parallels the Amur River from the Sungari to its tributary, the Nonni. In the southwest lie the hills and mountains of Jehol.

North of the former Chinese Eastern Railway the Khingan Mountains have a Siberian-type larch and birch forest; to the south is a Mongolian-type steppe. There is little agriculture, largely of hay; the chief occupation is dairying; and the few settlers are lumbermen, hunters, or pastoralists. Much of the region lies in the Inner Mongolian Autonomous Region, a reflection of its geographic and historic orientation.

Although the province of Jehol lies outside the Great Wall and was once Mongolian in orientation, it is now essentially Chinese in culture. The higher areas were formerly forested and formed an imperial hunting ground, but the timber has now been cut from most accessible areas. Forests are noticeably more abundant on the shady north slopes.

The geographic region here described has a dry continental climate with Mongolian-style winters. Agriculture is feasible only in the southern valleys. The topography is so unfavorable that access to many areas has been difficult, but new automobile roads and railways have made them easier to reach.

Large amounts of coal are produced along the eastern margin of Jehol.

The crops include millet, kaoliang, and spring wheat. Opium has been widely grown in Jehol. Its culture is common in the less accessible areas of interior China, where expensive transportation makes it necessary to grow cash crops that are easily shipped.

8 Regions of South China

*South China / The Yangtze Plain / The Szechwan Basin / The
Central Mountain Belt / The South Yangtze Hills / The Southeastern
Coast / The Canton Hinterland / The Southwestern Uplands /
Hainan*

SOUTH CHINA

South China belongs to the east-coast humid
subtropics, with summer monsoon rainfall.
Winters are short and cool rather than cold;
snow is almost unknown. The amount of rainfall, 40 to 80 inches, makes the landscape
green throughout the year. Flood, drought, and
famines are uncommon. Whereas the North
has large areas of level land, perhaps 40 per
cent in all, the South is dominantly hilly, with
less than 15 per cent in plains.

Southern China is distinct in environment
and in history. Not all the people are racially
Chinese; many are descendants of early tribespeople who took on aspects of Chinese culture
and in part intermarried as the ethnic Chinese
moved south of the Yangtze. Whereas the Chinese in the north speak of themselves as Han
people, referring to the Han dynasty at the
time of Christ, those in the far south are often
known as Tang people, from the dynasty of the
seventh to the tenth century during China's
advance to the Canton area. Several million

139

people in the southwest are racially Chuang or Thai, Lolo, Miao, or Yao. In addition, many proper Chinese in South China represent mass migrations from the north, notably the Hakkas.

This is a land of rice, in which we find much less diversification than in the wheat-millet-kaoliang region of North China. Along with rice culture go flooded fields, often terraced, and water buffalo. Two crops are raised a year, but farms are smaller and cultivation more intensive than in the north, so that the net income per farm family is only slightly higher because of the double cropping.

For the entire area of Agricultural China, the pre-Communist surveys of J. Lossing Buck showed an average of 0.45 acre of crop land per farm person; for his rice province of South China the figure is 0.37, while in the wheat province of North China the acreage is 0.56 per farm dweller. If all crops are converted into the equivalent of grain, and if all laborers are put on a uniform work basis, the average annual yield at that time for South China may be estimated at 1,520 kilograms per person in contrast to 1,231 for North China. The per capita average for all China was 1,393, as compared with 20,000 kilograms for the United States. Under Communist direction the per capita yield has apparently gone down, while that of the United States continues to rise. While poor tenure conditions have long been important, no amount of redistribution can solve the basic man-land ratio.

The boundary between the North and the South is clearly marked by climate, natural vegetation, soil, crops, and culture. In the west it follows the crest of the Chin Ling Mountains; near the coast it lies near the Hwai River whose clear-water southern tributaries drain riceland, while the muddy northern tributaries flow through fields of kaoliang and millet.

Both the North and the South are dominantly rural. On the whole, South China has larger and more modern cities, and has had more overseas contacts.

The South may be divided into eight geographic regions: the Yangtze Plain, the Sze-

chwan Basin, the Central Mountain Belt, the South Yangtze Hills, the Southeastern Coast, the Canton Hinterland, the Southwestern Uplands, and Hainan. To these may be added Taiwan, considered in a separate chapter because of its political status.

THE YANGTZE PLAIN

Water is the key to the geography of the Yangtze Plain. On either side of the river is a network of canals, and in several areas there are large lakes. Transport is by river steamer and junk, or by launches and canalboats. Since rice is the characteristic crop, most fields are flooded for half the year. This is a green world, very different from the brown landscapes of North China.

The Yangtze Plain probably averages 1,500 people per square mile, and 70 per cent of the area is in cultivation. Both figures are higher than those for any other region in China and betray the intensity with which man crowds this fertile lowland. Though the region lacks compactness, it has coherence. The shape is irregular since boundaries follow the alluvial plain. From east to west the distance is 600 miles; from north to south it varies from about 20 to 200 miles. The area is 75,000 square miles, and the population numbers some 110 million.

Whereas many characteristics are common throughout, the region may be subdivided into the delta below Wuhu and the flood plains and lakelands of the middle Yangtze. The delta occupies most of the province of Kiangsu and part of Chekiang. The middle Yangtze lies in Anhwei, Kiangsi, and the twin provinces of Hupei and Hunan. These latter take their name from the Tungting Hu, or Lake, with respect to which they lie north and south.

Although the Yangtze is comparable in length to the Hwang, it flows through a region of three times the rainfall and carries much more water. The city of Ichang has received 39 inches in five days, and at times one heavy rain may follow another. As much as a cubic

The funnel-shaped Hangchow Bay is famous for its tidal bore. At spring tides the water advances with a front which may be 6 to 10 feet high. (*Ah Fong*)

mile of rain has fallen on the mid-Yangtze basin in a single storm.

During the floods the Yangtze carries a volume of 2,500,000 cubic feet per second, as compared with a mean annual discharge of 770,000 cubic feet per second. At times the river has inundated 40,000 square miles, roughly the area of Ohio, but fortunately, disastrous floods are uncommon. This is in part because of the storage capacity provided by the marginal lakes such as the Tungting, Poyang, and Tai, and the network of smaller waterways, where the rise of a few feet involves the storage of a large volume of flood water. Unlike the Hwang, the Yangtze is not overloaded and is able to carry its burden of sediment to the sea. This load amounts to 600 million tons a year, and its deposition in the delta is advancing the shore line one mile every 70 years.

Much of the Yangtze Plain is geologically so young that the land has not yet been built up much above sea level. Even at Ichang, 1,000 miles inland, the elevation of the river is but 295 feet. Low water at Hankow is only 39 feet above sea level, but the maximum flood stage reaches 98 feet. Tides extend 200 miles up river. The large lakes on either side of the river represent unfilled parts of the original lowland. When the Yangtze rises in summer, these lakes are filled by backwater from the river. The Tungting Lake then measures 1,450 square miles, and the Poyang covers 1,075 square miles. During the winter the basins become almost dry. The Tai Lake in the delta varies less in size and covers about 1,330 square miles. Comparable lakes are present along the lower Hwai River, with a total area of 2,000 square miles. If portions of these lakes could be drained, the reclaimed land would add materially to the area available for crop cultivation.

The Yangtze provides a splendid avenue of communication. Next to the Rhine it may be the busiest river in the world. Where islands divide the river, there are a few troublesome sand bars; elsewhere the channel is sufficiently deep for ocean steamers of 4,000 tons to reach Hankow, 630 miles upstream, at all seasons, and for 10,000-ton boats with 25-foot draft in summer. This inland port normally handles 5 per cent of China's foreign trade. River boats easily reach Ichang at the foot of the gorges. These gorges mark the western limit of the Yangtze Plain.

Three major tributaries join the Yangtze within the region. From the north flows the Han, at whose mouth is Hankow. On the south the Yuan and Siang flow through Tungting Lake, and the Kan reaches the Yangtze via the Poyang Lake. The lowland plains around these rivers form further subdivisions of the region as a whole.

The Hwai River, which flows eastward between the Yangtze and the Hwang and marks the northern limit of the Yangtze Plain, presents unique problems. The Hwai is sometimes referred to as a river without a mouth, since its lower course was usurped by a shift in the Hwang, and the river discharges into shallow depressions. Floods have been recurrent.

No area in the world has such a network of canals. Most of them are navigable for small boats, and these waterways are the roads of the region. They are especially abundant south of the Yangtze and east of the Tai Lake. Since the water table is near the surface the canals are normally full. In one measured square mile, which appears representative, they have a total length of 27.8 miles, with an average spacing of 380 feet. The mileage in this small part of the delta may approximate 150,000 miles, and for the region as a whole there may be 250,000 to 500,000 miles of navigable waterways. With an average width of 10 feet, these canals represent 10 per cent of the total area. The most famous is the Grand Canal,

started in the seventh century and completed in the thirteenth to carry tribute rice to the capital at Peking.

Climatic conditions provide a growing season of 300 days free from frost, so that at least two crops a year may be raised. Since rainfall lines in this part of China extend nearly east and west, the region has a fairly uniform rainfall of 40 to 50 inches. From March through August the rainfall amounts to 5 inches a month, with a maximum in June. January and December are the only months with less than 2 inches. Fall and winter are the most pleasant seasons, with clear skies and average temperatures below 50°F from October through February. Summers are oppressively hot and humid. Shanghai frequently experiences three weeks during which the daily maximum exceeds 100°F, while for two months the daily maximum may average 97°F. Climatic extremes are suggested by occasional snow on palm trees.

Although the Yangtze Plain has a larger percentage of city dwellers than any other region, nearly three-quarters of the people are farmers. Nowhere in the world is farm land more intensively utilized. Many districts have a farm population in excess of 2,500 per square mile. Only five areas in Asia duplicate this congestion: the Chengtu Plain in Szechwan, the delta

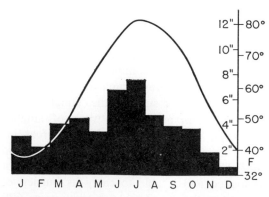

SHANGHAI. Elevation 23 feet, average temperature 61°F, annual precipitation 45 inches. Snow rarely falls; summer temperatures frequently exceed 100°F.

around Canton, the Kanto Plain centering on Tokyo, the lowlands of Java, and the lower Ganges Plain.

Tiny fields are the rule. Because of meticulous care, crop yields are large per acre, but on account of the excessive labor required, the return per person is low. China's agricultural problem is not so much to increase the total harvest as to raise the per capita yield. Rice is the standard summer crop; wheat, beans, and barley are the chief winter crops. Winter cultivation is common, with two-thirds of the fields yielding a second harvest. Vegetables are widely raised. Water buffalo and oxen are the characteristic farm animals.

The two distinctive crops are cotton and silk, both produced more extensively here than in any other part of China. Cotton is important in the delta, and is processed in the large mills in Shanghai. Fully one-third of China's cotton is grown in this region. Some of the finest silk in the world is produced in the immediate hinterland of Shanghai, where in some localities one-quarter of the land is devoted to mulberry cultivation. Silk is obtained from cocoons spun by the silkworm, which is fed on mulberry leaves. Mulberry trees, trimmed to bush size, yield 70,000 pounds of leaves per acre. These leaves are fed to silkworms, which eat four to six times a day during their 30-day life. To produce a pound of silk requires 150 pounds of mulberry leaves. China has lost most of her export market for silk, but because of the domestic consumption her pre-Communist production probably led the world.

The Yangtze Plain has a dozen cities whose population exceeds 500,000, and many more of over 100,000. More than elsewhere these are semimodernized cities with extensive Western developments.

Shanghai is important because in its hinterland live some 300 million people, one-tenth of the human race. Few other cities in the world so dominate such a market, nor is Shanghai likely to have a rival. The city is the entrepôt for the Yangtze and occupies the most feasible site for a modern port near its mouth. Even if the Yangtze valley should develop new outlets westward via Burma or south through Canton, the trade of Shanghai will doubtless increase even faster than any diversion. No other Chinese port is so close to Japan, and the location midway along the coast is a commercial advantage. The population exceeds 7 million, twice the size of the closest rival, Peking. Shanghai ranks next to Tokyo as the largest center in Asia, and holds fourth or fifth place among world cities.

When the city was opened to foreign trade in 1843, it was already one of the busiest ports

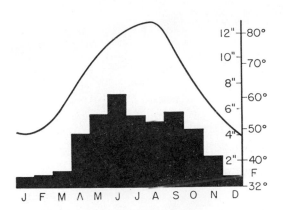

CHUNGKING. Elevation 755 feet, average temperature 66°F, annual precipitation 43 inches. Szechwan has a long rainy season; frost is rare.

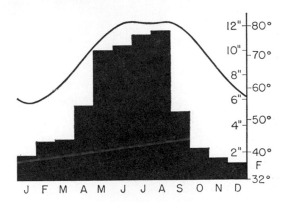

CANTON. Elevation 29 feet, average temperature 72°F, annual precipitation 65 inches. The growing season continues throughout the year.

of China, although entirely devoted to domestic commerce. Since then its growth has been phenomenal. Shanghai's prosperity was due in part to geography and in part to the economic security provided by the old International Settlement with its extraterritorial rights. When trade flourished in the interior, it brought business to Shanghai, and when civil warfare gripped the country, people and wealth sought refuge here.

The wide mouth of the Yangtze does not provide a suitable location for a harbor. Instead, Shanghai lies 14 miles to the south, up the winding Whangpoo River. Extensive dredging has provided a 30-foot channel along the Whangpoo, but enormous sand bars in the estuary of the Yangtze, known as the Fairy Flats, provide a low-water depth of only 20 feet, and large ships must wait for high tide, which normally measures 15 feet. The site of the city is a mud flat barely above high tide, with no bedrock for at least 1,000 feet down. On this foundation have been built 24-story buildings, which were, when erected, some of the tallest outside the Americas.

Present-day Shanghai has grown out of three separate political areas: the old walled city and two adjacent areas set apart under the Treaty Port arrangements for foreigners a century ago. The latter included the French Concession and the International Settlement, which came to provide the commercial core of metropolitan Shanghai.

During recent decades the Municipality of

Many cities in the Yangtze delta are intersected by canals, which provide an avenue for transport as well as a water supply. These steps lead to the back doors of the houses and shops. (*George B. Cressey*)

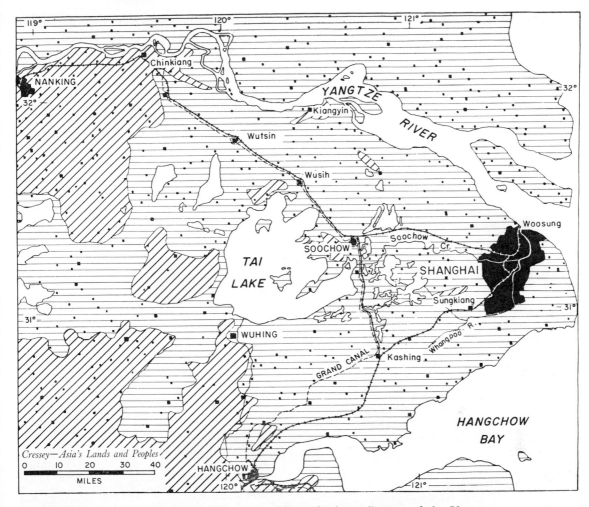

Shanghai lies on both sides of the Whangpoo River, the last tributary of the Yangtze.
Nanking, Soochow, and Hangchow are other delta cities of importance.

Greater Shanghai has spread on both sides of the Whangpoo toward the Yangtze.

Shanghai is primarily a commercial city, with industry dependent upon foreign contacts rather than local raw materials. Cotton and silk are the only resources produced in the immediate hinterland. Nevertheless, its location has made Shanghai an important center for heavy industry, and it contains plants for steel, shipbuilding, and machinery. Half of China's imports and exports normally pass through Shanghai, and despite the absence of nearby resources, the city has accounted for almost half of all China's industry. Among world ports, pre-Communist Shanghai ranked eighth in tonnage of ships entered. No other port in China had such extensive steamship connections. The city is thus China's cultural front door. Prior to the Second World War, the foreign population of Shanghai included 75,000 persons, among whom were 5,000 Americans.

Five hours southwest of Shanghai by rail is Hangchow, and two hours to the west is Soochow, linked in the Chinese expression "Heaven above, Soochow and Hangchow below." Hangchow is famous for its beautiful scenery and Soochow for its beautiful women. Each city is noted for satins and embroidery. The population of each exceeds a half million. To the east of Hangchow are Shaohing and Ningpo, each with over 250,000 people.

Nanking was the seat of government during the Sung and Ming dynasties before 1416, but most signs of its former magnificence are gone except the name "southern capital" and its 22-mile long city wall. New boulevards and mod-ern government buildings were built during the period when Nanking was the capital of the Nationalist government after 1928. The population considerably exceeds a million. The city lies on the Yangtze 200 miles northwest of Shanghai, with railroad connections to Shang-hai, Tientsin, and westward.

Hankow, at the mouth of the Han River, and its twin city of Wuchang, on the south bank of the Yangtze, dominate central China. Together with nearby Hanyang, the three cities are col-

Shanghai is the metropolis of China. The waterfront along the Whangpoo River is lined by some of the finest buildings in all Asia, all built in pre-Communist days. (*Ewing Galloway*)

The Yangtze bridge at Wuhan not only links the triple city area of Hankow, Wuchang, and Hanyang but provides through rail connections between Peking and Canton. (*China Photo Service*)

lectively known as Wuhan and have a population of 2 million. Hankow lies 630 miles up river from Shanghai, three to four days distant by boat. Railways lead north to Peking and south to Canton, linked by a 3,762-foot bridge. Hankow's water traffic not only follows the Yangtze east and west but also leads northwestward up the Han River and southwestward through Tungting Lake to the Siang River. Hankow is the most modern of the three cities, with buildings along the waterfront that rival those of Shanghai. Wuchang is the capital of Hupei province. Wuhan, at the crossroads of rail and water transport, has become both a commercial and an industrial metropolis. Giant steel mills draw on nearby iron ore, but coal must be brought several hundred miles, thus increasing the cost.

THE SZECHWAN BASIN

Western China has long been relatively inaccessible, so that it has not shared in the modernization which characterizes the coastal provinces. The land behind the Yangtze gorges thus remained undeveloped until the Second World War compelled China to rediscover its own interior. When the seaboard was overrun by the Japanese, Free China emerged in the far west. The basin of Szechwan is a notable example of these western revitalized areas.

Szechwan is the most populous of China's provinces, with a total of over 60 million inhabitants. Of this number, some 55 million live within the geographic region here described. In area, Szechwan is one of the largest provinces, exceeded only by Yunnan and Kansu among the traditional 18 provinces south of the Great Wall. Out of a total area of 117,197 square miles, the Szechwan Basin occupies about 75,000 square miles; the remainder is mountainous. The average population density within the region is thus 750 per square mile, highest of any region that is not a plain.

The Szechwan Basin is a land of hills and low mountains, cut by swift rivers flowing through steep-sided valleys. The region is underlain by soft shales and sandstones of the Cretaceous age, which are purple, or in some places red, in color. These gave the region its name of the "Red Basin."

Central Szechwan is a structural basin with numerous sharp anticlines and gentle synclines, trending roughly northeast to southwest. Much of the area was once a peneplain at a height near the present hilltops. As streams became entrenched, harder anticlinal areas of limestone and sandstone remained as ridges. Falls and rapids mark the outcrop of these formations along the streams and account for the gorges that characterize many tributaries. Most valleys contain several natural terrace levels. No more than 5 per cent of the basin is level, and the only plain is the alluvial fan around Chengtu.

Elevations along the Yangtze decrease from 820 feet at Pingshan in the west to 590 feet at Wanhsien in the east. Elsewhere the region is generally under 2,000 feet in height. Szechwan takes its name from the "four rivers" that drain into the Yangtze. These are the Min, which enters the Yangtze at Ipin, the To at Luhsien, the Kialing at Chungking, and the Wu from the province of Kweichow.

The climate of Szechwan has numerous surprising features. Although the region is far in the interior and surrounded by imposing mountains, the rainfall is about 40 inches. Seasonal temperature extremes are small. Winters rarely have snow or frost, except in the north, and there is a January average of 50°F and a July average of 80°F. The frost-free period is 330 days. Cold Mongolian air is kept out by the barrier of the Chin Ling Mountains to the north. The province has a great deal of cloud

and mist, so that the humidity is usually high. Rain may fall gently for several days in winter yet the amount be too little to measure; summer months have thundershowers. After the summer rains the level of the Yangtze may rise 75 feet, and more than twice that much in the gorges.

In easternmost Tibet, overlooking the Szechwan basin, is Mount Omei, one of the sacred mountains of China. The elevation is 10,145 feet with bold cliffs facing the east. In one year the recorded rainfall amounted to 311 inches. Despite its location of 600 miles from the ocean this mountain area has the heaviest precipitation of any station in China.

Agriculture is thus carried on under favorable circumstances, although the hilly topography requires extensive terracing. Dozens of terrace levels rise on many hillsides, some of them only 5 feet wide. Forty per cent of the region is cultivated. The Szechwan Basin grows a greater variety of crops than any other region; both the wheat, millet, and corn of the North, and the rice, rapeseed, and sugar cane of the South are represented. Rice is the usual summer crop wherever water is available for irrigation; it is planted in April or May and harvested 100 days later. Sweet potatoes are important on the dry hilltops. Wheat is a winter crop. Silk and tea are widely produced, together with some cotton, tobacco, and opium. Tung or wood oil is a major commercial crop, used as a quick drier in varnish. Citrus fruits are grown south of the Yangtze.

Crop yields are well above the national average; about 75 bushels of rice and 25 bushels of wheat are produced per acre. The farm-population density per square mile of cultivated land numbers some 2,000 people. Rice supplies more than half the food energy, with one-seventh from corn.

The landscape of the Szechwan Basin is distinctive. Other regions are as green and intensively developed, but nowhere else is so much land terraced. In fact, nowhere else except in Loessland is it so easy to construct terraces, for the bedrock is soft and weathers easily. Even 45-degree slopes have tiny steps of level land. Water wheels line the swifter streams and as they are turned by the current, lift irrigation water to the fields. Elsewhere water is obtained by chain pumps, often operated by water buffalo. Clusters of trees and bamboo surround the houses, with many banyan, cypress, pines, and some oaks and palms. Few parts of China are so highly praised for their beauty.

Beneath the surface occur extensive deposits of salt and coal, together with some iron ore, natural gas and petroleum, copper, and gold. A half million tons of salt are obtained from the brine of native wells, some of them over 1,000 feet deep. Coal production is

largely from the basins of the Kialing, Min, and To rivers. Modern industry is confined to the vicinity of Chungking.

Chungking lies nearly 1,400 miles up the Yangtze, but is accessible by 200-foot boats. The city occupies a strategic site on a high hill where the Kialing River joins the Yangtze. The original city wall dates from 320 B.C. The population of the municipality amounts to 2 million, partly a result of wartime developments when Chungking was the capital. New roads have been cut through the old city, and modern buildings up to seven stories in height have taken the place of the old. Prior to 1927 there was not a wheeled vehicle inside the city wall and not many streets wide enough for such con-

Farm buildings commonly surround a courtyard where grain is dried and household operations are carried on. This view is near Hsintsin in Szechwan. (*Courtesy United States Air Transport Command*)

veyances. Chungking is the commercial center of the province. In location and industry, the city has some parallels with Pittsburgh. Both cities lie on high ground at the junction of navigable rivers, both have nearby coal, and both produce steel.

The second city of the Szechwan Basin is Chengtu in the far west, within sight of the Great Snowy Mountains of Tibet. Chengtu is on the alluvial plain of the Min, near where it leaves the Azure Wall of mountains. This plain has an area of 1,730 square miles and a population of nearly 5 million: a density of some 3,000 people per square mile. Few other spots on earth are so fertile and productive, in part because of a remarkable irrigation system, developed in the third century B.C., which involves the annual removal of silt from the canals. Chengtu is rich in history and culture, but has only limited modern developments. Its population is about a million.

One major problem of the Szechwan Basin has been the difficulty of transportation, both internally and to the rest of China. Steamships on the Yangtze date from 1898, but freight rates are very high because of the hazards of navigation through the gorges. Railroads now lead north to Shensi and south to Kweichow. Most domestic freight still moves by river boat.

THE CENTRAL MOUNTAIN BELT

Between the Yangtze and the Hwang is a mountain zone which accounts for the abrupt contrasts between dry North China and the humid South. Toward the west the mountains are Tibetan in character; near the latitude of Nanking, where they die out, they have become mere hills. The northern slopes are dry, but south of the crest monsoon rains result in forests and rice culture. The Central Mountain Belt is the southern limit of loess and the northern boundary of extensive rice, tea, mulberry, and bamboo culture.

This region separates the wheat-eating Chinese of the north from the rice-eating population of the south. It also marks important cultural and historic boundaries, for revolutions in the past have commonly been limited to one side or the other of this mountain area. To cross the mountains in winter is to pass from the dusty frozen lands of Kansu, Shensi, or Honan to the green fields of Szechwan, Hupei, and south Anhwei.

This region is part of the Kunlun Mountain system which originates far to the west in the Pamirs. Where the range enters China in southern Kansu it is known as the Min Mountains and rises to 15,000 feet; farther east in Shensi elevations are over 10,000 feet and the ranges are called the Chin Ling, a name which is often used for the whole range east of Tibet. In Honan are the 6,000-foot Funiu Mountains; in Anhwei the hills between the Hwai and the Yangtze are but 3,000 feet in height and are termed the Tapieh Mountains; the name Hwai-yang also appears on some maps.

In addition to this sequence along the northern margin of the Central Mountain Belt, there is a parallel chain of mountains to the south of the Han River, which flows eastward through the western part of the region. In northern Szechwan these mountains are called the Tapa; farther east they cross the Yangtze as the Gorge Mountains.

Since the western half of the Belt is rugged, most of the people live in the eastern hills where level land amounts to 5 or 10 per cent. The chief city is Nancheng (Hanchung) on the Han River, set in a miniature Chengtu Plain.

Not only does the Central Mountain Belt separate the North from South China, it also isolates the Szechwan Basin from the Yangtze Plain. The Yangtze gorges provide some of the finest scenery and most difficult navigation in China. The river descends 300 feet in the 200 miles from Wanhsien to Ichang, and the current flows as fast as 13 knots. The principal gorges occur where the Yangtze cuts across folds of hard limestone. Sheer cliffs rise 1,000 to 2,000 feet. Vessels up to 2,000 tons are used during the high-water period in summer, but so much power is required and the risks are so great that freight rates are high. Native junks

The Yangtze Gorges form one of the most difficult areas of river navigation on earth; in places the current measures 13 knots. This is the entrance to the Kweifu Gorge above Ichang. (*Courtesy United States Navy*)

operate throughout the year, but must be dragged up through the rapids by long cables, pulled by lines of coolies on shore.

The hydroelectric potentials are very large, and grandiose schemes look forward to giant power plants. One proposal calls for a dam in the Yangtze gorges 600 feet high with an electric capacity of 13.4 million kilowatts.

THE SOUTH YANGTZE HILLS

The Yangtze River drains four regions after it leaves Tibet: the Szechwan Basin, the Central Mountain Belt, the Yangtze Plain, and the South Yangtze Hills. The hills include a large area south to the watershed. The region lacks internal coherence as a geographic entity, but conditions of life are essentially uniform.

Four north-flowing streams, all but the easternmost of which are tributary to the Yangtze, guide the economic life. These are the Yuan and Siang in Hunan, which reach the Yangtze via the Tungting Lake; the Kan in Kiangsi, which flows via the Poyang Lake; and the Chientang River which enters the sea in Chekiang province. In each instance the major city of the valley lies in or near the Yangtze Plain to the north. These are, respectively, Changteh, Changsha, Nanchang, and Hangchow.

These rivers and their tributaries carry a great volume of traffic on native junks but are of limited value for powered navigation. Where streams become too shallow for even the smallest boats, bamboo rafts extend the navigable distance. Thus almost every city is served by some water transport. Modern automobile roads have revolutionized the accessibility of the region. Journeys that once required days are now a matter of hours.

Hills of reddish sandstone are characteristic. Except for mountains along the various provincial borders, elevations are under 2,000 feet. Level land is restricted to river-flood plains and to the rolling topography on summit levels; elsewhere slopes are fairly steep. Terracing is widespread.

Surprisingly large areas are in forest, mostly in remote sections. Fir, pine, and bamboo are systematically grown for export to cities along the Yangtze. The most extensive of these forest areas are in western and southern Hunan in the basin of the Yuan River. Where the original vegetation has been cleared from the hillsides, whether for lumber or for cultivation, excessive erosion has occurred. After the land is abandoned it does not return to forest but becomes covered with wild grass.

Several uplands lie within the region, such as the Lu Mountains in northern Kiangsi with the summer resort of Kuling, the Hung Mountains in southern Hunan, and the Nan Ling system next to Kwangtung. Each exceeds 4,000 feet.

This is the warmest and wettest part of the Yangtze valley. Rainfall everywhere exceeds 50 inches, and in the higher areas is as much as 70 inches. Temperatures are neither excessively high nor low, with frost occurring only rarely. The average annual relative humidity exceeds 80 per cent. This high moisture content helps to keep the landscape always green. Whereas prolonged drought may turn the Yangtze Plain brown, such conditions seldom occur here. At least 300 consecutive days are frost-free. Oranges, palms, tung-oil trees, and bamboo reveal the subtropical nature of the climate. Soils are red podsols and much leached.

Rice is the universal summer crop wherever irrigation is feasible. Almost everywhere it oc-

cupies half of the crop land, and in many places the area approaches 100 per cent. Shortly before the harvest, a second planting is often put into the same fields in alternate rows with the first crop, since the growing season is not long enough for two successive crops. Uplands are unirrigated and devoted to tea, rapeseed, and sweet potatoes. Winter crops include such staples as beans, oil seeds, and wheat.

Tea is a distinctive crop, with characteristic flavors in each valley, and even on the sunny and shady sides of the same hills. Nearly 3 million acres in China are devoted to tea plants, of which two-thirds are in the South Yangtze Hills. Siangtan in central Hunan is especially famous. Hunan and Kiangsi commonly cure the leaves in such a way as to make black tea, while green tea is produced in Chekiang and Fukien.

Cultivated land amounts to one-fifth of the total, of which three-quarters is irrigated. Surveys show 2,000 farm people per square mile of cultivated land. This population density is higher than for most regions so far considered, but is surpassed by those farther south. The total population amounts to some 75 million in an area of 150,000 square miles, or an average including city dwellers and farmers alike of 500 per square mile.

The South Yangtze Hills fortunately have conspicuous mineral wealth. Coal is widespread and is produced especially at Pingsiang in Kiangsi. Iron ore is mined at Tayeh and elsewhere near the Yangtze. These supply the great steel mills near Wuhan. The nonferrous metals are distinctive, and include antimony from central Hunan and tungsten from southern Kiangsi, both among the most important occurrences in the world for these unusual metals. Zinc and lead have been mined for many years. High-grade kaolin clays provide the basis for porcelain, famous for centuries and found in museums throughout the world.

The Canton-Hankow Railway and the east–west line linking Hangchow with Nanchang, Changsha, and Fengkieh (Kweichow) have opened the region to modern trade.

THE SOUTHEASTERN COAST

A variety of factors give geographic personality to the Southeastern Coast. The coast line is embayed and has led to the region's extensive maritime interests and the skill of her people as sailors. No other region is so oriented to the sea or so detached from interior China. Typhoons are recurrent and yield heavy rainfall. Race and language are complex. Millions of Chinese in Southeast Asia count this as their ancestral home.

The coast is a subsiding shore line with drowned valleys and offshore islands that once were hilltops. Hundreds of sheltered harbors provide havens for native junks, but in only a few localities is there sufficient access to the hinterland to give rise to a commercial port. The irregular coast reflects the rugged topography of the interior. This is a hard and rocky land, largely underlain by granite, rhyolite-porphyry, and other resistant formations. Here and there are softer rocks, and these give rise to scattered basins or rounded hills; elsewhere there are rugged mountains.

An analysis of the land forms of that part of Chekiang province which lies within this geographic region shows that about 5 per cent are coastal flat lands; 1 per cent are interior lowlands; less than 1 per cent are rolling hills (with 4- to 10-degree average slopes); 90 per cent are mountain lands (10- to 25-degree slopes); and 3 per cent are steep lands (with slopes over 20 degrees). Topographic conditions in Fukien are probably comparable, but eastern Kwangtung has more level land and more gentle slopes.

Along the western border of this region are a series of mountains that rise to 4,000 and 6,000 feet. Those in southern Fukien are the Taching Mountains; farther north are the Wuyi Mountains, sometimes romanized as Bohea.

This is a hot and very wet region, with 50 inches of rainfall on the lower coastal areas and over 80 inches on the interior mountains. All months have some rain, but from May through September the monthly average is over 6 inches.

Typhoons, most common during the late summer, bring torrential rains. The destructive force of the wind is limited to the immediate coast, but heavy rains extend throughout the region. Fukien is somewhat drier than the other provinces since it lies in the rain shadow of Taiwan. As a result of heavy precipitation some areas have a subtropical rain forest. Commercial forests, with systematic replanting, enable the region to export lumber to the entire China coast.

Communications have been difficult, but railways open the interior. Since overland roads leading to the rest of China are limited except in the far north and south, contact with the other provinces as well as within the region has been by sea. Each river-mouth city has its independent hinterland. Thus Wenchow, Foochow, Amoy, and Swatow dominate subregions of their own, and each valley has its own unique customs and speech. In the days of the clipper ships, Foochow shipped 65 million pounds of tea a year; today it is noteworthy for its fine lacquer.

The coastal zone from Shanghai to Canton is characterized by linguistic and psychological confusion. In Fukien alone there are 108 dialects. Many people in Kwangtung are Hakkas, "guest people" who once lived in Honan. Each port has large numbers of boat people who spend their entire lives afloat; they are in part of South Seas origin. Yunnan and Kweichow have even greater racial differences, but they relate to tribesmen rather than to nominal Chinese stock as along the coast. Fortunately the radio, motion pictures, and standardized school pronunciations increasingly make people mutually intelligible; but cultural contrasts persist everywhere.

Since the land offers so little, many people have turned to the sea. Fishing boats dot the coastal waters, especially in the Chusan archipelago of Chekiang. Seagoing junks sail north to Tientsin and south as far as Singapore. Modern Chinese steamships draw many of their crew from this coastal school for seamen. Millions of emigrants from Amoy, Swatow, and elsewhere have gone to the Indochina States, Malaya, Indonesia, and the Philippines. Their remittances to relatives at home amount to millions of dollars each year.

With an area of only 70,000 square miles, the region supports about 40 million people. Only 15 per cent of the area is in cultivation, and the crop area per person averages less than one-fifth of an acre.

THE CANTON HINTERLAND

Canton was the first port for foreign trade and has had the longest contact with Westerners. It is also the home of most of the Chinese who now live in the United States and Europe. Arab and Persian traders came to Canton in A.D. 300 and were followed by the Portuguese in 1514 and later by the Spanish and Dutch. When modern trade began early in the nineteenth century, this was the only port at which foreign vessels might call, and this was the main port of call for American clipper ships. Here also came the first Protestant missionary, Robert Morrison, in 1807. Millions of Cantonese have gone overseas and have brought or sent back money and ideas which have helped to make their region progressive.

The Canton Hinterland occupies much of Kwangtung and Kwangsi, and is more or less coextensive with the Si Kiang basin, plus the coastal area to the south.

This is tropical China, for most of the Canton Hinterland lies within 25 degrees of the equator. There is a long, wet summer with excessive humidity and high temperatures from mid-April until mid-October; then follows a relatively cool and dry winter until mid-February, after which there are two months of transition with fog and muggy weather. This region is as wet as the Southeastern Coast, having 70 inches or more of rain along the coast and less in the interior. The maximum precipitation occurs in August—nearly 12 inches—but June and July are nearly as wet. Even winter months have 1 or 2 inches. Snow falls only on the

highest mountains, and there but rarely. The Nan Ling Mountains along the northern border are the wettest area in China, although isolated stations elsewhere may have more precipitation.

Here as elsewhere in eastern China, the chief source of moist air masses is the South China Sea. Its relation to Chinese rainfall is comparable to that of the Caribbean and Gulf of Mexico to the United States.

Summer temperatures are high, since the sun is directly overhead in June, but the cloudiness keeps maximum temperatures in the 90s rather than around 100°F as in Shanghai or Peking. Many people commonly wear white tropical clothing for several months of the year. Cold air masses from Mongolia seldom reach the valley of the Si Kiang, though occasional frosts kill banana plants and other tropical vegetation.

These climatic conditions are reflected in the soils and natural vegetation. Before the arrival of man, most of the region was covered by a rain forest. Except on river-flood plains and deltas, soils are red in color with lateritic tendencies. They are low in humus and so badly leached that their fertility is poor. The colloid content is so low that they erode badly. Heavy and repeated fertilization is essential. Most hillsides should have been kept in the original forest; where this has been destroyed, tall coarse grasses have taken possession of the surface. Such rank growth covers about one-third of the region.

The fruits of the area further suggest the low latitude: They include oranges, bananas, pineapples, lichees, olives, and figs. Sugar cane is also grown.

The Canton Hinterland is a region of two successive rice crops. The first crop is planted in March and harvested in July, and the second is grown between August and November. Although the yield for each harvest is the lowest in the country, the double crop produces a large yield per acre. Over three-quarters of the cropland is double-cropped in summer, but only one-tenth carries a third winter crop. Sweet potatoes are more common than else-

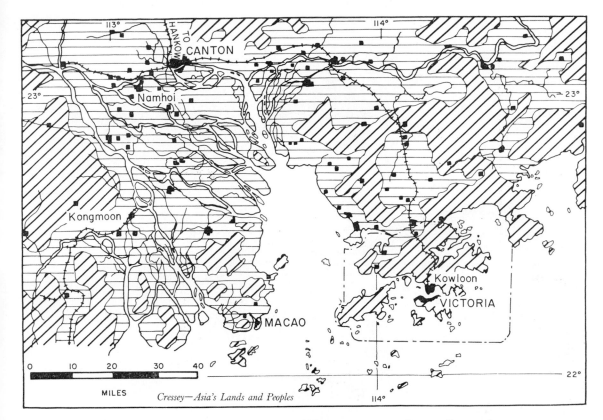

The twin cities of Victoria and Kowloon make up British Hong Kong. Canton lies on the Pearl River, a segment of the compound West River delta. Portuguese Macao dates from 1557.

where but are grown far less than rice; since they do not require irrigation, they are often raised on dry areas. Poorer people eat dried shredded sweet potatoes as a substitute for rice.

Silk is important in the delta around Canton. Many farmers also raise fish, devoting four-tenths of their farm to ponds and six-tenths to mulberry fields. Part of the fish food is supplied by residual materials from the raising of silkworms, and the fertile mud from the pond bottoms is used in turn to enrich the mulberry fields.

Cultivated land in the entire region amounts to some 15 per cent of the total area, and 70 per cent of this is irrigated. Pre-Communist land values were the highest in the country, with prices well above the national average. No less than 2,500 farm people occupy each square

mile of cultivated land. By far the most intensive utilization occurs in the level land around Canton.

Three major streams drain the area, each one converging on a common delta. In the east is the Tung or East River, in the center is the Pei or North River, and the third and longest is the Si or West River. The Si enables steamers of 6-foot draft to reach Wuchow, 200 miles from the sea, at all seasons. Each river is extensively used by motor launches and junks. These rivers flow through very hilly topography. Fully 85 per cent of the region is in hills and mountains; considerably more if the delta is excluded.

Where these streams reach the sea, they have built a compound delta. Unlike those of the Hwang and Yangtze, this delta is not a

Canton lies on the Pearl River or Chu Kiang, a part of the delta complex of the West, North, and East Rivers. The Pearl is too shallow for oceangoing vessels but is extensively used by small vessels. (*Eastfoto*)

broad plain, but rather a fragmented area of alluvium which surrounds many hills and is cut by wide distributaries. Its area is 2,900 square miles, and the population exceeds 10 million —a figure which means a density of well over 3,500 people per square mile. A shorter stream in the delta is the Chu or Pearl River, on which lies Canton. While the Pearl River basin is separate from that of the three other rivers, it is connected with them by waterways which are navigable for small craft.

The province of Kwangsi has unique limestone-solution topography, nowhere surpassed, though equaled in Yugoslavia and Puerto Rico. Isolated vertical walled hills rise 100 to 600 feet above the plain, with the picturesque effects which characterize Chinese landscape paint-

ings. In some areas remnants of an older surface are cut by deep sinkholes and canyons; elsewhere the area is a confusion of steep slopes with only a trace of the original upper surface and the beginning of lower plains. In the still more dissected areas broad plains have developed near ground water, with only isolated steep hills as remnants of the original mass. These hills are residuals, left by ground-water solution, and are associated with features such as caves, underground drainage ways, and sinkholes, where the roofs have collapsed and only occasional pillars remain. The area is a classic example of karst topography.

The city of Canton, sometimes known as Kwangchow, was founded in 1053. It thus dates from the time when Chinese immigrants from the north drove out the Thai people. The city was known to Arab and Indian traders in early times. Canton was one of the first cities to tear down its city wall and open wide streets; the city is now in part modern and in part old style. The population exceeds the 2 million count.

Canton dominates all of China south of the Yangtze valley, commercially and intellectually. The city serves a rich hinterland, up the three rivers and also along the coast. Unfortunately, the Pearl River is too shallow for large vessels, and it is necessary for West River steamers to go out around the delta to reach the city. Deep water is available 9 miles down the Pearl River at Whampoa, although much dredging will be necessary in order to create a modern ocean port.

The island of Hong Kong was ceded to Great Britain in 1842, and in 1898 additional territory was leased on the mainland for a 99-year period. The advantages have been both geographic and political. The harbor is excellent, and its location along the major shipping lanes to Europe and to America made it an important port of call. In normal years Hong Kong is one of the half-dozen busiest ports on earth. The city also has served as an entrepôt for smaller ports from Foochow to Haiphong, but as trade and facilities develop at these lesser ports the need for Hong Kong will diminish. The city of Victoria, often called by the name of the island, is picturesquely situated at the

The city of Victoria lies at the base of the mountainous island of Hong Kong; across the bay on territory leased from China is Kowloon. Only a few ports in the world handle more traffic. (*Courtesy British Information Service*)

foot of an 1,825-foot peak. Across the bay is Kowloon, with rail connections to Canton and central China. Hong Kong was established as a free port, so that trade has flourished. If Canton can develop sufficient business with proper commercial facilities, Hong Kong may lose much of its importance.

During the first half of the twentieth century, British Hong Kong and the International Settlement of Shanghai served as havens of refuge during times of disorder within China, and as commercial centers of great international importance during periods of peace. With the emergence of Communism on the mainland, Hong Kong received 2 million refugees and has become a major center for the manufacture and export of industrial products, including textiles. Its population exceeds 3 million.

Nearby Portuguese Macao was settled in 1557 and is the oldest foreign possession along the China coast. Within its dozen square miles live a half million people.

THE SOUTHWESTERN UPLANDS

The topography of the Southwestern Uplands may be subdivided into three areas, each a much dissected plateau, which form a giant set of stairs from the lowlands of the Canton Hinterland to the highlands of Tibet. Western Kwangsi has a general level of 2,000 feet; Kweichow lies about 3,000 feet above sea level; most of eastern Yunnan is above 6,000 feet. The general trend of rivers and ridges is from northwest to southeast; hence, travel at right angles involves crossing a series of mountains and valleys. Level land in the region as a whole is between 5 and 10 per cent. Earthquakes have been severe in western Yunnan.

Toward the east, in Kwangsi, only a few traces of original summit levels remain, and much of the land is at lower elevations so that most settlements lie in open valleys. Central Kweichow is so extensively cut by deep valleys that level land is almost absent, and most settlements lie in narrow valleys; agricul-

tural possibilities are limited. The hard limestone hills are not easily terraced. Soil erosion has been very destructive and has so depleted the hillsides that cultivation is less extensive than formerly; this is one reason for the poverty of the province. In Yunnan the few plains all lie on undissected interstream uplands, and the widely spaced young valleys are narrow and deep. There are several lakes and old lake basins on the Yunnan Plateau, notably near the cities of Kunming and Tali. Karst topography is in its infancy in Yunnan, in full development in Kwangsi, and of intermediate character in Kweichow.

Although the region is subtropical in latitude, the moderating factor of altitude makes the temperatures mild and the seasonal range low. Highlands in the tropics enjoy some of the most pleasant climates in the world. Conditions vary according to local elevation. At Kunming the January average is 50°F, and in July it is 70°F; extremes have never exceeded 90°F or dropped below 29°F. The rainfall average is 42 inches, with only minor variations. Half the total falls in July and August. The growing season is over 325 days, but the cool weather permits only one summer crop of rice. Two-fifths of the fields raise a winter crop.

The Southwestern Uplands have a great variety of native peoples. Chinese have lived here for 2,000 years, but the area has remained semicolonial in government and the Chinese have pushed the aborigines or tribesmen into the hills or steeper valleys rather than assimilating them. Although Yunnan and Kweichow lie in the far southwest, 2,000 miles from the capital at Peking, yet the Chinese speak some of the best Mandarin heard outside the Yellow Plain. More than half the people are of non-Chinese stock. Non-Chinese people include the Miao, Lolo, Chungchia, and many others, each with distinct languages and culture. In many areas effective Chinese control is only a matter of the past century, so that the 1953 census had to include rough estimates rather than an enumeration. These racial contrasts are reflected in the agricultural pattern. The Chinese occupy the good land and raise rice; the tribesmen live on the hillsides and raise corn, millet, and barley.

Although conspicuous changes in transportation and industry arose out of the westward orientation of wartime China, most of the region is tens of miles from a railway or modern road, and few of the latter are paved. Where transport is by means of coolie carriers, the cost of rice is doubled if carried a two days' journey. If agricultural products are to be exported, high-value cash crops are necessary. Opium at times supplies this need but thereby preempts much of the best land. Tea is exported to Tibet. New crops might be found in lumbering, livestock, fruit, sugar cane, cotton, or tung oil. All these must wait upon improved access to outside markets.

This region is the largest in Agricultural China, but the percentage of cultivated land is among the lowest; it is estimated by the writer at 4 per cent, and by Buck at 7 per cent for this southwestern rice area. Nowhere else are there so many people per square mile of cultivated land. Buck reported a pre-Communist farm population of 2,636 per square mile of crop area; this certainly now exceeds 3,000. Even allowing for possible errors in computation, this average is extraordinarily high. Since so much of the land is naturally poor, the density represents intensive effort and low standards of living. The average farm is only 1 or 2 acres in extent.

The Uplands have a variety of mineral wealth. Yunnan produces modest amounts of coal, copper, and iron, and leads all China in tin output. Kweichow yields small amounts of coal and mercury.

Kunming, with a population of a half million, is the terminus for a narrow-gauge railway from Haiphong in Vietnam, built by the French late in the nineteenth century. A second avenue to the outside world is provided by the wartime Burma Road, which crosses extremely difficult country in the gorges of the Salween and Mekong rivers. A railroad to Burma would give China an important back door to the Indian Ocean and thence to Europe.

HAINAN

Hainan is the most tropical region of China. The area is 13,000 square miles, slightly smaller than Taiwan. The island is separated from the mainland by a strait 15 miles wide, and has an area of 14,000 square miles. The population numbers some 3 million, one-third of whom are Lois or Li tribesmen rather than ethnic Chinese.

Much of the island is mountainous, with elevations which reach 4,428 feet in the Five Finger Mountains. A coastal plain occupies the northern quarter of the island and extends around the western and eastern shores, with mangrove swamps along the sea. Rice is the chief agricultural product, and there is a small production of coconuts, rubber, and timber from the tropical forests. Crops of coffee and cocoa reflect the low latitude. Extensive deposits of high-grade iron ore have been developed and were shipped to Japan prior to the Second World War.

The chief city is Kiungshan in the north, served by the port of Hoihow.

China's territorial claims include a number of small islands scattered through the South China Sea as far as 4°N latitude, including the Spratly and Paracel groups.

9 Regions of Outer China

Inner Asia / Inner Mongolia / Sinkiang / Tibet

INNER ASIA

Interior Asia has two large areas with less than 10 inches of rainfall: One lies northwest of the Pamirs in Soviet Middle Asia; the other is to the east in western China and Mongolia. Most people live in oases along mountain-fed streams or favored areas with slightly higher rainfall; elsewhere this is the home of the pastoralist rather than the farmer, of nomadic encampments rather than fixed settlements. Although grazing utilizes far more land than does farming, paradoxically most of the population is sedentary.

Outer China covers 1½ million square miles, but the population is no more than 15 million.

One-half of the area is a rolling upland plain, one-half highland plateau and mountains. Everywhere the dominant note is aridity. Most of this dry area of western China is without drainage to the sea. The few withering streams drain inward rather than to the ocean; that is to say they are centripetal rather than centrifugal, and basins are not filled to overflowing as in humid lands where precipitation exceeds evaporation.

Three political areas are involved, each with somewhat confused political status. Traditional Mongolia may be divided into Inner and Outer Mongolia, named from their position with respect to the rest of China. Outer Mongolia has been independent of effective Chinese rule since

1913 and obtained its legal independence from China in 1946. The country, now known as the Mongolian People's Republic, is considered in a separate chapter.

Sinkiang has had full provincial status since 1878, but its remoteness from the capital has rendered political control difficult. The province has at times been somewhat oriented toward the Soviet Union, especially after the construction of the Turk-Sib Railway parallel to the frontier, but the construction of the Trans-Chinese Railway has effectively tied it to the rest of China.

Historic Tibet is also divided into two sections, both integral parts of greater China. Nearer Tibet lies closer to the traditional provinces, and is administered as the provinces of Chinghai and Sikang, the latter now a part of Szechwan. Farther Tibet includes the bulk of the great plateau, but its boundaries are vague. Conventional lines as shown on maps have little validity with the local inhabitants. Chinese authority was negligible between 1911 and 1940; during the early part of that period British influence was strong.

These major political districts roughly form geographic regions; if not entirely homogeneous in its physical pattern, each one is at least a unit in cultural coherence. Inner Mongolia includes the southern edge of the Gobi Desert and the encircling steppelands. Sinkiang has three parts: the Tarim Basin, the Tien Shan Range, and the Dzungarian Basin. Tibet occupies the great plateau from the Himalaya to the Astin Tagh, high but for the most part as dry as the lowlands. In most of these areas ethnic Chinese are a minority.

Half of China lies here in the interior. Although its economic influence is negligible, politically it has had profound significance since the earliest dynasties. Time after time migrations which started in this arid interior have swept south across China and also westward into Europe. This is the "Pulse of Asia," as Ellsworth Huntington has titled his book, and many of the secrets of Old World history will be better understood as we learn the story of

fluctuating rainfall in Inner Asia. Two thousand years ago under the Han dynasty, Chinese rule extended west of the Pamirs into the basin of the Aral Sea. Under Genghis Khan and his grandson Kublai, the Mongols built up the largest land empire prior to the Soviet Union and its satellites.

Overland travel is a major problem. Railroads are widely spaced, and automobile roads are few and poor. Caravans of two-humped Bactrian camels or ox carts are the traditional means of communication across the plains, with yak as pack animals in the highlands. Distances are measured in days rather than in miles. Thus the cart or caravan trip from Kashgar in western Sinkiang to Peking normally requires four to five months for 2,900 miles, while an additional two months are needed to reach Hulun in northeastern Mongolia. In contrast, Kashgar is but two weeks by horseback from the Soviet Union. The 675 miles from the Great Wall north to Ulan Bator in Outer Mongolia, which can now be covered in less than a day by rail or in three days by car, require 30 to 45 days by camel. Two months are involved in the caravan journey from Koko Nor in northeastern Tibet to Lhasa in the south, but there is now a truck road and a nearly completed railway. Effective political control has been difficult under such handicaps.

INNER MONGOLIA

Although most of the Gobi Desert will be considered in Chapter 11 on the Mongolian People's Republic, the fact that Inner Mongolia covers 451,620 square miles and has a population of 8 million calls for some consideration in these chapters on China. Most of these people are now Chinese farmers rather than Mongol pastoralists, although grazing accounts for the bulk of the land in use; few traces of nomadism remain.

Inner Mongolia originally referred to the area between the Great Wall and the Gobi proper, much of it a semiarid grassland with fair grazing potentials. In 1911 the area was

Mechanized dry farming has pushed north of the Great Wall onto the chestnut-brown soils of Inner Mongolia. This is a crop of oats 90 miles north of Kalgan. (*Courtesy James Thorp*)

broken up into four provinces, known from west to east as Ningsia, Suiyuan, Chahar, and Jehol. Although the latter was absorbed into Japanese-dominated Manchuria, its original orientation was toward the desert. To these four provinces, or at least the drier parts of them, the Communists added the semidesert fringe of Liaoning and Heilungkiang in western Manchuria in 1947, thus creating a crescent-shaped area known as the Inner Mongolian Autonomous Region. These Manchurian areas include land on both sides of the Great Khingan Mountains. From end to end the distance exceeds 1,500 miles. The capital is at Kweisui, or Huehot, near the bend of the Hwang Ho.

The Great Wall was China's attempt to set a limit between farmer and shepherd—between the lands of adequate and inadequate rainfall. But since deserts are areas of fluctuating precipitation, the arable limits expand and contract with passing decades. Time after time throughout Chinese history, rainfall outside the Wall has increased to the point where it has been sufficient for crops, and Chinese colonists have pressed 100 miles or more into Mongolia. The nomads in turn were able to retreat toward the then wetter core of the usual desert area. Later on, in drier cycles when the rains failed, dust-bowl conditions developed along the fringe of cultivation, and the farmers were obliged to retreat southward. The nomads in turn moved outward, eventually invading the cultivated areas south of the Wall. The Great Wall was an attempt to stabilize a shifting climatic boundary. It failed because, like all deserts, the Gobi did not stay put. Similar to-and-fro migrations are known to have taken place around the eastern and northern limits of Mongolia.

Inner Mongolia has been the scene of considerable Chinese colonization within recent decades, reaching to latitude 42°N outside the Great Wall north of Kalgan. Soils are fertile, but rainfall is variable; the only possibilities for further settlement depend on large-scale mechanized dry farming.

Although Chinese farmers tend to criticize the Mongol herdsmen for not cultivating the soil, it is clear that once the surface is disturbed serious erosion may follow.

The great Jesuit travelers, Huc and Gabet, describe the area north of Peking as follows.[1]

Towards the middle of the seventeenth century, the Chinese began to penetrate into this district. At that period, the whole landscape was still one of rude grandeur; the mountains were covered with fine forests, and the Mongol tents whitened the valleys, amid rich pasturages. For a very modest sum, the Chinese obtained permission to cultivate the desert, and as cultivation advanced, the Mongols were obliged to retreat, conducting their flocks and herds elsewhere.

From that time forth, the aspect of the country became entirely changed. All the trees were grubbed up, the forests disappeared from the hills, the prairies were cleared by means of fire, and the new cultivators set busily to work in exhausting the fecundity of the soil. Almost the entire region is now in the hands of the Chinese, and it is probably to their system of devastation that we must attribute the extreme irregularity of the seasons which now desolate this unhappy land. Droughts are of almost annual occurrence; the spring winds setting in, dry up the soil; the heavens assume a sinister aspect, and the unfortunate population await, in utter terror, the manifestation of some terrible calamity; the winds by degrees redouble their violence, and sometimes continue to blow far into the summer months. Then the dust rises in clouds, the atmosphere becomes thick and dark; and often, at midday, you are

[1] E. R. Huc: *Travels in Tartary, Thibet, and China,* London: Routledge (1928) I, 4.

environed with the terrors of night, or rather, with an intense and almost palpable blackness, a thousand times more fearful than the most sombre night. Next after these hurricanes comes the rain: but so comes, that instead of being an object of desire, it is an object of dread, for it pours down in furious raging torrents. Sometimes the heavens suddenly opening, pour forth in, as it were, an immense cascade, all the water with which they are charged in that quarter; and immediately the fields and their crops disappear under a sea of mud, whose enormous waves follow the course of the valleys, and carry everything before them. The torrent rushes on, and in a few hours, the earth reappears, but the crops are gone, and worse even than that, the arable soil also has gone with them. Nothing remains but a ramification of ruts, filled with gravel, and thenceforward incapable of being plowed.

Spectacular mineral developments have begun to enliven the empty landscape, notably around the oil fields of western Kansu and the iron and coal developments near Paotow outside the great bend of the Hwang Ho. Salt from desert lakes is an old product. Railroads have brought new accessibility, with the line to Outer Mongolia and Siberia and the railroad to Sinkiang.

This elongated Autonomous Region, classified on ethnic and thus administrative grounds, is scarcely a geographic unit. In the north, parts of the Great Khingan are well forested; some of the area is flat and semidesert as in the Ordos or Gobi borderlands; elsewhere there are mountains and the dissected edge of the Mongolian escarpment. Along the Hwang Ho are large areas of irrigated land, though the soil tends to be too saline for cultivation. Near the Hwang and the Liao, elevations are under 1,000 feet, while farther north the plateau averages 3,000 feet, and mountaintops rise to twice that elevation. Rainfall averages range from 20 inches to scarcely one-tenth of this figure.

Only 3 per cent of the region is cultivated. In addition to millet, kaoliang, and wheat, new crops include soybeans, linseed, and sugar beets.

SINKIANG

Sinkiang commands the chief low-level gateways between Oriental and Occidental Eurasia. Highways have crossed the province since the dawn of history, at one time to link ancient China with the Roman world. This was the route of early Europeans and of the monks who brought Buddhism from India. Into China came jade from the Kunlun, and westward moved silks and porcelains. Trade and security, even more than colonization, have been China's territorial interest in this area.

The great highway of central Asia, now paralleled by a railway, leads west from Sian, one of China's former capitals in Shensi, to Lanchow and then follows the long arm of Kansu through the oases of Wuwei, Kanchow, Kiuchuan (Suchow), past China's ancient front door at the Jade Gate near the end of the Great Wall, to Ansi. The road follows the base of the Nan Shan Range, stepping from one irrigated area to another along the edge of Mongolia. Until 1940 the only means of travel was on horseback or by springless two-wheeled carts.

West of Ansi the original Silk Road entered Sinkiang and followed the southern edge of the Tarim Basin past Lob Nor to Yarkand, but the oases are now largely in ruins, and the route crosses extremely desolate country. The abandonment of this route may have been associated with climatic changes.

The present road strikes north from Ansi across the barren desert to Hami at the foot of the Tien Shan or "Heavenly Mountains." Here the trail divides. One route leads along the oases south of the mountains through the Turfan Depression to Kashgar, where the 12,700-foot Terek Pass leads across the Pamirs to Soviet Fergana. The other and currently more important road lies north of the Tien Shan through Kitai to Urumchi, or Tihwa, capital of Sinkiang. Three roads lead west from Urumchi to the Turk-Sib Railway in Soviet territory: one via Kuldja and the Ili valley; another through the famous Dzungarian Gate;

the third crosses the frontier near Tahcheng.

This Imperial Highway in the past required 30 days of travel from Peking to Sian, 18 cart stages from Sian to Lanchow, 20 days more to Kanchow, 18 stages each of bitter desert travel to Kiuchuan (Suchow) and Hami, and then 36 days of "bitter and sweet" travel to Urumchi. Three more series of 18 stages each led from Urumchi to Kashgar. This represented 120 days of actual travel, or five months, allowing for the usual rest stops. Automobiles now link these cities over fair desert roads, but the trip is not one to be taken lightly since few supplies are available en route. The new Trans-China Railway roughly parallels the ancient road and has brought Urumchi within a few days of Peking.

Difficult trails lead south from Kashgar via Yarkand over high Tibetan passes to India, but the Buddhist pilgrim route led far to the west through Afghanistan.

None of these routes along the Nan Shan and Tien Shan offered much attraction to early nomadic wanderers with large flocks, since long stretches of pastureless country intervene between oases. Farther north, along the base of the Altai Mountains, the grassland is continuous and provides an easy avenue to western Asia along the valley of the Black Irtysh River.

Sinkiang, now known as the Uighur Autonomous Region, covers some 660,800 square miles, and has a population of 6 million. Of these only 500,000 are nomads. Eighty per cent of the people are Uigurs, of Turkic stock and Islamic religion. (Sinkiang is sometimes known as Eastern or Chinese Turkestan because of the prevalence of Turkic culture—in which respect it resembles Soviet Middle Asia.) Kazaks may number 10 per cent; ethnic Chinese account for fewer than 10 per cent of the population. Unlike Mongolia and Tibet where Chinese influence is a matter of recent centuries, Sinkiang has been under Chinese control off and on since the Han dynasty in 200 B.C. At distant Kashgar, however, China has exercised complete control for only 450 out of 2,000 years. In contrast to Manchuria, where the Chinese have occupied the land as agricul-

The oases of Sinkiang, hot and dry, are noted for their sweet melons and grapes. This is a Uighur girl in Turfan. (*Eastfoto*)

tural settlers, in Sinkiang they are merely traders in the oases. Chinese control has been less since Islam replaced Buddhism in the fourteenth century. Serious civil war has occurred several times during the twentieth century. Soviet influence has frequently been strong and at times the control of the central Chinese government only nominal.

Despite the remoteness of Sinkiang, notable changes have taken place in recent decades. Stations for the improvement of agriculture and animal husbandry have been established, mining and industry are undergoing development, and major improvements have taken place in communications. The province contains large amounts of low-grade coal and iron ore, considerable oil, and several mineral deposits.

Geographic Sinkiang is somewhat smaller than the political province, for the former does not include the large section of the Tibetan Plateau shown on most maps within the political boundary. Five major subregions are involved. Next to Tibet the alpine but arid ranges

of the Astin Tagh and Kunlun rise to over 20,000 feet. The desolate Tarim Basin lies next to them on the north, rimmed by oases. In the center of Sinkiang rises the rugged and snow-crowned Tien Shan Range. Farther north is the semiarid Dzungarian Basin, and the semiarid Altai Mountains lie next to Mongolia. The Tarim Basin is one of the driest deserts in the world, but Dzungaria is comparable to the moister parts of the Gobi.

Sinkiang is a land of oases. Most of the plains are too arid for grazing, and the mountains are too rugged. Wherever semipermanent streams descend from the highlands, fed by melting snow, irrigation ditches spread the water over their alluvial fan. Each such oasis commands a bit of desert, an irrigated area with a principal city, barren foothills, and well-watered mountain valleys upstream. Each settlement is largely independent of its neighbors, isolated by desert and mountains.

The only significant oases along the south of the Tarim Basin next to the Astin Tagh are Yarkand, with an area of 1,240 square miles, and Khotan, with an irrigated area of 1,400 square miles. The most important settlements lie in the northern Tarim Basin at the southern base of the Tien Shan. In the west is Kashgar with 1,790 square miles under cultivation. Farther east is the Aksu oasis with 1,780 square miles. Other centers are Turfan, famous for its raisins and dried fruit, and Hami, renowned throughout China for the sweetness of its melons. The population of these oases averages 400 people per square mile, and the cities themselves have populations of a few tens of thousands.

The oases of Dzungaria are less noteworthy. No settlements of importance line the Altai, where the more abundant grassland changes the economy from irrigated agriculture to grazing. At the northern foot of the Tien Shan are Wusu, Urumchi, Kitai, and Barkol. Urumchi, also known to the Chinese as Tihwa, is the capital of Sinkiang. The city numbers 250,000 people and commands an oasis of 1,330 square miles.

Safe agriculture is limited to areas of dependable irrigation. Wheat, kaoliang, millet, beans, rice, excellent fruit, tobacco, and cotton are the chief crops. Widespread ruins of abandoned cities and ancient irrigation systems suggest more cultivation and a larger population in the past, presumably owing to more abundant rainfall. Not all such evidence may be so interpreted, however, for some settlements are known to have been abandoned because of the diversion of water upstream, the development of alkali or saline soils, or political troubles. Any expansion of crop acreage is tied up with reorganization of the water supply. Dry farming may offer some possibilities in Dzungaria.

Many oases are supplied by underground tunnels, known as *karez* from their Persian name, often several miles in length, which bring water down alluvial slopes. These horizontal wells prevent evaporation losses and are close enough to the water table to check seepage. Where they collapse, an oasis may have to be abandoned.

The great mountain system of Sinkiang is the Tien Shan, which has a length of 1,000 miles in China plus its westward continuation into the Soviet Union. This is the highest range in Asia north of Tibet. Elevations within Sinkiang reach 23,616 feet in Khan Tengri in the west and 17,712 feet in the Bogdo Ola north of Turfan in the east. Numerous long glaciers descend from extensive snow fields. Part of the topography is very rugged; elsewhere there are uplifted peneplains and open valleys covered with alpine meadows.

To the west the Tien Shan system divides to surround the broad and fertile Ili valley, which drains to Lake Balkhash. Ili is famed in Chinese history as the most remote place of banishment for political prisoners. On the east the Tien Shan fades into hill lands in the Mongolian Gobi.

Along the Soviet frontier in the west are a series of ranges which completely close in the Tarim Basin and almost block passage westward from the Dzungarian Basin. Only three lowland gaps cross these mountains. In the far north is the valley of the Black Irtysh at an elevation of about 1,500 feet between the Altai and the Tarbagatai, with heights of 13,553 and 11,910 feet near the frontier, respectively. Farther south is another corridor near Tahcheng, not so low but much used. The classic Dzungarian Gate at 1,060-foot elevation is a graben between the Tarbagatai and the Dzungarian Ala-tau which here form the northern spurs of the Tien Shan. This is the lowest pass in all central Asia, famous for its strong winds.

The main river of Sinkiang is the Tarim. All tributary streams that descend from the encircling mountains seek to reach it, but many are used up for irrigation en route. So much water is lost by seepage, evaporation, or diversion for irrigation that the Tarim progressively becomes smaller. Only one stream from the south persists across the desert. The Tarim gives its name to the entire basin, the central part of which is the nearly rainless Taklamakan Desert. Much of the Taklamakan is filled with great sand dunes, more developed here than anywhere else in Asia except in southern

Arabia, so that travel across the central desert is virtually impossible. Fine dust derived from the beds of withering streams and the deflation of soft sediments has been blown into accumulations of loess on the encircling mountain slopes. Since the Tarim Basin is encircled by high mountains, neither water nor sediment can escape.

Lob Nor is the terminal lake for the Tarim River. This salt lake in southeastern Sinkiang has had a unique history. Two thousand years ago it occupied a site near 90°E and 41°N, with the now ruined trade city of Loulan on its banks. Later the river was diverted southward, and a new lake developed 2 degrees farther west and 2 degrees to the south, leaving the original Lob Nor Basin a salt-encrusted flat. The explorer Sven Hedin has shown that the Tarim has now returned to its earlier course and that the original site of Lob Nor is again a lake. The alternation from basin to basin appears to be the result of sedimentation, raising the level of first one, then the other. When the basin is dry, wind deflation excavates a part of the silt.

In addition to the main basin there is the famous Turfan Depression, 928 feet below sea level.

To the north of the Tien Shan is Dzungaria, unlike the Tarim Basin in several particulars. Its plain is open on both east and west; there is no unifying river; and sand dunes are less

The Pamir highlands in Sinkiang are the meeting point for many people. Homes are the round, felt-covered yurts. This Khalkas woman is weaving carpets. (*Eastfoto*)

developed. The longest stream is the Manass, a withering river which sometimes reaches its terminal lake of Telli Nor at an elevation of 951 feet. At times the lake is completely dry, for the basin becomes so full of silt that the river is diverted to the east. Since Dzungaria is somewhat humid, marginal rain-fed agriculture is possible in a few places.

No area in the world is so remote from the ocean as Sinkiang; it is almost entirely cut off from the moisture and the moderating influences of the sea. Few air masses ever reach it from the Indian, Pacific, or Arctic oceans. The Atlantic is even more distant, and westerly winds from that ocean must first cross the mountains of Europe and nearly 4,000 miles of Asia. Nevertheless, such rainfall as Sinkiang imports appears to be largely of Atlantic origin.

Whereas all of Sinkiang is arid, the Tien Shan separate an exceptionally dry south from a slightly less arid north. Thus the north slopes of the Tien Shan facing Dzungaria and the Atlantic, are more humid than those on the south facing the Taklamakan. An important fringe of poor grazing land follows the northern edge of the Tien Shan, and a much richer belt of steppe borders the southern Altai Mountains. These grasslands make it possible for nomads to migrate east and west with their flocks. Here are the routes used by the Mongols in invading

western Asia under Genghis and Kublai Khan. The Tarim Basin has no such continuous grasslands, and the population is limited to habitation in fixed oases, tens of miles apart.

There are few meteorological stations, but Urumchi reports 9 inches, Kashgar averages 3.5 inches, and Yarkand appears to have only 0.5 inch of rain a year. Precipitation fluctuates widely from year to year and includes both winter snow and summer rain. On mountain slopes the amount may reach 20 or 30 inches, with the maximum at intermediate elevations and drought above and below. Thus forests grow on the middle slopes of the Tien Shan from 5,000 to 9,000 feet, above which are upland meadows. Sheep and cattle from the lowlands are pastured on these grasslands during the summer. The snow line lies higher than 3 miles.

In this arid landscape temperatures from season to season and from day to night differ sharply. Few deserts in the world have greater extremes. Summer temperatures often exceed 100°F, with a July average of 80°F or more. The Turfan Depression has recorded a maximum of 118°F and a July mean of 90°F. In contrast, January averages are considerably below freezing, with several stations reporting less than 22°F, so that the few lakes and rivers freeze over. Hedin has measured −25°F at the beginning of January in the central Taklamakan.

TIBET

There is nothing in the world quite like Tibet. Three-fourths of the million square miles within this geographic region lies above 10,000 feet, and in large areas all elevations exceed 16,000 feet. Within the Himalayan and Karakoram ranges alone there are 50 summits over 25,000 feet high. Much of the country is a desolate highland plain almost without vegetation or nomadic possibilities. In some of the lower valleys in the southeast a milder climate and adequate rainfall permit some agriculture.

Tibet is so variously defined that we need to

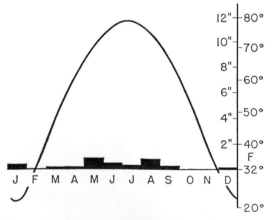

KASHGAR. Elevation 4,296 feet, average temperature 55°F, annual precipitation 3 inches. Most of Sinkiang is arid.

Much of Tibet is very cold throughout the year so that fur clothing is essential. This photograph is of a horseman and his daughter. (*New China News Agency*)

clarify the situation by comparing the extent of topographic or geographic Tibet, the great highland between the Tarim Basin and the plains of India, with the various political divisions involved. In the far west Kashmir has many Tibetan characteristics, as do the parts of Pakistan and India which reach into the Himalaya. Nepal and Bhutan are independent kingdoms, once tributary to China as was most of the south slope of the mountains. Eastern Tibet includes parts of the provinces of Chinghai, Sikang, Kansu, and Szechwan. A large area in the northwest is theoretically within Sinkiang. This leaves less than half of the plateau for Farther Tibet, the Chinese territory governed from Lhasa and now known as the Tibetan Autonomous Region. Farther Tibet is credited with 349,419 square miles and about 1,500,000 people. The entire region of geographic Tibet may have twice that population.

Within Tibet are seven physical regions, as follows: the Himalayan system in the south, made up of three parallel ranges; the Karakoram Mountains in the west, between the Himalaya and the Kunlun; the Tsangpo valley north of the Himalaya; the Chang Tang Plateau, covering much of northern Tibet; the Astin Tagh and Kunlun systems in the north; the Tsaidam and Koko Nor Basins between the Astin Tagh and the Kunlun in the northeast;

and the Land of the Great Canyons in eastern Tibet, often known as Kham.

The Himalaya extend 1,500 miles in a great arc. The southernmost range, termed the Siwaliks or Outer Himalaya, rises abruptly from the plain of the Indus and the Ganges. Although elevations reach 5,000 feet, the Outer Himalaya are known as foothills. To the north are the Lesser Himalaya, 7,000 to 15,000 feet. The Great Himalaya, still farther north, have an average crest line of 20,000 feet and form the theoretical boundary of China. In this range are most of the giant peaks, such as Nanda Devi, 25,645 feet, Kanchenjunga, 28,146 feet, and Mount Everest, 29,028 feet, known to the Tibetans as Chomolungma. Further details on the Himalaya will be considered in the chapters on South Asia.

The Karakoram Mountains in the west are said to be the whitest, snowiest, and iciest range outside polar regions. They include the world's second highest peak, K^2, with an elevation of 28,250 feet. Within this area are numerous glaciers 30 and 40 miles long. The famed Karakoram Pass, 18,317 feet in elevation, lies to the northeast outside the Karakoram Mountains.

The Tsangpo is the local name for the upper Brahmaputra River where it flows eastward across southern Tibet. Since this area contains the central or U province with Lhasa as capital, it is sometimes known as Central Tibet. Within this region are several other important towns, such as Shigatse and Gyangtse. This is the lowest part of Farther Tibet and the most populous. The Tsangpo flows at an elevation of 12,000 feet and is more or less navigable by native craft for 400 miles above the gorges where it turns into India. Although the peaks of the Himalaya rise 10,000 to 15,000 feet above the Tsangpo lowlands, the passes from India are no more than 3,000 feet, and several of them are only a few hundred feet above the floor of the valley.

The largest part of Tibet lies in the region of Chang Tang, extending from 80 to 92°E, and from 31 to 36°N. This part of the plateau is a series of desert playa basins and massive but low mountains, all at elevations over 16,000 feet. Scoured by the wind, baked by the sun, and cracked by frost, these desolate uplands have a grandeur of their own but are not a feasible home for man.

Within Chang Tang are hundreds of lakes, both fresh and salt, and many square miles are whitened by a surface crust of salt or alkali. Some salt lakes are known not as lakes but as salt pits; potash, soda, and borax are found around their margins. The largest lake of the region is Nam Tso (Tengri Nor), with an area of 950 square miles. The Chang Tang is too cold and dry for grass, trees, or cultivated crops. For eight months or more the ground is frozen, but in summer large areas become swampy, especially where external drainage is lacking. Scores of partly explored mountains trend roughly east and west. The southernmost range is a massive chain, variously known as

The highlands of Tibet and Sinkiang provide grazing lands for many sheep and yak. These Yuku herdsmen are in the Chilien Shan. (*Eastfoto*)

the Kailas or Nyenchen Tanglha, and described by Sven Hedin as the Trans-Himalaya. The average elevation is greater than that of the Himalaya, as are also the passes, but the peaks are lower. Other important ranges farther north are the Tanglha, the Dungbura, and the Hohoshile.

The Astin Tagh and Kunlun systems are the northern counterpart to the Himalaya. The Astin Tagh rises directly from the Tarim Basin of Sinkiang to heights of 17,000 feet. Its eastward extension in Kansu is called the Nan Shan, of which the Richthofen Mountains form the outer range with elevations touching 20,000 feet. The Kunlun Mountains lie close to the Astin Tagh where they join the Pamirs in the west, but diverge eastward. There is a fairly continuous series of peaks of 20,000 feet and over in the west. Toward the east, elevations are somewhat less, and the chain is known as the Amne Machin, which continues into China as the Min and Chin Ling.

The Tsaidam and Koko Nor Basins are enclosed between the eastern Astin Tagh and Nan Shan. The former is a vast desert swamp at an elevation of 9,000 feet, with important oil deposits; the latter holds a beautiful lake at a height of 10,500 feet in the midst of a mountain-rimmed basin. Koko Nor has an area variously given as 1,600 to 1,800 square miles and is the largest in Tibet; like most other basins it is salty. Both areas are semidesert with very meager pastoral possibilities.

Eastern Tibet is a land of great valleys and intervening high ranges, with a general northwest to southeast orientation. It is known to the Tibetans as Kham, or as the Land of Great Canyons. Here flow the Hwang, Yangtze, Mekong, Salween, and their many swift tributaries. Although the rivers flow at elevations of slightly over a mile, there is so little level land in the valleys that most people live at altitudes between 9,000 and 13,000 feet. Because of the more abundant rainfall, extensive forests cover the lower slopes.

In southeastern Tibet these four rivers plus the Brahmaputra approach within 400 miles

of one another, but on leaving the plateau they diverge so that their mouths are 2,000 miles apart. Since each river is in a deep gorge and intervening ridges are sharp-crested, travel between India and China is very difficult. No important routes have ever crossed them to link the two countries.

The easternmost mountains, bordering Szechwan and Yunnan, are known to the Chinese as the Tahsueh Shan, or Great Snowy Mountains. Numerous peaks exceed 20,000 feet and are glacier-clad. As an evidence of decreasing moisture northward toward the heart of Asia, the snow line rises from 13,500 feet in Yunnan to 18,000 feet in Kansu. The highest peak is Minya Konka, southwest of Kangting (Tatsienlu); the elevation is 24,900 feet.

The climate of Tibet is conditioned by its great elevation and by the encircling mountains. High altitudes and thin air join with intense insolation and strong radiation to produce sharp temperature contrasts between day and night as well as sharp changes from the dry winter to the somewhat moist summer. Conditions differ widely, for whereas the vicinity of Lhasa has a mild *Cwb* climate (Koeppen symbols), and the eastern valleys are *Dwb*, the northern plains are a cold desert, *ET/BW kw*, and the windward slopes of the Himalaya have subtropical conditions.

The difference between temperatures during the day and at night may exceed 80°F within 24 hours. In the short summer the thermometer may reach 90°F while in winter travelers have recorded −40°F. The winter cold is intensified by strong winds.

Most of Tibet is cut off from the summer Indian monsoon by the Himalayan barrier, especially in the west, where winds parallel the mountain front. In the southeast, moisture-bearing winds occasionally blow up the valleys of the Brahmaputra, Salween, Mekong, and Yangtze Rivers and bring summer rain to the Tsangpo lowland. Almost none of this moisture crosses the Nyenchen Tanglha Range. Most of interior Tibet receives less than 10 inches of precipitation per year.

The shortage of water over much of Tibet discourages any habitation in a large part of the plateau and makes travel hazardous. Most of the population live in the south and east, where lower elevations provide meager agricultural and grazing possibilities. Chief food is parched barley, or tsamba, and a tea made from sour milk and brick tea as in Mongolia.

In the southeastern agricultural districts seed cannot be sown before May. Autumn comes early, and the crops must be gathered by the middle of September, for night frosts then become very severe, even at elevations as low as 12,000 feet above the sea.

The yak is the typical draft animal, a long-haired form of cattle, whose shaggy appearance exaggerates his proportions. Both yaks and mules carry about 170 pounds each, but while loaded mules travel 20 to 25 miles a day and donkeys 10 to 15 miles, yaks cover even less. The yak needs a longer period for grazing than the other animals since he is fed no grain, but no other animal is so well adapted to Tibetan travel. Sheep and goats, carrying 20 to 25 pounds each, are also used for transport purposes in western Tibet.

Four ancient highways focused on Lhasa and were used for commercial caravans and pilgrims. The North Road leads northeast across mountains nearly 20,000 feet high past Koko Nor to Sining west of Lanchow. Caravans take about 50 days for the journey, preferably traveling in summer on account of the more abundant grass and water as well as the warmer weather. Yaks are used across the Chang Tang in summer and camels in winter.

The Chinese Road, also known as the Tea Road, runs east from Lhasa over high mountains and deep valleys via Changtu and Paan (Batang) to Kangting (Tatsienlu) west of Chengtu. Since this road leads at right angles to the trend of the mountains, the route presents great difficulties but is used extensively. Both the North and Chinese Roads are now paralleled by a truck road, and along the former a railway has penetrated Tibet.

The South Road from Lhasa leads to Gyang-tse, whence trails continue to India. Mail normally covers the 330 miles from Lhasa to Gangtok in India in eight to ten days.

The main West Road runs up the valley of the Tsangpo past Lake Manasarowar to Gartok on the upper Indus and continues to Leh, the capital of Ladakh, 900 miles from Lhasa.

In the far west are trails that connect India and Sinkiang, either across the Burzil and Hunza Passes from Srinagar to Kashgar, or farther east over the Karakoram Pass.

Lhasa is the Mecca of Tibet and the dream city of travelers throughout the world. The city lies in a sheltered valley where it is possible to raise vegetables, apples, and peaches, and many flowers. Bamboo and trees grow well, but the hillsides have been denuded for fuel. The city has electric light, telephones, and an airport. The crowning feature of the city is the monastery palace of the Dalai Lama, known as the Potala. This is the climax of Tibetan architecture and one of the most majestic buildings in the world.

Climatological records at Lhasa indicate a more mild climate than was previously recognized, certainly unrepresentative of most of Tibet. The city lies at 12,243-feet elevation and is surrounded by mountains that rise 3,000 and 4,000 feet above the smooth floor of the Lhasa River. Lhasa has two distinct seasons, the rainy or growing season from May to September, and the dry or cold season of the remaining months. Spring and autumn are brief. Local topography obscures wind directions, but the southeast monsoon is clearly developed in summer. In winter the westerly winds tend to be stronger and last longer. Mean temperatures range from 32°F in January to 64°F in June, with an annual average of 48°F. The latter is exceptionally mild for the latitude and altitude. The highest temperatures are in May, before the heavy rains, as in the Ganges valley. Frost occurs on 225 days a year. The annual rainfall varies from 18 to 198 inches; its range is indicative of the uncertainty of monsoon penetration. There is plenty of sunshine at Lhasa, and even in the

The city of Lhasa is now linked to eastern China by two automobile roads, so that Shanghai is but 20 days distant. The city is dominated by the Potala, the great shrine of Lamaism and the traditional seat of the Dalai Lama. (*Eastfoto*)

rainy season it is unusual not to see patches of blue sky.

Lamaism governs many aspects of Tibetan life, political as well as spiritual. Control was traditionally divided between the Panchan Lama at Tashi Lumpo, as spiritual head, and the more politically powerful Dalai Lama at Lhasa. Monasteries serve as centers of industry and learning, as well as meccas for religious pilgrimage.

Chinese interest in Tibet dates from 650, when a Chinese expedition entered Lhasa. In 1209 Tibet was conquered by Genghis Khan, and in 1270 Kublai Khan became a convert to Lamaism and set up the rule of priest-kings. Chinese control continued intermittently until 1911, when it was interrupted for a few decades until reasserted under the Nationalist and later under the Communist governments. While Tibet has had periods of quasi-independ-

ence, Chinese suzerainty has been continuous.

Over the centuries, the limits of Tibetan and Chinese culture have spilled across the Himalaya and extended down the south slopes as far as the Terai swamps at the base of the mountains. These swamps in turn have marked the traditional northern limit of Hindu culture. During the period of British rule in India, the political boundary was unilaterally pushed to the crest of the mountains, thus including the south slopes within India and its related states of Nepal and Bhutan. In the area north of Assam, British and Indian maps thus show the boundary along the crest of the Himalaya, the so-called McMahon line, dating from 1914 but never ratified, whereas both Nationalist and Communist maps locate the boundary at the base and very close to the Brahmaputra. Similar disputed areas are present in Ladakh in northern Kashmir.

10 Taiwan

Nationalist China / The Taiwan Landscape / Laboratory for Asia? / References on Taiwan

NATIONALIST CHINA

The island of Taiwan lies astride the Tropic of Cancer in the same latitude as Cuba, but has only one-third of the latter's area. Fukien is 100 miles to the west; Shanghai and Hong Kong are each 400 miles distant; Kyushu lies 600 miles to the north; and Luzon is 200 miles southward. Thousands of miles of open Pacific separate Taiwan from North America.

Taiwan has a history which dates back to several centuries B.C. when it was occupied by people known as the Longkius. Malays arrived in the sixth century, and their descendants live in the mountains, where they are now classed as aborigines.

Relations with mainland China began in 605, but extensive settlement did not occur until the fourteenth century. The Japanese visited the island at an early date. In 1590 the Portuguese bestowed upon it the name Formosa, or "beautiful island." In 1624 the Dutch settled in the south, followed in the north two years later by the Spanish, who were shortly driven out.

After the Manchus had captured Peking in 1644, they pressed southward, driving remnants of the Ming Chinese before them. In

1661 some of these refugees crossed to Taiwan and expelled the Dutch. At this time the Chinese population of the island numbered about 100,000 people. For a time the island then formed an independent kingdom but could not hold out against the mainland and was incorporated into China in 1683.

Following the Sino-Japanese war of 1895, Taiwan was governed by Japan until 1945. In 1949, when the Nationalist government under Chiang Kai-shek lost control of the Mainland, it retreated to the island. Thus there came to be two rival governments, the Republic of China under the Kuomintang on Taiwan and the People's Republic of China under the Communist Party, each insisting that it was sovereign over all China. The situation of three centuries ago thus finds some parallel today.

The population of Taiwan represents several groups, each reflecting a distinct wave of immigration. Among the earliest arrivals were the Malays, 200,000 of whom live in the interior mountains. The foothills are occupied by a million Hakkas from Kwangtung, who came at least two centuries ago. The western plains are the home of 5 million Hoklos from Fukien, migrants of the eighteenth and nineteenth centuries. Nearly 2 million Mainland refugees arrived after 1945, and now dominate the cities.

Taiwan covers 13,952 square miles, only one-third of the area of Chekiang, which is the smallest of the Mainland provinces.

The population increase presents some sober facts. In 1624, the total was about 25,000 Chinese plus unknown numbers of natives. Following the Manchurian conquest of 1683, immigration from Fukien and Kwangtung was encouraged, and by the mid-eighteenth century the island total reached a million. This figure had doubled by 1895 when the Japanese took possession. The census of 1905 listed 3,156,706; that of 1943 showed 6,585,841. In 1960 the total reached 10,466,000, plus 600,000 members of the armed forces, and included some 2 million Mainland refugees. This represented a density of 750 people per square mile, making Taiwan one of the most crowded of all countries on earth.

Industrial developments under the Japanese, plus the arrival of large numbers of urban Mainlanders, has led to the rapid growth of cities. The capital at Taipei has a population of nearly a million, while four other cities exceed 200,000. Several city names begin with the *tai* of Taiwan, followed by the character for their compass location: *pei*-north, *nan*-south, *tung*-east, *si*-west, or *chung*-middle. We can thus understand the names of Taipei, 14 miles from its seaport at Keelung, Tainan, near the main southern port of Kaohiung, Taichung in

Nationalist China Data [1]

Area (Taiwan)	13,952 square miles
Population (Taiwan)	10,947,000 (1961 est.)
Taipei (capital)	854,061 (1959 est.)
Kaohiung	438,429
Tainan	324,137
Primary and secondary pupils	2,625,274 (1961)
University students	35,000 (1961)
Rice	1,912,018 metric tons (1960)
Refined sugar	845,702 " "
Coal	3,962,000 " "
Cement	1,183,101 " "
Pig iron	24,444 " "
Electricity	3,628,000,000 kilowatthours (1960)

[1] *Britannica Book of the Year,* 1962.

Water wheels, largely made of bamboo, lift water for irrigation in this scene on Taiwan. (*Courtesy International Cooperation Administration*)

west central Taiwan, and the east-coast city of Taitung.

In addition to Taiwan, the Nationalist government controls the 64 small islands of the Pescadores group, one-third of the distance to the Mainland, and also a number of tiny islands within sight of the China Mainland.

THE TAIWAN LANDSCAPE

Many aspects of Taiwan resemble those of Mainland China. If it were not for political realities, the island might be considered as one of the geographic regions of South China, analogous to Hainan.

The general configuration of the island is that of a tilted fault block, sloping to the west from a range of 2-mile–high mountains along the eastern axis. Frequent earthquakes indicate that faulting is still under way. The highest elevation in the island is known to foreigners as Mount Morrison, 12,956 feet. This peak gives its name to the entire range. Thirty peaks exceed 10,000 feet in height. Slopes on the east descend precipitously to the sea, but between part of the central range and the Pacific are the Taito lowland and mountains. Fertile coastal plains with their dense population border the western shore. Land which is even approxi-

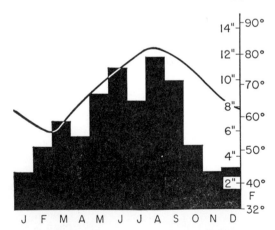

TAIPEI. Elevation 30 feet, average temperature 72°F, annual precipitation 84 inches. Taiwan is both warm and wet.

176   TAIWAN

mately flat totals only 15 per cent of the island. A west-to-east cross section is not unlike that from the central valley of California across the Sierra Nevada, with the Taitung lowland graben corresponding to Owens Valley and Lake Tahoe.

Tropical conditions prevail except in the mountains, where there is alpine vegetation. Lowland temperatures never reach freezing and seldom approach 100°F. The shores are bathed by the warm Kuroshio, the Pacific equivalent of the Gulf Stream. The island is exposed to both monsoons, with continental winds during the winter of special importance. This northeastern monsoon lasts from early October till late March, and since its direction coincides with the trade winds to be expected at these latitudes, strong winds result. Steamers along the west coast at times barely make headway.

The southwest summer monsoon from early May to late August is weaker, since it is opposed by the trade-wind tendency. Both monsoons bring copious precipitation, particularly to the north, where heavy orographic rainfall results. Occasional summer typhoons bring torrential rainfall to the abrupt eastern slopes. The annual precipitation in the western lowland varies from 40 inches near the coast to double that amount in the hills. Within the mountains rainfall is among the heaviest in the world, with a recorded maximum of 289 inches. Rapid runoff and excessive erosion result.

The northern port of Keelung is known as "the rainy city," since it records 200 rainy days a year and has received as much as 203 inches in twelve months. This may be one reason why the port of Kaohiung in the far south, with little rain, is widely used for loading and unloading cargo which might be damaged by moisture.

Taiwan has become a major producer of pineapple, with three crops in five years. (*Hamilton Wright, courtesy Chinese News Service*)

Seventy per cent of Taiwan is in forest. Where the lowlands have not been cleared, there is a tropical cover of camphor, cypress, bamboo, and other forms of trees, many of them of commercial value. Mangroves border the shallow western coast. Broad-leaf forests prevail between elevations of 1,500 and 6,500 feet. These include large camphor trees, and at higher elevations, oak, maple, and chestnut. Mixed forests occur on mountain slopes from 6,500 to 10,000 feet elevation, with both deciduous and coniferous trees such as huge cedars, rhododendrons, hemlocks, and pines. Pure coniferous forests are present above 10,000 feet, along with grasslands above the tree line.

Agriculture follows the South China pattern. One sees the characteristic flooded rice fields, generally terraced, and crops of sweet potatoes, tea, bananas, and corn. Water buffalo, pigs, ducks, and Chinese farm implements are all part of the landscape. Only a quarter of Taiwan is cultivated, but two-thirds of the cropland is irrigated. Many fields raise two or even three crops in a year. The population density in terms of cropland alone exceeds 2,000 per square mile.

Rice, the dominant food crop, occupies half the cultivated acreage. Production slightly exceeds domestic consumption; two harvests a year are common. Sweet potatoes, introduced long ago from China, are the main food of the poorer folk. Sugar cane is grown especially in the west and north, and large shipments of raw and refined sugar are made. Bananas and canned pineapple are significant exports. Another export is tea, which is widely grown in the north. Green varieties are dried rapidly and only partly fermented; black tea results when drying is delayed to permit oxidation and full fermentation. Oolong, or brown and amber tea, is a major export to the United States.

Taiwan once supplied three-fourths of the world's natural camphor, but now that synthetic substitutes are available, the natural product has lost its monopoly. Several thousand dollars worth of camphor may be obtained from a single large tree.

Taiwan is not highly mineralized. A fair

Sugar is Taiwan's major agricultural export. Heat and insects cause workers to cover their heads and arms. (*Courtesy International Cooperation Administration*)

One interpretation of the name Taiwan is "terraced hills," of Formosa, "beautiful"; both are typified in this landscape. (*Courtesy International Cooperation Administration*)

grade of coal is mined in the north. Hydro-electric developments have provided an important source of power. Salt is evaporated along the western coast. Though a variety of metals is mined, production is limited. The chief ores are those of copper, gold, sulfur, and manganese.

LABORATORY FOR ASIA?

Taiwan serves as an experimental laboratory for what may be done elsewhere in East and South Asia. As with many other areas, it experienced a colonial period when its economy was distorted to serve imperial objectives. As elsewhere, there was little preparation for self-government. Since independence, the island has had the benefit of massive foreign aid and technical guidance. Agricultural reform and research, industrial development under both state support and private initiative, and widespread social change have produced excellent results.

As a result, Taiwan now has the highest standard of living of any part of Asia outside of Japan. How much of this represents sound economic progress and how much has been made possible by American assistance may not be clear until the island stands on its own feet and until it is no longer necessary to support an army of a half million soldiers.

Although Taiwan is small, its topography is varied and offers a replica of many Mainland environments. At the same time the island is without notable assets which might make the experiment unreal. Thanks to strenuous efforts, the island now feeds itself and has a modest surplus for export. Subsistence presents no real difficulty; Taiwan's problem is rather to readjust to new economic and political realities.

Agriculture supports two-thirds of the population, but to maintain and increase the output will require skill and capital. Careless cultivation of steep hillsides has resulted in excessive erosion, which in turn chokes valley bottoms and takes them out of cultivation. Since very little new land remains to be brought into agricultural use, Taiwan may have reached or passed the peak of its crop acreage. Increased attention to conservation is important.

Irrigation is essential in many areas, especially in the seasonally dry southwest. Additional reservoirs, canal systems, and the development of ground water should materially increase crop yields, in part through growing a second or third crop each year.

Fertilizers are widely employed and still offer considerable promise. Taiwan ranks second to Japan in the application of commercial fertilizers, using them at the rate of 45 pounds per capita, or 130 pounds per cultivated acre; in comparison, the figures for Japan are 79 and 515, respectively.

Mechanization is sometimes thought to offer a panacea for Asian agriculture, but Taiwan's terraced cultivation, tiny fields, and interculture make its application difficult.

Tenancy was widespread under Japanese rule; but land reform has been introduced and rents reduced. Eighty per cent of all farmers now own their land. In all these agricultural developments, the magic initials have been JCRR, which stand for the Joint Commission for Rural Reconstruction, a Chinese-American program of research, development, and education which has been outstandingly successful.

Industrialization lacks a raw-material base. Sugar is the major commercial crop. The accessible forests largely consist of mixed subtropical hardwoods rather than of solid stands. Copper is the only plentiful mineral, along with sulfur and a little manganese. Petroleum is almost lacking, but there are several hundred million tons of low-grade coal. Fortunately, hydroelectric potentials are considerable. As a result, industrial workers represent 15 per cent of all those employed on Taiwan.

Despite these limitations, Nationalist China has made good progress. If some of the developments on Taiwan since 1949 could have been duplicated on the Mainland prior to the withdrawal of the Nationalists, China might not have turned to Communism. And if there is to be a change on the Mainland it may come through the demonstration of what democratic free enterprise can show on Taiwan.

References on Taiwan

See also general references on China, Chapter 4.

*Chen, Cheng-Siang: "Land Utilization in Formosa," *Geog. Rev.,* XLI (1951), 438–456.

Chen, Cheng-Siang: "The Pescadores," *Geog. Rev.,* XLIII (1953), 77–88.

Gage, Eugenia: "Industrial Developments—Formosa," *Econ. Geog.,* XXVI (1950), 214–222.

Ginsburg, Norton S.: "Taiwan: A Resource Analysis of an Oriental Society," *Econ. Development and Cultural Change,* I (1952), 37–52, 110–131.

*Hsieh, Chiao-Min: "Formosa, Rich Island of the Far East," *Jour. Geog.,* LI (1952), 45–55.

Shen, T. H.: "Food Production and Administration in Taiwan," *Sci. Monthly,* LXXIV (1952), 253–268.

11 Mongolia

The Mongolian People's Republic / Life in the Desert /
Gobi Land Forms / References on Mongolia

THE MONGOLIAN PEOPLE'S REPUBLIC

There are three Mongolias. To the south and east is the Inner Mongolian Autonomous Region of the People's Republic of China, consisting of semiarid lands outside the Great Wall and in dry western Manchuria. To the north and within the Soviet Union is the Buryat Autonomous Republic, formerly known as Buryat Mongolia, occupying a forested area on both sides of Lake Baikal. Both of these two regions include large numbers of non-Mongolian people, Chinese and Slavic respectively, who outnumber the original inhabitants. In the cen-

ter lies the independent Mongolian People's Republic, much of it in the Gobi Desert but including grassy plains and wooded mountains in the north. This is the traditional Outer Mongolia, once a part of China and so named with respect to its distance from Peking, in contrast to the more accessible Inner Mongolia

Mongolia reached its golden era during the twelfth and thirteenth centuries when Genghis Khan (1162–1227) and his grandson Kublai Khan (1259–1294) conquered much of Asia. Still earlier history goes back to the Huns in the third century B.C., followed by periods under the Turks, and the Uighurs. From 1691 until 1911, Mongolia was under the rule of the

Manchus. After their overthrow, Mongolia declared its independence, but this was not legally recognized by the Chinese government until 1945.

While the Mongolian People's Republic has been a Soviet-style state closely aligned with the U.S.S.R., there is nevertheless a distinct urge for nationalism. Until 1950 the only contact with the outside world was through Soviet territory; in that year came recognition by the People's Republic of China and the reestablishment of trade southward. In 1961 the country was admitted to the United Nations.

Although Pan-Mongol nationalism has dreams of reestablishing a Greater Mongolia and memories of Genghis Khan still provide a political rallying point, the present *status quo* seems assured by the presence and rivalries of two powerful neighbors. Historically, the area has turned southward, but several decades of Soviet support have given the Mongolian People's Republic a strong northward orientation. The Soviet Union and China are now engaged in "socialist competition" on the territory of traditional rivalry. Foreign trade with the U.S.S.R. involves the import of machinery, automobiles, and gasoline in exchange for wool, furs, and livestock. China supplies textiles, tea, and food in exchange for horses.

Foreign contacts increased with the availability of the Trans-Mongolian Railway in 1956. This line shortens the trip from Moscow to Peking by 700 miles. A few other lines in the far east connect with Soviet railways.

Geographic Mongolia is enclosed on the north by the Siberian frontier, largely mountainous and forested; on the east by the Great Khingan and Jehol Mountains; and on the south by the hilly areas along the Great Wall next to Loessland. Only in the west, adjoining Sinkiang, is the geographic boundary uncertain. The region covers upwards of 1 million square miles, roughly twice the area of the Mongolian Republic. Population estimates for Greater Mongolia are highly uncertain, with a possible total of 3 million Mongols. Inner Mongolia may count 1½ million people of Mongol blood, while Buryats, Kalmuks, and Tuvinians in the Soviet Union total ½ million. The Mongolian People's Republic is credited with a population of about 1 million, three-quarters of whom are Khalkhas. The urban population accounts for one-fifth of the whole. The area of the republic measures 591,119 square miles.

The chief city and capital is Ulan Bator, formerly known as Urga, with a population of about 200,000. This was one of the historic centers of Lamaism. The city has woolen textile mills, a shoe factory, a modern dairy, a flour mill, and numerous small factories. Other towns are in the 10,000 category. North of Ulan Bator and opposite the Soviet city of Kyakhta is the frontier town of Altan-Bulak. Other settlements are trading villages, such as Choibalsan in the east or Uliassutai and Kobdo in the northwest.

Mongolia's mineral resources include low-grade coal, with the production of several hun-

Mongolia Data [1]

Area	591,119 square miles	
Population	1,075,000 (1960 est.)	
Ulan Bator (capital)	170,000 (1960 est.)	
Primary and secondary pupils	124,000	
University students	4,000	
Wheat	256,500 metric tons (1960)	
Livestock	23,500,000 " " (1958 est.)	
Coal	790,000 " " (1959)	
Electricity	70,400,000 kilowatthours (1959)	

[1] *Britannica Book of the Year*, 1962.

Ulan Bator is Mongolia's only city. Here is the government building, with the statue in the foreground of Sukhe Bator, the revolutionary hero. (*George B. Cressey*)

dred thousand tons a year near Ulan Bator, some oil in the central Gobi, salt from desert lakes, and a small production of gold.

LIFE IN THE DESERT

The Mongolian People's Republic is a land where much of life depends on grass, and this in turn on scanty rainfall. Agriculture is possible in only a few areas; mining is largely undeveloped; there are few trees for forestry and few water bodies for fishing; and industry is lacking outside the capital.

In the central Gobi the rainfall is under 8 inches, and the desert surface is nearly barren. Around the margins of the true desert the rainfall rises to 12 inches, and it is in this steppe that the nomad finds his home. Higher elevations in the northwest intercept more rainfall and have local forests. The only agricultural possibilities are in the extreme north.

The chief means of livelihood, then, is animal husbandry. Flocks of sheep, cattle, horses, and camels are pastured on the grassland, and since the grass seldom grows tall enough to be harvested, the animals must go where it is. Inner Asia is the home of nomadic people who are continually on the move. Their felt-covered yurts are found from the valley of the Volga to that of the Amur. From their animals come food, clothing, shelter, transportation, fuel, and wealth. When the rains fail and the grass withers, life is impossible. In few environments does man live so close to nature. Centuries of rigorous life in an exacting environment have long since weeded out the unfit.

Within the Mongolian People's Republic there are 25 million head of livestock, half of them sheep. Horses and cattle each number over 2 million. Since camels are being replaced by trucks, their total is under 1 million. Wool

Old transport waits for the new along the highway near Ulan Bator at the crossing of the Trans-Mongolian Railway, a short cut from Siberia to China. Two-humped Bactrian camels have been an essential element in Mongolian nomadism. (*Sovfoto*)

and hides are an important export, formerly moving to China but currently sold to the Soviet Union.

Sheep are the most useful of the animals. They provide wool for the felts that cover the yurts, sheepskins for clothing, milk in summer plus cheese and butter which may be stored for winter, mutton in winter, and dung for fuel.

The food of the Mongols is largely derived from their flocks; only a little barley, millet, flour, and brick tea are bought from passing caravans. Milk, butter, cheese, and mutton are the chief items in the diet. Sour milk is the basis of the staple drink, a concoction of tea, salt, and butter, often with parched barley and bits of cheese. This is drunk piping hot from a wooden bowl. Since water is scarce in the steppe, dishes are seldom washed.

Nomadic characteristics are gradually changing, especially under Communist attempts to develop herding cooperatives and to settle peo-

ple in fixed locations. Thousands of acres have been cultivated with machinery and dry-farming techniques, but the precipitation and growing season are both marginal.

The Gobi is the most northern of all deserts and the most continental. Other parts of Asia have drier climates, but none experience a greater range of temperatures. In winter the thermometer regularly drops to −30 and even −40°F. Summer days often record 90°F in the shade, and exposed rock surfaces may be heated to 150°F. Nights are always cool. The annual day-and-night average for Ulan Bator is near freezing.

Winters and spring have only a light snowfall, seldom covering the ground to a depth of more than a few inches. Herds may thus graze on dried grass throughout the winter. Summer is the rainy period. Ulan Bator reports 8 inches, but the rainfall decreases southward and westward so that the central and western Gobi is the driest area. Unlike the torrential downpours of tropical deserts most rainfall occurs in showers or a protracted drizzle. Since such showers may be local in distribution, nomads in quest of grass must be frequently on the move. Some precipitation is convectional, but much of it is cyclonic or due to the frontal action of moving air masses.

In the absence of adequate instrumental records, climatic characteristics must be determined in terms of vegetation. Most of the Gobi is a dry steppe rather than a true desert, listed in Koeppen symbols as *BS*. Patches of true desert, *BW,* are usually mapped in the south and southwest, where there is an almost complete absence of vegetation and numerous sand dunes. The northern hills and mountains with their forest cover appear to be *Dw,* a cold temperate climate with a dry winter.

The Mongols were traditionally believers in the Lama variety of Buddhism, similar to that of Tibet. Monasteries received one monk from every family and were the chief centers of fixed settlement. Many lamaseries possessed considerable wealth in herds as well as in buildings and money. The Lama hierarchy once exercised much temporal as well as spiritual power. The status of lamaism has been changed with the arrival of Communism, so that only a few monasteries exist today, and only a few hundred lamas remain out of the one-time hundred thousand.

GOBI LAND FORMS

Two-thirds of Mongolia lies in the flat Gobi; the other third is made up of hills and mountains to the north and west. From every side the rolling Gobi desert is approached over a mountain rim, inside which the surface gradually descends. Within these encircling mountains the monotony of boundless desert plains continues for hundreds of miles, broken here and there by rugged mountains or dissected badlands.

The ancient rock floor is a complex of hard formations, much folded, faulted, and locally injected with igneous rocks. In some cases the original sedimentary rocks have been altered to crystalline gneiss and schist. Granite is present in many areas.

Despite wide differences in age, hardness, and structure, these ancient rocks have been worn down to essentially flat surfaces. The highest of them is known as the Mongolian peneplain. Across it one may drive an automobile for miles without obstruction. Few areas on earth have been eroded to such flatness, and one passes across rocks of notably different resistance to erosion with scarcely a topographic break. Here and there are residual monadnocks. This nearly perfect plain lies at an elevation of 5,300 feet in southern Mongolia and at over 6,000 feet near the Arctic Divide, with lower elevations in the center.

At altitudes lower than the Mongolian peneplain there is another remarkably smooth erosion surface known as the Gobi peneplain. Although the elevation varies considerably, it commonly lies around 4,000 feet. This surface is developed on the softer sediments, Cretaceous and younger, which have accumulated in

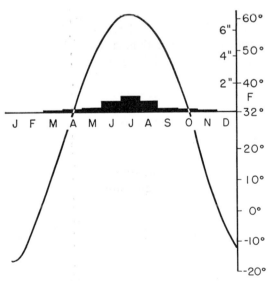

ULAN BATOR. Elevation 4,347 feet, average temperature 27°F, annual precipitation 8 inches. Mongolia experiences continental extremes of temperature.

Every village has its school. This teacher and her prize students are in Tsetserleg. (*George B. Cressey*)

down-warped basins. It also is extraordinarily level, with little relation between land form and the underlying rocks.

From place to place, this Gobi peneplain is interrupted by shallow, undrained hollows that range in size from 200 yards to 10 miles in length, and from 20 to 400 feet in depth. These are known as the Pang Kiang erosion surface, not sufficiently perfect or widespread to be a peneplain. Whereas these hollows have relatively flat floors, they are never so perfectly level as the Gobi upland. In most cases they contain intermittent playa lakes. The bluffs that descend from the Gobi plain to the Pang Kiang floor are here and there carved into badlands by innumerable gullies. Although the rainfall is low, the runoff from occasional showers, perhaps years apart, does considerable work. Depressions of the Pang Kiang type appear to be excavated largely by wind work in the

softer and less cemented recent sediments. As a result of this deflation, a veneer of shifting sand covers the adjoining uplands, especially around their southern and eastern sides.

Sand dunes are not extensively developed in Mongolia or in any other part of central Asia except the Taklamakan Desert. For the Gobi as a whole they probably cover less than 5 per cent of the entire desert, chiefly in the southwest.

The larger part of the Gobi is covered with a thin veneer of gravel or small stones, forming a desert pavement. During the passage of time, all surface sand and silt have quite generally been removed by wind and water, and these residual pebbles remain to armor the underlying rocks or soil. All finer material has been swept out of the desert; loess is entirely absent in central Mongolia, present instead in the surrounding grasslands.

Within the plains of Mongolia several major basins or broad depressions, known as talas, have been defined by Berkey and Morris. In the northeast, extending into northwestern Manchuria, is the Dalai tala, roughly parallel to the Great Khingan Mountains. Its northern part is occupied by a chain of lakes, some of them in the Amur drainage system; to the south lies rougher country with lava flows and recent volcanoes. The Iren tala lies in the central Gobi, on the direct route between Ulan Bator and Kalgan (Wanchuan). This is undulating country, which rises from the center at 2,930 feet to 5,000 and 6,000 feet in the broad swell that surrounds it; within it are at least seven minor basins. The Gashuin tala lies in the southwest, between the Gurban Saikhan Mountains and the Nan Shan Range; its chief stream is the Etsin Gol. The eastern part is known as the Alashan Desert. The Ordos Desert inside the great loop of the Hwang River represents a fourth basin.

In northwest Mongolia are a series of structural basins bounded by faulted mountains, much smaller than the warped talas just described. These are known collectively as the Valley of the Lakes.

Most of the mountains of northern Mongolia are associated with the great system of ranges that extends north into Siberia. From west to east these are as follows: Next to Sinkiang are the narrow Altai, which rise to 13,553 feet at the Siberian border and continue southeastward 900 miles to the middle of Mongolia. North of the Valley of the Lakes are the Tannu-Ola, which form the southern boundary of the Soviet Union. To the east the Sayan Mountains mark the Mongolian frontier to the Selenga River. East of the Tannu-Ola and south of the Sayan is a confused mountainous area known as the Khangai Mountains, a dissected dome rather than a range. East of the Selenga valley are the Kentci Hills, in part mountainous.

References on Mongolia   See also general references for China, Chapter 4.

Geisler, Richard A.: "Recent Developments in Outer Mongolia," *Far Eastern Survey,* XXVIII (1959), 182–188.

Jackson, W. A. Douglas: *Russo-Chinese borderlands,* Princeton, N.J.: D. Van Nostrand Co., Inc. (1962).

Lattimore, Owen: *Nomads and Commissars: Mongolia Revisited,* New York: Oxford University Press (1962).

Montagu, Ivor: *Land of the Blue Sky: A Portrait of Modern Mongolia,* London: D. Dobson (1956).

Montagu, Ivor: "Mongolian Visit," *Geog. Mag.,* XXVIII (1955), 119–129.

*Rupen, Robert A.: "Inside Outer Mongolia," *Foreign Affairs,* XXXVII (1959), 328–333.

*Wiens, Herald J.: "Geographical Limitations to Food Production in the Mongolian People's Republic," *Annals, Assn. Amer. Geogs.,* XLI (1951), 348–369.

12 The Two Koreas

The Korean Peninsula / The Physical Environment / Livelihood /
The Two Koreas / References on Korea

THE KOREAN PENINSULA

Divided Korea faces many baffling problems. Not the least of them concerns the fundamental question of livelihood for 35 million people in an area of 85,286 square miles, of which only one-fifth is potentially arable. The two Koreas together have about the same area and crop acreage as New York and New England without Maine, and half again as many people, but with nothing like the income from industry or urban commerce needed to purchase food or other goods from the outside. The average man, woman, or child in Korea must secure almost his entire living from less than a half acre of cultivated land. Even if Korea were united, this problem would remain.

Thirty-five years of imperial rule by Japan, preceded off and on by centuries of foreign domination, ill equipped Korea for self-government. Of more pressing importance were the postwar political confusions left in the rival occupation by Soviet and American troops north and south of the 38th parallel, an artificial line which roughly split the peninsula in half.

Although surrounded by two powerful neighbors, from each of whom Korea has borrowed cultural elements, the Koreans have nevertheless developed an independent way of life. The people are ethnographically distinct.

Despite the fact that they have alternately been subject to the Chinese, Mongols, Manchus, and Japanese, and to some degree to the Russians and Americans, the Koreans have their own language, literature, culture, and national ambitions. It was via the peninsula that Japan gained much of her Mainland culture. To protect this cultural nationalism Korea early sought to emphasize her isolation, and thus she gained the title of the "hermit nation." Unfortunately, internal strife frequently made her prey to aggression.

One of Japan's avowed objectives in the Sino-Japanese War of 1894 to 1895 and again during the Russo-Japanese War of 1904 to 1905, was to give the peninsula its independence from China. But after a short protectorate, Korea was formally annexed to Japan in 1910, instead of being granted independence. Koreans did not welcome Japanese rule, and there were numerous uprisings.

Japan's occupation of Korea resulted in economic problems for both countries. To Korea Japanese exploitation brought widespread material improvements in communications, agriculture, and mining. But the relative livelihood

This Korean farmer in his old-style dress looks across a characteristic landscape of cultivated lowlands and forested hillsides. (*Horace Bristol from Three Lions*)

of the Korean farmer declined because of a disproportionate increase in population, in tenancy, in debt, and in imports over exports. The Japanese occupation tended to impoverish the average Korean. To Japan, Korea became a source of food and raw materials, such as rice, cotton, fish, iron ore, gold, and other minerals; a market for manufactured goods; an outlet for nonagricultural colonists; and a strategic approach to the Mainland. But possession of Korea was not a blessing to the average Japanese. Korean laborers are willing to work for lower wages and thus undercut the Japanese standard of living. In fact, the Korean farmer is almost the only one in the world who has been able to compete successfully with the Chinese. Large numbers of Korean workers migrated to the industrial and mining districts of Japan, and this cheap labor displaced Japanese workers. Prior to the Second World War there were 1¼ million Koreans in Japan, twice as many as there were Japanese in Korea. At the same time there were 1½ million Koreans in Manchuria.

With the collapse of Japan after the Second World War, troops of the Soviet Union occupied the area north of the 38th parallel, while American troops occupied the south. Once independence was secured, the divided nations had to readjust their economy from colonial dependence upon Japan to a combination of internal self-sufficiency and new external trade relations.

Korea has its own distinctive geography, unlike that of either Japan or China. Rice fields are common to both, but those in Korea appear to represent a slightly lower intensity of land use. Many Korean hills have been deforested, are now covered with scrub, and show serious erosion. Volcanic landscapes are found along the Chinese frontier and in some small patches in the interior of the peninsula. The offshore island of Cheju (Quelpart) is also volcanic. None of the volcanoes of Korea are active.

The uniqueness of Korea is most noticeable in its cultural aspects. Houses are substantially built with mud walls, and their floors are heated by passages underneath which circulate smoke from the kitchen fire. Rural settlement is commonly in villages, often located at the edge of the hills; but in the northern interior isolated, wooden-shingled farmhouses are common. Neither roads nor irrigation canals are so numerous as in Japan. Green fertilizer and compost replace the human manure of Japan and China. Most noticeable is the difference in appearance and dress, although the white clothing of the Koreans of past decades is being changed to darker colors.

Korea is a land of wide differences, so much so that generalizations can be valid only region

South Korea Data [1]

Area	38,031 square miles
Population	24,994,117 (1960 census)
Seoul (capital)	2,444,883
Pusan	1,162,614
Taegu	678,277
Primary and secondary pupils	4,610,000 (1960)
University students	100,000
Grain	23,413,741 long tons (1960)
Rice	15,949,473 " "
Cement	357,856 metric tons (1960)
Electricity	1,697,000,000 kilowatthours (1960)

[1] *Britannica Book of the Year*, 1962.

by region. Not only are there contrasts in topography, climate, and land use, but cultural differences related to waves of settlement and external contacts have produced a diverse human geography. The major differences are between the more continental and less agricultural north, and the peninsular south. The arbitrary line of the 38th parallel which was chosen to separate Soviet and American spheres following the Second World War broadly marks these differences.

Korea as a whole is transitional between continental China and insular Japan. During the winter the fields of southern Korea are green with barley or winter wheat, while the north is covered with snow. In summer flooded rice fields dominate the south, while the northern farmer cultivates hardier grains, in part on fire-cleared slopes. Three-fourths of the rice is grown in the south. Since Korea extends through 9 degrees of latitude, temperature contrasts are to be expected. The south raises cotton as well as rice and winter wheat or barley; the center grows rice, oats, corn, and winter wheat; the north produces a single crop of potatoes, oats, millet, barley, and some rice in the valley bottoms.

A second contrast is between the east and the west. The eastern part, facing the Sea of Japan, is the more mountainous and less accessible. Most of the plains are in the west and lead to an embayed coast line. It is these plains which support the bulk of the population, for only here is widespread cultivation feasible.

THE PHYSICAL ENVIRONMENT

Korea is a land of mountains. From the air they seem to be without number; range after range, they extend to the horizon so that the land resembles a sea in a heavy gale. High mountains are uncommon; it is their profusion here that is impressive. No plain is so extensive that the encircling mountains cannot be seen on a fair day. Although mostly small, these plains are vital, for in this one-fifth of the 85,286 square miles Korea's 35 million population is crowded.

Beneath the surface is a complex of granite, gneiss, ancient limestones, and metamorphic rocks. Patches of sedimentary formations occur, especially in the southeast. Recent deposits are confined to small areas. The gneiss is resistant and generally forms highlands; granite may be eroded to more rounded forms at lower elevations.

The Chinese frontier is marked by two rivers and a mountain range. The Yalu, which flows southwestward, forms a pronounced cultural boundary. The Tumen drains northeast, but across it Koreans have migrated for centuries. Between the headwaters lies the volcanic Paektu-san, or Paitou Shan in Chinese, with a maximum elevation of 9,000 feet. At the sum-

North Korea Data [1]

Area	47,862 square miles
Population	8,252,000 (1960 est.)
Pyongyang (capital)	500,000 (est.)
Primary and secondary pupils	2,040,000 (1960)
University students	50,000 (1960)
Grain	3,800,000 metric tons (1960)
Coal	11,000,000 " "
Steel	641,000 " "
Cement	1,800,000 " "
Electricity	9,200,000,000 kilowatthours (1960)

[1] *Britannica Book of the Year*, 1962.

mit is a large crater lake comparable to that in Oregon.

Much of the northern frontier is an uninhabited land with magnificent forests of spruce, fir, larch, and pine. Open valleys are few. The geologic development and erosional history of the north have given rise to the Kaima Plateau, a rolling upland, in some places lava-capped, dissected by deeply entrenched rivers and disrupted by some minor ranges. There is an abrupt transition eastward from this interior upland, marked by sharp fault escarpments. To the southwest the descent is more gradual to the mountains, valleys, and plains of northwestern Korea.

The geographic regions of northern and southern Korea are separated by a valley, part of which is a lava-capped graben which cuts the peninsula along a northeast–southwest line followed by the railroad from Genzan to Seoul. South and east of this valley, Korea is dominated by the Taebaek Mountain Range which parallels the east coast. This is a maturely dissected block, with summits more than 5,000 feet in elevation, which slopes gently to the west but descends abruptly to the Sea of Japan. The most picturesque scenery occurs in the

Kumgang San, or Diamond Mountains. The Naktong Basin of the southeast is divided from the rest of the peninsula by a range, the Sobaek, trending southwest from the southern Taebaek. There are many other ranges caused by old earth folds or recent tectonic activity which confuse the structure of southern Korea.

Most rivers rise in the mountains near the Sea of Japan and flow westward into the Yalu and Tumen systems or westward to the Yellow Sea. None of them are long. Thus the widest alluvial plains are on the west, and the economic life of these areas might have tended to move toward the continent, had it not been for Japanese occupation. In contrast to the few harbors on the east, the western and southern embayed coast lines with their many islands provide better shelter for fishing vessels or modern steamers, although the high tides are a handicap.

The climatic characteristics of Korea more nearly resemble those of central and northern China than of Japan. There are considerable contrasts between winter and summer in the different regions. Because of the location of the peninsula on the margin of the Asiatic winter high-pressure area, monsoonal drifts of cold, dry air come from the north and west during the cold season. The passage of cyclonic storms, especially strong in the spring and fall, brings nonperiodic variations to the winter weather. These storms cause more precipitation in the south than in the north; even so it is slight compared with the summer rains. Snow may stay long on the ground in the north, but it melts quickly in the mild temperatures of the south. The northern interior has bitterly cold winters; only in the extreme southern fringe of the peninsula is the mean January temperature above freezing. The frost-free period varies from 130 days in the northern interior to 180 days in the center and 225 in the south.

Summers are hot and humid, with a marked concentration of rainfall. Much of this rainfall is convectional in origin and occurs in thunderstorms. Regional temperature contrasts are not so sharp in summer as in winter, although the

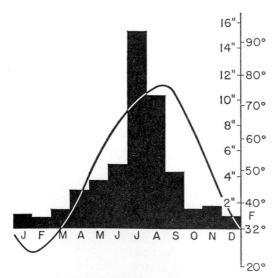

SEOUL. Elevation 285 feet, average temperature 52°F, annual precipitation 49 inches. Korea has a pronounced summer concentration of rainfall.

The Hwachon dam in South Korea parallels even larger hydroelectric projects in North Korea. (*Courtesy International Cooperation Administration*)

northern interior and northeastern littoral are distinctly cooler than the southern. Within Korea precipitation varies mainly with orographic position; the highest amounts are in the south with over 60 inches in the Sobaek Range; the least are in the sheltered upper Yalu Basin of the north, less than 25 inches. Since most of the precipitation occurs during the growing season, agricultural needs are normally well supplied. Occasional torrential storms, caused by typhoons or sharp convection, may do much damage.

Sharp seasonal contrasts are characteristic, as is shown by the extremes at Seoul where the maximum is over 100°F and the minimum −10°F. The relation to the continental interior of Asia makes these extremes greater in the north and in the interior than in the south or along the coast.

Climatic conditions somewhat resemble those in eastern North America, modified by the peninsular character of Korea and by the greater continentality of Asia. Temperatures at all seasons are somewhat lower than those at corresponding latitudes in the United States.

Nearly three-quarters of Korea is forest land. In the densely settled areas most of the commercial timber has long since been removed, so that only a cover of scrub trees and grass remains. The best timber resource still available is along the Chinese border, where there are excellent stands of spruce, fir, larch, and pine. In the mountain lands of the south, the forests are dominantly pine with some oak and elm. The chief use of these forest lands is for domestic firewood. The little bamboo that is cultivated in protected patches in the extreme south is a crop rather than a natural cover.

The peninsula of Korea has several minerals

of value. Mineral production and associated industries were greatly expanded by the Japanese during the Second World War. These included aluminum works, chemicals, nonferrous refining, machinery, and munitions, all for export. Iron ore is an important mineral, mined in the northwest and northeast. Most of it was once shipped to Japan, but there are blast furnaces and steel mills southwest of Pyongyang (Heijo) and elsewhere. Gold has been known for many decades, and there were American mining concessions even before the period of Japanese occupation. Both placer and lode deposits are widely scattered. The annual yield amounts to several hundred thousand ounces. Coal is widespread with an output of several million metric tons. Two-thirds of the reserves are anthracite, with mines near Pyongyang in the north and in less accessible deposits in southeastern Korea. The remainder is poor lignite. Copper, silver and tungsten are mined. Graphite is one of the more unusual resources, but although the quality is excellent, competition with deposits in Ceylon makes the yield fluctuate.

Among power resources are hydroelectric projects, especially those which utilize the Yalu and its tributaries. The 350-foot high Suifeng Dam, built in 1944, generates 640,000 kilowatts.

LIVELIHOOD

Seventy-five per cent of all Koreans live on the soil, and 10 to 15 per cent more depend indirectly on agriculture. There is little profit to most people from mining, forestry, or industry. Centuries of intensive cultivation have so impoverished the land that crop yields are low. Fertilization would help, but poverty-stricken farmers have difficulty in making the necessary adjustments. The population density for the peninsula as a whole exceeds 400, while in terms of cropland alone many areas support 1,500 people per square mile.

Korean agriculture is characterized by the intensity of human labor. Only the simplest tools are available, and there is neither capital nor experience for the use of elaborate machinery. Crop yields per acre are often low. During the American period in South Korea, agricultural experimentation materially increased yields and quality. The average holding per farm family is scarcely 3 acres, but most of the farms are smaller and are diminishing in size.

Double cropping is common, especially in the southern areas where climatic conditions are favorable. In terms of 100 as representing single-crop utilization, the extreme southeast has a figure of 192, in contrast to 109 in the northeast.

The economy of Korea is tuned to the cultivation of rice, which is the major crop even though it occupies only one-third of the cultivated land. Almost all the rice is irrigated, but two-thirds of the flooded fields are precariously dependent upon variable rainfall for their necessary water. Both yield and acreage fluctuate considerably from year to year. Prior to the Second World War two-fifths of the rice crop was shipped to Japan to meet the deficiency there. This left an inadequate food supply for Korea, which was partly corrected by the import of millet from Manchuria.

Barley represents the second most important crop and is the principal food for many of the people. It occupies an acreage about three-fifths that of rice but represents only one-fifth of the value. In southern Korea barley is a winter crop planted during October or November in the drained rice paddies or on dry fields and harvested in June or July. In the north, where winters are more severe, it is sown in the spring. Soy and other varieties of beans occupy positions in acreage and value similar to that of barley. Millet is also important in the northwest; wheat is grown in the same area. Other crops include oats, buckwheat, corn, white and sweet potatoes. An important crop, particularly in the north, is grain sorghum. This is called kaoliang by the Chinese; the Korean calls it *susu,* derived from the sound of tall grain moved by the wind. There are many vegetables, especially turnips and cabbage, used in *kimchi,* the Korean pickle. Excellent pears and apples are grown.

Southern Korea is well suited for the growing of American varieties of cotton; native varieties are grown in the northwest. The growth of mulberry and the production of silk are widespread subsidiary agricultural occupations.

Korean cattle are of good quality. There are many oxen and cows, an average of one to every two farmhouses. Pigs and chickens are common.

Climatic conditions divide Korea into two major agricultural regions, the northern and southern. The climatic and agricultural boundary tends to run from southeast to northwest. Although the two agricultural regions are roughly equal in size, more than three-fourths of the rice is grown in the south together with almost all the cotton, barley, and sweet potatoes. Northern Korea specializes in the hardier grains in addition to rice.

It is important to realize that the 38th parallel, which divided Soviet and American spheres after the war, roughly reflected this fundamental contrast in economy, although the dividing line was established for other reasons.

One of the unfortunate features of farming in the northern interior and in the central mountain sections is the practice of "fire-field" agriculture, or burning the hillsides in preparation for planting a temporary crop. On the extensive areas of state forest land squatters illegally burn the brush or grass in order to fer-

Foot-operated water wheels such as this are a common method of lifting irrigation water. (*Courtesy International Cooperation Administration*)

Seoul is a city of nearly 3 million people. The tall building is a department store; beyond the corner is a bank. (*Courtesy International Cooperation Administration*)

tilize the soil preparatory to planting crops of millet, oats, or potatoes. After one or two years fertility diminishes and erosion becomes serious, so that the fields must be abandoned. Prior to the Second World War fire-cleared fields measured a million acres, one-eleventh of the cultivated area.

Korea's population has grown rapidly. In 1913 the total population was but 15,459,000. This figure rose to 24,326,327 in 1940, and exceeded 33 million by 1960. After allowing for emigration to Japan and Manchuria, this figure represented a natural increase of over 2 per cent per year. Some two-thirds of the total population live in what is now South Korea.

The long-standing problem of Korea is the achievement of acceptable livelihood for so many people on so little good land. Whenever political stability is lacking or economic conditions are upset, Korea's population faces catastrophe. The margin of welfare and stability is precarious even with favorable climate and sound guidance.

The cities, which in the past existed largely for administrative or market functions, have become the centers of modern industrialization. The largest city is Seoul, the governmental, financial, and cultural center of South Korea, with a population of over two million. Other major cities of the South are Taegu, with a half million people, and the seaports of Pusan at the railway terminus opposite Japan, over one million in population, and Inchon with over 250,000, the gateway of Seoul on the west coast. North Korea's capital is Pyongyang (Heijo), with a half million people.

THE TWO KOREAS

Korea became independent in 1948, following forty years of rule by Japan. Unfortunately, postwar differences between the Soviet and American zones led to the creation of two countries, the Republic of Korea in the south, with its capital at Seoul, and the Democratic People's Republic of Korea in the north, governed from Pyongyang.

Although North Korea is somewhat larger in area, three-quarters of the people live in South Korea, several million of them refugees from North Korea or repatriates from Japan. The density of population in South Korea is more than twice that of North Korea.

South Korea leads in agriculture and the production of nonferrous minerals, including tungsten, copper, and graphite; North Korea leads in production of coal, iron, gold, hydro-electricity, and in heavy industry. Whereas the former has extensive international trade, the latter is largely oriented toward Communist China and the Soviet Union. Railways, urban prosperity, and material progress are more developed in the south.

Many economic problems confront Korea. The decades under Japan were designed to fit the colony into imperial needs for markets and for raw materials, and the subsequent division, with its American and Chinese support, has further distorted the normal economy. The viability of the two halves of the country without foreign support is uncertain.

Despite the division, both Koreas have made notable progress. Agricultural production has risen, in part because of mechanization and fertilizers, as has that of fishing and lumbering. North Korea produces 10 million tons of coal and 1 million tons of iron ore. South Korea mines 3 million tons of coal but only $\frac{1}{4}$ million tons of iron ore. In both halves of the country the economy is unbalanced; thus South Korean exports represent only 5 per cent of the value of its imports.

References on Korea

See also general references on Asia in Chapter 1.

Fisher, Charles A.: "The Role of Korea in the Far East," *Geog. Jour.,* CXX (1954), 282–298.

Ladejinsky, W.: "Chosen's Agriculture and Its Problems," *Foreign Agriculture,* IV (1940), 95–122.

McCune, Shannon, with Arthur H. Robinson: "Notes on a Physiographic Diagram of Tyosen (Korea)," *Geog. Rev.,* XXXI (1941), 653–658.

McCune, Shannon: "Physical Basis for Korean Boundaries," *Far Eastern Quarterly,* V (1946), 272–288.

McCune, Shannon: "Southeastern Littoral of Korea," *Econ. Geog.,* XXIII (1947), 41–51.

*McCune, Shannon: *Korea's Heritage: A Regional and Social Geography,* Rutland, Vt.: Tuttle (1956).

*Trewartha, Glenn T., and Wilbur Zelinsky: "Population Distribution and Change in Korea, 1925–1949," *Geog. Rev.,* XLV (1955), 1–26.

Zaichikov, V. T.: *Geography of Korea,* New York: Inst. of Pacific Relations (1952).

13 Japan's Prospects

The Japanese Landscape / Geographical History / Population Problems / Location / References on Japan

THE JAPANESE LANDSCAPE

Few countries have the charm of Japan. Verdant hillsides, painstaking cultivation, artistic gardens, and courteous people combine to create a delightful landscape. Wherever the land permits, miniature rice fields crowd so closely that there is scarcely room for roads or villages. This intricate field pattern, in varying shades of green or brown according to the maturity of the crop, gives the dominant note to the cultural landscape. Tea and mulberry climb the slopes; forests and clumps of bamboo partly hide the shrines and temples among the hills.

If all Japanese landscapes were merged into a single scene and viewed from the air, one might look down upon a micropattern of hills and mountains interlaced by winding ribbons of alluvium. At one side would be the inescapable sea, fringed by rocky cliffs and tiny deltas. Wherever water is available and the land can be terraced one sees rice fields and here and there clusters of farm houses surrounded by fruit or mulberry trees. Many villages extend along highways, river levees, or the seacoast. Larger settlements center about feudal castles or shrines. Railroads are more important than automobile roads, and the inevitable hydroelectric transmission lines intro-

198

duce a modern note to the rural scene. Modern industry dominates metropolitan areas and spills over into the smallest towns. Everywhere one sees the hand of man.

This is a very human landscape, long settled and intensively developed. Archibald MacLeish has graphically described the pressure of man on the land as follows: [1]

Japan is the country where the stones show human fingerprints: where the pressure of men on the earth has worn through to the iron rock.

There is nothing in Japan but the volcanoes and the volcanic wastes that men have not handled. There is no getting away from men anywhere; from the sight of men in the open houses or from the shape of their work in the made fields or from the smell of their dung in the paddy water.

In other countries a farm is meadows and a wood lot and a corner that the plow leaves: room to turn about and time to turn about in. In Japan a farm is as rigid and tight a thing as

[1] Archibald MacLeish: "Of Many Men on Little Land," *Fortune,* September, 1936. Quoted by permission.

a city lot—a patch here and triangle here and a square or so somewhere else: every road corner of land diked and leveled off even though the growing surface is less than a man's shirt; every field soaked with manure and worked and reworked as carefully and as continuously as a European farmer works a seedbed . . . nothing thrown away, nothing let go wild, nothing wasted.

Nature has obviously exercised a closely guiding hand, for the correspondence between the cultural pattern and the physical surroundings is intimate. Agriculture shows a mature adjustment to land forms, and population distribution follows food possibilities, whether from land or sea. Vertical differences in climate and soils bring modifications from place to place but do not greatly disturb the general picture within Honshu, Kyushu, and Shikoku. Hokkaido to the north is newer and different.

Despite the pressure for food, surprisingly large areas of waste land are to be seen; much of Japan appears to be unused. Large areas are forested, either naturally or with trees planted for erosion-control projects. Some of

Japan Data [1]

Area	142,727 square miles
Population	93,418,501 (1960 census)
Tokyo (capital)	8,310,027
Osaka	3,011,563
Nagoya	1,591,935
Yokohama	1,375,710
Kyoto	1,284,818
Kobe	1,113,977
Primary and secondary pupils	21,579,254
University students	653,253 (1958)
Rice	12,501,000 metric tons (1959)
Barley	1,241,000 " "
Wheat	1,416,000 " "
Fish catch	5,205,682 " "
Coal	52,608,000 " " (1960)
Steel	15,348,000 " "
Cement	22,536,000 " "
Raw silk	16,032 " "
Petroleum	29,904,000 litres (1960)

[1] *Britannica Book of the Year,* 1962.

this unused land is in wild bamboo grass or brushland on mountain slopes, fit neither for grazing nor for tree crops. Many forest plots supply charcoal for domestic use. Elsewhere idle land represents stream terraces with excessively coarse soils where cultivation is impractical. Other areas of sandy flood plains or coastal swamps are unfit for agriculture.

Field patterns are best seen at the time of rise transplanting when the tiny flooded fields gleam like mirrors. There are no fences, and only low dikes separate each plot. Where the slope is gentle, rectilinear patterns prevail; on hillsides the dike system follows the contours. Unless irrigation water is easily available, rice fields seldom rise much above the valley floor.

Above the irrigated fields may be sloping terraces for tea or mulberry or fruit. Almost everywhere the pattern of surface configuration guides the land use. In the new agricultural districts of Hokkaido the farms average 10 acres, and were originally laid out along American lines, but in Old Japan farms of about 2 acres are the rule.

The unpainted exteriors of Japanese houses tend to be drab to Western eyes, except for the lattice windows. Walls are of thin wooden siding or of mud and straw plaster on a wattle foundation. Roofs were once characteristically covered with thatch in the country or with tile in the cities, where the fire hazard is greater. Sliding lattice partitions with translucent paper

Most Japanese living rooms have a slightly raised corner where a flower display or some object of beauty is placed; this is known as the tokonoma. Before one enters the home he removes his shoes, so that floors remain clean. (*Courtesy Japan Air Lines*)

Industry and urban life have brought basic changes in housing, so that these concrete apartment houses are scarcely identifiable as Japanese. (*Courtesy Japanese Consulate General, New York City*)

in place of glass are artistic and well adapted to a subtropical climate but are ill suited to the cold and snowy winters of the north.

There are no stoves for heating, although on the colder west coast houses are built with the Korean device of allowing smoke from the kitchen fire to circulate through a brick baffle which extends under the earthen floors of the adjoining rooms. Elsewhere a charcoal brazier supplies enough heat to warm one's hands before writing or doing fine work.

The charm of Japanese houses lies not in the exterior, but in the enclosed courtyards with their formal gardens. Even the better residences are often entered through a simple gateway crowded between shops along the street. Only temples and inns have attractive exteriors.

Japanese cities show but limited functional zoning. The predominance of one- and two-story houses produces a flat urban skyline, interrupted perhaps by the ancient feudal castle or shrine which served as the original nucleus. Both village and city streets are surprisingly similar in the structure of buildings, the types of business, and general character. Shops open directly on the narrow street without doors or windows and are boarded up at night. In many business places the owner lives in the rear or upstairs.

In parts of Tokyo and Osaka the Westernization is striking. Modern subways, a blaze of neon lights, excellent department stores, and people in European dress give a cosmopolitan air. Tokyo is in tune with cities the world over; it is the most modern city in all Asia. An American has little difficulty in finding someone along the downtown streets who speaks or at least reads English. The central parts of Kobe, Yokohama, and Nagoya are somewhat similar.

Contrasts and contradictions mark the rapid transition from centuries of seclusion to world awareness. Few nations have so transformed their national life as has Japan since 1868 when the Emperor Meiji ascended the throne. Many of these adjustments are psychological, but the material evidences are widespread. Rural landscapes have changed less than the urban, but everywhere one sees signs of the new. Nevertheless, Japan is not merely becoming Westernized; rather she is skillfully remolding her own life to be in tune with the world. Acceptance of some Western techniques should not be regarded as mere copying; instead, the Japanese are grafting branches of material civilization onto the parent stock of their indigenous culture.

GEOGRAPHICAL HISTORY

Japanese origins are shrouded in obscurity. The earliest authenticated records date from the third or fourth century of the Christian era, although legendary history places the first emperor, Jimmu, in 660 B.C. Several racial elements have contributed to the people and culture of today. Some strains which came from the south are Indonesian, Malayo-Polynesian, and southern coastal Mongoloid; others are northern Mongoloid who originated within Asia. In terms of physical ethnography, the contribution from the south is slightly dominant; culturally, Asiatic influences are stronger.

Much of this blending preceded the beginnings of the Christian era and can be deciphered only by archeological evidence. The Japanese adoption of Confucianism, Buddhism,

and Chinese culture under the Tang dynasty during the seventh to tenth centuries is well known. On the other hand, house types and short stature point southward. One illustration will suffice. The Japanese custom of eating raw fish is found also in the East Indies, in Ceylon, and in Madagascar, but almost nowhere on the continent. A few alien tribes of boat people in southern China eat uncooked fish, but not the Chinese themselves.

Thus from the beginning the Japanese have been a mixed group, influenced by imported cultures. Unlike self-sufficient China, Japan has been accustomed to cultural borrowing and adaptation. Such a historical frame of mind, with its willingness to learn from others, may help to explain the rapidity with which modern Japan has accepted ideas from Western culture. This adaptability was demonstrated after the Second World War by the speed with which the Japanese took on the externals of American democracy. We should remember, however, that in a country whose roots are so ancient, European culture will remain for decades no more than a veneer.

Within the islands are three ancient centers of culture. In southern Kyushu lies the Satsuma area, which received racial and cultural contributions from the coast of South China, from the South Seas, and possibly from Oceania by way of the Ryukyu archipelago. On the west coast of Honshu was the local Izumo culture, closely allied to that of Korea and the Amur valley tribes. The Yamato culture flourished in central Honshu and gave rise to the present civilization of Japan; it is in part a fusion of Satsuma and Izumo types. The Yamato area had early contacts with central and northern China, Korea, and even India.

Each of these early cultures was to some extent superimposed on that of the indigenous Ainus, an early human type which once covered most of the islands but is now found only in northern Hokkaido. The beginnings of Japanese life were all in the southwest, in Kyushu and western Honshu. As time progressed, the pre-Japanese inhabitants, the Ainus, were

The development of the Japanese Empire began in the seventh century when the original inhabitants, the Ainu, were gradually pushed northward from western Honshu. At the height of Japan's conquest during the Second World War, she controlled an area from Wake Island 5,000 miles west to Burma, and from the Aleutians 4,500 miles south to the Solomon Islands, with a land area of 3,500 square miles.

Many country homes are covered with thatch roofs and have paper-covered lattice windows. This farm near Nara specializes in producing silk. (*Moulin, from Ewing Galloway*)

pushed northward, but only with much difficulty. Lake Biwa marked an important boundary in early historic times, and the main island was not completely conquered until the close of the tenth century. Some of this advance may have been due to the pressure for more rice land.

Five centuries of feudalism preceded the modern era, with a hierarchy not unlike that of medieval Europe. Nobles lived in castles surrounded by moats and were supported by warriors dressed in coats of mail.

Japan's overseas expansion began with the Ryukyu, or Liukiu, chain of islands, acquired in 1609 and in 1876 to 1879. Taiwan, or For-

mosa, was seized in 1895, and the Kuriles, or Chishima-retto, were taken over in 1875. The Ryukyu and Taiwan were once nominally under Chinese control; the Kuriles had been a matter of dispute with Russia.

Modern imperialism started with the first Sino-Japanese War (1894–1895), fought ostensibly to give Korea its independence from China. With the treaty of peace, Japan sought the Liaotung Peninsula in southern Manchuria, but was forced by pressure from Russia, Germany, and France to accept instead an indemnity from China. A few years later, Russia secured permission to build the Chinese Eastern Railway across Manchuria en route to Vladivostok and later built a branch south to Dairen and Port Arthur in the Liaotung Peninsula. Thus Russia became established in the same area that Japan had sought previously. This led to the Russo-Japanese War of 1904 to 1905, from which Japan secured southern Sakhalin and economic concessions in southern Manchuria. In 1910 Korea was formally annexed; its first Japanese occupation had occurred in the seventeenth century.

At the time of the Russian Revolution of 1917, Japan and the United States joined in sending an expedition into Siberia as far as Lake Baikal. Each country agreed to send 7,500 soldiers, but Japan sent 72,500 and withdrew only on strong diplomatic pressure from Washington. At the same period she took over northern Sakhalin, but had to return it later.

During the First World War Japan seized German concessions in Shantung which were not returned to China until the Washington Conference of 1922. At the end of the war Japan was awarded a mandate over the German islands in the Pacific north of the equator: the Caroline, Marshall, and Mariana groups.

Manchuria became the puppet state of Manchukuo after the Mukden incident of September 18, 1931. Fighting spread south of the Great Wall in 1937.

The attack upon Pearl Harbor on December 7, 1941, offered still further opportunities for expansion on the Mainland and to the south. Japan's attack on the United States grew out

The seaside resort of Kamakura, 30 miles southwest of Tokyo, is noted for its great bronze Buddha, the Daibutsu, which is 700 years old. (*Courtesy Japan Tourist Association*)

of her desperation in not finding adequate live-lihood on her own terms within her own sphere. Now that she is reduced to the area of the original islands, her trade problem can be solved only by good relations with both sources of supply and markets.

In Japan's quest for empire she originally had but few assets: chiefly location and a virile and dynamic people. Although the homeland was poor, surrounding areas added important resources. At the height of her conquests in 1942, Japan extended from the Aleutians 4,500 miles south to the Solomon Islands, and from Wake Island 5,000 miles west to Burma. This involved a land area of 3,250,000 square miles with a population of 300 million. Time was temporarily on Japan's side, for no other nation ever conquered so much or such rich territory so quickly or so easily.

Control of the mandated islands plus Southeast Asia and China gave a new meaning to defense in depth. The empire was able to sell this space in exchange for time, but unlike the experience of China, time was not eventually on her side. Japan proper is relatively compact and accessible and thus vulnerable to attack. Her temporary security in the Second World War came from the acquisition of outer territories. Without these, it seems unlikely that she can ever again challenge the United States.

Following her defeat in the Second World War, Japan lost southern Sakhalin and the Kuriles to the Soviet Union; Taiwan and her interests in Manchuria reverted to China; Korea became independent; and the United States took over the mandated areas as well as other islands in the south.

Japanese imperialists had two territorial goals. One group, led by the army, favored expansion on the continent; the other, dominated by the navy, pointed to the South Seas. China offered a market and certain raw materials. Action in the northwest also provided a buffer against the Soviet Union and its ideology. One of the reasons for acquiring Korea was to secure protection against Russia; to render Korea secure, Manchuria was desirable, and in turn

Mongolia; eastern Siberia would similarly be a safeguard; hence the appetite grew with the eating.

Ambitions in the South Seas referred vaguely to the Philippines, Indonesia, Malaya, Thailand, and the Indochina States. Here are important resources of iron and many other metals, petroleum, rubber, lumber, rice, vegetable oils and fibers, and potentially of cotton. The prospective markets are large, and (of equal significance) there is room for colonization in warm, rice-growing lands. All this was part of a Greater East Asia program by which Japan hoped to obtain military security and economic self-sufficiency.

Postwar Japan covers 142,727 square miles, about the size of California, whereas the prewar empire had an area of 262,948 square miles including the mandated islands.

Japan's place in the world cannot be understood without an appreciation of her psychology and ideology. During the centuries when she shut herself from intercourse with the outside world, even from China, it was but natural that an attitude of superiority should have developed. Knowing no outside power, Japan regarded her own culture as the most desirable. When Western civilization suddenly broke in during the nineteenth century, the Japanese were keenly disappointed that Europe did not grant equality to the arts and achievements of the Orient. This oversight was unfortunate for the West since Oriental culture was of a high order.

What had been a feeling of superiority was suddenly changed to one of inferiority. It is an interesting commentary that only when the Japanese had demonstrated military competence in 1904 to 1905, and again during the two World Wars, did the country receive cultural recognition. Underlying much of Japan's current program is this desire for respect and political equality. Japan wants desperately to be understood, to acquire face through appreciation by the West.

When the first Japanese went overseas, there was a tendency for commercial representatives and naval officers to visit England, for army men to go to Germany, and for thousands of students to come to the United States. These early educational relations have continued; many influential Japanese once studied in American universities. No country enjoys a larger measure of basic good will and admiration than does the United States, although momentary differences may reverse the picture. Japan's own culture is secure, but many ideas from her neighbor across the Pacific find their way into her life and thought.

No one can understand Japanese geography without an appreciation of the cultural and spiritual urge which lies behind it. Expansion in Asia was not merely a search for food, livelihood, and security. Behind the lure of empire was the desire to bring to other lands the blessings of a culture which to the Japanese appeared to be a better way of life.

POPULATION PROBLEMS

Japan's greatest assets and likewise her greatest problems concern people. About 100 million live on four islands no larger than California. For many years, the net annual increase has been over a million people. Where can these islanders live? What can they do? How shall they be fed? Population increase has been so rapid that it repeatedly threatens to outrun the productive capacity of soil and mineral resources. No problem is more pressing.

Japan is insular, without much room for expansion at home, and her people are ambitious. Emigration has been unpopular, industry insecure, and foreign trade unpredictable. Territorial expansion was once sought as a panacea, since with overseas political control it was hoped that raw materials and markets would be assured. Japan's skill in meeting her population problems since the Second World War has been remarkable, notably the fact that she was able to balance her import-export budget.

The 100 million people are distributed in close relationship with land forms. Wherever there is level land and fertile soil, no matter

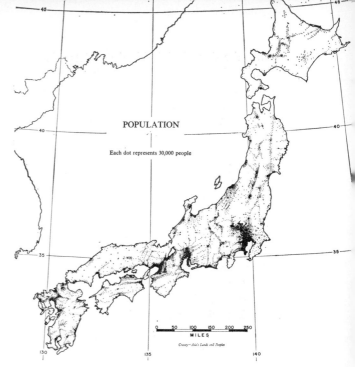

POPULATION

Each dot represents 30,000 people

MILES
0   50   100   150   200   250

Cressey—Asia's Lands and Peoples

Japan's people are strikingly concentrated in the coastal plains and interior valleys, with the densest population extending from the Kanto Plain westward to the Inland Sea.

If the maps of Japan appear crowded, it is because they are reproduced on the same scale used for the other major divisions of Asia.

how surrounded by mountains, there are people. Modern urbanization only emphasizes this pattern since all cities are in the lowland plains. So close is the man-land correspondence that a map of rural population is at the same time a good representation of land forms, or equally of cultivated land. Vertical zonation is obvious, for the areas of population concentration are all lowlands, and the density decreases with altitude. Most Japanese live near sea level.

Nearly half of the people of Japan live in what are defined as "densely inhabited districts." These consist of areas which contain more than 10,000 people per square mile and are over 800 in number. Despite their importance, the aggregate area of the districts amounts to only 1 per cent of Japan.

Four great metropolitan regions stand out, led by Tokyo-Yokohama, which counts over 15 million people, three-quarters of whom live within the densely inhabited districts. The conurbation is known as Keihin. The population of the Osaka, Kobe, and Kyoto area, called the Hanshin conurbation, exceeds 10 million; it also has three-quarters of its people in the crowded areas. Nagoya with its surroundings constitutes the third metropolitan area, but only half of its 5 million people live within the densely inhabited district. The industrial cities of northern Kyushu form the fourth area, with a total population of 3 million, of whom three-fifths are concentrated in the built-up district.

In striking contrast to the urban congestion, almost one-fourth of Japan has a population density of less than one person per square mile. Most of this includes areas of steep slopes, volcanic rocks, or unusable soils.

Few regions have uniform population distributions. Even the pattern of the Kanto Plain around Tokyo is highly irregular, owing to the distribution of land available for rice. Almost everywhere mountains interrupt settlement, so that isolation and difficulty of access characterize the human scene. Fragmentation and microdetail are as true of population patterns as of surface configuration.

Annual population figures for the 2½ centuries of the Tokugawa regime (1602–1867) are remarkably uniform, with little variation from 28 million. After the restoration of the Emperor Meiji in 1868, the population increased rapidly. It doubled by 1925 and will double again by 1970. In some measure, these additional millions are the responsibility of Admiral Perry, who forced open Japan's doors in 1853 and brought in the disrupting influences of the Western world.

Japan's amazing population increase is shown by the following census figures:

1920	43,500,000
1930	55,391,000
1940	73,114,308
1950	83,199,637
1960	93,418,501

Although both birth and death rates have fluctuated considerably, the net increase of population in most years has reached 1 million.

In terms of total area, the population density exceeds 650 per square mile. Excluding Hokkaido, the average reaches 800. Few countries in the world exceed these figures. Yet such figures become meaningful only when seen in the light of the cultivated area, and in these terms, Japan has more than 4,000 people for each square mile of tilled land.

With 100 million people and no room for more agriculture, Japan faces her greatest difficulty. Yields per acre have increased remarkably, but one wonders how long this improvement may continue. Emigration has failed to care for the surplus, since the Japanese show little inclination to colonize either their own Hokkaido or subtropical areas such as Brazil. Immigration barriers keep them out of many countries.

Faced with agricultural overpopulation, the country has turned to industry; but without an adequate base of supplies or a rich market at home, industrial Japan must first import raw

The Japanese people are remarkably clean and tidy. (*Courtesy Japan Air Lines*)

materials and then export manufactured goods. A policy of international good will would thus seem economically imperative. So long as foreign trade flourishes there will be factory jobs for many people.

Japan's skills and resources should easily make her an excellent second-category nation, but they scarcely qualify her for the domination of the western Pacific and eastern Asia.

Population increase represents one of the great problems of the twentieth century, both for Japan and for all the world. Every nation has a moral obligation to maintain a satisfactory balance between its numbers and the productive capacity of its domain, unless it is willing to accept a progressively lower standard of living. The world's good land is nearly all occupied, and the regulation of population has become one of the most essential of international problems. Reckless increase without corresponding technological advance can lead only to chaos, poverty, and a troubled world.

LOCATION

Five hundred miles of enclosed seas separate Japan from China, and to the east the United States lies beyond 4,000 miles of open ocean. Closer than either are Korea and Soviet territory, only a few tens of miles distant. Japan's island location, necessitating a maritime relation to her neighbors, is the key to much of her geography.

Is Japan a gateway to Asia? Is the country to become an avenue from America and Europe for trade and understanding, or is Japan to be the leader in Asiatic unity? Can Japan hold her economic and political initiative in the western Pacific, or will China overshadow her? The answers to these questions must all start with an evaluation of place, for location is the most significant of all environmental considerations.

If our concepts of space in the Pacific were derived from an understanding of the globe rather than from flat maps, the significance of Japan's location in regard to the United States would be better understood. Japan is not merely somewhere far to the west of the Golden Gate, one of a half dozen areas across the Pacific, to each of which we take a different route; instead, Japan lies just beyond Alaska along the main great circle route to Asia.

Every direct steamship or air route from San Francisco, Seattle, or Vancouver to the China coast, and on to the Philippines, Singapore, or Indonesia either touches Japan or is within a few miles of its shores. The airway from San Francisco to Manila via Hawaii and Guam is 2,000 miles longer than the direct route from Seattle to Manila via Tokyo.

Location imparts commercial advantages to Japan, for here meet two of the world's great ocean trade routes. One of them originates in Europe, crosses the Indian Ocean to Singapore, and moves north past Hong Kong and Shanghai to Kobe and Yokohama. The other starts from North America and passes westward via Japan to the China coast and the Philippines. Japan thus faces two ways, with unique access to markets. No part of Japan is more than a few tens of miles from the sea. Millions of Japanese have had maritime experience.

Islands have the advantage of accessibility and at the same time of relative security. Japan is fortunately well supplied with harbors. This means that outside ideas may penetrate easily and that social adjustments evolve more readily. An insular position often brings safety. Until 1945 no invader had ever landed on Japanese shores. The Mongols had tried under Kublai Khan in 1281, but a typhoon intervened.

Japan covers 142,727 square miles spread across 3,413 islands. Four large islands make up 97 per cent of Japan. The largest is Honshu in the center. This is the mainland and economic core of the country. In the southwest lie Shikoku and Kyushu, and to the north is the frontier island of Hokkaido. Hundreds of smaller islands cluster around these larger lands.

Between Honshu, Shikoku, and Kyushu lies the Inland Sea. Dotted with green islands and

The charm of Japanese architecture is reflected in this winter photograph of the Kinka-kuji Temple, or Golden Pavilion, in Kyoto, which dates from 1394. The city was once the capital of Japan and still has unique charm. (*Courtesy Kyoto Bureau of Tourist Industry*)

surrounded by historic shores, this is Japan's economic and cultural Main Street.

Americans should not have too much difficulty in visualizing the basic setting, for Japan extends from the latitude of Georgia to that of Nova Scotia. Both Japan and eastern North America face an ocean and thus have an east-coast climate, but it is erroneous to stop with this observation, for Japan is surrounded by seas while the ocean only borders the United States on the east. A better comparison would involve isolating a coastal American strip 200 miles wide and moving it several hundred miles to sea.

Some of Japan's problems resemble those of Britain; both have comparable area and population, and both must export manufactured goods in order to import needed food. Each is the major island area in its respective ocean, and each has had enemies on the mainland. But whereas the British Isles have a west-coast maritime climate, Japan lies on the east coast and is alternately maritime and continental. Britain also enjoyed the advantage of an early start and has ex-colonial ties across the oceans not available to Japan. The British remain uncertain as to whether they are Europeans, or citizens of a world commonwealth, or primarily allies of North America. Few problems in the Atlantic world are more significant than the relative widths of the English Channel and the Atlantic Ocean. In like manner, the Japanese have looked toward the Asiatic mainland, toward an empire southward, and toward a Pacific alliance with the United States. An international orientation is inescapable. But where shall Japan turn? Only island areas have these options.

The Pacific is a wide ocean, and the relations between its margins are still immature. Though commerce has grown, cultural understanding lags. No Pacific community similar to that around the Atlantic has yet fully developed, but as contacts increase so must understanding.

Japan appears to be geographically well endowed to be an important second-class power, but not more. While her island position gives her material advantages of accessibility and maritime interests, she is poor in many basic resources. Ideas and cultural leadership are other matters. Japan's future is assured if she is willing to pattern her life in terms of her notable cultural achievements and geographic environment. Only misfortune can accompany overexpansion.

References on Japan

Two of the best volumes on the geography of Japan are Glenn T. Trewartha: *Japan, A Physical, Cultural, and Regional Geography;* and Edward A. Ackerman: *Japan's Natural Resources and Their Relation to Japan's Economic Future.*

The following lists do not include references to the many excellent studies in Japanese, often with English summaries, in the *Geographical Review of Japan* and the *Japanese Journal of Geology and Geography.*

See also general references on Asia in Chapter 1.

*Ackerman, Edward A.: *Japan's Natural Resources and Their Relation to Japan's Economic Future,* Chicago: The University of Chicago Press (1953).

Beardsley, Richard K., John W. Hall, and Robert E. Ward: *Village Japan,* Chicago: The University of Chicago Press (1959).

Bishop, Carl W.: "The Historical Geography of Early Japan," *Geog. Rev.,* XIII (1923), 40–62.

Dickerman, Nelson: "Mineral Resources of Japan," Washington: *Foreign Minerals Survey,* II, no. 5 (1945).

Erselcuk, Muzaffer: "Japan's Oil Resources," *Econ. Geog.,* XXII (1946), 14–23.

Eyre, John D.: "Water Controls in a Japanese Irrigation System," *Geog. Rev.,* XLV (1955), 197–216.

Eyre, John D.: "Japanese Land Development in Kojima Bay," *Econ. Geog.,* XXXII (1956), 58–74.

Eyre, John D.: "Sources of Tokyo's Fresh Food Supply," *Geog. Rev.,* XLIX (1959), 455–474.

Eyre, John D.: "Japanese Inter-prefectural Rice Movements," *Econ. Geog.,* XXXVIII (1962), 78–86.

*Ginsburg, Norton S. (ed.): *The Pattern of Asia,* Englewood Cliffs, N.J.: Prentice-Hall (1958).

*Hall, Robert Burnett: "Tokaido: Road and Region," *Geog. Rev.,* XXVII (1937), 353–377.

Hall, Robert B., Jr.: "Hand Tractors in Japanese Paddy Fields," *Econ. Geog.,* XXXIV (1958), 312–320.

Kojima, Reikichi: "The Population of the Prefectures and Cities of Japan in Most Recent Times," *Far Eastern Quarterly,* III (1944), 313–362.

Mathieson, R. S.: "The Japanese Salmon Fisheries; A Geographic Appraisal," *Econ. Geog.,* XXXIV (1958), 352–361.

Nuttonson, M. Y.: *Agricultural Climatology of Japan and Its Agro-climatic Analogues in North America,* Washington: Amer. Inst. of Crop Ecology (1949).

Nuttonson, M. Y.: *Ecological Crop Geography and Field Practices of Japan, Japan's Natural Vegetation, and Agro-climatic Analogues in North America,* Washington: Amer. Inst. of Crop Ecology (1951).

Orchard, John E.: "Industrialization in Japan, China Mainland, and India—Some World Implications," *Annals, Assn. Amer. Geogs.,* L (1960), 193–215.

*Science Council of Japan: *Regional Geography of Japan: Guidebook,* Tokyo: Kokonshoin (1957).

Thompson, John H.: "Urban Agriculture in Southern Japan," *Econ. Geog.,* XXXIII (1957), 224–237.

*Thompson, John H., and Michihiro Miyazaki: "A Map of Japan's Manufacturing," *Geog. Rev.,* XXXXIX (1959), 1–17.

Thompson, John H.: "Manufacturing in the Kita Kyushu Industrial Zone of Japan," *Annals, Assn. Amer. Geogs.,* XLIX (1959), 420–442.

*Trewartha, Glenn T.: *Japan: A Physical, Cultural, and Regional Geography,* Madison, Wis.: University of Wisconsin Press (1945).

14 The Japanese Environment

Land Forms / Climate / Forests and Soils / Mineral Resources

LAND FORMS

Water and land combine to make Japanese geography a matter of both hydrography and topography. The country is both insular and mountainous. Seas not only encircle the islands but also penetrate the land and the culture. Land and water are everywhere so near each other that one is always within sight of mountains or sea.

The Pacific Ocean is encircled by a series of rugged young mountains from Cape Horn through Alaska and Japan to New Zealand. Along the coast of Asia these form a festoon of mountainous island arcs, each with its ends curving inward toward the continent. Japan occupies one of these arcs; the Kuriles and the Ryukyu form similar arcs to the north and south. From north to south these arcs enclose the Sea of Okhotsk, the Sea of Japan, and the East China Sea.

If we could take away the ocean, the Japanese archipelago would stand out as a great mountain range, with peaks rising 5 and 6 miles above the ocean floor. To the east and south are conspicuous troughs, descending to more than 30,000 feet below sea level. And if we could change geological history to slow-motion speed, we might observe how frequently volcanoes, faulting, and crustal folding have disturbed the configuration of Japan.

Scattered sedimentary rocks reveal that the

213

QUATERNARY LANDFORMS

■ Alluvium
▨ Diluvium

0 50 100 150 200 250
MILES

Cressey—Asia's Lands and Peoples

Only 15 per cent of Japan is level, divided between the present-day alluvial plains, in most cases graded to sea level, and the uplifted and dissected diluvium which forms terraces a few tens or a hundred feet above the alluvial surfaces.

LANDFORMS AND
GEOGRAPHIC REGIONS

H   Hokkaido
NH   Northern Honshu
KP   Kanto Plain
CH   Central Honshu
WH   Western Honshu
S   Shikoku
K   Kyushu

H

NH

KP

WH

CH

S

K

0   100   200   300   400
MILES

Cressey—Asia's Lands and Peoples

islands have been submerged at various times, while widespread lava flows, ash deposits, and intrusions betray repeated igneous activity. In origin and topography Japan is so young that there has not been time to round off the edges. Slopes are unusually steep and summits jagged.

Within this mountainous framework, Japan has nearly 200 volcanoes, of which 60 have been active within historic times. Fujiyama is the most famous of the active peaks, although it has not erupted since 1707. Since many of the active volcanoes are high and isolated, they are significant elements of the landscape.

Mount Fuji, known to the Japanese as Fuji-san, rises to 12,390 feet and has a crater 720 feet deep. The symmetrical cone has a slope which reaches 37 degrees toward the summit, the angle of rest for loose cinders. The volcano, though dormant since 1707, had experienced a dozen eruptions in the preceding 1,000 years. The 1707 eruption produced great clouds of ash, which turned day into night over Tokyo. The only present activity is a small fumerole on the summit. While Fuji is now inactive, no volcano can be considered dead until enough time has elapsed to erode the cone.

Earthquakes are common. Seismologists record about 1,500 minor shocks a year. Destructive quakes occur about once in three years, but commonly affect only small areas. There are seven principal seismic zones: (1) offshore along the margin of the continental shelf and the Japan deep, (2) along the coast of the Sea of Japan, (3) the western Inland Sea, (4) from Osaka past Lake Biwa to Tsuruga, (5) the Fossa Magna and Fuji zone, (6) the Nasu volcanic chain in northern Kyushu, and (7) the Ishikari Depression in Hokkaido. Where the earthquake centers are near large cities, great damage results, as at Tokyo and Yokohama on

Six-sevenths of Japan is hilly or mountainous. The seven geographic regions are as follows, reading from north to south: Hokkaido, Northern Honshu, the Kanto Plain, Central Honshu, Western Honshu, Shikoku, and Kyushu. (*Base map by Erwin Raisz*)

September 1, 1923, when 91,344 people perished in the resulting fire. Earthquake destruction is especially devastating on unconsolidated soil such as underlies many delta cities. When the displacement occurs beneath the sea, great "tidal" waves may be generated, known as tsunami.

More than 1,000 hot springs dot the islands; some are related to volcanic intrusions; others owe their temperature to heat generated by friction along fault zones. Health resorts have developed around many hot springs.

Within Japan is an infinite complex of topography, and yet essentially the same repetition of associated land forms. The islands have intricate patterns of microdetail rather than the gross structures of China. Two-thirds of the slopes are over 15 degrees, and less than 15 per cent of the land is approximately flat.

The country has no large plains, and mountains are everywhere within sight. Land that is even approximately level is limited to discontinuous fragments of uplifted sea floor, interior basins filled with debris, alluvial flood plains and deltas, and the dissected terraces of earlier streams. Valley floors have a noticeable slope, and down them during the rainy season flow turbulent yet overloaded mountain streams, whose braided courses are strewn with sand and cobbles. On either side dikes guard the adjoining fields, for so much deposition has occurred that the bed of the stream may be level with or above the surrounding countryside.

Not all the nearly level land is usable.

Japan has nearly 200 volcanoes, one-third of them more or less active. This is the eruption of December 1958 on Asamayama in Central Honshu. The crater has a circumference of 1.2 miles. (*Bruce Thompson, courtesy Japan Society*)

Coastal swamps and stony river beds almost defy reclamation. The largest areas of unused level land are former flood plains and coastal plains which now stand as terraces a few tens or even hundreds of feet above present stream levels. These upper surfaces, graded to sea level when the land was lower but now uplifted and dissected, are known as diluvial terraces, in contrast to the present-day undissected surfaces called alluvial. In some plains they cover one-fourth to one-half of the lowland area. Since diluvial terraces are built of sand and gravel and have a low water table, they are of limited use for Japan's great crop, rice. Irrigation is difficult since they lie above stream gradients and are too porous to hold standing water.

Scattered and discontinuous plains, peripheral and interior, form the principal home for the 100 million Japanese. The total level area does not exceed 20,000 square miles, no larger than half the state of Ohio. The four main islands contain about three dozen lowland areas large enough to identify, ranging from the Kanto Plain near Tokyo, with an area of about 2,500 square miles, of which more than half is in diluvial upland terraces, to strips a few hundred yards in width and a few miles in length. In addition to the Kanto Plain, the principal lowlands are the Kinai Plain around Osaka and Kyoto, the Nobi Plain near Nagoya, the Echigo Plain near Niigata on the western coast of northern Honshu, the Sendai Plain in the northeast, and the Ishikari, Tokachi, Nemuro, and Central Plains in Hokkaido.

Japanese rivers are short; the longest is but 229 miles from source to mouth. Because of their swiftness as well as the variation in seasonal flow, few of them are suitable for navigation. There are many possibilities for hydroelectric power development, but sites for large reservoirs are seldom available. Lake Biwa near Kyoto is the largest fresh-water body.

Fringing the sea are two types of coast line, one with cliffs and offshore islands, the other low and often swampy and usually near the mouth of a short torrential stream. The coast is highly irregular and has numerous large embayments on the Pacific side. The ratio of 1 mile of coast line to 8.5 square miles of area, in contrast to 1 to 13 for Great Britain, shows how close the Japanese live to the sea. It is probable that 90 per cent of Japan's actual coast is almost inaccessible, either on foot or by boat.

The geomorphic pattern of Japan may be grouped in either of two twofold divisions. The north differs from the southwest, and even more the Pacific side differs from that next to the Sea of Japan. These four areas meet west of Tokyo in the Central Mountain Knot, or Japanese Alps, known to the Japanese as the Hida Range. East of the range is the down-faulted Fossa Magna. Between the young folded mountains on the Pacific side that form the Outer Zone and the Inner Zone of block mountains lies a linear series of faults and tectonic depressions. From the island of Kyushu in the southwest to Hokkaido in the north, this boundary is marked by bold fault scarps and grabens. Contrasts between Pacific and Asiatic sides are especially marked in the southwest.

The Outer Zone along the Pacific has well-developed parallel ridges and depressions. The mountains are high and rugged, with few plains, and are underlain by a regular arrangement of crystalline schists and of altered and folded sedimentaries. Volcanic rocks are rare in the south but abundant in the north, especially in Hokkaido.

The Inner Zone is a series of fault-block plateaus, dissected into steep-sided hills and mountains. The geological structure is that of elongated domes with ancient sedimentary rocks and granitic intrusions, greatly disturbed but without regular folding. Faulting and volcanic activity are widespread. The Inland Sea lies between the Inner and Outer Zones and occupies a series of submerged fault blocks, whose former mountain peaks now project as islands. Whereas few summits in the Outer Zone exceed 3,500 feet, altitudes of 6,000 feet are common in the Inner Zone.

Central Japan is cut by a transverse low-

Japan has two types of lowland surfaces: alluvial flood plains graded to present river levels and older surfaces, now uplifted and in process of dissection, known as the diluvium. While the former can be irrigated and hence made to produce rice, the latter are above stream levels and may be too sandy to hold irrigation water.

land which extends from the Pacific to the Sea of Japan, known as the Fossa Magna. Along the western margin of this depression is a fault scarp over 6,000 feet high, and at its base are a series of grabens. Great volcanoes have been poured out along this fault zone, notably Mount Fuji. The highest elevations and most alpine topography of the country are found just west of the Fossa Magna, with several peaks in excess of 10,000 feet.

Vertical zonation dominates the Japanese scene. Delta plains are bordered by diluvial terraces. Above them rise low foothills of weak Tertiary sediments which merge with high mountains carved in crystallines or old sedimentary rocks. Enclosed within these moun-

tains are numerous alluvial basins at various elevations. Alpine land forms are found near the highest summits. Throughout the geographic story to follow, the greatest contrasts are between elevations rather than between north and south. Climate, forests, agriculture, land use, and settlement all reflect this characteristic layering with altitude.

An accurate knowledge of land forms is thus basic in the understanding of how people live in Japan. With only one-seventh of the land approximately level and much of the rest too steep to be terraced or otherwise utilized except for forests, the Japanese face inescapable problems. Viewed from the sea, Japan rises hill upon hill; seen from the land, the pano-

The Hida Range, known to Westerners as the Japanese Alps, dominates central Honshu west of Tokyo and provides rugged assignments for alpinists. The central peak is called the Yari or spear. (*Ewing Galloway*)

rama is water, water everywhere. The two dominant aspects of her physical setting are thus the restricted extent of level land and insularity. Over large areas the Japanese are plainsmen enveloped in mountains; elsewhere they have become fishermen.

CLIMATE

Japan generally enjoys favorable climate, but conditions cannot be judged by latitude and solar insolation alone. The islands are warmer than comparable parts of China to the west, yet cooler than Mediterranean lands on the same parallel. Since the islands lie off the east coast of a great land mass, powerful continental influences are modified by marine conditions.

The islands have an extent of 1,500 miles, and the irregularities of topography introduce sharp vertical contrasts. Climatic conditions in Japan correspond somewhat to those in eastern North America, between Georgia and Nova Scotia, except that during both summer and winter Japan has higher humidity. The most populous part of Japan lies in the latitude of the Carolinas, 400 miles south of the American center of population.

During the summer a gentle flow of hot, moist air moves over Japan from the Pacific. In winter months conditions are reversed, with strong winds, cold and dry, from Siberia. Thus tropical Pacific air masses dominate one season, while polar continental air masses rule the other; of these, the latter are the more dynamic.

Several centers of action account for this basic circulation. During the winter the semi-permanent anticyclone south of Lake Baikal pours great quantities of very cold, dry air over eastern Asia. Two main streams of this air cross Japan; one moves eastward to the Aleutian winter low-pressure area, and the other and stronger is drawn southward to the equatorial low beyond the China Sea. This merging of clockwise winds from the continental high-pressure area with oceanic counterclockwise low-pressure circulation develops the outblowing winter monsoon.

With the arrival of summer, conditions are reversed. The high temperatures of northern China and Mongolia give rise to an area of low pressure, producing an inblowing cyclone; at the same time, high pressure over the north Pacific is intensified and feeds the stationary Asiatic low. The result is the summer monsoon.

The winter monsoon blows from the northwest over Japan. The summer monsoon has weak winds which are less dependable; they come from the south and east to Japan. Although the winter circulation produces marked temperature contrasts from north to south, summer conditions are more nearly uniform throughout. Thus the north–south January gradient is 2.6°F per degree of latitude, whereas in the summer it is but 1°F. The average January range from southern Kyushu to central Hokkaido is 29°F; in July the difference amounts to only 9°F.

Superimposed on these monsoon tendencies is a parade of cyclonic and anticyclonic storms, moving northeastward out of China. These introduce a nonperiodic element, especially during the winter and spring seasons.

During winter months most of the disturbances come from the Yangtze valley; at other seasons the sources are both central China and the lands farther north, even including Siberia. These traveling storms move the length of the Japanese islands and continue via the Aleutians and Alaska to the United States.

During June and July weak tropical lows cross Japan and bring warm, sultry weather.

The rains of this period occur during the time of the plum blossoms and are known as the "plum blossom rains" or *Bai-u*. This is a time of cloudiness, high humidity, protracted gentle rain, and high sensible temperatures. Convectional showers occur in the summer months, often in the warm sector of cyclonic storms.

When cyclonic whirls cross Japan during the time of polar continental air movements from Asia, the back side of each cyclonic storm, with its northern circulation, combines with the outblowing winter monsoon from the same direction to produce powerful northwest winds, while on the forward side of the low the two wind tendencies are in opposition. The reverse tends to occur in summer, when the southerly component of the cyclonic storm supplements the southern monsoon, except that neither cyclonic storms nor the movements of tropical Pacific air masses are so well developed at this season. At all times the front and back of each cyclonic whirl tend alternately to augment or to cancel the monsoon tendency.

Typhoons, a third factor, still further influence this circulation. These storms are apt to pass over or near Japan once or twice a month in the late summer and fall. It is often said that typhoons most often occur between the two hundred and tenth and two hundred and twentieth days of the lunar year, thus early in September. Although less severe than along the shores of China, the storms may cause serious damage. Destructiveness from typhoon winds is limited to the southern coasts, but torrential rain may be widespread, with resulting floods from mountain streams. Typhoons may bring 15 inches of rain in 24 hours, even 39 inches on one occasion. Single storms may cause damage amounting to several hundred million dollars.

The principal oceanic circulation in the western Pacific is the Kuroshio or Black Current, the largest current in any ocean, with a volume 5,000 times that of the Mississippi. It is often known as the Japan Current. The temperature of the water rarely drops below 68°F, and may reach 80°F in summer. It bathes the southeastern shores of Japan but turns eastward away from the coast near Tokyo. A branch of this warm circulation enters the Sea of Japan, where it is known as the Tsushima Current. Thus summer winds from the Pacific pass over the Kuroshio and are warmed.

A minor cold current from the north, the Oyashio or Okhotsk Current, hugs the western coasts of Hokkaido and northern Honshu. Its temperature rarely exceeds 65°F. Thus winter winds from Asia are moderated in temperature and given an increased moisture content as they cross the Sea of Japan. Since the warm offshore Kuroshio lies to leeward of the islands, it is scarcely effective in winter. The situation is somewhat comparable to the Gulf Stream and Labrador Current in the Atlantic. Fog is a common result when warm air passes over cold water.

All parts of the islands have adequate precipitation, but relief makes the rainfall pattern very patchy. Several stations in the south along the Pacific receive over 125 inches, and there is a similar precipitation maximum along the central part of the Sea of Japan side. Rainfall in interior basins drops below 40 inches only in a few localities. Except along the west coast, the precipitation maximum at most stations occurs during the summer, a result of the monsoon plus Bai-u and typhoon rains. Winter winds are dry as they blow out from the interior of Asia, but in crossing the Sea of Japan

Many Japanese mountains receive heavy snowfall, so that ski areas are accessible to most cities. This is the Iwappara area in Niigata Prefecture. (*Courtesy Japan Tourist Association*)

they acquire some moisture and may yield heavy snowfall on the western slopes of Honshu and Hokkaido. Snow remains on the ground along the west coast as far south as central Honshu; on the Pacific side, in contrast, only the northern end of the island has a snow cover.

August is the hottest month. Tropical clothing is worn everywhere during the summer even in Hokkaido, and the high humidity and sultry air are enervating. South of Tokyo, books, shoes, and clothing are quickly covered with mildew in summer. Mosquito nets are required almost the year round in southern Japan.

Since the populous part of Japan is toward the south, many people make summer trips to mountain or seaside resorts. For one not accustomed to the humidity, it is particularly desirable to avoid the period of the Bai-u rains that occur from June to July.

The frost-free period, essentially equivalent to the growing season, ranges from 120 days in the interior of Hokkaido and 160 days in mountainous Honshu to 240 days along the southeastern coast. Southern Kyushu has 300 frost-free days. Thus two crops of rice may be grown in parts of Kyushu, Shikoku, and the southern peninsulas of Honshu.

Various attempts have been made to subdivide Japan into climatic divisions. In the Koeppen classification, all of Kyushu, Shikoku, and northern Honshu, except the northern highlands, belong to the *Cfa* (mild winter, always humid, hot summer) type, while Hokkaido is classed as *Dfb* (severe winter, humid, cool summers), or *Dfa* in mountainous Honshu.

There are thus three major climatic regions. The first covers most of Hokkaido, with four months of mean temperatures below freezing and only 120 to 150 days of growing season. Precipitation on the lowlands ranges from 30 to 40 inches, decreasing toward the north.

Central Japan, the second division, is characterized by moderate climates, a mean annual temperature below 68°F, and 175 to 220 frost-free days; rainfall amounts to 40 to 60 inches. Within central Japan are three subregions: the southwest tip of Hokkaido, somewhat warmer

than the rest of the island; the Sea of Japan province with abundant winter snow which exceeds the summer precipitation; and the Pacific province, characterized by a summer precipitation maximum and mild, sunshiny winters. This large region includes all of eastern and southern Honshu and northern Kyushu.

A third climatic division is found in southern Japan, with mean annual temperatures of more than 68°F, 240 to 300 days when crops may grow, and up to 125 inches of rain.

There is a noticeable contrast between the cloudy and cool coast of the Sea of Japan, known as the shady side, and the warm Pacific coast, known as the sunny side.

Despite the wide contrasts, all lowland areas have adequate warmth and rainfall for agriculture. Slight differences in altitude result in marked differences in land use. Variations in orographic rainfall, temperature gradients, air drainage, and the length of critical growing periods restrict certain crops to certain elevations. This vertical zonation brings together within a few miles horizontally the climatic zones that would otherwise lie 1,000 miles apart. Bamboo and rice are within sight of snow fields and the tree line. Japan's climate is as micropatterned as its topography.

FORESTS AND SOILS

Half of Japan is still covered with forest, though little of it is virgin growth. An additional 15 per cent is in brush or fields of wild, coarse grass. Almost all of this is in mountainous areas, and about a quarter of the forests are in areas which are economically inaccessible. Except for a few alpine meadows above the tree line, trees almost everywhere represent the climax vegetation. Broad-leaved trees account for half of the forest area, with conifers representing a third.

Thanks to the absence of Pleistocene glaciation, the flora is exceptionally rich and diversified, with a range from palms and orchids to maples and pines. Hillsides are clothed in rich verdure, in striking contrast to Chinese provinces in the same latitudes. Bamboo, properly a grass rather than a tree, is widespread as far as northern Honshu.

Fall foliage is especially splendid. With the arrival of autumn, Japan, Manchuria, and the northeastern United States are the finest areas in the world for brilliant yellow and red leaves of maple, oak, and other deciduous trees. In the spring Japan's flowering plum and cherry trees are renowned. The magnificent stands of ancient cryptomeria which surround temples, shrines, and old castles attest to the Japanese appreciation of trees.

The vertical zonation of vegetation is noticeable in a country so mountainous as this. One may stand on the deck of a vessel along the shores of Japan and see this stratification rising from subtropical forms at sea level through successive climatic zones to boreal forests at heights of a mile or so. On the higher peaks one sees tundra zones next to summer snow fields. Climate paves the way for this zonation of vegetation, which in turn influences soil types and thus land use. The beauty of travel in Japan is the wide variety of landscapes which are accessible in a short horizontal distance. These transitions, plus the mingling of relict forms of vegetation, make mapping of forest types difficult.

In general, a subtropical forest covers lower elevations as far north as central Honshu near latitude 37°N, with broad-leaved evergreens such as camphors and some oaks.

Temperate mixed forests in northern Honshu and western Hokkaido are economically the most important for lumber. Maple, birch, beech, poplar, and oak mingle with fir, pine, hemlock, and cedar. Cryptomeria and pine are the chief commercial timbers. As one goes southward, these forms rise above sea level. In central Japan the boundary lies at 1,800 feet on Mount Fuji and somewhat above 3,000 feet in Kyushu.

Boreal forests cover the summits of the higher mountains in northern Honshu and the lowlands in eastern Hokkaido; fir and spruce predominate. Temperatures in the subtropical forest zone range from 55 to 70°F; in the temperate forest zone the mean annual temperature varies between 43 and 55°F; in the boreal forests averages are below 43°F.

Creditable progress has been made in reforestation, both for future timber and for flood control. On eroded slopes and near the headwaters of streams, large areas have been planted as protective forests, and the traveler cannot fail to be impressed with the care that has been used. Since lumbering methods often leave bare, steep slopes of loose ash or soil, erosion proceeds quite rapidly if the surface is not protected.

Charcoal is an important forest product and the chief household fuel. Many villages have their communal areas where charcoal is produced for domestic needs, and it is a common sight to see lines of people coming out of the woods laden with bundles of fuel. The annual value of charcoal is three-fourths the value of sawn timber. Whereas timber comes largely from conifers, hardwoods are preferred for charcoal.

Despite improvements in many aspects of forestry, the supply is inadequate, so that both timber and wood pulp are imported. Oregon, Washington, and British Columbia are a large source of supply, and prewar imports were made from Korea and Manchuria. Hokkaido has the largest domestic reserves, but in most years cutting exceeds growth.

Japanese soils tend to be thin and immature, reflecting the underlying rock rather than climatic influences or vegetation. Most soils are without a profile. Soils in the north are podsolic; in the south they are lateritic. One unique type is the dark acidic volcanic soil known as *ando*.

Flood-plain and delta sediments form the best agricultural land, and sandy, recent alluvium is favored over the coarser diluvium. Volcanic soils are generally infertile, as they are derived from acidic lavas or ash. Herein is an important contrast with the rich basic lava soils in Java and the Philippines.

Podsolized soils of various types cover much

of Hokkaido and are present on higher elevations in northern Honshu. This location roughly corresponds to the area of boreal forests. Northern lowland Honshu is a region of brown forest soils, some of them slightly podsolized. The southern part of Japan has yellow and red forest soils with lateritic tendencies.

MINERAL RESOURCES

Japan is fortunate in having a wide variety of mineral wealth, but the reserves of most of them are inadequate. Only coal, copper, chromium, gold, silver, sulfur, and zinc are present in large quantities, and in few instances is there any surplus. Even the domestic production of coal meets only nine-tenths of the consumption, largely because of the necessity of importing coking coal. While none of the following minerals appear adequate, there is a small production of antimony, asbestos, lead, manganese, mercury, nickel, salt, tin, titanium, and tungsten. Japan is clearly short of iron ore. There seems to be little or no aluminum, cobalt, fluorite, magnesite, mica, molybdenum, and vanadium, or mineral fertilizers such as nitrate, phosphate, or potash. The modest status of Japan's mineral industry is indicated by the fact that it provides only 2 per cent of the national income.

Three commodities account for an overwhelming share of the total mineral output. Coal represents about one-half, followed by gold and copper. Despite her material handicaps at home, Japan has achieved a great industrial development on the basis of imported raw materials, such as coal, oil, and scrap steel from the United States, and iron and aluminum ores from the South Seas.

The following paragraphs will consider power resources, metals, and nonmetallic minerals.

Coal provides the largest source of heat and energy, closely followed by water power. Japan is comfortably supplied with coal and hydroelectricity but has very little oil or natural gas. Coal, which is widely distributed, is predominantly bituminous, of only fair quality; very

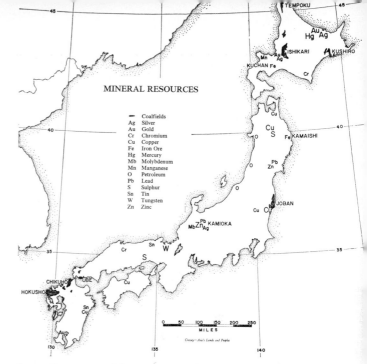

MINERAL RESOURCES

—	Coalfields
Ag	Silver
Au	Gold
Cr	Chromium
Cu	Copper
Fe	Iron Ore
Hg	Mercury
Mb	Molybdenum
Mn	Manganese
O	Petroleum
Pb	Lead
S	Sulphur
Sn	Tin
W	Tungsten
Zn	Zinc

Japan has a surprising amount of mineral wealth, although production is usually inadequate to meet domestic needs. The size of the symbol suggests relative importance within Japan.

little is suitable for even low-grade metallurgical coke. Coal deposits are found in Paleozoic, Mesozoic, and Tertiary rocks, the latter being by far the most important. Lignite is widespread. The reserves are thought to be adequate for 200 years, but most seams are thin and broken, and dip steeply. Ground water often presents a problem in mining.

Half of the reserves of coal are in central and southern Hokkaido, Kyushu, and east central Honshu. Since the development of modern mining, the leading area of production has been northwestern Kyushu, which supplies about one-half of the output. Most of this comes from the Chikuho field south of Moji. Production in Hokkaido is increasing, and the island accounts for one-third of the national total. Next in importance is the Joban field north of Tokyo. The production in all Japan amounts to over 50 million metric tons. Since this amount is inadequate, several million tons of coking coal and anthracite are imported, formerly from Korea, China, and Indochina, but after the war, from the United States. Japanese coal is well suited for steamship boilers, and Nagasaki was once an important bunkering point for steamers from Europe and across the Pacific.

Japan's reserves, even including all possible deposits, amount to less than 200 tons per capita as compared with 4,000 for the United Kingdom and 25,000 for the United States. Although production may continue for many years, and should prove adequate for domestic needs, there is little likelihood that Japan can increase her production to compete in heavy industries with the leading countries of the world. Any great industrialization must depend upon imported fuel.

The second great source of modern power is petroleum. Japan's chief producing districts are in the Niigata, Akita, and Yamagata prefectures on the Sea of Japan side of Honshu, and the Ishikari plain in Hokkaido. Most of the wells are shallow, and the oil is generally of poor quality. The supply is only one-tenth of Japan's annual needs, and is less than the daily yield in the United States. Despite strenuous effort over past decades, the geology of the country does not warrant the prospect that the output can be materially increased.

The rugged topography and heavy precipitation of the central mountains lend themselves to the development of water power, but the variable flow of most rivers has made it necessary to build standby thermal electric plants. Since canyons are narrow and offer little storage room, several dams are 500 feet high. Japan now has few undeveloped water-power sites, and they are mostly small in size and lack adequate reservoir storage to equalize the highly seasonal flow. Out of an ultimate theoretical production of 12 million kilowatts, three-quarters is already in use. The major consumption of electricity is in three load centers around the Japanese Alps: Tokyo and Yokohama; Kyoto, Osaka, and Kobe; and Nagoya.

Japan's resources of iron ore are notably insufficient. Reserves are small, and the iron content of most deposits is low. Less than a dozen deposits are in commercial production. The output of iron ore is largely from Kamaishi in northern Honshu and Kutchan in southern Hokkaido. To meet the deficiency, three-quarters of Japan's iron ore is imported. The supply once came from Korea, the central Yangtze valley, Malaya, the Philippine Islands, India, and Australia. Supplies from mainland Asia were cut off by the war. Although Japan imports much of her iron ore, the use of large quantities of imported scrap iron enables her to carry on a slight export of steel, even to the United States.

Copper is the second most important mineral product in Japan, and the country usually ranks sixth or seventh in world production. Although Japanese copper accounts for only 2 or 3 per cent of the world total, it forms a basis for her electrical industry. The production is from northern Honshu and Shikoku.

The production of gold and silver has long been of nominal importance, but in recent decades the output has grown rapidly. Japan ranks twelfth among world gold producers. Three-fourths of the silver output is obtained as a by-product in the smelting of copper.

Zinc is much more plentiful than lead, so that Japan ranks about sixth in world output. There are no domestic ores of aluminum. Less than half of Japan's manganese is obtained at home.

The most noteworthy nonmetallic resource of the islands is sulfur, one of the basic tonnage materials needed for industry. High-grade deposits are widely distributed, usually in association with volcanic rocks. In addition to native sulfur, there is also a production from pyrite, an iron sulfide which is also a source of pig iron. The availability of sulfur furnishes a basis for such industries as the manufacture of paper, celluloid, and rayon. Part of the production is usually available for export.

Salt is obtained from sea water, but since the high humidity does not favor solar evaporation, the final crystallization requires artificial heat. Production around the Inland Sea is barely sufficient for salt in foodstuffs, and most of the industrial needs, which are twice those of

The shores of northern Japan are lined with fishing villages which take advantage of fishing areas made possible by the Okhotsk current. These are crab boats, leaving the mother ship. (*Courtesy Japanese Consulate General, New York City*)

household salt, are secured from East Africa or elsewhere overseas.

Despite strenuous efforts for many years to increase the home supply of minerals, the percentage of import remains high, usually about 50 per cent.

The geology of Japan is now well enough known to suggest that she cannot look forward to great industrial developments based on her domestic mineral resources. There are barely enough minerals for internal needs, let alone world trade. What Japan has done in industry is a tribute to her resourcefulness rather than a result of the gifts of nature. Fortunately Japan does have coal, although it lacks coking qualities. Economic or political conditions may make it feasible to import ores from the mainland or from countries to the south. Japan's industrial future would appear to rely upon such indigenous resources as cheap power, specialized agricultural products, skilled labor, and ingenuity.

15 Livelihood in Japan

*Agriculture / Fishing / Economic Developments /
International Relations*

AGRICULTURE

Japanese agriculture is designed to produce the maximum number of calories per acre. This means a concentration on rice, wheat, and vegetables rather than on meat or dairy products. Since labor and fertilizers are used intensively, crop yields are high. Yet food remains one of Japan's major problems.

Japan is still a nation of farmers. Despite dramatic urbanization and industrialization, one-third of all the working population is engaged in agriculture. In 1930 the percentage was one-half, while at the beginning of the century the fraction was two-thirds. Even fac-

tory workers are closely tied to the land, for many of them were born on farms where their relatives still live. Agrarian reform following the Second World War resulted in most farmers owning their own land.

The area under cultivation amounts to 16 per cent of Japan's total area. This proportion compares with 12 per cent in China, 25 per cent in India with Pakistan, and 30 to 40 per cent in Western Europe.

Prior to the Second World War the ratio of cultivated land increased slowly, rising from 12 per cent in 1887 to 14 per cent in 1902 and 16 per cent by 1919. Since the 1930s the percentage has remained constant, as the cultivation of new areas has been balanced by the loss of marginal land which has gone out of use or has been taken over by urban areas which have spilled into the countryside. Pastures amount to an additional 4 per cent.

Apparently the economic maximum has been reached. Any further addition to the present cultivated acreage will depend upon expensive irrigation, drainage, or fertilization. Considerable areas of diluvial upland remain uncultivated, apparently because they are uneconomic for rice culture or other developments.

Since farm households number 6 million, the tilled area per family is about 2 acres; in comparison, the average farm in the United States measures 150 acres. This size is quadrupled in Hokkaido and reduced to little more than an acre in southwest Japan. As a result of generations of subdivision, many farms have come to embrace several widely scattered plots, which are in turn divided into tiny, unfenced fields, even as small as one-sixth or one-tenth of an acre in size. In some localities governmental action has led to a consolidation of land holdings with some resulting increase in yields. The uneconomic fragmentation has its minor advantages, for a flood or crop failure in some fields may still leave the farmer with a yield elsewhere.

Rice accounts for over half of the crop area, most of it irrigated. Rice, the master crop, is the characteristic food from the south almost to the extreme north, although the trend is toward more wheat. As elsewhere in the Orient, rice is generally sown in seedbeds and transplanted by hand in flooded fields. Skillful cultivation, thorough fertilization, and scientific seed development have raised the per acre yield to the highest in the world.

Japanese canals, unlike those in China, are used for irrigation only and are thus mere ditches. In order to keep the land flooded,

Rice is first sown in seedbeds, shown in the foreground, and transplanted after a month to the prepared fields. (*Courtesy Japanese Consulate General, New York City*)

ridges a foot or so wide and high separate individual fields, and the surplus water is led from one level to another. Some of these miniature dikes may be planted with a row of mulberry trees, soybeans, or other crops. Elsewhere they form narrow paths, precariously slippery and winding for the bicyclist.

Two successive harvests of rice per year are found only on the extreme south coasts of Shikoku and Kyushu. As far north as Sendai two crops are interplanted, one maturing several weeks in advance of the other. Sixty per cent of the rice fields are left fallow during the winter; many remain flooded, since they are too low to be properly drained.

Winter cropping is negligible north of Sendai, but is common in the south. The index of double cropping reaches 170 in Kyushu, amounts to 140 around Tokyo, and drops to 110 in northern Honshu. Where rice fields are planted to fall crops, these are wheat, barley, rapeseed, or vegetables. Because of wet soil

Tea leaves are harvested several times a year. This scene is in Shizuoka Prefecture, Japan's leading area for tea. (*Courtesy Japan Tourist Association*)

the earth is heaped into ridges on which seeds are sown. Intervening depressions are often flooded by the winter rains.

Wheat, rye, barley, oats, and rapeseed account for about half of the area devoted to rice. They are grown as spring crops in Hokkaido or as fall crops farther south, either on paddy fields after the rice harvest or on diluvial uplands after a crop of beans or vegetables. With the introduction of Western habits of diet, the consumption of bread has increased. Sweet potatoes are a large crop in the south, with some white potatoes in the north. Carbohydrates represent an overabundant proportion of Japanese diet.

The domestic supplies of rice and wheat are normally inadequate for the expanding population, so that in most years several million tons must be obtained from abroad.

Despite the widespread use of tea, less than 0.5 per cent of all cropland is devoted to its production. Diluvial uplands and steep terraced hill slopes are commonly selected, especially in the vicinity of Shizuoka.

Silk was formerly the great cash crop of the Japanese farmer, and mulberry leaves for feeding the silkworms were raised in every district south of Sendai. One-fourth of all the upland fields in crops was once given over to mulberry, notably in central Honshu in the hinterland of Yokohama. In several interior basins, such as Suwa, mulberry occupied over half of the cultivated area. Many rice farmers in the lowlands have a small patch of mulberry or scattered trees around the house or fields. While mulberry trees will grow to considerable height, they are trimmed back to bush size so that the leaves may be easily gathered from the ground.

Synthetic substitutes have greatly reduced the market for Japanese silk.

Other cash crops are flax and hemp, pyrethrum for insecticides, tobacco, peppermint, and camphor. Common vegetables include the giant radish known as daikon for pickles; soy, kidney, and red beans; peas; and taro. Interculture is common, and several crops a year may be grown on the same field.

Fruit is widely and increasingly grown. Oranges lead and yield best in southern Japan. They are followed by persimmons, apples, pears, grapes, and peaches. Apples are raised in the highlands of Honshu and in Hokkaido.

The animal industry is small but growing. Dairy cows increased from 100,000 in 1935 to nearly 1 million by 1960, and the total number of cattle exceeds 3 million. Pigs number nearly 2 million, and there are 1 million sheep. The few horses are kept largely for draft purposes on the farm. The limited number of animals reflects the pressure of human population for food and may also be accounted for by the lack of good pasture land, the poor native grasses, the long hot summers, and the reluctance of the Japanese rice farmer to keep ani-

The pressure for food has led to the terracing of every available hillside. Rice and snow do not normally go together, but the Japanese have developed varieties which mature in Hokkaido during the hot summer. (*Courtesy Japanese Consulate General, New York City*)

mals. Orthodox Buddhists do not eat meat. From the earliest times fish has taken the place of meat as the main sustenance in the diet.

The production of food for 100 million people living on crowded islands requires that crop yields be at a maximum. Unfortunately Japanese soils are poor. The diluvium is usually sandy and sterile, uplands are leached, and soils developed on volcanic parent materials are infertile. Only by the most painstaking and repeated fertilization can adequate crops be grown. In the production of rice, the expense of fertilizer stands next to wages in the average cost. Commercial fertilizers, such as soybean or other oil cake, waste from fish or from silk cocoons, and prepared minerals supplement farm-supplied fertilizer, which includes compost, human excrement or night soil, and animal manure.

Modern science has contributed much to Japanese agriculture, chiefly through commercial fertilizer, seed improvement, and protection from crop diseases. Complex machinery is impractical in the tiny fields, so that the spade, hoe, and plow remain the traditional tools. Small two-wheeled tractors are coming into wide use. Since mechanical power for pumping irrigation water may be too expensive, water is lifted by man or animal power.

Japan needs more food, but can find little additional acreage. Increased harvests must come from the physical improvement of the existing cropland, better management, and new varieties of seeds or crops.

Westerners too often look at Asia in terms of their own special backgrounds and judge Oriental conditions by what they have supposed ideal. We should do well to consider the comments of Ambassador Edwin O. Reischauer, who writes: [1]

Japanese methods of agriculture, involving as they do an immense amount of arduous hand labor, seem primitive and inefficient to most Americans. With our simple faith in machinery

[1] Edwin Oldfather Reischauer: *The United States and Japan,* Cambridge, Mass.: Harvard University Press (1950), 58–59. Quoted by permission.

we often feel that mechanization of agriculture in Japan would not only save labor but would also increase production. Unfortunately, saving labor in a densely populated land like Japan means nothing unless the labor saved can be profitably employed in other tasks, and the concept that production can be increased by mechanizing farming is a complete fallacy as far as Japan is concerned. Tractors are used to a slight extent in the island of Hokkaido, but they are of little use in the narrow hillside terraces and tiny paddy fields that make up so much of Japan's farm land. And even on the broader stretches of flat fields, mechanization of the sort common in this country would on the whole decrease the yield rather than increase it. Machines have not been invented which till the soil as effectively as the great Japanese hoe with its two-foot blade. Nor have machines been invented which can equal the skill and loving care of the individual farm wife transplanting rice seedlings by hand. It would be as practical to mechanize the growing of flowers around an average suburban home in this country as to mechanize a Japanese farm. Japanese farming is really gardening, with the prolific farmer and his family lavishing as much work and care on each square yard of their land as an American family would on its prize flower bed. . . .

Actually, Japanese farming stands at a high level of achievement, given the special relationship of man to land existing in Japan. The tools and techniques used, while recklessly extravagant of manpower, make the most of every cultivable scrap of land, which is as it must be wherever men are overabundant and land is scarce.

Wide variations in agriculture exist from place to place within Japan. These will be discussed in Chapter 16 on the regions of Japan.

FISHING

Crowded Japan looks out on a friendly sea. Typhoons occasionally devastate the shores, but there are innumerable protected harbors. Sheltered waters such as the Inland Sea invite the fisherman and trader. The waters around Japan comprise the greatest fishing grounds of the world; both in tonnage and value the catch exceeds that of any other country. The annual

The seas which surround Japan provide the richest fishing grounds in the world, thanks in part to the mixing of warm and cold ocean currents. Fish largely replace meat in Japanese diet. (*Courtesy Japanese Consulate General, New York City*)

catch is over 5 million tons, almost a quarter of the world's fish supply. Fish and other marine products are one of the basic exports from Japan. These pastures of the sea furnish a considerable part of the Japanese diet, for fish is an integral item in every meal, as important as meat in European countries.

Fishing interests characterize all the shores of Japan, even where there are no harbors. The calm Inland Sea, the stormy borders of the Sea of Okhotsk, and the coasts of Honshu each have their fishing villages. In many instances, these settlements fringe a mile or more of narrow gravel beach backed by mountains, so that virtually no level land is available for agriculture. Houses line the shore just above high-tide mark, often clinging to the cliffs. The beach is strewn with boats, nets, and racks for drying fish. Contact with the rest of Japan may be exclusively by boat. Many of these villages reflect the poverty of those who engage in the industry. About a million Japanese are fishermen, some the year round, others seasonally.

Off the east coast flows the warm northbound Kuroshio or Japan Current with a branch that enters the Sea of Japan, while the cold current known as the Oyashio moves southward from the Sea of Okhotsk to the Sea of Japan. The warm Kuroshio waters thus surround south and central Honshu. They provide a rich habitat for a number of species, including sardines, mackerel, and tuna, and supply the largest total catch. The cold Oyashio area surrounds Hokkaido and spreads along the Asiatic coast to Korea; it is notable for herring, salmon, and cod. Between the two currents lies a shifting zone of mixed waters, found especially on both sides of northern Honshu; here the catch fluctuates widely from year to year as the currents shift.

Varied environments are hospitable to many kinds of aquatic life. The limited supplies of food on the land, the coastal character of the population, and the highly indented shore line all tend to push people to the sea. Within the present century fishing has expanded from a littoral and small-boat industry to one that ranges from the sub-Arctic to Antarctica. The annual catch varies according to biological conditions, ocean currents, and economic factors. There is some indication that the seas around Japan may have been "overharvested" and that conservation may be needed.

Coastwise and near-shore fishing account for half of the yield, with the leading items in order as follows: sardines; seaweeds for food, fertilizer, fodder, or iodine; salmon; cuttlefish; yellowtail; and shellfish. Most of the near-shore catch is obtained in picturesque sailboats or rowboats which return home each night.

Deep-sea fishing represents a growing part of the total industry. Sardine, cod, bonito, shark, mackerel, and tuna are the principal fish. Modern refrigeration has made it possible for Japanese vessels to operate at great distances, even along the coasts of Alaska and Chile. Floating canneries prepare large amounts of crab and salmon for export. There is also some whaling, coral and pearl collection, and aquaculture on the land. Several Japanese whaling ships visit Antarctic waters.

After Japan's emergence toward the close of the nineteenth century, she built a merchant marine that now ranks among the world leaders. This rapid maritime expansion reflects the intimate familiarity with the sea and its ways which is a feature of Japan. Fisheries are schools of seamanship, for those who live on the water learn to read the clouds and find their way over horizonless seas.

ECONOMIC DEVELOPMENTS

Few aspects of twentieth-century Japan are more spectacular than the rise of modern industry. Although most of the modern factories are in the larger cities, even rural landscapes have been changed. Modern factories literally pop out of the rice fields. Cities have grown enormously and have cosmopolitan cores, although residential sections are still in the old style. Towering factories with their smoke and noise are increasingly common; in addition to Western-style industry there are many small plants, often family-owned.

Current population increases cannot be absorbed on the farms; hence a large labor surplus is available to industry at nominal cost. Wages, which were once very low, have been considerably raised, but since costs of urban living have increased even faster, the lot of many factory employees is marginal.

Japanese industry was once highly monopolistic and achieved its start through government subsidies. Most of it was in the hands of a few great families, for instance, the Mitsui, Mitsubishi, and Sumitomo. Through various corporations these families, known as the Zai-batsu, owned banks, shipping lines, textile mills, heavy industries, import and export firms, and even controlled much of the handicraft. The activity of these giant combines extended Japan's trade to the corners of the world. Wherever there was a market for goods that Japan was able to produce, these firms made her a serious competitor.

Since Japan is deficient in many raw materials, the foundation of her export industry is the fabrication of other people's raw materials into articles to fit the tastes and pocketbooks of overseas customers. Her profit lies in the value added by manufacture.

The distribution of industry corresponds with

Japan ranks sixth in world steel production, although both coking coal and much of her iron ore must be imported. (*Courtesy Japanese Consulate General, New York City*)

The Strait of Shimonoseki forms the western entrance to the Inland Sea, with a succession of wharves and industry along the narrow coastal plain. A tunnel now leads to Moji, in the distance. (*Courtesy John H. Thompson*)

the belt of densest population, which can offer labor supply and consumption potential. The local availability of power from hydroelectricity and coal, the proximity of harbors for importing overseas raw materials, a supply of workers, and access to markets are prime factors in locating Japanese industry.

The shores of the Inland Sea plus an extension eastward to Tokyo mark the leading industrial area of Japan. The distance from Nagasaki to Tokyo is 600 miles, and along this line is a discontinuous collection of factory towns. Four areas stand out: Northern Kyushu, Osaka-Kobe-Kyoto, Nagoya, and Tokyo-Yokohama. Within each area are industrial landscapes which are scarcely to be distinguished from those in the West.

Northern or Kita Kyushu has had European contacts longer than any other part of Japan, chiefly at Nagasaki with the Portuguese and Dutch, who introduced shipbuilding. This city was an early coaling port for European steamers, but most of them now call at Moji instead. The district has abundant coal, although it is not of good coking quality, and is well situated for the importation of overseas iron ore. Kita Kyushu thus accounts for a significant share of Japan's steel and heavy industry, including cement, glass, and chemicals. Since level land is at a premium, there is an irregular succession of industrial towns along the coast for many miles. The urbanized area on both sides of the Strait of Shimonoseki is often referred to as Kammon. The chief center is at Yawata near

Moji, where blast furnaces and steel mills produce several million tons a year.

Osaka, Japan's leading industrial city, specializes in the country's traditional product, cotton and synthetic textiles. Steel fabrication, shipbuilding, and heavy industry are increasingly important both here and in nearby Kobe. The combined industrial area is known as Hanshin. Whereas Osaka has ample level land, Kobe unfortunately lies on a narrow alluvial fan with inadequate room for industry.

Inland Kyoto, the old imperial capital, is in marked contrast to the Hanshin area. It is not a modern industrial city; instead, it specializes in artistic crafts, such as silk weaving, pottery, cloisonné, lacquer, bamboo, bronze, and toys.

The Osaka-Kobe-Kyoto region lacks both cheap power and raw materials, but it does have skilled labor and a central location. More than a million factory workers live here, and account for 20 per cent of Japan's industrial production.

Nagoya is a replica of Osaka in bay-head location and products, chiefly textiles, automobiles, and machinery for industry. The pottery business is centered here, thanks to nearby kaolin deposits. The labor force exceeds some 750,000 people.

Tokyo and Yokohama have more industrial diversification than Osaka and tend more toward light industry. In the hinterland lies the chief silk area, and Yokohama is the closest port of shipment for the American market. Silk reeling and weaving, the manufacture of machinery and electrical goods, printing, and a wide variety of skilled-labor industries are found here, including the making of optical

Scores of modern industrial cities can duplicate the landscape of this chemical plant. Most industry is located near tidewater to take advantage of imported raw materials and to facilitate exports. (*Courtesy Japanese Consulate General, New York City*)

goods and cameras. Electrical power is available from the nearby mountains.

The Kanto Plain around Tokyo holds Japan's largest concentration of industry, with more than a million factory workers and nearly 25 per cent of the country's total output. Industries focus on the Keihin conurbation, centered on Tokyo, Yokohama, and intervening Kawasaki. Excellent port facilities provide for the importation of raw materials and the export of manufactured goods, and the dense population furnishes manpower and a concentrated domestic market.

INTERNATIONAL RELATIONS

Japan must trade to live. Imports are essential even for basic livelihood, and to pay for them Japan must find markets. Overseas political relations are of pressing domestic concern. Few nations have developed world trade so rapidly. Since the opening of Japan in 1853, the country has made enormous strides in its international position. External expansion was especially noticeable between the First and Second World Wars.

In the international market Japan's great assets have been a considerable measure of skill and efficiency, cheap labor, and nearness to Asiatic consumers. Essential raw materials being scarce, exports must rest in part on imports. As long as Japan can add enough secondary value to basic raw commodities through manufacturing, and as long as she is not faced with too high tariff walls, she can probably command a market. The real test is comparative inventiveness and commercial skill. Japan can secure markets only so long as she makes a cheaper or better product than her competitors and enjoys international good will.

The first contacts with Europe came with the arrival of the Portuguese and Dutch at Nagasaki in the middle of the sixteenth century, but this trade was shortly suppressed and later restricted to one Dutch ship a year. Not until the treaties arranged by Admiral Perry in 1854 were foreigners permitted to carry on commerce, and the conspicuous developments date from the Meiji Restoration in 1868.

The First World War presented great commercial opportunities to Japan, since Europe and America were unable to supply their normal markets. The Second World War resulted in widespread destruction of her industrial capacity but was followed by spectacular recovery.

It is imperative for Japan to import if she is to maintain anything approaching her present standards of living. This would be true even if all exports should cease. In his definitive analysis of Japan's resources and needs, Ackerman concludes as follows: [2]

Japan is confronted with the necessity of importing, *for domestic use alone,* at least one-fifth of its food requirements, more than half of its wood and fibre requirements, nearly nine-tenths of its petroleum requirements, nearly one-half of its phosphate, more than three-quarters of its potash, half of its iron, four-fifths of its lead, a substantial portion of its salt, all its aluminum, and nearly all its tin, antimony, and many other minor items. . . .

If Japan can muster enough foreign exchange to purchase these needed materials in world markets, and still maintain a balanced trade account, as is hoped, the solution to these deficiencies will be forthcoming, and Japan will be self-supporting.

During the twentieth century the character of Japanese trade has undergone several changes. An early concentration on manufactured imports is changing to the purchase of raw materials such as raw cotton and wool, wheat and other foods, iron ore, scrap steel, minerals, petroleum products, chemicals, and machine tools. Likewise in exports the emphasis has shifted from raw silk, cotton textiles, and variety goods to complex manufactured items such as ships, optical goods including cameras, electrical items such as transistors, sewing machines, and quality merchandise.

[2] Edward A. Ackerman: *Japan's Natural Resources and Their Relation to Japan's Economic Future,* Chicago: The University of Chicago Press (1953), 564. Quoted by permission.

Because of her dependence upon essential imports, Japan suffers when world prices rise. On the other hand, she profits greatly at times of world surplus when many nations are willing to sell their products at prices below costs.

In order to solve the political aspects of her import needs, Japan once endeavored to set up a closed financial system in eastern Asia known as the "yen bloc." But neither Manchuria nor China proper supplied Japan's material deficiencies. Cotton could be grown on the Mainland, but boycotts handicapped the supply. Coal, iron, and salt were available, but the war with China restricted production. Only after her conquests in southeastern Asia following 1941 did the "Greater East Asia Co-prosperity Sphere" include a self-sufficient economic realm; but this situation did not last. In normal times, China was Japan's best customer, to the mutual profit of both nations. The extent to which this trade will return depends on political conditions.

The United States was once in second place but now leads, largely on account of Japanese purchases of cotton, coal, oil, iron, and automobiles; sales to America include textiles and cheap as well as complex manufactured goods.

At present the Japanese buyer can seldom afford American-made consumer goods, but as her standard of living increases, Japan will become a better customer. If the United States wishes to enlarge its trade to Japan, it is obvious that it should buy more in return.

Japan's great potential market lies in eastern and southern Asia, and there too may be found many of her basic needs. But whether this trade is to be captured by Japan or China, or whether these areas of new nationalism will develop their own industry, remains a major question.

Until late in the nineteenth century the policy of nonintercourse with foreign nations prohibited the construction of ocean vessels, so that navigation was limited to coastal regions. The first modern shipyards were built in 1891, and from this time on the construction of steel vessels increased rapidly. During the mid-twentieth century Japanese shipyards built some of the largest oil tankers in the world. In 1960 the country was in fifth rank among maritime powers with over 6 million gross tons, representing truly a remarkable postwar recovery.

Japan has 758 seaports, of which 36 are open to foreign ships.

16 Regions of Japan

The Kanto Plain / Central Honshu / Western Honshu and the Inland Sea / Shikoku / Kyushu / Northern Honshu / Hokkaido

THE KANTO PLAIN

Within Japan are wide variations in environment and life. Seven geographic regions are recognized: the Kanto Plain, Central Honshu, Western Honshu and the Inland Sea, Shikoku, Kyushu, Northern Honshu, and Hokkaido.

On almost any kind of map of Japan, the Kanto Plain around Tokyo is conspicuous. In its geologic history, surface forms, land use, and population concentration, this is an outstanding region. Nowhere else is there so much approximately flat land; yet even here the surface is far from level. Most of the region is a compound alluvial fan built by the many rivers

that pour out of the Central Honshu mountains. Uplift has rejuvenated the streams, which now have flood plains graded to a lower base level. Dissected diluvial terraces thus alternate with alluvial floodplains. Elsewhere there is uplifted coastal plain, floored by sediments laid down beneath the sea. Many of the rivers flow between dikes; when these are overtopped by flood waters, wide areas of farm land are inundated. Sand, coarse sediments, and volcanic ash predominate. Portions of the region near the seacoast to the east are occupied by coastal swamps and unfilled lakes. In this section a few hard rock hills rise above the general level of the terrain.

In many respects the Kanto landscape is representative of Japan. Midway between north and south, the climate is a fair sample of humid, subtropical conditions. Rainfall amounts to 58 inches in Tokyo with a maximum in September that is eight times the December minimum. Snow falls during two or three weeks of the mild winter but does not remain long on the ground. As the growing season lasts 220 days, multiple cropping is feasible during the hot summers.

Some 20 million people live in an area of 5,000 square miles. The plain is the largest compact settlement and contains about one-fifth of the population of Japan. The Kanto Plain is the most modernized of all regions, and its great port at Yokohama is Japan's principal front door to the United States.

Arable land within the Kanto district amounts to 2,500,000 acres. This means that about two-thirds of the area is actually under cultivation.

Irrigated rice dominates the low alluvial valleys and coastal plains and occupies 40 per cent of all arable land. One-seventh of the rice in Japan is grown in the Kanto Plain. Rice fields generally lie fallow during the winter or are planted to a crop of green manure. Increasing amounts of wheat and other dry grains are grown during the winter season. Near many of the farm houses are small patches of mulberry, tea, or tobacco.

Upland agriculture on the flat-topped diluvial terraces is less continuous than on the lowlands. Irrigated rice is uncommon; instead, there are fields of vegetables, beans, peas, sweet potatoes, wheat, millet, or buckwheat. Extensive areas are planted to mulberry trees, and one-fourth of all Japan's silk is produced on the Kanto Plain, with an even larger amount in the nearby mountains. In some upland districts from 30

The Kanto Plain around Tokyo is Japan's largest area of level land, intensively used for rice where not crowded with settlements. In the flatter parts of the delta, houses follow the natural levees.

to 50 per cent of the cultivated land has been devoted to the growing of mulberry during the years when silk prices have been high. In addition, these uplands are the center of Japan's limited production of tobacco. Tea is widely raised. Where winter crops are to be planted, wheat and barley are sown. Large areas of flattish diluvium are still in wild grass or woods. Terrace margins facing the lowlands are steep and usually in forest. The Kanto Plain is the northern limit of broad-leaved evergreen hardwoods.

Population densities are high on the lowlands, ranging from 1,000 to 4,000 people per square mile. On the uplands the crowding is represented by one-half to one-quarter of these figures. Tiny villages are always in sight, and there are well over one hundred cities and towns.

The great metropolitan center is the twin city of Tokyo and Yokohama. Although separate politically, they function as one and are often known as Keihin. From center to center is but 18 miles, and the intervening area is solidly filled with residential and industrial suburbs. This urban area serves not only the Kanto Plain but all of northern Honshu, and in a real sense the entire nation as well.

The southern shore of Honshu is characterized by a series of long bays, usually of tectonic origin and now in the process of being filled by delta growth. The easternmost of these is the Sagami-Tokyo embayment, locus of the great 1923 earthquake. The city of Tokyo lies at the head of the bay on the compound delta of the small streams that drain the Kanto Plain. Most of the bay near Tokyo is too shallow for ocean vessels, but dredging operations have made a deep-water harbor. The chief port is Yohohama, halfway to the open sea, which handles several times as much tonnage as that which enters Tokyo directly.

Tokyo does not owe its greatness to the sea alone. It has been important since the sixteenth century, when it became the capital of the Tokugawa Shoguns and their feudal Daimos. After the Emperor Meiji was restored in 1868,

the imperial capital was moved here from Kyoto. Tokyo is today the political, social, educational, cultural, and commercial center of the Empire. Clustered here are the head offices of the great industrial houses, the center of government, the leading universities, and the greatest wealth.

The eastern part of the city lies on a low river flood plain, interlaced with canals which serve commerce and industry. The western and residential section is on a dissected terrace. On a spur of this upland lies the old Shogun castle, now the imperial palace. From it streets radiate in a cobweb pattern, cut by two concentric moats now largely filled in to make roads. Since subsidiary castles of lesser chiefs also had their radiating streets, the city pattern is complicated. After the great fires that followed the earthquake of September 1, 1923, and again after the air raids of the Second World War, when large parts of the city were destroyed, wide avenues have replaced many narrow streets. Downtown Tokyo is marked by splendid department stores, banks, and office buildings. These are of concrete and steel, designed to be earthquake-resistant; few are over eight stories in height, as they are limited by law to 100 feet. Dominating the sky line is a 1,092-foot television tower, built in the style of the Eiffel Tower.

Industry in the Tokyo-Yokohama area is diversified; both small workshops and large factories are represented. Textiles, machinery, electrical goods, optical equipment, food, chemicals, novelties, rubber, glass, paper, and printing are each important. Shipbuilding and ship repair are significant along the waterfront. The only local raw material is silk, and most of the filatures for reeling silk are in villages outside the city. Coal, iron, raw cotton, and other supplies are all imported. Electric power is abundant.

Prior to 1932, Tokyo covered 31 square miles and had a population of 2,070,000. By the annexation of surrounding cities and some purely rural land, the area rose to 223 square miles, with a population of 6,778,804 in 1940.

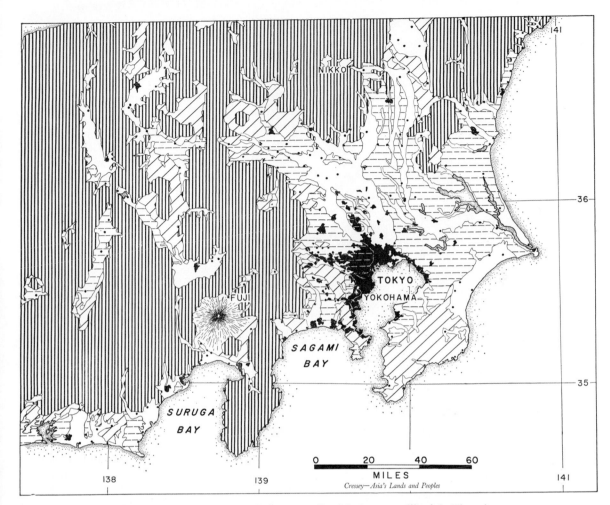

The Kanto Plain is Japan's largest lowland, in part alluvial, in part diluvial. The city of Tokyo lies on each type of surface. Mount Fuji is visible from Tokyo on a clear day. The alluvium is unshaded; the diluvium is represented by broken horizontal lines; hills are shown by diagonal lines; mountainous areas are in vertical lines.

This increased in 1960 to 8,310,027 people, making it the largest city in the world.

Yokohama is a newer city than Tokyo, and its growth is largely the product of industry and foreign commerce. Splendid wharves accommodate the largest vessels in the Pacific. The population numbers 1½ million. The combined population of the Tokyo and Yokohama metropolitan area in 1960 numbered 15,805,-776.

Excellent rail services lead out from Tokyo and make it the chief railway center of the na-

tion. There are several hundred miles of railway within the Kanto Plain itself. Express trains on the Japanese narrow-gauge line cover the 348 miles to Osaka in a little over six hours, and the time will be further reduced with the completion of a high-speed standard-gauge line, Japan's first.

Many places in Japan compete for the greatest charm, but perhaps no interior spot is more lovely than the temple city of Nikko, which lies at the edge of the hills just north of the Kanto Plain. Beautiful pagodas and shrines, sur-

Japanese architecture reaches its climax in the Yomeimon Gate at Nikko, the scenic center 90 miles north of Tokyo. (*Courtesy Japan Tourist Association*)

rounded by giant cryptomeria trees, provide the background for Japanese temple architecture at its best.

CENTRAL HONSHU

The central portion of Honshu is the most mountainous region in Japan. Numerous peaks approximate 10,000 feet, and level land is restricted to isolated basins or coastal margins. Giant volcanoes and fault scarps give parts of the area a rugged and inhospitable topography. These are the Hida Mountains, often known as the Japanese Alps. Unfavorable land forms create a blank on the population map. On the other hand, wherever level land is present, so is man.

Medieval Japan was linked together by a series of imperial highways which were still important during the seventeenth, eighteenth, and nineteenth centuries. These connected government centers and various shrines, and were used by great numbers of officials, merchants, and pilgrims. Few were suitable for wheeled vehicles. The most famous of these highways was the Tokaido, which linked the imperial capital, then at Kyoto, with the feudal capital at Tokyo, 300 miles to the east. Other roads from Kyoto led to the western end of Honshu, one along the northern or shady side and the other skirting the Inland Sea along the sunny side.

The mountainous Honshu coast has always been a barrier to travel along the Tokaido highway from Kyoto to Tokyo. South of Mount Fuji there was once a gateway, and this gave rise to the names Kanto, meaning east of the barrier, and Kwansai, the region around Kyoto and Osaka, to the west of the gate.

Lowland climates in Central Honshu are not

very different from those in the Kanto Plain, but sharp differences in altitude and exposure introduce pronounced climatic variations. On the shady Sea of Japan side, rainfall amounts to 80 and 100 inches, the maximum occurring in winter. Winters are cool and long, with cloudy weather and considerable snow in the mountains. Along the sunny Pacific side, the 60 to 80 inches of rain occur largely in the summer, partly associated with typhoons and Bai-u rains. Interior basins, with 40 to 50 inches of rain, are among the driest parts of Japan. Frosts are an agricultural hazard at higher elevations.

Some portions of the area are developed and prosperous; others more isolated are poor and backward. The lack of progress is especially noticeable on the west coast, which is Japan's back door, where there are few large cities or ports and little industry, and where landless farmers represent a holdover from feudal times. Such conditions have given rise to emigration from these areas to Hokkaido and to Brazil.

The outstanding geologic feature is a structural lowland that cuts across the island from north to south. This great graben, known as the Fossa Magna, is bordered by towering ramparts, especially on the west. Along the fault lines numerous volcanoes have built huge cones of lava and cinders, in some places entirely filling the transverse lowland. Minor faulting has produced local basins, now deeply filled with steep-sloping alluvial fans and diluvium.

The greatest of the volcanoes is Fujiyama, variously written as Fuji or Fujisan, which rises

Symmetrical Fuji supplies a common theme for Japanese art. Winter snow covers the lower slopes, and the summit is bare for only two months. The volcano lies 70 miles west of Tokyo, from which it is visible on clear days. (*Courtesy Pan American World Airways*)

to 12,390 feet. Fuji is surrounded by a series of five lovely lakes, in which artists delight to mirror the mountain. Each season, each side of the mountain, and each time of day has its unique charm. Thousands of tourists climb to the summit during July and August, the only relatively snow-free months. There is a weather station on the top, where the January-February average is near 0°F, and winter temperatures have dropped to −40°F. At this high altitude the boiling point of water is reduced to 180°F.

The northwestern and southeastern shores of Central Honshu both have discontinuous narrow strips of arable land along steep alluvial fans or terraces.

Rice is the dominant crop almost everywhere but is handicapped in the mountains by limited level land, coarse soil, marginal rainfall, and cooler summers. Where double cropping is possible, wheat or barley follows rice.

Several specialized crops are important. Chief among them is the growing of mulberry leaves in interior basins where rice does not do well. Cheap land and cheap labor favor mulberry. The trees are tolerant of poor soil and do not require irrigation. The Suwa Basin is the most important sericultural center in the world, with as much as 40 per cent of all its cultivated land in mulberry. When the silk market in the United States or Europe expands, mulberry cultivation in the Suwa area climbs higher and higher up the slopes; with decline in silk export, mulberry gardens recede, and apples or grapes take their place. About one-third of the silk of Japan is produced in Central Honshu.

Central Honshu also supplies half of the crop of green tea, chiefly in the hinterland of Shizuoka. This is the northern limit of oranges, which are raised extensively along the south coast. More daikon for pickle is grown around Nagoya than elsewhere.

Landscapes usually show a dominance of rice on the irrigated valley floors, surrounded by variable amounts of mulberry on the lowlands and rising up the slopes, and tea on terraced hillsides. Villages tend to lie next to the hills, often at the mouths of valleys. Unused hillsides are clothed with forest. Small mines in the mountains produce copper, lead, zinc, and silver. Fishing is significant along both coasts.

A few places deserve mention. On the north coast is the city of Kanazawa with a population of a quarter of a million. This is the largest city on the west side of Honshu, but the chief port is Fushiki, 25 miles to the north. Within the mountains at an elevation of 3,180 feet is the well-known summer resort of Karuizawa.

The one great metropolis is industrial Nagoya, at the head of Ise Bay and on the Nobi Plain, third largest lowland in Japan. The Nobi Plain covers 700 square miles and has a population of some 5 million; the topography and land use is comparable to the Kanto Plain. The city of Nagoya lies on a low terrace 4 miles from the head of a shallow bay, but its port of Yokkaichi is much inferior to Tokyo's Yokohama or Osaka's Kobe. Port improvements at Nagoya make it possible for large oceangoing vessels to enter, and the city ranks fourth among Japan's ports. The population numbers about 2 million, so that Nagoya is the third largest city of Japan. The imports include wool from Australia, raw cotton from India, lumber from the United States, and miscellaneous raw materials from much of the world. Exports consist of cotton cloth and chinaware.

WESTERN HONSHU AND
THE INLAND SEA

No other part of Japan has the maturity of landscape and intensity of occupancy that is characteristic of the shores of the Inland Sea. Here are the richest culture and the most perfected land use. Before modern industry invaded the area, agriculture had reached a climax in adjustment, with seemingly complete utilization of all available fields. This region is the heart of old traditional Japan, and ancient cultural forms reflect the long history.

The Inland Sea is Japan's Main Street: an avenue for commerce bordered by busy cities, a rich fishing area, and a region of picturesque scenery. (*Courtesy Pan American World Airways*)

Population crowds the land even more than in the regions already considered. Western Honshu is also a region of great industrial importance.

The Inland Sea, known to the Japanese as the Setouchi, is Japan's Mediterranean. Through it moves both internal and external commerce. Thousands of vessels, with sail or engine, transport cargo from one port to another, and through the sea pass all trans-Pacific steamers, as well as those bound from Yokohama to Europe or the South Seas. Quite possibly as many vessels use the Inland Sea as use the English Channel. Sheltered waters and many harbors make the sea an important fishing region. Clear blue skies, mirrorlike water,

and countless islands with forests or rice terraces contribute to the beauty of one of the most picturesque spots in the world.

Although Western Honshu lies in the latitudes of Italy and Greece and has comparable temperatures, Japan represents an eastern continental rather than a west-coast situation. The Inland Sea has twice the rainfall of the European Mediterranean and no dry summer. Monsoon winds bring a summer rainfall maximum to the sunny south coast, but the bordering mountains keep some of the moisture from the interior, so that the precipitation of 40 inches or less in the inland plains must be amplified by an elaborate system of wells, ponds, and irrigation canals. On the shady north coast there is a winter maximum with some snow. The mountains have two and three times the lowland rainfall, but the runoff is seasonal and of limited value for irrigation or hydroelectric power unless reservoirs are constructed.

The frost-free period averages 220 days near the Inland Sea and somewhat less along the Sea of Japan. Temperature contrasts within the region are not pronounced, for elevations seldom exceed a half mile. Summers are uncomfortably hot, with high humidities till September. Winters are mild, and snow is rare. Except on the north shore winter cropping is common. The high productivity of the land does not mean greater farm income, but rather smaller farms, with the average between 1 and 2 acres.

Unlike mountainous Central Honshu, the western part of Honshu is merely hilly; large areas of granite have been eroded into rounded hills. Interior basins are not numerous. A complicated system of block faulting furnishes the pattern for streams, and the Inland Sea itself is a series of dropped blocks, the islands being remnants of a dissected peneplain. Wherever approximately level land occurs, there is an association of swampy delta or coastal plain alluvium, partially dissected diluvial terraces, and older and higher diluvial terraces often made up of very coarse material. Artificial terracing for rice is more widespread than elsewhere, with steps to the top of the hills in some locations.

Rice is everywhere the principal crop; yields in this region are the highest per acre in the nation. Mulberry trees and tea bushes are widespread on the slopes. On account of the prevalence of winter cropping, Western Honshu is the most significant area for wheat and barley. Rye, rapeseed, and legumes are of some importance. Citrus fruits and apples are common. Near the cities are large areas of vegetables, fruit, and flowers. Local specialization has made some localities famous for watermelons, peaches, and strawberries. The tea grown near Uji, south of Kyoto, is especially well known. Along the south shore of Honshu are raised the reeds that are woven into the tatami mats which invariably cover the floors of Japanese homes.

Some rice fields are too poorly drained to be planted to a winter crop, but nearly three-fourths of the upland fields raise a second crop, and a few even a third. Intertillage is common, and one may find combinations such as alternating rows of mulberry, persimmons, and tea. A thousand years of population pressure have pushed cultivation to its limits.

Many farmers supplement their income from crops by fish culture in the ponds and moats that surround the villages. A large number of those who live near the northern or southern shore are part-time fishermen. The abundant sunshine and high temperatures along the Inland Sea make it a favored coast for the extraction of salt from sea water. The final evaporation takes place over coal fires.

Within the region is Japan's greatest industrial area, that around Osaka and Kobe. Textiles, metal industries, and shipbuilding are outstanding. Though mineral resources are lacking, plentiful labor and favorable location stimulate industry. In Western Honshu are found the old crafts and arts for which Japan is famous. Communications by water and rail are excellent throughout the region, although the north coast is much less favored.

Western Honshu and the Inland Sea include three subregions: the Kinki district in the east around the great cities of Kobe, Osaka, and Kyoto; the sunny south side of Honshu with the offshore islands; and the shady Sea of Japan side. Whereas all share most of the characteristics just described, each has its personality. In fact, one never stops subdividing Japan, for successive generalizations each have their exceptions when applied to smaller and smaller areas.

The Kinki district includes five fault basins, separated by low mountain barriers. Each is in part swampy, and some contain lakes. To the northeast is Lake Biwa, Japan's largest lake, surrounded by only a limited area of level land. West of it is the Kyoto Basin, south of which is the Nara, or Yamato Basin. Only two

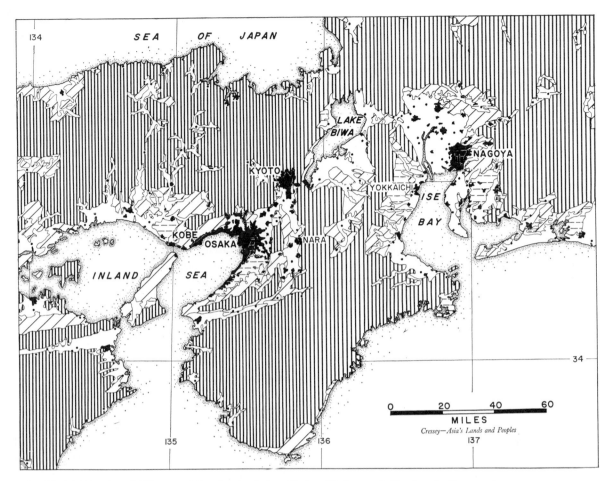

The Kinki District of Western Honshu includes Osaka, Kobe, and Kyoto; farther east lies Nagoya. The narrow width of Honshu is illustrated by the presence on this map of the Pacific Ocean, the Sea of Japan, and the Inland Sea.

of the lowlands reach the sea: the delta around Osaka and the unimportant Kino graben to the south.

The rivers of the Kinki subregion are diked to protect adjoining fields, and as a result, deposition is confined to the channel so that dikes must be raised repeatedly. Near Lake Biwa this process has gone so far that the bottoms of some streams are 20 feet above the surrounding plain. In a few places railroads and highways are carried under the river by tunnels on the level rather than over them by bridges. When the dikes break disaster follows.

Many rural areas were laid out according to a rectangular land pattern known as the Handen brought from China during 645 to 655. Roads and canals conform to this scheme, which is restricted to the Kinki area.

The Kinki area takes first place in history and culture. For eleven centuries Kyoto was the imperial capital and thus the center of arts and crafts. The city is still the home of craftsmen who produce handsome lacquer, porcelain, cloisonné, bronze, and silk textiles. Modern-style industry concentrates on high-quality weaving, dyeing, and ceramics. Kyoto has its own personality of dignity and charm, without the noisy and dirty modernity of the other large cities. It fortunately escaped damage during the Second World War. The city is laid out with wide streets in a rectangular pattern around the old palaces and temples, in the style of Peking. Its unspoiled palaces are visited by millions of tourists a year. The population is about 1½ million.

South of Kyoto lies Nara, the cradle of Japanese history and the first center of government. Its temples, national shrines, and natural beauty make it a rival to Nikko as a tourist goal.

Osaka is Japan's premier industrial center, producing fabrics, steel, machinery, ships, rolling stock, chemicals, and a host of modern products. Osaka's smoking factories and crowded residential streets are the antithesis of lovely Kyoto. Here are one-fourth of the nation's factory workers, who produce one-third of its manufactured goods. The city lies on a delta at the head of a shallow bay, with adequate room for expansion. Numerous canals and rivers simplify barge transportation but require 1,600 bridges within the city.

During recent years the harbor has been dredged so that 20,000-ton ocean vessels may be accommodated. The original absence of port facilities led to the development of Kobe, 16 miles to the west. The combined conurbation is known as Hanshin. Kobe still serves as Osaka's entrepôt for overseas trade, but Osaka itself now ranks third, next to Kobe and Yokohama. If domestic and overseas commerce are combined, Osaka is the first port of Japan. When Japan was opened to foreign trade, Osaka, because of its nearness to Kyoto, was already the most important domestic trading center.

The Osaka area produces a wide variety of goods. This is the major center for cotton textiles. Although there is no local iron ore or coal, the fabrication of steel is important. Smoke, smells, and slums are characteristic. The population numbers over 3 million.

Kobe lies on an alluvial fan at the base of mountains which restrict its inland growth and cause it to expand along the shore toward Osaka. Since Kobe is the chief port of call for foreign shipping, it is but natural that it should show many Western influences. The harbor has facilities for the largest ocean vessels in the Pacific, and there is a heavy movement of freight. Kobe is doubly fortunate in its maritime position. Almost all ships from Canada, the United States, or the Panama Canal include a visit to Kobe en route to other parts of Asia. Likewise ships from Europe to eastern Asia, together with those from Australia and the East Indies, invariably proceed to Kobe. Japan thus lies on two of the major ocean highways. The number of vessels which enter Kobe and Osaka annually place it along with New York and London among world ports.

The Japanese have always differentiated between the shady Sea of Japan side and the sunny Pacific side of their islands. The northwest shore of Honshu is known as the San-in, since it is dark, stormy, and snowy. In contrast, the southeast margin is the San-yo, bright and sunny. The San-in coast receives the winter continental monsoon from across the Sea of Japan, with resulting cloud and snow. The San-yo coast is under the influence of the summer oceanic monsoon. Salt may be evaporated from sea water, and citrus fruits are grown to the south, but not to the north.

In Western Honshu, neither shore has much arable land, although the margins of the Inland Sea are more hospitable. The northern coast is less indented and has fewer harbors. Despite the lack of shelter, or perhaps because of the scarcity of farm land, fishing is important along the Sea of Japan. Korean influences are noticeable in the San-in area.

The western entrance to the Inland Sea is guarded by the twin cities of Shimonoseki and Moji, on either side of the mile-wide straits. Shipping prefers Moji on account of its coal and steel, but Shimonoseki became important as it was the rail terminus for the larger island. A railway and highway tunnel now links Moji and Shimonoseki. Many cities lie along the San-yo between Shimonoseki and Kobe, chief of which is Hiroshima.

SHIKOKU

The island of Shikoku is the smallest of the main Japanese group and the least important. The topography is maturely dissected, and its high mountains and steep slopes strictly limit agriculture and handicap communications. A major geologic boundary runs east and west through the island, marked by the great fault scarp which separates the Inner and Outer Zones of Japan. To the south is a series of parallel ridges and valleys underlain by ancient folded rocks; to the north is granite eroded into hills similar to the topography across the Inland Sea.

Both geologically and geographically, southern Shikoku is rather similar to southern Kyushu and to the Kii peninsula of Honshu south of Osaka.

In the north, agricultural conditions closely correspond with those in Western Honshu, just described. On the south shore a more nearly tropical climate with 300 days free from frost permits the growth of palms, camphor and wax trees, and two successive crops of rice. The summer monsoon brings heavy rainfall to the mountains of Shikoku, so that precipitation on the south slopes exceeds 75 inches. In the lee of the mountains near the Inland Sea the rainfall is only half that amount. In addition to wet rice, there are the usual dry crops of rye, barley, buckwheat, sweet potatoes, and mulberry.

Lumbering and fishing are the chief occupations, and the island is an important producer of paper. In the mountains near the Inland Sea is a large copper mine at Besshi. Shikoku has no volcanoes.

There are few cities, little industry, limited railroad service, and a considerable area with but sparse population.

KYUSHU

Although Kyushu lies in the southwest corner of Japan, it has an important history and is one of the ancient centers of Japanese life. The island is closest to China, and has long had contacts with the South Seas through the steppingstones of the Ryukyu Islands. The highly indented coast line encourages fishing activities, and people from Kyushu have long been accustomed to life on the sea. The old Satsuma culture was based on these overseas contacts. Customs and dialects still differ from those on Honshu. There are only a few modern cities.

More than elsewhere, volcanic landscapes are dominant in Kyushu, and there are several active craters; but less than half of the island is occupied by old lava flows or ash deposits. There are two separate areas of vulcanism, one around Mount Aso in the center, the other the volcano of Sakurajima in the south. Population pressure is so great that rice terraces and dry fields have been pushed far up the slopes, and 100,000 people live within the supercrater or caldera of temporarily quiescent Mount Aso. The island is divided into two equal parts by the same structural boundary that cuts the island of Shikoku.

This is the warmest part of subtropical Japan. Summer temperatures are higher than elsewhere and much more oppressive because of the humidity. The winter monsoon, from which the island is unprotected, in these latitudes brings no snow or low temperatures. Agriculture is intensive but not unusual. Double cropping is common, with rice often planted as the second crop in mid-July, following dry grains. Sweet potatoes are widely grown, being a dependable crop and the poor man's food. Originally raised in China, sweet potatoes moved from there to the Ryukyu Islands and thence to southern Kyushu and eventually to the rest of Japan. Each successive area refers to the sweet potato by a name that indicates its importation from the adjoining region. Much of the island is forested, so that lumber and paper mills are important.

Southern Kyushu is more distinctly tropical than the northern part of the island. One sees here rural houses covered by simple thatched roofs, dense vegetation, and abundant bamboo, bananas, and oranges. Tobacco and sweet potatoes, along with sugar cane, beans, taro, and vegetables, supplement rice culture, which covers but one-third of the arable land. This is the smallest proportion outside Hokkaido, and both yields and quality are poor. Kyushu has several specialized horse-breeding areas utilizing the wild grasses of the uplands.

The city of Nagasaki, north of the structural escarpment which cuts through each of the main islands, has been a significant foreign-trade port for several centuries, and for a long time was the only gateway for Occidental culture. Dutch and Portuguese traders have made Nagasaki conscious of the outside world since the middle of the sixteenth century. The city is closest of all Japanese ports to China, and express steamers from there normally reach Shanghai, 500 miles distant, in a day. Nagasaki's foreign contacts are furthered by the presence of nearby coal suitable for steamship use, and prior to the substitution of fuel oil, it was customary for many steamers from Europe or North America to take on supplies here. Nagasaki has lost much of its commercial importance and ranks low among Japanese ports. It is still, however, an important shipbuilding center.

About half of the nation's coal is mined in the Chikuho Basin in the extreme northern part of the island. This coal, of Tertiary age, is subbituminous and must be mixed with imported coal in order to make metallurgical coke. There are several dozen large mines, but operations are complicated by faulting. The region supplies the Japanese market as far north as Nagoya, beyond which supplies come from the Joban district near Sendai or from Hokkaido.

Coal from Chikuho and adjacent fields has given rise to a great concentration of heavy industry on the southern side of the Strait of Shimonoseki. In a belt some 25 miles long and usually less than a mile wide from Moji west to Yawata and Fukuoka, there is a continuous succession of coal docks, ore piles, blast furnaces and steel mills, cement works, flour mills, sugar refineries, paper mills, oil refineries, glass works, machine shops, and unattractive factory towns. The industrial area of North Kyushu has an aggregate population of 3 million. The Yawata plant and its subsidiaries account for one-fourth of Japan's pig iron and steel.

Since level land is limited, many of the factories are directly on tidewater. The area is well situated midway between supplies of coking coal and ore from the continent or the South Seas, and the domestic markets for its products. The straits are a converging point for all East

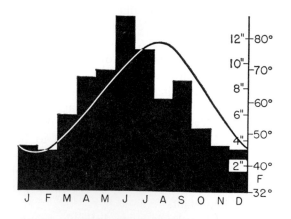

KAGOSHIMA. Elevation 18 feet, average temperature 63°F, annual precipitation 88 inches. Southwestern Kyushu has a more pronounced monsoon rainfall than the rest of Japan.

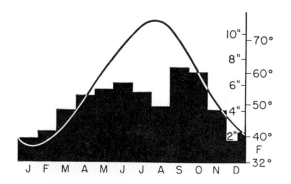

TOKYO. Elevation 19 feet, average temperature 58°F, annual precipitation 62 inches. Since the base line for rainfall corresponds to 32°F, it is obvious that Tokyo seldom has snow.

Asian traffic, but neither Moji nor Shimonoseki is an important port for passengers. Freight facilities are well developed.

Kyushu exhibits wide contrasts. Heavy industry dominates a small corner of the landscape, but isolation characterizes the life of most rural areas, especially south of the dividing escarpment. Southern Kyushu has important gold and copper mines.

Two subtropical island groups adjoin Japan. Directly south of Honshu are the Ogasawara or Bonin Islands, the most famous of which is Iwo Jima. South of Kyushu are the Ryukyu; Okinawa is the principal island. These southern island groups have a tropical climate with heavy rainfall and low seasonal range of temperature. Destructive typhoons visit the area during the summer. Sweet potatoes are everywhere more important than rice. Important developments in sugar-cane production have characterized recent years. Coconuts, tapioca, and taro reflect the low latitude.

The Ryukyu group includes 55 small islands near the edge of the continental shelf with a total area of 935 square miles. Several are volcanic, and level land is limited on each. Coral reefs fringe the shore. Overpopulation has led to emigration to Japan proper and to Hawaii.

The archipelago was once a Chinese dependency, then known as the Liukiu Islands.

NORTHERN HONSHU

Despite the overall unity of the Japanese islands, there is clearly marked variation from place to place. Few countries, certainly none in Asia, have so much detail in land pattern or land use within so small an area. Over 100 distinct geographic regions have been recognized, of which a quarter are in Northern Honshu. The generalizations necessary in the present study cannot do justice to this diversity.

Northern Honshu is the largest of all regions south of Hokkaido, the most recently developed, and the least densely populated. Parts of the area have been cultivated for little more than a century, and expansion is still under way. Subtropical conditions merge into a temperate climate, and the growing season ranges from 160 to a maximum of 200 days, according to latitude and altitude. Tea, sweet potatoes, and bamboo are absent, double cropping is uncommon, and mulberry is only locally important. Winters are long and cool, and many places have snow on the ground for four months. The original forest consisted of maple, birch, chestnut, poplar, and oak. These climatic and vegetation conditions have given rise to brown forest soils.

Three north–south mountain ranges with intervening lowlands give a parallel arrangement to the topography, which is reflected in the linear pattern of cultivated land and population distribution. Each of these zones has its interruptions, so that the feasible sites for settlements are isolated. The central range is the highest and is crowned by a number of volcanoes, several of which reach a mile in height; elsewhere elevations are but half that figure. Structurally, the eastern range is the dividing line between Inner and Outer Japan. There are a few coastal plains, especially in the west, and several of the interior lowlands reach the sea through breaks in the mountains; elsewhere level land is absent along the shore.

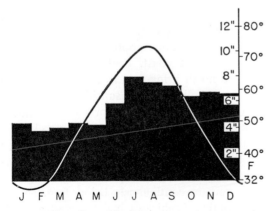

AKITA. Elevation 33 feet, average temperature 52°F, annual precipitation 73 inches. The west coast of northern Honshu receives heavy snowfall, derived from winds which cross the Sea of Japan.

Off Northern Honshu on the Pacific side there is a cool current, the Oyashio, and as the warm summer monsoon blows over it, condensation produces considerable fog. As a result, summers along the east coast are cooler and drier than on the west. The Sea of Japan side has a slight winter precipitation maximum which is due to the heavy snowfall, often 10 feet in depth. When the snow does not melt until spring, the planting of crops may be delayed. The heaviest snowfall is on the west coast of central Honshu in the vicinity of latitude 37°N rather than farther north where average temperatures and hence precipitation are lower. Railroads have many miles of snow sheds, but service may be interrupted for days at a time. In many towns along the Sea of Japan and in the mountains, the houses are built with projecting eaves, known as *gangi,* which shelter the sidewalks and thus permit access in winter when the snow is deep. Strong winter gales make it necessary to weight house shingles with large stones.

There are few harbors along either coast, but the cool waters provide such a favorable habitat for marine life that fishing is an important industry.

Farms average 3 to 4 acres, but are twice as large farther south where double cropping is feasible. Rice is grown wherever it may be irrigated; other crops are favored by cooler conditions. White potatoes and beans do well, as do millet, buckwheat, and barley. Three-quarters of Japan's apples are raised here, and have a flavor superior to those grown in the south. Cherries are another fruit. Horse raising is a thriving business.

Northern Honshu has a number of relatively important natural resources. Copper is mined at several centers. The coal mines at Joban south of Sendai constitute one of Japan's three major sources of fuel. North of Sendai are large blast furnaces at Kamaishi. Along the Sea of Japan are the country's leading petroleum fields, especially near Niigata in the Echigo Hills. Intensive developments have failed to develop satisfactory production from their limited reserves. Gold, silver, sulfur, and hydroelectric power are also produced in the central mountains.

The small percentage of level land has restricted population. Cities are few and industries lacking. There is little overseas trade. The two urban centers of Northern Honshu are Sendai on the east coast, and Niigata on the west; each lies in an elongated plain along the sea, with areas of 580 and 700 square miles, respectively.

HOKKAIDO

Hokkaido is Japan's northland, a frontier of settlement with a population density but one-sixth that of Honshu. Since this region is the newest part of Japan, much of it still has a pioneer landscape. Hokkaido is the remaining home of the aboriginal Ainu, of whom only 15,000 remain. These non-Japanese peoples once lived in southern Honshu.

Sixty per cent of the island is covered with a boreal forest, underlain by peaty or podsolic soils. The land that is potentially arable amounts to only about 14 per cent, but the restrictions of a short growing season as well as of peripheral location permanently handicap development.

This northern island, lying in the latitude of Nova Scotia, has an eastern continental marine climate with severe winters. Rainfall on the agricultural lowlands approximates 40 inches. Along the east coast, cool offshore currents from the north bring fogs as in northern Honshu. There is little winter sunshine in the west, and one interior station reports but 44 hours for the entire month of January. The two largest cities of Hakodate and Sapporo average less than three hours of sunshine a day during January. Daily average temperatures during the winter remain continuously below freezing for four months. Asahizawa has reported a minimum temperature of −41°F, and in Sapporo, farther south, the thermometer has dropped to −16°F.

The winter monsoon begins at the end of

The mountains of Hokkaido, Japan's northland, occasionally receive heavy winter snows which may block communications for days. The island lies in the latitude of Oregon. (*Pix*)

September or early in October and continues until late in March. Strong northwest winds, occasionally of gale strength, bring snowstorms of unusual intensity. A snow cover of several feet is common in the west, occasionally reaching a depth of 6 feet. The summer southeast monsoon from May to September is intermittent and weak. Since this warm air passes over the cold water of the Oyashio, chilled by melting sea ice from the Bering Sea, considerable fog results in June and July in the east. Late summer is the most pleasant period.

The frost-free period is generally less than 150 days, and in the north drops below 90, which is the minimum growing period for the most rapidly maturing varieties of rice. Unfortunately, these averages vary widely from year to year. Hazards of unseasonable frost and occasional drought make agriculture somewhat precarious.

Although many aspects of Hokkaido's geography differ from that of the islands to the south, there is a similarity in the association of mountains and lowlands. Coastal terraces are more widespread than elsewhere in Japan. The lowest plains represent alluvial deposits, often poorly drained. Diluvial terraces and ash fields are widespread. Two north–south mountain ranges cross the island, intersected by an east–west series of volcanoes. Where they meet, elevations exceed a mile.

The extractive industries of mining, forestry, and fishing are relatively more important than elsewhere in Japan. The island contains the largest coal reserves, but they are unfortunately much disturbed by faulting and folding.

Many of the remaining Ainu live around the shores of Lake Akan in Hokkaido. (*Courtesy Japanese Consulate General, New York City*)

A dozen mines produce a fair quality of bituminous coal that makes a poor but usable coke. Deposits of iron ore are inadequate and must be supplemented by imported supplies. These form the basis for the great steel and iron industry at Muroran. Copper, gold, silver, and sulfur are also secured. Hokkaido produces one-sixth of Japan's timber, some of which is made into paper on the island; reserves are abundant. About one-fifth of the fish catch is accounted for here, and there are numerous canneries. Small fishing settlements line the coast. The resources of Hokkaido are remote from the chief centers of Japanese population.

With the development of railroads in the decade following 1880, farmers from the southern islands began to come into the Ishikari Plain. Though the plain is Japan's second largest lowland, it measures only 800 square miles. Most of the island was in 1880 an unoccupied wilderness. As a result of extensive agricultural experimentation, the Japanese have learned how to grow rice in this northern climate, and it exceeds wheat in acreage. Beans, apples, white potatoes, sugar beets, cherries, and hay replace tea and mulberry as cash crops. Hokkaido is the only place where oats are important. Peppermint and large white asparagus are specialized crops, largely exported to the United States and Europe.

Hokkaido has the most extensive dairy industry in the country, shipping considerable quantities of canned milk and butter. Some of the cattle are kept in American-style barns and fed from corn-filled silos, a reflection of the early agricultural advice supplied by American experts. Horses are much more numerous than on the farms in other regions. Another result of early American influence is seen in the use of "Giddap," "Whoa," "Gee," and "Haw."

Despite the differences in climate, Japanese immigrants have transplanted their conventional subtropical crops such as rice, and have also brought with them subtropical house types with paper windows, without adequate modification for the severe winter conditions. Farms average 10 acres in size, usually in one continuous unfenced plot. Roads are laid out in accordance with rectangular land surveys, drawn prior to settlement, and fields conform to the road pattern. In contrast to the clustered settlements elsewhere in Japan, in Hokkaido individual disseminated farmsteads dot the landscape.

Life in Hokkaido has not been attractive to the average Japanese farmer, and early colonization was largely the result of government subsidies. The population did not reach 1 million until 1905, but it grew to 5 million by 1960. The agricultural population accounts for nearly 40 per cent of the total. Colonization authorities believe that there may be room for a million additional farmers, although expensive irrigation and drainage will be required to bring more land into cultivation, and it is thought that the urban population may be increased by approximately 2 million. The chief cities are the capital of Sapporo in the Ishikari Plain, the steel center of Muroran, and the seaport and rail terminus at Hakodate.

The comparative neglect of opportunities for settlement within this island emphasizes the essentially subtropical character of Japanese culture and the unwillingness of the people to leave their homeland and settle in lands where rice is not easily raised. Thus the total number of Japanese settlers outside of Japan numbered only 1 million before the Second World War, of whom half were in Manchuria. This figure contrasts with 10 million Chinese who have left China. Japanese emigrants living in Brazil number 200,000; there are 150,000 on the United States mainland, another 150,000 in Hawaii, and only 2,500 in all Europe.

THE SOUTHEAST ASIAN REALM

Southeast Asia is a green world of islands and peninsulas, so underpopulated and underdeveloped that there is a surplus of raw materials for export. Much of the realm has recently emerged from a colonial status, with resulting problems of political and economic development.

"Reduced to their essentials, the problems of Southeast Asia are: self-protection, self-support, and self-government. They arise out of the strategic importance and untold wealth of the area, which the Communists covet, and the determination of the peoples of Southeast Asia who have recently achieved their independence to govern themselves and rise to a position of dignity, quality, and honor in the international community." (Carlos P. Romulo: "The Position of Southeast Asia in the World Community," in Philip W. Thayer, ed.: *Southeast Asia in the Coming World*, Baltimore: The Johns Hopkins Press (1953), 252. Quoted by permission.)

Rice paddies in Java. (*Courtesy Standard Oil Co. of New Jersey*)

17 The Indo-Pacific Realm

Peninsulas and Islands / Population Patterns / Historical Development /
References on Southeast Asia

PENINSULAS AND ISLANDS

The Southeastern realm spreads across an area considerably larger than the United States, but since half of the overall area is water, the land measures 1½ million square miles. Most of the realm lies within a 1,500-mile radius centered on Saigon. While the territory is large, its insular and peninsular character makes it relatively accessible. The east–west dimensions are those of North America; from north to south the range is equivalent to that from Mexico to Peru. Here live well over 200 million people in a handful of sovereign nations. Although the total population is impressive, the people of the realm still lack technical skill and accumulated capital. Except for remote Siberia, Southeast Asia as a whole is the newest and most underdeveloped part of the continent.

The realm has had a number of names, but Southeast Asia is now generally accepted. The islands have been variously known as the Indies or East Indies, with or without the Philippines. Some of the mainland has been termed Indochina. The British and some Indians have called the area Farther India; the Chinese refer to it as Nan Yang, the South Seas. Since the realm lies between two oceans and two cultures, it may appropriately be described as Indo-Pacific.

This is the maritime tropics, spread across the equator from 25°N to 10°S. Climatic conditions are quite unlike those to be found in the continental areas of equatorial Brazil or the Congo. Though temperature and humidity are high, there is often a cooling breeze. The pattern of land and sea creates three geographic provinces: the mainland peninsular area of Burma, Thailand, and the Indochina States; [1] the insular area of Indonesia and Malaya (for although the latter is attached to the mainland its geography is essentially insular); and the Philippine archipelago, also maritime but different in climate and culture.

Unlike China or India, each of which has a unity supplied by its culture, the realm has little sense of community; nor is there appreciable intrarealm trade. Such coherence as Southeast Asia may possess derives from its location and physical features rather than from internal human or economic considerations.

The character of the realm must be understood from its overall location and from its relation to its two powerful neighbors, China and India. This is the least continental and most peripheral part of Asia, isolated from the interior by towering mountains. It shares monsoon characteristics with India and China, but the seasonal development is less pronounced. In geopolitical terms, here is Rimland rather than Heartland.

While Southeast Asia is not today an area of major economic strength and is a target rather than a center of political power, it enjoys basic assets in its commanding location and in its unrealized potentials. It is the richest of the world's tropical lands. By the end of the twentieth century the world may be obliged to reassess its place in the world.

A thousand years ago the coasts of this area were the meeting place for Indian and Chinese traders. Chinese junks have long journeyed to Luzon, Java, and Thailand; in Malaya they met

[1] The term Indochina States refers to the area of former French Indochina, now divided into Viet Nam (both North and South), Laos, and Cambodia.

Arab vessels and exchanged their goods for merchandise from India and Europe. Indian colonists carried Buddhism and, later, Islam to Indonesia. It was through Southeast Asia that China and India had their major commercial contacts, rather than overland across Tibet.

The oceans and their river extensions are still the main avenues for both internal and overseas trade. Only negligible commerce crosses any of the land frontiers, and none at all moves overland to India. All Philippine and Indonesian commerce is perforce by ship. Except for the subsistence farmer, who knows only his immediate earth and sky, the orientation is seaward.

Unlike land-dominated realms, which commonly find their focus in a river or a central lowland, Southeast Asia has no single clearcut meeting place unless it be at the West-created port of Singapore. Physical compartmentalization has led to political fragmentation; no ancient empire ever united the entire realm or even half of it. The realities of the current world may argue for federation and cooperation, but the bases for unity are few.

One reason for this fractionalization lies in the colonial history of the last two centuries. Burma was British until 1948; Indochina was French until 1949; Malaya secured its independence from Britain in 1957; Indonesia ceased to be Netherlands India in 1949; and the oldest ex-colonial nation, the Philippines, dates only from 1946. Most of these new nations still look "homeward" for their official language, railway equipment, export markets, and political guidance. Only Thailand has been "free," and even here British influence has been important.

Southeast Asia has also become a contest zone between the totalitarian and the free worlds; here British and American political and economic interests now meet Soviet and Chinese politics and aid. Still earlier, the realm was an objective in Japan's "Greater East Asia Co-prosperity Sphere."

As India and China plan expansion, their goals overlap here. India may look forward to

POLITICAL
DIVISIONS

0   200   400   600   800
MILES

Cressey—Asia's Lands and Peoples

The countries of Southeast Asia range from maritime Indonesia, whose east–west dimensions exceed those of the United States, to land-locked Laos, the size of Pennsylvania. The only cities which exceed a million in population are Jakarta, Surabaya, Manila, Singapore, Saigon, and Bangkok.

260   THE INDO-PACIFIC REALM

Modern Thailand has some of the finest contemporary architecture and native culture of Southeast Asia. These dancers are in Bangkok. (*Courtesy Trans World Airlines*)

transforming the Indian Ocean into an Indian lake, where her interests will be dominant from Cape Town to Singapore. China has long looked to the South Seas as an area of colonization, a source of raw materials, and increasingly as a market for her expanding industry. Where these objectives are blocked, political action may follow. Chinese territorial claims already encompass all islands in the South China Sea to within 4 degrees north of the equator.

Singapore and the Strait of Malacca are a gateway to the western Pacific, much as the Panama Canal commands its eastern approach. Whatever the future of the Pacific world, South-

east Asia holds one of the gateways. The geostrategic problem of the Southeast Asian realm, still leaderless, is to capitalize on its commanding location at the meeting place of the Pacific and Indian worlds.

Southeast Asia's emerging role in international affairs has well been described by Amry Vandenbosch and Richard Butwell.[2]

The world has become considerably smaller since that distant day in the sixteenth century when the Spanish ships of the daring Magellan

[2] Amry Vandenbosch and Richard Butwell: *Southeast Asia among the World Powers,* Lexington, Ky.: University of Kentucky Press (1957), 10–12. Quoted by permission.

reached the Philippines from across the wide Pacific, and this has had important consequences for all nations. . . . In modern times . . . it is true to say that Southeast Asia has been far from the main arenas of conflict in world politics. . . . Southeast Asia, though an aspect of the rivalry between the Western states, was not a key area in the international struggle for power. This changed with Japan's rise to power in Asia in the nineteen-thirties. . . . The geography of decreasing distances among the nations of the world and the not unrelated expansion of European politics into world politics thus combined to bring Southeast Asia closer to the threshold of conflict in modern international relations. It did not, however, bring it quite over that threshold.

The factor which has accomplished this more than any other has been the rivalry between the United States and the Soviet Union in the years since the end of the Second World War. . . .

The nationalist revolutions of the postwar years which catapulted European colonialism out of Southeast Asia left a vacuum in the wake of the Western withdrawal. As the cold war between the United States and the U.S.S.R. increased in intensity in the years after 1945, the importance of Southeast Asia in world politics loomed larger. It would appear greater today than at any other time in modern history. It is in the light of its role as a "battlefield" in the Western-Communist conflict that its continuing divisions and its economic backwardness are to be appraised. . . . Whether it likes it or not, and the so-called "neutralist" foreign policies of some of its states would seem to indicate it does not, Southeast Asia is today very much a part of the world about it.

POPULATION PATTERNS

The most striking feature of the population map for Southeast Asia is the uneven distribution of people. This would be even more obvious if one might make a circuit by plane. A few alluvial lowlands are almost as crowded as anywhere in Asia, but many uplands are as empty as Mongolia or Tibet. For the realm as a whole, the density is 100 people per square mile. See map on page 291.

Several areas with densities in excess of 500 per square mile stand out. One is the delta of the Red River in North Viet Nam; another is the Mekong lowland in South Viet Nam. Thailand and Burma have their concentrations in the Chao Phraya (Menam) and Irrawaddy deltas. Spots of dense population appear in the southern Celebes, parts of coastal Sumatra, and in some of the Philippine Islands. Most striking of all are Java and Bali, where the density for the islands as a whole considerably exceeds 1,000 per square mile and in places is double that figure.

This pattern is not surprising since three-quarters of all the people in the realm are farmers, and they naturally live on the most available land. Modern reclamation will certainly add new farm lands, and the map of a century hence should show major changes in land use and population concentration. Although urban growth is everywhere striking, only one-seventh of the population live in cities.

Each country has a master city, several times larger than its nearest rival. Rangoon in Burma is three times the size of Mandalay. Bangkok, capital of Thailand, is twenty-five times larger than Chiangmai. Neither Saigon nor Hanoi in South and North Viet Nam, respectively, has any close rival. In the Malay Peninsula, Singapore is five times the size of Kuala Lumpur. Manila has ten times the population of its Philippine rival, Cebu. Jakarta is twice as large as Surabaya, its Javanese competitor, even though both exceed a million people.

All the million-category cities are seaports, and all except Bangkok, being creations of foreign enterprise, once included a large population of the original colonial power. Chinese are numerous in each, notably in Singapore, where they form three-fourths of the population. Each metropolitan city represents large foreign capital investments for harbor, industrial, and municipal facilities; parts of each are thoroughly cosmopolitan in their appearance. Only indigenous Bangkok has exotic attractions for the tourist.

Most of the present population clusters exist in relative isolation from their neighbors. Few roads or railways link the several countries or even the population pockets within them. Since most contacts have been by sea, every major city is also a port. The detached character of the several islands is matched on the mainland by the isolating factors of terrain and vegetation. Nowhere does the realm find cultural avenues or a cultural focus.

Ethnic diversity is as obvious as is uneven distribution. Malays dominate much of the area; but the term includes many variations. Malays are basically Mongoloid and represent a long drift of people out of southern China. While most groups have preferred the lowlands, some have been pressed into mountain areas. Some known movements date back to the second millennium B.C. Other groups appear to have Negrito or Australoid origins, especially in Indonesia; some have Caucasoid back-

grounds. Chinese traders and colonists have penetrated Southeast Asia for several centuries and currently number some 10 million, many of whom still retain Chinese citizenship. Thailand and Malaya lead with 3 million Chinese each; Indonesia, the Indochina States, and Singapore count over 1 million apiece; Burma has over 300,000; Western Borneo and the Philippines each have more than 100,000. Indian immigrants, chiefly laborers in Burma or Malaya, are less numerous but may number 2 million.

With the rise of nationalism, each of the host countries is insisting that resident aliens become citizens or return to their homeland. This creates special problems for the Chinese if their country of residence recognizes only Communist China.

Dense populations and intensive land use characterize most lowland areas. These rice fields in North Viet Nam reflect old river patterns of the Song-ka, 100 miles south of Hanoi. (*Courtesy United States Air Force*)

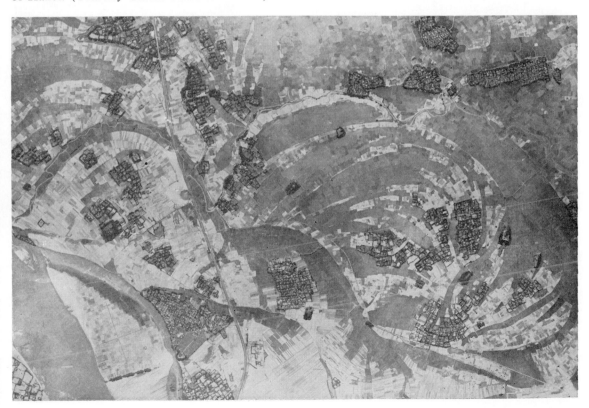

Large sections of Southeast Asia appear to be underpopulated. If overall densities should approach those of China and India, the realm might rival them in total population. Here is room for several hundred million people. And everywhere population is expanding rapidly. Java has grown nearly tenfold in a century. The problem lies not in overall numbers but in the problem of raising per capita incomes more rapidly than the increase in population.

HISTORICAL DEVELOPMENT

The fragmented character of the Indo-Pacific realm has been reflected in its history. In the absence of a solid internal base, the realm as a whole and many of its parts have always been subject to external influences. No single empire or even a single culture ever dominated even half of the area until the brief episode of Japanese control during the Second World War. Twentieth-century political coherence or cooperation is scarcely to be expected.

Most authenticated history reaches only to the beginning of the Christian era, although some monuments may date back to the second millennium B.C. The earliest inhabitants may have been Negroid people who were pushed into the mountains or onward toward Australia by successive waves of South Mongoloids whom we know as Malays; these people came overland from the north. Indian colonists

Java has had a tradition of culture for a thousand years. During the eighth and ninth centuries, the people, who were Buddhists, built this great monument, or stupa, known as the Borobudur. The carvings on the four terraces are particularly rich. (*Satake*)

The ruins of the great temple city of Angkor in Cambodia provide a souvenir of the Mon-Khmer civilization, which flourished from the ninth into the thirteenth century. The magnificent carvings have been termed "lace on stone." This temple was erected to Vishnu. (*Courtesy Pan American World Airways*)

moved along the coasts about 2,000 years ago and set up communities in Java and the Mekong valley. Somewhat later, Chinese settlers migrated and moved along the Annam coast.

The first sea-based empire was that of Sri Vijaya, which developed in northern Sumatra and on both sides of the Strait of Malacca from the fifth into the eighth century, with continuations into the fourteenth century. A rival empire then arose in the Java Sea, that of Madjapahit, where Hindu culture reached its flower in Southeast Asia. This was the civilization which produced the monuments at Borobudur in central Java.

On the mainland the various political units were river- rather than sea-oriented, at times having upriver and downriver divisions. Suc-cessive waves of Tibeto-Burman and South Chinese people pressed down the valleys: Lao, Thai, Shan, Annamese and many others. One empire was that of the Mon-Khmers which reached its zenith in the twelfth century, when Angkor rivaled the great cities of ancient Europe. Two centuries later arose the Shan empire and the beginnings of modern Thailand.

While India never ruled much of Southeast Asia, Chinese empires frequently extended well into the peninsula, so that at times the court in Peking received tribute from Burma, Thailand, Viet Nam, Laos, Cambodia, and even Malaya. Though China's territorial claims to these areas may be marginal, she still regards them as "lost territories," and they are so shown on both Nationalist and Communist maps.

Water buffalo, or carabao, are coextensive with rice culture, for they are well adapted to the high temperature and humidity of the realm. This photo is from the island of Mindoro in the central Philippines. (*Courtesy United Nations*)

In addition to the cultural and commercial penetration by China and India, Arab traders cruised the coasts, and in the thirteenth century Islam was brought from India by spice merchants who used the port of Malacca as their base. Muslim culture came to penetrate most of Indonesia except Bali and Mindanao, though it made little progress into the Southeast Asian mainland, which was Buddhist.

European penetration began in 1511 with the capture of Malacca by the Portuguese, who were seeking spices. The Spanish under Magellan arrived in the Philippines in 1525 and based their claim on the Treaty of Tordesillas, by which the Pope divided the world between the Portuguese and Spanish along a meridian which presumably circled the poles through Brazil.

Later on came the Dutch, French, and British. The last two were primarily interested in India, but the Dutch sailed directly from the Cape of Good Hope, and avoiding the Strait of Malacca, established their settlement in Java in 1600. Only in the Philippines and in Java did European administration permeate the native culture; elsewhere the effect was probably less than that of the Chinese traders under the Ming dynasty (1368–1644), or of Japanese merchants prior to 1637.

Great Britain started to bring Burma under her domination in 1824, largely to protect India. As British control pushed eastward, French influence appeared on the other side of the realm in Cochin China in 1862, and by 1893 spread to the adjoining states, which came to be French Indochina. By mutual agreement in 1896, Thailand was preserved as an independent buffer state. Farther south, agreements between the Dutch and British left the former secure in the Netherlands Indies but gave the British free rein in Malaya.

At the time when European powers arrived in Southeast Asia, the realm was a patchwork of petty principalities, sultanates, and kingdoms—dozens in number and with highly uncertain boundaries. Some states paid tribute to others, even to two or more at the same time, but a demand for tribute did not necessarily imply sovereign control. On such a fluid structure, European control imposed sharp but ill-conceived boundaries which often paid little attention to tribal distribution. Many of these lines have resulted in twentieth-century disputes. For instance, millions of Thais live outside Thailand.

Alongside the indigenous changes which have taken place in recent centuries, a major penetration was made by Chinese and Indian laborers, merchants, and capitalists. Immigrants from each country set up cultural enclaves which have resisted assimilation; the unwillingness of many Chinese to accept local citizenship presents a recurrent problem. Singapore is thus more of a Chinese than a Malay city. Several of the large coastal cities are products of immigration.

European and American imperialism has given each former colony a distinct cultural orientation. Filipinos, with a lingering Spanish heritage, speak English and trade with America. Burma is no longer related to the British Commonwealth, but in language and commerce the country still looks to England. The same is true of the former French protectorates. Portuguese Timor is the last of the colonial areas.

So strong is this outward orientation that people in Rangoon know less of Manila or Saigon than they do of Washington or of Paris. Jakarta is quite unaware of life in Bangkok. The people of the Philippines know far less about next-door Indonesia than they do of American history, and except in the concern of a few people in Manila, Thailand might as well be on another continent. Each of the new nations tends to look toward its former colonial ruler rather than to its neighbor.

The several European powers had varied motives in adopting their methods of administration, but none sought a balanced economy for their colonies. In some ways the Dutch were the best colonial administrators, and their capital investment in the Indies was greater than that of any other power in Southeast Asia. The Dutch were the only European people who were willing to settle in their colonies for life. In most countries an overdependence on one or two exports, such as rice, rubber, or sugar, came to be the rule; the lack of diversification brought economic problems as the world price fluctuated.

The British sought strategic advantages and a market for their merchandise. The Dutch had little to sell but wanted an opportunity for capital investment; the inscription on the old office of the Dutch East India Company in Amsterdam still reads: "The cost comes before the profit." American investments in the Philippines were limited, but the islands' export trade in sugar, copra, and abacá was made possible only by preferential tariffs in the United States. French efforts brought little economic profit and may rather have centered on prestige and a search for manpower. Thailand remained free, but came within the British economic sphere.

More than elsewhere in Asia, this was a colonial area not of one power but of a half dozen. Each country faces the outside world but turns its back on its neighbors. Southeast Asia clearly lacks cultural unity.

If Southeast Asia is to achieve integrity in the face of imperial pressures from China and India or from the Soviet Union and America, and is to carry weight in the world of the twenty-first century, some federation would seem desirable. Although Indonesia represents the largest bloc of population, an all-Malay union with the Philippines and the Malay peninsula seems remote. Singapore might provide a logical focus, but its population is too Chinese. The three continental areas of Burma, Thailand, and the Indochina States have many similarities but lack mutual understanding and economic motivation.

Everywhere an intense nationalism seems to preclude union. Centuries of cultural fragmentation combine with geographic fractionalization to block political cooperation. Each country has visions of past grandeur and may wish to recover areas which it lost centuries ago.

References on Southeast Asia

The standard reference is E. H. G. Dobby: *Southeast Asia,* with a bibliography. Local studies are considered in the *Jour. of Tropical Geography* (Kuala Lumpur). See also general references on Asia in Chapter 1.

Broek, Jan O. M.: "Diversity and Unity in Southeast Asia," *Geog. Rev.,* XXXIV (1944), 175–195.

*Dobby, E. H. G.: "Winds and Fronts over Southeast Asia," *Geog. Rev.,* XXXV (1945), 204–218.

Dobby, E. H. G.: "Some Aspects of the Human Ecology of Southeast Asia," *Geog. Jour.,* CVIII (1946), 40–54.

*Dobby, E. H. G.: *Southeast Asia,* 7th ed., London: University of London Press (1960).

Fryer, D. W.: "The 'Million City' in Southeast Asia," *Geog. Rev.,* XLIII (1953), 474–494.

Ginsburg, Norton S.: "The Great City in Southeast Asia," *Amer. Jour. Sociology* (1955), 455–462.

*Ginsburg, Norton S. (ed.): *The Pattern of Asia,* Englewood Cliffs, N.J.: Prentice-Hall (1958).

International Bank of Reconstruction and Development: *The Economic Development of Malaya,* Baltimore: The Johns Hopkins Press (1955).

*Pelzer, Karl G.: *Pioneer Settlement in the Asiatic Tropics,* New York: Amer. Geog. Soc. (1945).

*Robequain, Charles: *Malaya, Indonesia, Borneo, and the Philippines,* New York: David McKay (1958).

*Spencer, Joseph E.: *Asia, East by South,* New York: Wiley (1954).

Unger, Leonard: "The Chinese in Southeast Asia," *Geog. Rev.,* XXXIV (1944), 196–217.

Zelinsky, Wilbur: "The Indochinese Peninsula: A Demographic Anomaly," *Far Eastern Quarterly,* IX (1950), 115–145.

18 The Southeast Asian Base

Structure and Surface / Climate / Vegetation / Soil

STRUCTURE AND SURFACE

The divisions of Southeast Asia, peninsular and insular, have related structures. Both contain young mountains, and both contain old stable blocks. The presence of the South China Sea and its many shallow embayments, such as the Gulf of Siam or the Java and Celebes Seas, should not imply any lack of geologic unity or physical coherence. At the same time the area is more fractionalized than other parts of Asia, with resulting cultural diversity.

Eastern Tibet, like the Pamir area farther west, appears to be a complex knot or core area from which great mountain ranges radiate like the arms of an octopus. The Himalaya and the Kunlun extend westward; the Chin Ling and the Nan Ling reach eastward across China. To the south are several great north–south ranges whose topography is clear but whose structural history is imperfectly known.

One of these radiating mountain chains forms the boundary between Burma and India and extends, half buried, in an arc through Sumatra and Java. Another marks the frontier between Burma and Thailand and continues through Malaya. Still a third range extends to the southeast through Viet Nam. A fourth line of mountains, trending to the southeast, divides Viet Nam from China.

Other structures appear in the Philippines— and probably continue in Celebes and Borneo

269

LANDFORMS

Cressey—Asia's Lands and Peoples

Much of Southeast Asia is mountainous and in part volcanic. Cultivation and population concentrate in the deltas and coastal plains, but large areas remain underdeveloped. Half of the realm is peninsular; half is insular. (*Base map by Erwin Raisz,
modified by Edward Soja*)

as well—as parts of the circum-Pacific arc which borders East Asia from Kamchatka southward through Japan.

Two of these alignments, Tertiary in age, encircle the submerged Sunda Platform. This is one of the old stable areas of Asia, in part an ancient peneplain. The Sunda Platform was probably above sea level during the Glacial period, when the ocean was lowered by the removal of so much water to build up the continental ice sheets. The Platform, now slightly submerged, in most places is less than 150 feet deep. Comparable but much smaller stable areas, now above sea level, are present in central Burma, central Thailand, and Cambodia.

The arcuate mountains of the Sumatra-Java chain and of the Philippines are evidences of crumpling between the rigid Sunda massif, as an extension of the Asian continent, and the encircling active areas of the Indian and Pacific Oceans. The Indonesian arc has a length of 3,000 miles and contains more than seventy active volcanoes in addition to scores of semi-extinct cones. Earthquakes are recurrent. The Philippine arc is shorter but almost as active. In both arcs the mountains rise steeply from the floor of the adjoining ocean.

A volcanic and seismic zone forms the outermost part of the Burmese-Indonesian arc; within it is a folded zone rich in oil-bearing formations in Burma, Sumatra, and Borneo. The interior of the Southeast Asian realm is a stable area, without earthquakes or folding since the Cretaceous period, and underlain by ancient rocks. Here and there this inner area has metalliferous zones containing tin, iron, lead, silver, tungsten, aluminum, manganese, and chromium.

The great rivers of continental Southeast Asia have several unique characteristics. Each is controlled by geologic features, so much so that the Salween and Songkoi, or Red, Rivers flow in structural trenches. Each river has few tributaries in its upper course and its basin widens out toward the mouth, the reverse of the normal trend. Each carries a large volume of water from the heavy monsoon rainfall. Near latitude 28°N the airline distance from the Irrawaddy to the Yangtze is only 30 miles, and the Brahmaputra flows 70 miles farther west; yet the mouth of the Yangtze is half a continent distant from the mouth of the Brahmaputra.

The Irrawaddy has the longest lowland, 800 miles in length, and a delta which measures 40,000 square miles. The Salween is without an extensive delta. The lowland of the so-called Menam River is 300 miles long, and its delta covers 26,000 square miles. (Actually its name is Menam Chao Phraya, since *menam* simply means river.) The Mekong, largest river in the realm, has an irregular lowland which, together with the delta proper, covers at least 100,000 square miles. The Songkoi, or Red, has a delta which measures some 5,400 square miles.

Three types of land forms dominate Southeast Asia: young tectonic or volcanic mountains, dissected peneplains, and recent alluvial plains.

Most mountains are under 10,000 feet, although elevations reach twice that figure in northern Burma, and several volcanic peaks exceed 2 miles in height. Although many of these mountains are contemporary with the Himalaya, the heavy rainfall and tropical weathering has led to rapid erosion, so that bedrock is seldom exposed. Mountainous land forms characterize the ranges which finger southward from eastern Tibet, as well as the island arcs which encircle the Sunda Platform.

Parts of Borneo, Malaya, southern Thailand, and Cambodia have a topography which reflects an old peneplain surface, the product of a long period of erosion under long-continued crustal stability, now more or less dissected. These areas include the deeply dissected Shan Plateau in Burma, covering 200,000 square miles between the Irrawaddy and Salween; the 60,000 square-mile Khorat Platform in Thailand between the Chao Phraya and Mekong Rivers; and the low lying Cambodian Saucer, 45,000 square miles in extent. All are under-

Indonesia's most famous volcano is Krakatoa, located between Java and Sumatra. The eruption of 1883 blew the former cone 17 miles into the air and left sea water 1,000 feet deep. This is the new ash cone known as Anak Krakatoa, the child of Krakatoa. (*Courtesy Indonesian Information Office*)

lain by old strata. A similar peneplain surface apparently continues beneath the Sunda Sea in Indonesia.

Flood plains, deltas, interior basins, and emerged coastal plains occupy about one-tenth of Southeast Asia, but they provide the habitat for most of the people. Rapid sedimentation is the product of rapid erosion. Many deltas are advancing seaward 150 to 300 feet a year; both the Irrawaddy and Mekong Rivers are building the coast seaward at the rate of 200 feet annually.

As river mouths advance, the river bed builds upward. As soon as the surface of the water rises slightly above that of the surrounding land, the river usually changes its course. Every large delta thus has a network of abandoned distributaries, with intervening marsh lands. Each flood adds its layer of fertile silt, and preserves the flatness of the land.

Along many low coasts mangrove swamps have developed on a large scale. The vegetation traps river-borne sediment and helps the land to grow seaward. Thus one-third of Sumatra has been formed by coastal sedimentation, some 60,000 square miles in extent. Inland swamps are found in many poorly drained areas, such as the Tonle Sap marshes along the lower Mekong River or behind natural levees. Since most swamps are tree-covered, reclamation has been difficult.

The most advantageous areas for agriculture are the broad alluvial plains near Rangoon, Bangkok, and Saigon, where periodic flooding provides an ideal environment for growing rice.

CLIMATE

Southeast Asia lies astride the equator. This is the zone of the doldrums, an area of low pressure and rising air which is due to solar heating. The normal circulation is thus for air masses to move toward the equator from both hemispheres. While the air is drawn in from north and south respectively, the effect of the earth's rotation, described in Ferrel's law as the Coriolis force, turns these winds to their right in the Northern Hemisphere and to their left in the Southern Hemisphere. They thus become the northeast and southeast trade winds, respectively.

These trade winds meet in the intertropical convergence zone, an area of rising air, sharp squalls, and exceptionally heavy showers. This is sometimes known as the equatorial front, analogous to the fronts of intermediate latitudes. But whereas the latter involve air of dissimilar properties where one air mass overrides another, the intertropical convergence zone is merely a broad zone involving similar air. Unlike fronts elsewhere, horizontal forces are weak; instead, the air is marked by vigorous upward movement and strong convection. Calms are frequent, as is implied in the term doldrum. Where opposing winds do meet, perhaps with somewhat different character, shear action produces sharp eddies or squalls which may become quite violent.

As the overhead sun shifts north or south of the equator with the season, the trade-wind circulation moves with it. Here is where it becomes important to apply Ferrel's law, for the northeast or southeast direction of the trade winds applies only within their respective hemispheres. Thus when trade winds from the southeast, where they have had a left-hand deflection, cross the equator, they become turned to their right and move as southwest winds.

This idealized situation is modified by the fact that on either side of the Southeast Asian realm are two continents, Asia and Australia. Although their size is quite unequal, each has a seasonal alternation between high and low pressure, at opposite times of the year in the two hemispheres. Quite apart from the equator-induced trade winds, air masses stream out of high-pressure Asia during its winter toward Australia, which then is experiencing summer with low pressure. These winds result from descending air over the Asian continent, so that the air is cold and dry, and it may require passage over hundreds of miles of warm seas to erase its original character.

Our understanding of Southeast Asian air masses has been clarified by E. H. G. Dobby, who has plotted their monthly course, as shown in the maps on page 275. January winds blow strongly from the northeast, as a combination of trade winds and outblowing monsoon circulation which originated in the heart of Asia. They are thus relatively cool and only somewhat moist, and yield moderate rain on windward slopes. As these winds cross the equator they are deflected to their left. They then meet the southeast trades, in part blowing out from Australia, along an intertropical convergence zone which lies 7 degrees south of the equator; here rain may be quite heavy.

In July, conditions are reversed. The trades of the Southern Hemisphere, many of which have developed high humidity during their passage across warm seas, cross the equator and become southwest winds. This circulation covers the entire realm, pushing aside any convergence zone or restricting it to a north–south belt through Thailand between roughly parallel winds which move in from the Bay of Bengal and the South China Sea. Heavy rain results, especially on mountain slopes.

This to-and-fro circulation is the monsoon; in reality it is more complicated than here described or anywhere understood. The monsoon circulation is by no means uniform, for there are differences between insular equatorial Indonesia, and the semicontinental mountains 20 degrees north of the equator. Mountain ranges affect the path of the monsoon, as may also high-level jet-stream winds, which are as yet little understood.

No other part of Asia has such uniform year-round temperatures. The sun shines high overhead, and the sunshine duration varies little from month to month. Near the equator and at sea level, average monthly temperatures vary only 2 or 3 degrees. At Singapore the range is from 78 to 81°F, while Jakarta varies between 78 and 79°F. Farther north the monthly range differs more widely, as at Bangkok with 78°F and 87°F. The adjoining tropical seas are the hottest in the world.

The diurnal temperature range is much greater. Singapore often has a 12°F difference between day and night. It has been well said that "night is the winter of the tropics." The highest and lowest temperatures for the year may occur within twelve hours of each other.

It is well to emphasize that equatorial cities never experience temperatures as high as those in continental interiors. The all-time maximum at Singapore is 97°F, or at Jakarta, 98°F. Farther from the equator, temperatures rise, as is shown at Manila with 101°F or Saigon with 104°F. What makes the tropics oppressive is the continuation of high temperature and the uncomfortable humidity.

Temperature is so strikingly reduced by altitude that elevations above a mile may be classed as resort areas. The only parts of Southeast Asia where elevations are high enough for snow lie in northern Burma and Viet Nam, but frost is occasionally experienced above 10,000 feet on the Indonesian volcanoes.

Most trade-wind or monsoon air masses which enter the realm have crossed warm seas for thousands of miles, even though their source area may have been partly in dry Asia or Australia. They are thus moist and balmy, and the resulting rain makes the realm the wettest on earth. While tropical air may be nearly saturated, rain results only when the air has been cooled by convection or by rising over mountains. Sea-level stations outside the doldrums are seldom very rainy unless there are nearby orographic influences.

Most of the islands and coasts receive at least 80 inches of rain, well distributed through the year, and exposed mountain slopes may have twice this amount. Rain-shadow areas, as in interior Burma or Thailand, receive as little as 40 inches. Rainfall on exposed areas gives rise to a tropical rain forest; in the rain shadow, because of the high evaporation, there is a savanna grassland. Every month is effectively wet near the equator; farther away there may be months with less than 2 or 3 inches of rain. It is the distribution of monsoon rain, rather than any variation in temperature, which gives Southeast Asia any semblance of seasons.

Where the monsoon is best developed, rain alternates with drought, or at least there is a seasonal distribution of moisture. Thus the west coasts of Burma, peninsular Thailand, and Malaya have heavy rain during the period of onshore winds from June through September, while east-coast areas, such as the Philippines and Viet Nam, have their rainiest season from October into March.

Since this moist tropical air is unstable, especially toward the intertropical convergence zone, strong vertical currents may develop. Cumulonimbus clouds rising to 10,000 feet may develop in a half hour, with vertical winds of 100 miles an hour. Several inches of rain may fall in an hour. Thunderstorms are very common.

Many tropical areas experience a daily routine much as follows: During morning hours the sun warms the air so that it becomes progressively lighter and rises, forming high cumulus clouds which condense to give heavy rain, often with sharp thunderstorms. Equilibrium is reestablished by afternoon, and by sundown the sky becomes clear as cooler air descends. Stars twinkle at night. The next day the same sequence recurs: a clear morning, then clouds and rain, and clear weather once more. Sportsmen thus make a date for tennis next Thursday after the rain.

In Koeppen climatic terms, Afi climates prevail over most of Indonesia, Malaya, and Mindanao; in other words, climates with monthly temperature averages always above 64°F and 2.4 inches of rain, and with a range between

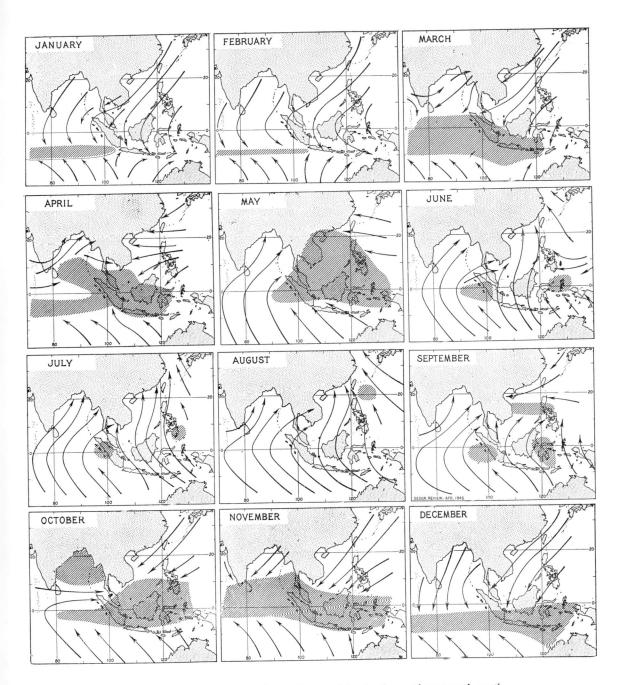

Southeast Asia lies astride the equator and is influenced by both northeast and southeast trade winds, as modified by the land masses of Asia and Australia. As this circulation shifts with the seasonal tilt of the earth, it gives rise to the monsoons. Doldrum areas are shaded. (*E. H. G. Dobby, courtesy American Geographical Society*)

coolest and warmest months of less than 9°F. *Awi* climates, with a slight dry season, are present in eastern Java and beyond. Most of the Philippines and western Burma have an *Amw* climate: hot, with a short dry season but with so much rain during the rest of the year that the soil usually remains moist. Thailand and the Indochina States are classed as *Aw*, hot and rainy, but with a few dry months and with a slight seasonal temperature shift.

VEGETATION

Before the arrival of man, most of Southeast Asia was a vast woodland, with a lush evergreen tropical rain forest where moisture was abundant, a more open deciduous forest where there was a monsoonal variation in rainfall, and with pockets of savanna grasslands in the areas where the excess of evapotranspiration over precipitation precluded trees. Mangrove forests or coconuts bordered many coasts. Nature ran riot, and tens of thousands of species have been counted.

Since primitive people lacked tools with which to clear the trees, only in modern times has the forest been attacked. Most agricultural clearings were made by fire, and were temporary. Little truly virgin forest remains. Uncleared forest growth, still relatively primeval, occupies as much as half of Southeast Asia.

An impression of the boundless forest is given by George Maxwell. Although he writes of Malaya, the description applies to much of the undeveloped parts of the realm.[1]

In a Malay village one may better realize the manner in which the forest hems in the cultivated area. The settlement is generally situated on the banks of a river. By the water's edge are the houses, built under the shade of fruit-trees, and behind them are the flat, irrigated padi-fields. On all sides this area is shut in by a dark heavy line that uprears itself, around and above it, like the

[1] George Maxwell: *In Malay Forests,* London: Blackwood (1930); quoted in Donald Moore (ed.): *Where Monsoons Meet,* London: Harrap (1956), 12–13. Quoted by permission.

walls of a prison. This line is the forest edge; and thence the forest spreads in every direction, miles upon miles, until some other village is reached; there it opens out again, and sweeping round the clearing, as a wave encircles some ocean rock, closes in again behind it and continues, over mountains, over plains, until the sea is reached.

But it is when he views it from a mountain peak that the stranger can best see the extent of the forest. He will then discover, what the Malay can never for a minute forget, that he lives his life in the midst of a forest which is as much apart from him as it is around him. The fact that it extends, interminable, far beyond the horizon on every side, then for the first time makes its indelible impression upon his mind.

On the slopes of the nearest spur each individual tree stands clear, each giant form showing the swelling roundness of its wealth of bough and leaf. Tier upon tier, the trees stand thickly massed, without a break, from the level of the plain to the height of the topmost trees that show their heads against the sky-line. Deep, dark, sombre green is the colour of this near range; here and there one may catch glimpses of lighter shades, a few scattered patches perhaps of sage green where some trees, after fruiting, are putting forth a new flush of leaves; possibly there may be a speck of vivid red that marks a tree whose young shoots assume an unusual colour. But the contrast only accentuates the prevailing tone.

Beyond these hills, which are not perhaps more than a few miles away, rises a range that is clad in purple. At this distance the mass of trees shows through the clear atmosphere, not with the shape of each individual tree, but with a uniform raised and rounded toughness that covers alike mountain crag and mountain ravine.

In some places in the plains between the two ranges one may perhaps see the lighter green that marks a cultivated area, or a gleam of white sand where alluvial tin-mines show like islands in the sea.

Beyond the purple mountains rise other ranges, and though, of course, you cannot see it, you know that the forest sweeps on through wide hidden valleys and wonderful places rarely trodden by man, until it reappears in sight upon another range.

The mountain-chains melt from purple to blue,

Much of Southeast Asia is still covered by a tropical rain forest, with dozens of species within a short distance. This road leads to a chromite mine on Mount Beaufort on Palawan Island in the Philippines. (*Canlas, courtesy International Cooperation Administration*)

and as they recede the roughness of the forest covering becomes a velvety pile, and then an even softer texture; and finally, where grey mists melt and dissolve in the distant haze, it is not easy to know which is forest and which is sky.

Tropical rain forests develop in areas with 80 or more inches of rain, either well distributed throughout the year or so abundant that there is no effective dry period in the soil. Trees grow in several stories. On the ground there may be scattered shrubs, bamboos, canes, mosses, and ferns. Above them is a layer of shade-loving trees 20 to 50 feet high, whose crowns form a continuous canopy. Still higher are a variety of tall, isolated trees, many belonging to the family Depterocarpia, which rise with straight trunks to 100 and even 200 feet as they reach for the sun. Where the trees form a nearly continuous canopy, only scattered shafts of sunlight reach the ground, and the surface vegetation may be sparse. Only 1 per cent of the outside light reaches the soil, so that a photographer may find time exposures necessary even at midday.

Woody creepers, often several hundred feet long, climb into the sunlight and spread in festoons from tree to tree. Epiphytes, such as orchids and wild figs, become adjusted to living, self-contained, above the ground.

Tropical forests are remarkable for the many

kinds of trees, with dozens of species within a few hundred feet; for the most part they are hardwoods. Many of these have no commercial value, and those for which there is a market are usually so scattered that it may be impractical to get them out. Since scores of unmarketable species are intermingled with the more desirable trees, it is not feasible to cut and move out the few varieties for which there is a current need. Furthermore, many tropical trees contain damaged wood, due to the many insects and to the tendency to rot under conditions of high temperature and high humidity.

Commercial lumbering is usually limited to the areas where only a few species grow and where access is easy. Stands of single species are more common in the monsoon forests, where teak is a valuable product, widely used for decks on ships. Ebony, sandalwood, and lauan, or Philippine mahogany, are also important. If the present forests could be cleared and if solid stands might be grown, Southeast Asia could be a large producer of cabinet woods and of cellulose for pulp and paper.

Many secondary forest products are locally important. Rattan, a long climbing cane used for baskets and furniture, is found from sea level to the higher mountains. The pith or marrow of the sago palm is an important source of starchy food, and provides a change from the diet of rice and corn. Sago flour is exported for use in puddings and as a stiffener in textiles. Many palm trees yield sugar or alcohol and fermented beverages. Wood oils are obtained from certain trees, usually from their nuts. Camphor is distilled from several trees; tannin is obtained

Lumbering operations in Southeast Asia are beginning to provide the world with splendid tropical hardwoods, such as Philippine mahogany or lauan. These logs have been cut north of Davao in the southern Philippines. (*Courtesy Caltex*)

from mangrove bark; and resins such as turpentine are a product of pine forests. The gum known as gutta percha, once obtained from wild trees, is now produced on estates. Although bamboo is properly a grass rather than a tree, it forms a valuable forest product. Some tropical bamboos attain a height of 100 feet and a diameter of 4 inches. Where some of the original forests have been cleared, man has replaced them with artificial forests of rubber, coconut and oil palm, and kapok, or with trees trimmed to bush form such as tea and cinchona.

While elevation brings cooler temperatures, to match mid-latitude conditions, the heavy rainfall results in a thick blanket of moss which covers the ground and may hang in great festoons on the trees.

Large animals—elephants or tigers—are rare, but there is a wealth of arboreal fauna. Most of this animal life has an Asiatic origin, in contrast to Australian fauna to the east. Between the two lies Wallace's line, which extends north and south from points east of Java and Borneo but including (as modified) the area of the Philippines.

SOIL

The widespread impression that tropical soils are highly fertile is largely mistaken. Vegetation runs riot, but when the land is cleared and crops planted, it is at once apparent that many soils are sterile and unproductive—even though the underlying parent material may be the same as in temperate lands.

The heavy rainfall of Southeast Asia and the high temperatures combine to leach the soil thoroughly. All substances which are soluble in water, no matter how slowly, are gradually dissolved and carried away in solution by the ground water, eventually to reach the sea. These soluble substances are the very ones which supply mineral nutrients to vegetation. Fresh parent material may be added by the gradual decay of the underlying bedrock or through its exposure by erosion and by the ac-

cumulation of alluvial deposits, but the usual result is that wet tropical soils are constantly being impoverished. Since leaching increases with heavier rainfall and is accelerated by high temperatures, soils decrease in fertility accordingly. Thus areas with a dry period or lower temperatures due to elevation may be more productive. Clay originates from the decomposition of the feldspars in igneous rocks. Where present in the soil, clay has the ability to hold some mineral plant foods and to slow down the leaching process. Sandy soils become leached more rapidly.

Soil is not merely altered mineral particles. It also contains organic material in varying amounts. The total amount of organic matter produced each year by a tropical rain forest is very great, probably exceeded nowhere. In the tropics, however, humus is always at a disadvantage, for the higher the temperature, the more rapid the rate of decay. Oxidation and the work of a myriad number of microorganisms quickly destroy all fallen trees or other vegetation. While decaying vegetable matter steadily accumulates as trees die, it is continuously depleted as bacteria complete its breakdown. Where soil is moist and temperatures remain above 75°F the breakdown by microorganisms is so much more rapid than the supply that humus is almost absent, despite the profuse vegetation. One may walk through many tropical forests and scuff away the litter of recently fallen leaves only to find iron-stained sandy soil directly on the surface. Such soil is almost devoid of any black carbonaceous matter and is very low in soluble mineral nutrients.

If soils thus tend to be infertile, one may properly question how it is possible for forests to grow. The answer is that trees send roots deep into the unleached subsoil, and the accumulating surface litter of vegetation just barely keeps ahead of decay. Once the forest is cut over and the supply of fresh humus is gone, soils reveal their intrinsic sterility, for the cycle of nutrients is broken. Even a heavy application of fertilizer may be of little value if

Many Javanese landscapes include these three components: symmetrical volcanic slopes, terraced rice fields, and coconut palms. This is a view of Garoet volcano, seen from Ngamplang. (*Courtesy Indonesian Information Office*)

there is no clay to adsorb it and retard its removal into the ground water.

Heavy rains not only accelerate the leaching of the soil; on unprotected slopes they may cause rapid erosion. Bare surfaces are rare in the natural forest, but agricultural clearings on hillsides may lose an inch of top soil in a single rain.

Three soil situations call for special comment: replenishment through the accumulation of alluvial deposits, the character of volcanic soils, and the development of laterite.

Many of the people of Southeast Asia live on flood plains, deltas, coastal plains, or interior basins where fresh silt and plant nutrients continually accumulate to offset leaching. Such soils may continue to yield crops without seri-

ous depletion for many years, as in the deltas of the Irrawaddy or the coastal plains of Java.

Indonesia and the Philippines contain large areas underlain by lava flows of basic chemical composition, and volcanic activity still continues. Not all volcanic soils are fertile, but those with a basaltic base tend to break down into clays which are productive, in contrast to igneous rocks with a more acidic composition. Basic lavas contain calcium, magnesium, iron, and usable phosphorus, whereas acidic forms of lava tend to yield less in the way of plant nutrients.

Southeast Asia has dozens of the most active volcanoes on earth. These frequently erupt great quantities of fine ash and other ejecta. The immediate neighborhood may be buried beneath several feet of ash, which destroys all vegetation; farther away and downwind the layer of fine material may amount to a fraction of an inch. This volcanic material weathers within a few decades, producing extraordinarily fertile soil whose productivity may persist for many years; before it is lost new eruptions usually occur. Hence the great fertility of the terraced rice fields in Java.

While these rejuvenating conditions prevail in most of Java and Bali, parts of Sumatra and the other Indonesian islands either lack the frequent accumulation of ash or it is of more acid character. For reasons such as this the outer islands of Indonesia may never develop the phenomenal population density which characterizes Java.

Parts of the mainland of Southeast Asia, and to some extent the nonvolcanic islands, are characterized by laterite, more or less perfectly developed. Its development involves a tropical process, related to the temperature and organic content of the ground water, which results in the complete decomposition of the silicates, followed by the progressive elimination of the magnesium and calcium compounds. The percentage of the remaining iron and aluminum is so much increased that they may become almost a commercial ore. Laterization is a biochemical process which takes place only where the ground water is low in humic acids. The result is an illuviated horizon of red or yellow slaglike and vesicular or pisolitic limonite and associated compounds which form a rock rather than merely a tropical red soil. The word laterite is often used carelessly, and should not be applied to a soil per se.

Three other factors are necessary to develop complete laterization: nearly level land, a fluctuating water table usually associated with the monsoon, and very long periods of time without appreciable tectonic uplift or erosion.

True laterite is a rock, formed *in situ* as an environmental by-product regardless of the underlying formations. As formed, it lies below the surface and has a thickness of 10 feet or more. When freshly exposed, laterite is soft, porous, bright red, and easily cut into building blocks; once exposed to the air, it becomes rock hard. It has long been quarried for building purposes, as is shown in the ruins of cities a thousand years old.

The tectonic stability of eastern Thailand, Cambodia, and Borneo accounts for development of laterite in these areas in contrast to its absence in much of the Philippines and Java, where changes in elevation have been frequent and erosion accelerated. In general, the requirements for laterite development are better met in peninsular India than in Southeast Asia.

Since laterite is thoroughly leached, any soil later formed from it is of necessity sterile. This is a factor in the low fertility of interior Thailand. Because there is little hope of natural improvement in fertility where laterite is present, moderate erosion may prove a blessing if it exposes relatively more fertile subsoil. This is especially true in flat areas which have long had tectonic stability. On the other hand, the bedrock beneath humid tropical areas may become decomposed to depths of 100 feet and more; once the protective blanket of surface vegetation is destroyed, slopes may become seriously gullied.

19 Livelihood in Southeast Asia

Land Use / Mineral Potentials / International Trade / Geographic Provinces

LAND USE

No other part of the continent has developed such specialized agriculture for export as Southeast Asia. Much of the world turns to the realm for its rubber, coconut and palm oil, abacá or Manila hemp, sisal, kapok, sugar, spices, quinine, tobacco, or rice. The demand for these commercial crops has led to the development of large plantations or estates, financed and managed by outside capital. In many places the entrepreneurs have cleared the forest and imported a labor force. Considerable capital is usually involved.

In promoting the cultivation of rubber, agri-

cultural research has been expensive. European management and profit expectations raise the price, and several years must elapse before trees come into bearing. Alongside the rubber estate a native farmer with no overhead may plant a few trees, possibly borrowed from across the road. Since his livelihood is based on subsistence crops, any income from rubber is a net profit; when thousands of such small farmers bring supplies to market the price may drop below costs on the estate.

Two methods of subsistence production are characteristic: wet-field rice in the plains and migratory fire-cleared plots in the hills, both of which involve negligible capital or outside skill.

282

Lowland rice is generally transplanted from seedbeds into puddled paddy fields. It may also be sown broadcast, in which case the fields are merely plowed and the seed scattered before the land is flooded. Where rainfall is heavy and frequent, irrigation may be unnecessary.

In the burnt-over type of production on well-drained upland soils, forest clearings are made by cutting the brush and accessible branches and girdling the trees at the beginning of the dry season; when the clearings are dry, the area is burned, and the ash fertilizes the poor tropical soil. The soil need not be plowed; instead, seed such as corn is planted in holes an inch deep made by a stick. After two or three harvests, weeds choke out planted crops, and the clearing is abandoned. The land then reverts to forest and is not again cleared for a decade, by which time the weeds have been killed by shade trees.

This practice is named *caingin* from its development in the Philippines; in Thailand it is called *tam rai* cultivation; in Burma, *taungya;* in Assam, *jhum;* in Ceylon, *cheena;* and in Indonesia and Malaya, *ladang.* At least one mountain tribe in north Burma attempts systematic reforestation of abandoned caingin fields.

In many areas the fields grow up to coarse cogon grass or bamboo rather than forest; this is primarily because the cogon is burned annually and only a few dwarf trees can get started. Once the land is covered with cogon grass, it cannot be recultivated by native plows and becomes a permanent grassland or artificial savanna. The root system is so dense that only machine-pulled plows can turn the sod. These savannas are incapable of native cultivation, and the tough grasses are too coarse for pasturage.

This type of fire-cleared upland cultivation

Slash-and-burn temporary clearings characterize hillside agriculture in the less-developed areas of Southeast Asia. In this aerial view from Viet Nam there are recent clearings as well as abandoned and partly overgrown fields. Very little truly virgin forest remains. (*Courtesy United States Air Force*)

does not encourage erosion. The ash provides a temporary fertilizer on soils otherwise unable to produce an annual crop. Neither tools nor animals are needed, and good crops are often raised. On the other hand, the method requires large areas per person, much valuable timber is destroyed, and relatively useless grasslands are likely to result.

On the basis of United Nations data, less than 10 per cent of the realm is cultivated, half of that figure in Borneo, and as much as six times the average in Java. Rice is the great crop, accounting for three-fifths of the crop acreage; in Thailand the fraction rises to nine-tenths; in Malaya it drops to one-fifth. Almost all is wet rice, grown in fields which are kept flooded by irrigation or by the heavy rains.

Corn appears to rank second as a food crop, occupying an average of one-eighth of the cultivated acreage; this extensive cultivation is largely due to the importance of corn in Indonesia and the Philippines, where the fraction is one-fifth. Sweet potatoes and cassava are grown in some areas, as in Java, where they occupy one-tenth of the cropland. Rubber, especially in Malaya, and coconuts, mainly in the Philippines, represent large acreages.

On the basis of broad assumptions, we may conclude that cropland might be doubled or trebled—perhaps even more. Certainly no other part of Asia has such attractive potentials. Siberia contains large areas of virgin land but the restrictions of cold and drought appear to be nearly insuperable. The empty parts of China are also too dry or too cold. Insofar as Java is a guide, Indonesia as a whole might provide food for 500 million people.

Although many areas are in a stage of pioneer agriculture, it should be emphasized that pioneering is seldom a possibility for the individual farmer. Tropical rain forests are difficult to clear; swamp lands require elaborate drainage arrangements; irrigation presents engineering problems; and few farmers who have had a taste of the amenities care to move beyond the frontier.

After the forest has been cleared, persistent work is necessary to keep it from reverting to jungle. Where migratory farmers use slash-and-burn techniques, nature recaptures the land within three or four years. Rubber plantations temporarily abandoned during the Second World War were soon engulfed by the forest. Large areas in the Philippines and elsewhere, once cleared, have become covered by grasses so wiry that the land can scarcely be plowed.

Most of the agricultural exports of the realm are technical crops such as rubber, oils, and

Land Use in Southeast Asia [1]

(in thousand hectares)

Country	Total area	Arable land incl. fallow and orchards	Irrigated land	Forest and woodlands
Burma	67,795	8,614	502	45,274
Cambodia	17,251	2,500	5	9,300
Indonesia	149,156	17,681	5,090	90,825
Laos	23,680	1,020	650	14,208
Malaya	13,129	2,186	211	9,477
Philippines	29,940	7,296	873	15,875
Thailand	51,400	9,898	1,538	29,910
Viet Nam, North	15,523	1,300	—	8,850
Viet Nam, South	17,963	2,897	—	5,620
All Southeast Asia	385,837	53,392	—	229,339

[1] United Nations, Food and Agricultural Organization: *Production Yearbook*, 1960.

Tropical Asia is a major source of agricultural raw materials. These railroad cars carry sugar cane to a "central" in Java. (*Courtesy Indonesian Information Office*)

fibers. The great exception is rice, produced in surplus in Burma, Thailand, and South Viet Nam. Each year Rangoon, Bangkok, and Saigon normally have 1 or 2 million tons of rice for export. These help to make up the deficits elsewhere in South and East Asia. Despite rising demands abroad, increased domestic needs plus internal political problems have reduced the available surplus and at the same time raised the price. Subsidized American rice has also come into competition with that grown in the area.

Southeast Asia has provided an illustration of a primary producer turning out raw materials for export, but its economy is changing as population and local purchasing power rise and local industry emerges.

Economic activity is handicapped by the absence of good railway facilities. Burma has a limited internal system, but no links to India or its Southeast Asian neighbors. Thailand has the longest mileage of railways, with connec-tions which lead south to Singapore and east to Cambodia. Viet Nam once had a through link from Saigon into China, but the line has been cut along the border between the North and South. Laos is entirely without rail facilities, and Cambodia must depend on the Mekong River for contacts with Saigon. Java and Luzon are well supplied with railways, but most other parts of the East Indies have only limited mileage. Five international borders in Southeast Asia are without any railroad crossings, and for the realm as a whole the only outside connection is provided by the two lines that run into China.

The railway pattern reflects land forms and population distribution. Construction has largely been limited to the plains, and no railways cross the mountain backbones; hence the isolation of Burma from Thailand, or of coastal Viet Nam from the interior. Swamp lands impose another barrier, as is witnessed by the absence of a railway across the lower Mekong.

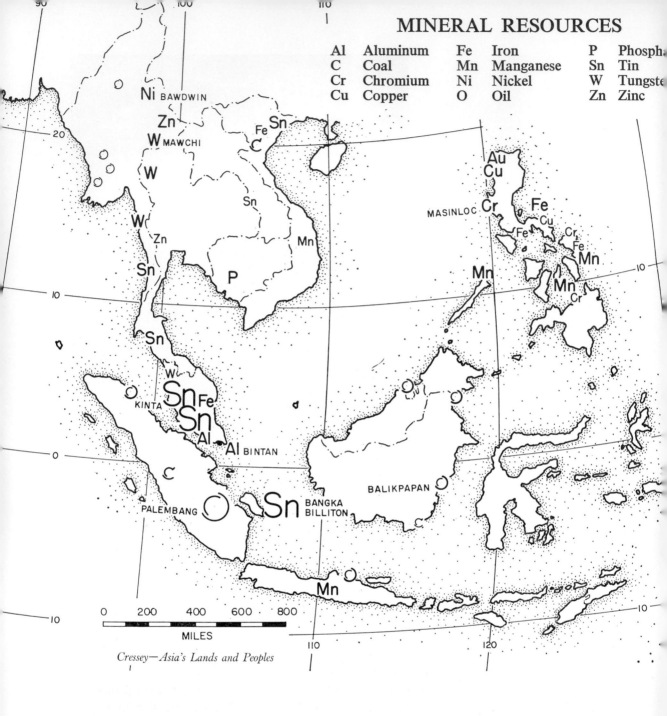

MINERAL RESOURCES

Al	Aluminum	Fe	Iron	P	Phosph
C	Coal	Mn	Manganese	Sn	Tin
Cr	Chromium	Ni	Nickel	W	Tungste
Cu	Copper	O	Oil	Zn	Zinc

Cressey—Asia's Lands and Peoples

Few parts of Asia appear to have greater undeveloped mineral assets, but only tin and petroleum are in large production. Coal is limited and poor. Most metals are shipped elsewhere for processing. The size of the symbols suggests world importance.

MINERAL POTENTIALS

Southeast Asia is abundantly supplied with mineral resources; the major exception seems to lie in the absence of coking coal. Most of the present production represents export items which are partly refined locally and then shipped elsewhere for final refining or fabrication. Oil and tin are examples.

Geological conditions vary too widely to warrant many generalizations. But we can say something about the location and amount of the resources. A belt of young petroleum-rich formations extends in a long arc from Burma south and east through the East Indies. Outside of it is a line of active volcanoes, and inside the crescent are large deposits of tin, iron, aluminum, manganese, chromium, and other minerals.

Two of the difficulties which confront geological exploration and mineral development throughout much of Southeast Asia are the dense cover of natural vegetation and the deeply weathered soil; fresh bedrock is rarely exposed. Many areas have only the most generalized geologic maps, and field studies necessitate work under very difficult conditions. Tropical weathering may extend to depths of 100 feet and more, and where laterite is present it may mask the underlying bedrock. Geologists may need to dig deep pits to find rock and examine its structure.

Tin is the unique mineral, and Indonesia now leads Malaya in its production. Iron ore, both rich and poor, moves to Japan from Malaya and the Philippines. Bauxite is mined near Singapore; rich chromium is present in the Philippines; Burma has been one of the world's

Tin is the most famous of the realm's mineral exports, produced both through lode mining and by placer operations from floating dredges which operate in their self-made lake. This is a scene on the Indonesian island of Billiton. (*Courtesy Indonesian Information Office*)

large producers of zinc and lead; and manganese is produced in the Philippines and elsewhere. Tungsten occurs in Burma, and gold is an important item in the Philippines.

Petroleum is obtained in Sumatra, with lesser amounts in Java and Borneo, but the only mainland occurrence is in central Burma. These lands possess the chief oil fields between the Persian Gulf and California, along with Japan and Sakhalin. The only good coal is in North Viet Nam, but subbituminous lignite is mined in several countries. The overall production exceeds 3 million tons a year.

Hydroelectric developments are in their infancy but hold some promise.

The preceding paragraphs refer only to resources in production. While much geological work remains to be done, it appears likely that the realm as a whole is richly endowed. Whether Southeast Asia is to become a significant industrial center depends on politics and capital, the growth of a local market, and relations with potential customers such as China and Japan.

Mining and industry have so far made little impress on the landscape. Areas are small and scattered, and only a small proportion of the labor force is so engaged. The impact is upon

The Benguet gold mines in the Philippines lie at an elevation of 5,000 feet, and have enabled the islands to become one of the important world producers. This photo is in the area of the Philippines' leading mountain resort at Baguio. (*Fenno Jacobs, from Three Lions*)

Oil wells such as these in Brunei have made the East Indies the leading source of petroleum between the Persian Gulf and California. (*Courtesy British Information Services*)

the economy and the culture rather than upon the land. Because of exploration and transport problems, most mining areas lie near the coast, especially where large tonnages are involved.

INTERNATIONAL TRADE

Southeast Asia has become a major area for foreign commerce, thanks in part to the available export surplus. Each year 1 billion dollars' worth of mineral commodities are shipped abroad, and the value of agricultural products is twice as large. These exports enable the realm to be a large buyer of machinery and manufactured goods. Only Indonesia imports food.

The exports are highly localized. Malaya and Singapore provide more than one-third of the total trade. Cambodia and Laos scarcely enter international commerce at all. Indonesia ranks high in totals but low in per capita value. On a per capita basis, North Borneo leads, with annual exports of some $300 per person, twice those of Malaya.

The emphasis on basic agricultural production and the underpopulated character of the realm is suggested by the large surplus of agricultural products. Rice leads, with an annual export of several million tons, normally from Rangoon, Bangkok, and Saigon. Sugar follows, especially from the Philippine Islands and Java. Rubber ranks third in tonnage, with large shipments from Indonesia and Malaya, and lesser amounts from Thailand, Burma, South Viet Nam, and Cambodia. Copra and coconut oil are major products in the Philippines and Malaya. Palm oil is shipped from Indonesia, and hemp from both Indonesia and the Philippines.

Trade in these tropical products faces many uncertainties. If demand warrants, the output of natural rubber or of coconut products could be quadrupled, and much more. The same is true of sugar, tea, and coarse fibers. From time to time high prices appear tempting and acreage is greatly increased, notably in rubber. But with oversupply, or with an increased use of synthetics, or with competition from Africa, or a general decline in world prices, prices collapse and the local economy suffers.

Mineral commodities also account for large-tonnage shipments. Petroleum is well in the lead, especially from Sumatra and Borneo. Iron ore moves abroad from the Malay Peninsula and the Philippines, for Southeast Asia lacks suitable coking coal for blast furnace use. Tin is the realm's most distinctive mineral, exported from Malaya, Indonesia, Burma, and Thailand. The list of other basic commodities in production includes gold and chromium from the Philippines and aluminum ore from the vicinity of Singapore.

These various raw materials move to the more industrialized countries: to Japan, to Anglo-America, and to Western Europe. With the foreign exchange which they produce, the realm is able to import both necessities and luxuries.

GEOGRAPHIC PROVINCES

The Southeast Asian realm or subcontinent may be divided into three geographic provinces, each with its physical and cultural personality. Each in turn is made up of numerous regions.

Although a part of Asia. the Southeast is isolated from the rest of the continent by imposing mountains. Valleys such as those of the Salween and the Mekong might be expected to provide an overland avenue from China; but the rivers flow through great canyons amid broken terrain so that travel is almost impossible. Most human contact has thus been by sea rather than overland; even the winds reach the realm across the seas.

The first province is the semicontinental north, made up of Burma, Thailand, and the Indochina States. In general, this is an area of roughly north–south mountain ranges, a half dozen in number, separated by valleys whose great rivers take their rise in the edge of Tibet: the Irrawaddy, Salween, Mekong, and the Songkoi, or Red, plus the lesser Chao Phraya.

This is a part of Monsoon Asia with its seasonal wind shift and wet or rainy periods; hence the deciduous forest cover. Grassy savannas occur in rain-shadow locations. Life in each country is concentrated in the alluvial plains, where rice culture dominates. The quasicontinental province of Burma, Thailand, and the parts of Indochina is essentially homogeneous in development and potentials. Unfortunately, it lacks internal political coherence or easy accessibility. One part has a historic British orientation; another was French.

The second geographic province is made up of the islands of Indonesia which surround the shallow Sunda continental shelf, plus the Malay Peninsula south of the Kra Isthmus near 10°N. The southern tips of Burma and Thailand are more insular than continental, and properly belong here. A million years ago the area may have been more continental than insular. Fluctuations in sea level during the Pleistocene glacial epochs several times provided dry land connections between the Sunda Islands. This is a maritime equatorial area with a nonseasonal climate and irregular convectional rainfall which brings turbulent flying. Equatorial rain forests once covered all but the higher elevations. The inhabitants are Malays rather than Mongoloids (as are those farther north) and tend to have

RURAL POPULATION

Each dot represents 30,000 People

Cressey—Asia's Lands and Peoples

The uneven distribution of population is obvious. Java is crowded, and similar concentrations appear in the deltas of the Irrawaddy, Menam, Mekong, and Red Rivers; elsewhere large areas are nearly empty. If developed, Southeast Asia might provide livelihood for a billion people.

fair rather than coffee-colored skin. Their life, like that of the people of peninsular Southeast Asia, who occupy an area comparable in extent, lacks a central focus or coherence; fortunately, it is less fragmented politically.

The third province comprises the Philippine Islands, also insular but with a seasonal rhythm, since the archipelago lies well north of the equator. The climate is that of the humid tropics, a maritime variant of the first province. The individual islands are smaller than most of those in the Indonesian group. Three centuries of Spanish control have resulted in a culture quite unlike that found elsewhere. One inheritance is Christianity.

Within these three provinces is a multitude of geographic regions, each with its unique personality. Some islands or groups form a unit; elsewhere, as in Java, there are recognizable contrasts within a single island. These regional contrasts will be considered in the following chapters.

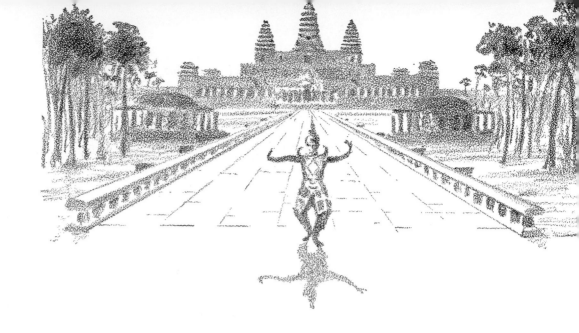

20 The Indochina States

*Historical Backgrounds / Two Rivers, One Cordillera / The Viet
Nams / Cambodia / Laos / References on the Indochina States*

HISTORICAL BACKGROUNDS

The term Indochina has always been unsatisfactory. If it refers to areas intermediate between the two great cultures of the continent it should include all Southeast Asia. If it refers to the present areas of the two Viet Nams, Laos, and Cambodia, it is inappropriate to imply much recent Indian influence. The name dates from the period of French control over the diverse lands comprised in her colony of Cochin China and the protectorates of Annam, Tonkin, Cambodia, and Laos.

Several streams of people and culture have flowed into the Indochina area. Chinese moved overland into the northeast, developing the areas which came to be known as Tonkin and northern Annam. Indian traders came by sea and established trading stations along the coast of Cambodia and the Mekong delta. One of the early peoples here were the Chams, possibly of Indonesian origin, who developed a small state midway between Annam and Cambodia. All these penetrations predated the Christian era, but they did not actively meet. The major overland movements which settled the area were from the northwest, especially those of the Khmers, who developed interior Cambodia during the seventh to the thirteenth centuries. Later came the Thai and many other

293

peoples, among them the Lao, moving out of Southwest China.

The ethnic map of present-day Indochina shows Annamese people occupying all the coast from the Red River to the Mekong including both deltas: Khmers in Cambodia, Thais along the central Mekong valley, remnant tribal groups in the central mountains, and mixed Thai and tribal people in the northwest.

Annamese far outnumber all other people together, probably making up 75 per cent of the total. Khmers account for nearly 10 per cent; Thais represent 5 per cent; and the others are Chinese, Chams, and many tribal groups such as the Moi.

Legendary history dates back to 2879 B.C., and as early as 207 B.C. there was probably a country known as the Kingdom of Viet Nam, the land of the people.

The earliest recorded history of Annam begins with 111 B.C., when a Chinese expedition set up a local kingdom which extended from South China into Tonkin; this later was incorporated into the Han dynasty empire of China. At that time the local inhabitants lived under primitive conditions, cultivating the soil with stone hoes and making little attempt to clear the forest or drain swamps. In 939 a revolt set up a native kingdom which came to be known by its Chinese name of Annam, meaning "peaceful south." A brief period of Chinese occupation in the fifteenth century was followed by another Annamite kingdom, later divided into Tonkin and Cochin China.

The kingdom of Cambodia, which dates from the second century, began as a collection of principalities near the lower Mekong and extended into what is now Thailand. During the zenith of its power, from 600 to 1200, the great buildings of Angkor, for which Cambodia is famous, were erected. Toward the end of the thirteenth century a member of a visiting Chinese embassy gave a vivid picture of the pomp of Cambodian royalty. There was an abundance of gold and silver in the trappings of the elephants and horses and in the huge parasols carried in the royal procession. The

decline of Cambodia was hastened by the spread of Thai tribes, moving out of southwest China in part under the pressure of Mongol invasions farther north. The city of Angkor was four times sacked by invading Thais, and was then abandoned to the jungle.

The Portuguese arrived in 1517, followed by the Dutch and the French. The latter came largely as missionaries, especially to Annam in the north. Their first territorial interest was in Cochin China, farther south, where an expeditionary force, after a decade of fighting, established their favorite contender on the throne. In order to consolidate his position, the new king of Cochin China also asked to become a tributary ruler under the emperor of China, a dual relationship which was unrecognized by Western law. Subsequent persecution of Christians led to French military action and the cession of three provinces to France in 1862.

The extension of French influence into Cambodia came at a time when that state, reduced from its ancient grandeur, was in a condition of vassalage to both Annam and Siam. The Khmers were thus favorable toward a French protectorate, which was established over Cambodia in 1864. When it was found that the Mekong valley did not offer a feasible avenue northward to China, French interests were shifted to the Red River and to Annam, where a treaty of navigation and protection was signed in 1874. This action was taken in the face of strong opposition from China, which continued to regard Tonkin as a vassal state until 1885. French acquisition of Indochina was completed by protectorates over Tonkin in 1874 and over Laos in 1893.

In this way the French Union of Indochina included Cochin China, Cambodia, Annam, Tonkin, and Laos. Although one of the smaller of French overseas territories, Indochina ranked first in population and took second place in the value of exports. Endless disagreements continued over the borders next to Burma, Siam, and China; British opposition was aroused whenever France pushed toward India. The Anglo-French convention of 1896 recognized Siam as a buffer state between expanding French interests in the east and British control over Burma.

Following the complicated events of Japanese occupation during the Second World War, and the postwar expulsion of the French, four independent states arose in 1954, of roughly equal size. They were the constitutional monarchy of Cambodia, with its capital at Pnompenh in the Mekong interior lowland; the constitutional monarchy of Laos whose capital is at Vientiane on the upper Mekong; and the two halves of Viet Nam, with a republic in the south centered on Saigon, and a Communist state, sometimes termed Viet Minh, in the north, with its capital at Hanoi, separated by a *de facto* boundary along the 17th parallel.

To include these countries in a single chapter or under a single name reflects their common French background but overlooks the lack of historic unity, the ethnic diversity, the artificial character of the boundaries, and the absence of geographic coherence. Indochina was one of the last parts of Asia to become colonial, and then to secure independence, but freedom has not yet resulted in peace or prosperity.

TWO RIVERS, ONE CORDILLERA

If the physical pattern of Indochina is simplified, we can recognize two major valleys: those of the Mekong and of the Songkoi or Red Rivers, with the rugged Annam Cordillera between them. Still other mountains lie along the Chinese border in the north, and in the extreme southwest.

The Mekong is one of the great rivers of Asia, some 2,700 miles in length. During the

The Mekong is the great river of the Indochina area. This view is in Cambodia between Kratie and Kampong Cham. (*Courtesy United Nations*)

early days of French penetration it was hoped that the river might provide an avenue into China, but several sections contain such swift rapids that boats take a month to move upstream from Saigon to northern Laos.

The delta is full of waterways. The Mekong enters the sea through five mouths, and associated streams as, for instance, the Saigon River flow immediately to the north. The compound delta measures nearly 15,000 square miles. Canals which have a depth of at least 6 feet total 1,000 miles. Several thousand junks and several hundred motorboats carry millions of tons of cargo. Upstream, seagoing vessels are able to reach Pnompenh and the Tonle Sap marshlands, especially in summer when there is a 20-foot channel.

From Kratie to the borders of China navigation is possible on many stretches but is interrupted by numerous rapids which necessitate frequent transshipment. Narrow canyons alternate with local plains. Even above Vientiane the river is 1,000 feet wide with a depth of 3 or 4 feet in the dry season. There is only negligible traffic in the upper section, so that Laos is more dependent on roads than water. Large-scale hydroelectric developments are for the future.

As befits a monsoon land, the Mekong carries a great volume of water during the rainy season. Some of this is temporarily stored in the Tonle Sap, a marginal lake which receives the flood waters of the Mekong, much as flood water is stored along the Yangtze. This natural reservoir reduces flood crests in the delta. The Cambodian plain which surrounds the lake is about twice the size of the Mekong delta; it is partly recent alluvium, partly underlain by horizontal sediments.

In North Viet Nam the important river is the Red, known to the French as the Fleuve Rouge and to the Annamese as the Coi or Songkoi. The length is 725 miles, only one-fourth that of the Mekong. Two tributaries are the Rivière Noire and the Rivière Claire (the Black and the Clear). Like the Mekong, the Red rises in China, and like the Mekong, it has numerous distributaries, so that the delta extends for 75 miles along the coast. The lowland area amounts to 5,400 square miles.

At Hanoi, near the head of the delta and 6 feet above sea level, the flow varies from 700 cubic meters per second in winter to 23,000 in summer. The latter equals the maximum discharge of the Danube and is twice that of the Nile or the Indus. Since the river level normally fluctuates by at least 25 feet, dikes have been built along all the distributaries to restrain flood waters. During the Annamese dynasty these dikes reached a height of 27 feet above sea level. Since the bed of the river is gradually rising because of the deposition of silt, the French raised the dikes to 37 feet; but since they were repeatedly overtopped, the height was further raised to 40 feet. When the dikes break and rice lands are flooded, famine follows. Elsewhere flooding may result from tidal inundation, so that maritime dikes are necessary.

Navigation is important on the lower reaches and it is also a vital factor upstream between the various rapids. The middle course is remarkably straight, doubtless reflecting tectonic control.

Although most of the people in the Indochina States live in the river plains, the bulk of the area is hilly and indeed mountainous. Level land covers no more than 15 per cent of the region. Through the center of Indochina extends a spur of the mountain complex which radiates from Yunnan and eastern Tibet, known as the Annam Cordillera. This is not a simple mountain range but rather a series of eroded plateaus dominated by high isolated peaks. The surface drops off steeply toward the east but slopes gently toward the Mekong. The Cordillera is thus difficult of access from the coast. The core of the southern range is a crystalline massif of early Paleozoic age with extensive lava flows associated with Tertiary fracturing. Farther north is an area of folded sedimentary rocks, squeezed between the Annam massif and similar ancient rocks across the border in South China. Elevations through-

The landscape in the Dien Bien Phu area of North Viet Nam has a combination of forested hills and terraced slopes, where irrigated rice provides the chief means of livelihood. Villages cluster at the apex of alluvial fans. (*Courtesy United States Air Force*)

out the Cordillera range from 3,000 to 8,000 feet, with a maximum of 10,306 feet.

Except along the Red and Mekong deltas, mountains closely approach the sea, leaving only a discontinuous coastal plain and a few small deltas. The combined level areas of the Annam coast total 7,700 square miles. Most of the shore line is inhospitable and without shelter; one important exception is the magnificent harbor of Camranh Bay.

To the west of the Annam Cordillera is an other north–south fold area which crosses western Cambodia and central Thailand, up to 4,149 feet in height. Between these mountains and the Annam Cordillera lies the geosyncline of the lower Mekong.

North of the Red River delta is a complex range of igneous peaks and limestone plateaus which mark the frontier next to China. Elevations reach 7,879 feet. Mountain alignments are generally northwest–southeast, as is that of the river. Many of the limestones are in an advanced stage of solution, with caves, underground drainage, and karst basins or poljes similar to the limestone topography of adjoining Kwangsi and Kweichow. Some of these spectacular erosion features, with their vertical walled residuals, extend into the Gulf of Tonkin, where they form a series of karst islands. A boat trip around these fantastic spires with their grottoes and tunnels is like roaming among mountain tops at sea.

One result of this river and mountain pattern is that the Indochina area lacks physical

This rice is being winnowed on the plains of Cai San in South Viet Nam, where large areas have been reclaimed for settlement by refugees from the north. (*Courtesy International Cooperation Administration*)

coherence. In place of one valley there are two, and between them lie isolating highlands. No single cultural focus is to be expected, nor a single political loyalty. Both rivers are partly navigable, but they lead nowhere. The deltas are productive, but agriculture proceeds with the hazard of widespread inundation.

THE VIET NAMS

Where there are now two Viet Nams, North and South, were once three French states: Tonkin in the north, an elongated Annam in the center, and Cochin China in the south. The first and third are crowded delta lands, espe-

cially congested in Tonkin. Viet Nam is the most promising of the several Indochina States, and even in its divided form the two halves each have far larger populations than the two other countries—over 15 million apiece.

In 1940 the area was occupied by Japan and used as a base for the invasion of Malaya. Following the war, independence forces under Ho Chi-Min forced out the returning French, and a cease-fire agreement in 1954 resulted in the division of Viet Nam into two roughly equal halves, with the boundary along the Ben Hai River, near the 17th parallel. The Communists gained control of the twenty-two provinces in the north, where they formed the Democratic

Republic of Viet Nam, leaving the thirty provinces of the south to the Republic of Viet Nam.

Viet Nam as a whole extends 900 miles from north to south, something like an elongated letter S, cut by the Annam Cordillera to make a dollar sign. At the two ends are rich rice areas, connected by a narrow coastal plain. The country has thus been likened to a coolie carrying-pole with baskets of rice at either end.

The curve of the coast line exposes the country to the two monsoons in different fashion. Moist summer winds from the Indian Ocean and the Gulf of Siam bring heavy rain to the Mekong delta and the westward side of the mountains. Saigon has an annual total of 81 inches, of which 71 inches fall from May through October. The southwest monsoon looses so much of its moisture on the windward

slopes of the Cordillera that the Annam coast lies in a rain shadow and is relatively dry in summer.

In contrast, the winter monsoon out of Asia picks up some moisture in its passage over the South China Sea and provides rainfall on the eastern slopes of the Annam mountains. Thus Hue, on the central Annam coast, receives 96 inches from August through January, while during the six summer months the total rainfall is but 20 inches. This is one of the wettest stations in Viet Nam, in part because of frequent typhoons.

Tonkin, in the far north, has a summer maximum, but every month has at least 1½ inches of rain. Since most of the winter precipitation comes in the form of a drizzle, it keeps the humidity high during the otherwise dry season

The delta of the Mekong in southern Viet Nam and Cambodia is a vast rice land, normally producing more than its population can consume, so that Saigon has a surplus for export. (*Courtesy International Cooperation Administration*)

and thus makes a winter rice crop possible. At least six-tenths of every month is cloudy.

Variability is a characteristic of Viet Nam rainfall. Several stations show a 1 to 3 range between the lowest and highest annual amounts, especially in the north; but any figures need to be evaluated against the evaporation rates. Even a year with normal rainfall may be agriculturally disastrous if one or two months at harvest time drop below the average. Excessive rainfall may be equally serious, as when typhoons bring 10 to 25 inches in a day.

High temperatures, heavy rainfall, and high humidity combine to yield luxurious vegetation. Vast rain forests remain in the mountains and even in the lowlands. A traveler along the central Annam coast describes the succession of rice fields, interspersed with

. . . bamboos of all sizes, palms ranging from mere fans to great masses of leaves, magnificent trees some of them bearing jackfruit on their trunks, coconut palms hugging the coast line, banana plants all but hiding the thatched huts, and above all the straight and slender arec-palm up which climbs the clinging betel vine.[1]

Most of the Vietnamese live in the deltas of the Red and the Mekong Rivers. Both are areas of new land where sedimentation is still in progress and the drainage pattern incomplete. Most of the area is so near sea level that it would be inundated during flood stages of the

[1] Harry Franck: *East of Siam,* New York: Century (1926), 110. Quoted by permission.

rivers or at times of high tide, if it were not for elaborate dike arrangements.

For most people rice culture provides the chief income, although prior to the Second World War there were the beginnings of plantations for rubber, coffee, and tea. In the north, which has been settled for centuries, fields are small and are worked by those who live on them. The south, namely the Mekong area of former Cochin China, was relatively empty when the French arrived. They parceled out large land holdings for themselves so that many farmers are tenants.

The two Viet Nams exhibit important geographic differences. Each centers on a delta, but that of the Mekong is much larger and less developed than that of the Red. North Viet Nam developed first, and the growth of the population has led to intensive agricultural development, with double cropping on half of the land. Since many rural areas have densities in excess of 2,000 per square mile, there is no surplus food.

Vietnamese people have lived in the south for only one or two centuries, so that there is still a surplus of land and of rice for export. Population densities in South Viet Nam are generally under 500 per square mile. Crop yields per acre are lower than in the north, and there are large areas of unused land; much irrigation is haphazard, depending on uncontrolled river floods.

Another major difference lies in mineral de-

North Viet Nam Data [1]

Area	60,156 square miles
Population	15,916,955 (1960 census)
Hanoi (capital)	643,576
Haiphong	369,248
Primary and secondary pupils	2,914,000
Higher education students	11,400
Rice	5,193,000 metric tons (1959)
Coal	2,000,000 " "
Electricity	200,000,000 kilowatthours (1959)

[1] *Britannica Book of the Year,* 1962.

velopment. North Viet Nam has excellent supplies of anthracite coal, with reserves of 20 billion tons and an annual production of several million tons near the port of Haiphong. Zinc, tin, and salt are also in production. Less geological work has been done in the south, and mining remains unimportant. Most French-directed industrialization lies in the north, where the best communications are also located.

Two cities dominate Viet Nam, each with a satellite. Hanoi, a city of a half million population, lies 100 miles inland near the head of the Red River delta, and is the capital of North Viet Nam. Hanoi was important in the days of Chinese control, and later became the Annamese capital until replaced by Hue in the seventeenth century. Under the French it became the capital of all Indochina. The shady boulevards, numerous squares, and imposing buildings make the old French area appear like a European city. Its seaport is Haiphong.

The metropolis of South Viet Nam and its current capital is Saigon, with its suburb of Cholon. The combined metropolitan area has over 1½ million people. The city lies 50 miles up the Saigon River, which, though rather narrow for large vessels, is 30 feet in depth. The port is connected with the Mekong through a canal known as the Chinese Arroya. Saigon is a new city, well laid out, and has been called

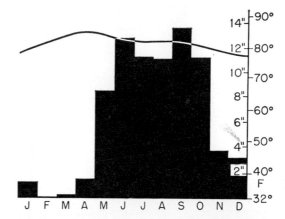

SAIGON. Elevation 30 feet, average temperature 82°F, annual precipitation 78 inches. The Mekong delta has a dry winter but receives so much summer rain that the landscape is always green.

the "Pearl of the East." Prior to the Second World War the city exported over a million tons of rice annually. Since Saigon shipping serves the nearby Mekong River, it is a major seaport.

Connecting Hanoi with Saigon is the old Mandarin Road, constructed in the days of the Annam empire and now paralleled by a modern highway and a railway. In imperial days few people other than officials traveled far. Avalanches frequently blocked the way in mountain sections; rivers could not be crossed when in flood; and sand dunes and beaches offered obstacles along part of the coast. Travelers who

South Viet Nam Data [1]

Area	65,958 square miles
Population	14,052,209 (1959 est.)
Saigon with Cholon (capital)	1,400,000 (1960 est.)
Tourane	110,348
Hue	102,814
Primary and secondary pupils	1,393,424
University students	9,217
Rubber	75,700 metric tons (1959)
Rice	4,381,000 " "
Electricity	280,000,000 kilowatthours (1959)

[1] *Britannica Book of the Year*, 1962.

New agricultural land has been developed in the central plateau of Viet Nam, where machinery is used to clear the forest and break the soil. This scene is near Ban Me Thout, the traditional home of nomadic Rhade tribesmen. (*Courtesy International Cooperation Administration*)

could afford it rode in sedan chairs carried by relays of coolies. Rest houses were established at frequent intervals where carriers could be changed, so that long journeys could be accomplished with little delay.

Midway along the Mandarin Road was the ancient capital of Hue, originally a Cham center and later an Annamese capital. Hue is one of the most picturesque towns in Viet Nam; it was built in Chinese style with some similarities to Peking, including nearby royal tombs.

CAMBODIA

The Kingdom of Cambodia takes its name from the city of Kambodja, founded by the Khmers about 435. Although repeatedly troubled by neighboring Thailand and Annam, and for nearly a century under French control, Cambodia has maintained its individuality, and a state of this name has existed for fifteen centuries. The country adopted its first constitution in 1947. Postwar developments have brought fewer problems than elsewhere in Indochina.

One asset lies in the country's ethnic unity, for nearly 90 per cent of the people are descendants of the ancient Khmers and speak a language unrelated to Thai, Laotian, or Vietnamese. Another advantage lies in the topographic coherence, focused on the Tonle Sap Basin and the lower Mekong valley.

Cambodia is about twice the size of Cuba and a little closer to the equator, but its land forms are quite different. Three-quarters of the country is a flat basin, only a few tens of feet above sea level, which surrounds the Tonle Sap or "great lake." To the south and west is the Elephant Range or Plateau, "round which the clouds gather." On the west the Cardamom Mountains rise to 5,000 feet, with steep slopes and dense forests. The northern border next to the Khorat Plateau of Thailand is formed by the terraces of the Dangrek Range. The eastern border of Cambodia is marked by the 3,000-foot Moi Plateau, home of primitive hill people.

Heavy rains are associated with the southwest monsoon, which blows from May through October. The encircling mountains receive as much as 120 inches of rain; most of the interior has at least 50 inches. Because of the high rate of evaporation this rain is barely adequate for agriculture, and some of the rice must be irrigated. The winter monsoon is generally dry, since any moisture which it may have acquired over the South China Sea is lost on the Annam Cordillera.

More than 50 per cent of Cambodia is forested. Water bodies account for 10 per cent— and much more during the flood season. Forty per cent of the land might be classed as arable, some of it a natural savanna, but not much more than 10 per cent is actually in agricultural use. Although Cambodia is the smallest of the Indochina States, it has the largest area of possible cropland. The present population of 5 million presumably represents only a fraction of the potential.

The most distinctive feature of the physical geography (and of the economy) is the Tonle Sap, at one time possibly an arm of the sea but cut off by sedimentation along the Mekong farther east. The lake is 100 miles long, 10 miles wide, and very shallow. It normally drains into the Mekong, but when the latter is in June flood the river rises 40 feet and the current in the outlet river from the lake is reversed. The Tonle Sap then spreads to a width of 50 miles, inundating forest and cropland, and thus increases its area from 1,000 to as much as 7,700 square miles. Because of the frequent flooding, many houses are built on stilts, and there are floating raft villages on the lake. The Tonle Sap is especially noted for the intensity of its fishing industry. As the waters recede from the flooded forests, with their abundance of organic food, bamboo weirs trap great numbers of fish. The annual catch approximates 65,000 tons.

Cambodia's economy is primarily agricultural. Rice accounts for 80 per cent of the crop area, and other farm products include corn, cotton, and tobacco. Nature is so lavish that a Cambodian proverb reads: "If it grows, why plant it?" Another saying is: "To destroy growing rice is as serious as to insult one's mother and father." Irrigation is largely haphazard, related to periodic flooding rather than to properly designed canals. Only a small part of the rice is raised as a second crop. Rubber and pepper are the two leading plantation products.

Ninety per cent of the population are rural, living near the Mekong and around the Tonle Sap Basin, leaving only 10 per cent for the fourteen provincial capital cities. Agricultural

Cambodia Data [1]

Area	66,606 square miles
Population	4,952,000 (1960 est.)
Pnompenh (capital)	355,180 (1959 est.)
Primary and secondary pupils	558,546 (1960)
Rice	1,451,000 metric tons (1960)
Rubber	37,100 " "

[1] *Britannica Book of the Year*, 1962.

Streams and canals intersect the lowlands of Cambodia and South Viet Nam and provide avenues for transporting rice. (*Courtesy International Cooperation Administration*)

built of laterite, faced with sandstone. They were adorned with magnificent carvings, "like lace on stone," as is shown at nearby Angkor Wat, the "Cambodian Parthenon," a vast temple erected to Vishnu.

Angkor was once one of the splendors of the world, and it is now one of the greatest collections of ruins to be found in any continent. After the city was abandoned in the fourteenth century, the buildings were overrun by the forest and remained unknown until 1861. The principal temple is 850 feet square and rises through a succession of terraces to a central tower 125 feet high. Hundreds of elaborate carved panels record Hindu epochs. Angkor has become a national symbol, and its ruins are shown on the country's flag. The older ninth-century ruins of Banyon are even more extensive.

The present capital city is Pnompenh, located on the Mekong near the confluence with the river which leads to the Tonle Sap Depression. The city has three parts: the French-designed European quarter around the *pnom,* or hill; the Chinese quarter with the main shops in the center; and the Cambodian quarter on the south. The city lies 150 miles from the sea and is normally accessible by ocean-going ships. The population is approaching a half million, many of them Chinese merchants or Vietnamese laborers.

Cambodia is no longer dependent on access to the outside world along the Mekong eastward to Saigon, for the country now has a seaport of its own south of Pnompenh at Sikanonville, named for a recent king.

LAOS

Laos is a land-bound island, 600 miles long and for the most part little more than 100 miles

development suffers from rural underpopulation.

Ninety per cent of the Cambodians are Khmers. Although their origin remains obscure, we know that they arrived from the northwest about 2000 B.C., displacing the earlier Cham people. The country was then Hinduized by migrations from India in the third century B.C. Chinese and Vietnamese are the leading minority peoples.

Khmer art flourished during two periods. The first, in the seventh century, was marked by brick temples with pyramid towers and painted stucco. The second period was associated with the building of the splendid capital at Angkor, which flourished from the ninth into the thirteenth century. This was a period of stone construction, and most structures were

wide. Although the country is the largest of the four Indochina States, it has few material assets and has the smallest and poorest population. The capital city of Vientiane lies on the Mekong 980 miles from the sea. Since river travel is interrupted by rapids, most traffic moves along the few mountain roads which cross into Viet Nam, or else over the Thailand railway from the Mekong to Bangkok.

The kingdom of Laos, formed in 1946, has descended from the ancient land of Lan Xang, the land of a million elephants, which was founded in 1353 after the Lao people had moved southward from China under pressure from Kublai Khan. Lan Xang endured until the end of the seventeenth century, and at its peak covered most of the Mekong valley, including areas now across the border in Thailand and Viet Nam.

The French protectorate did not begin until 1893 and ended with the Second World War, following which the region became a contest area between the Soviet Union, operating through North Viet Nam, and the United States, whose access was from the south. Since many of the people are related to the Thais, Thailand has always had strong political interests in Laos, and Bangkok is becoming a more important neighbor than Saigon.

One of the most obvious aspects of Laotian geography is the low density of population, only some 25 per square mile on the average. Many districts are nearly empty, and even in the denser areas the figure is under 200. The total population is around 2 million, less than 5 per cent of whom are urban.

At higher elevations live the Kha or Khmu. Whereas the Lao are Buddhists, the Kha are animists; whereas the Lao raise wet rice, the Kha engage in slash-and-burn agriculture and grow dry upland rice.

The third ethnic group are the Meo or Miao, who live in scattered mountain villages above 3,000 feet. Many other people live in Laos, both primitive mountain folk as well as urban Chinese and Vietnamese. The number and variety of different races makes coherence difficult.

Laotian economy is almost entirely based on subsistence agriculture, and this in turn rests on the heavy monsoon rains which begin in May. Rainfall ranges from 50 to 90 inches, and even more on mountain slopes. The climate is humid, but temperatures are moderated by elevation.

The Lao are predominantly wet-rice farmers, living in small villages where each family cultivates an area just large enough to supply its needs. All of life is oriented toward the soil.

Wet rice is raised only during the rainy season and is grown in two types of fields, one in the drier areas where some irrigation is available and the other where the rainfall is sufficient to keep the diked fields flooded. Only one rice crop is grown a year. Early varieties are planted in June for September harvest; regular paddy rice is started in May or June and harvested in November or December; and a late maturing variety is gathered in December or January. Dry-season crops are sometimes planted in the same fields.

Dry or upland rice is grown by mountain tribes who employ slash-and-burn or *rai* techniques. Trees and brush are cut in January at the beginning of the dry season and burned in April so that the ash may fertilize the soil.

Laos Data [1]

Area	91,428 square miles
Population	2,277,300 (1959 est.)
Vientiane (capital)	105,000
Primary and secondary pupils	79,117 (1958)

[1] *Britannica Book of the Year,* 1962.

Since stumps and roots remain in the ground, there is no plowing; instead, the rice is planted in holes made by a pointed stick.

Corn is the second crop, especially favored in the mountains. Opium is also a local cash crop.

This is a land of primary evergreen rain forests, where the trunks of the tropical giants rise straight and branchless to their dense crowns 80 to 100 feet above the ground. Below these is a lower level of smaller trees. Where slash-and-burn agriculture has repeatedly deforested an area, a secondary rain forest develops with a much denser low growth. Lower rainfall or well-drained soils may lead to a monsoon forest, more open than the rain forest. Teak is the only export timber.

Wild life is abundant, including domesticated elephants, which are the traditional symbol of royal court life.

Several resources offer a better future for Laos. The forests represent an untapped resource, including teak and cabinet woods. Tin is now mined, and there is some suggestion of other minerals. Hydroelectric potentials are very large, but will require cooperation with Thailand, which shares with Laos the common frontier of the Mekong River.

References on the Indochina States

See also general references for Southeast Asia, Chapter 17.

LeBar, Frank M.: *Laos,* New Haven, Conn.: Human Relations Area Files (1961).

McCune, Shannon: "Saigon, French Indo-China," *Jour. Geog.,* XXXVI (1937), 24–33.

McCune, Shannon: "The Diversity of Indochina's Physical Geography," *Far Eastern Quarterly,* VI (1947), 335–344.

Miller, E. Willard: "Mineral Resources of Indo-China," *Econ. Geog.,* XXII (1946), 268–279.

Pitts, Forrest R.: "The 'Logic' of the Seventeenth Parallel as a Boundary in Indochina," *Yearbook, Assn. Pacific Coast Geogs.,* XVIII (1956), 42–56.

Shabad, Theodore: "Economic Developments in North Viet Nam," *Pacific Affairs,* XXXI (1958), 36–53.

Steinberg, David J.: *Cambodia: Its People, Its Society, Its Culture,* New Haven, Conn.: Human Relations Area Files (1959).

Swann, Robert: "Laos: Pawn in the Cold War," *Geog. Mag.,* XXXII (1960), 365–375.

Webb, B. M.: "The Jewel of the Far East—Vietnam," *Canadian Geog. Jour.,* LXIV (1962), 3–15.

21 Thailand

The Land of the Thai / Thailand's Framework / Central Thailand /
Northern Thailand / Northeastern Thailand / Southern Thailand /
References on Thailand

THE LAND OF THE THAI

Since the first question in geography is "Where?" it may be appropriate to begin by examining the location of Thailand. Travelers by ship from Calcutta to Hong Kong must skirt the coasts of Burma and Indochina as they make the long journey via Singapore. The ports of Rangoon and Saigon lie near the main sea lanes and are in ready contact with world commerce. In contrast, Thailand is well to one side of the major highway. Cargo and passengers for Bangkok commonly transship at Singapore,

for none of the large Europe–to–East-Asia shipping lines make the detour. Bangkok was one of the least visited of the seaports of Southeast Asia, and Thailand remained little influenced by European contacts. Its unstrategic location may have been a factor in preserving its political independence.

This off-center location has been dramatically changed by the air age. Planes do not need to detour around the Malay Peninsula, and Bangkok is now a key point on one of the world's major airways. The Great Circle course from Calcutta to Hong Kong passes north of

Thailand and crosses terrain which is both inhospitable and closed politically. To avoid Chinese air space, planes must pass through Bangkok, and its airport has become one of the busiest in Asia.

One by-product of this centrality is that Bangkok has become the principal center for United Nations activities in Southeast Asia.

Another of the nation's international assets is that she owns the narrowest part of the Malay Peninsula at the Kra Isthmus. The possibility of constructing a canal at this point has been discussed for a century by rival British, French, and Japanese interests. Such a waterway would reduce the journey between Europe and East Asia by 600 miles and end the dominance of Singapore. The engineering problems involve the use of winding rivers with steep banks, and the necessity of cutting through a 250-foot ridge.

Thailand is the largest of the mainland countries of Southeast Asia, equal to the size of France and bigger than California. The overall extent is 1,000 miles from north to south, and half that from west to east, all of it within the tropics.

It has been suggested that the shape resembles an elephant's head, facing toward Indochina. The long southern peninsula represents the trunk; the mountains and narrow valleys of the north form part of the wrinkled skull; the Korat Plateau toward Laos suggests a flopping ear; the Gulf of Bangkok marks the elephant's mouth, with the delta plain and its rice lands occupying what would be the cheek. This comparison to an elephant has further meaning since elephants have supplied military power in battle and appear on the royal coat of arms; the elephant is a traditional symbol of good fortune.

The country has an area of 198,455 square miles and a population of some 25 million. This gives an average density of 125 per square mile, but the distribution varies widely, with many of the people concentrated in the plains around Bangkok. One province in the north has but 15 persons per square mile, while a southern province counts 450. Since the 1937 census recorded only 14.7 million, it is clear that with this rate of growth Thailand will someday need to consider population pressures. For the present, the country is still underpopulated.

In terms of cultivated land rather than of total area, the population density is 550 per square mile. Ninety per cent of the people live in towns with populations under 5,000, generally in agricultural villages numbering 500 to 750 inhabitants. Most farmers own their land, and except in a few mountain valleys of the north there is little rural poverty and no serious pressure of the people on the land. This situation is reflected in the availability of surplus rice for export.

Thailand is the oldest independent kingdom in Southeastern Asia, never conquered until its temporary submission to the Japanese in 1941.

Thailand Data [1]

Area	198,455 square miles
Population	25,519,965 (1960 census)
Bangkok (capital)	1,597,000
Primary and secondary pupils	3,888,800 (1958)
University (6) students	37,247
Rice	7,460,000 metric tons (1960)
Rubber	170,400 " "
Tin	12,240 " "
Electricity (incomplete)	339,111,526 kilowatthours (1959)

[1] *Britannica Book of the Year*, 1962.

The country has well been called a buffer state, for in 1896 France and Britain agreed by treaty to preserve it as an independent nation between their expanding territories in Burma and Indochina. The country was once called Siam, but since 1939, it has been known as Thailand, or Prathet Thai, the "land of the free nation."

Little is known about the early dwellers of Thailand. They appear to have been Negritos, who were later driven out by successive waves of Mongoloid people who made their way down the river valleys from the north and west. Their descendants are now the Mon, Cambodians, and Annamese. Still later, but before the Christian era, another wave of Tibeto-Burman people moved south along the Irrawaddy and entered Thailand. Peoples and cultures of India came in the sixth century, both directly and via Sumatra and Java. Another group of immigrants from the upper Yangtze valley were the Lao-Tai who arrived in numbers after their defeat by Kublai Khan in the thirteenth century, attracted by the decline of the Khmer empire in Cambodia. Their principal descendants are the present-day Thai, who make up 80 per cent of the population.

Although the Thai are the chief inhabitants, the Chinese population is also considerable, with some 500,000 who are still Chinese citizens and 3 million with some degree of Chinese parentage. Assimilation has been slow, and immigration is now restricted. Much of the retail and the import-and-export business is in Chinese hands; no other group is willing to work so hard for so little remuneration. Chinese shops are found even in small remote villages. Half of the Chinese live in the central area; others are in the tin and rubber areas of the south.

Thailand fortunately has little racial intolerance, although there has been some resentment against the Chinese in Bangkok. The unity in culture has been more important than any diversity in ethnic backgrounds. Over its history the country has borrowed extensively from all its neighbors, as well as from Europe.

THAILAND'S FRAMEWORK

Thailand has a simple physical pattern, that of a south-facing basin drained by a major river. Mountains enclose the country on the west, north, and southeast; to the east the boundary is chiefly along the Mekong River. Only one large stream is entirely within the country, the Chao Phraya, or Menam. To the west is the shorter Klong; the northeast is drained by tributaries of the Mekong.

The mountains of Thailand are a continuation of the complex that extends southward from the corner of Tibet through western Yunnan and Burma. Farther south these form the backbone of the Malay Peninsula and are known as the Tenasserim Range. A few peaks reach 8,000 feet in northern Thailand, but in most sections summit elevations are under a mile. The north and west is a country of parallel ridges and valleys, all trending north and south, in places arranged *en échelon*. The mountains which are made of limestone rise abruptly from the valley floors, but the others usually have lower foothills and intermediate slopes. Together, the mountainous sections of Thailand cover about one-third of the country.

Alluvial plains are limited to the vicinity of the rivers. Around Bangkok the Chao Phraya–Klong lowland extends up river some 250 miles. Narrow belts of alluvium follow the Mekong and its tributaries in the northeast, and southeast Thailand extends into the low plains of Cambodia.

Most of the remainder consists of rolling hills, chiefly old peneplains. The most important of these areas is the Khorat Plateau in the northeast, enclosed on the west and south by low linear mountains or scarps. This is a slightly dissected area, with an elevation of only a few hundred feet, underlain by horizontal red sandstones and other sedimentary rocks of Triassic age. Soils of low productivity limit the agriculture and thus the population.

Thick alluvial deposits obscure the underlying rocks in central Thailand. Igneous intrusions are widespread in the western mountains.

Granite batholiths form the core of all the main mountains.

The climate over most of Thailand may be divided into two seasons. The rainy period occurs during the southwest monsoon from the end of April until late in October, and is preceded by the hottest weather; the dry winter-season wind from the northeast lasts from November until mid-February.

Thailand is said to have a monsoon climate, but such a classification is an oversimplification. The migration of the heat equator north and south across Thailand twice annually means the passage of the doldrum belt, with its quiet air and the sky full of magnificent cumulus clouds, often thunderheads. Thus much of the rainfall is in localized thundershowers. The northeast and southeast trade winds, which theoretically blow on opposite sides of the doldrums, are considerably modified by the overall monsoonal conditions. Occasionally a typhoon will come directly across the South China Sea, fading out across Thailand. Such depressions bring rain over wide areas. For a week or so in winter, north winds from a high-pressure area over Asia accompany an overcast sky and bring markedly lower temperatures in interior Thailand.

Temperatures are moderate to high, as befits the intratropical latitudes. The prevailing temperatures, particularly in the central portion, are determined largely by the degree of cloudiness, or by its absence. Thus the season of highest temperatures is in late March, April, and early May. Once the rains are well started, that is, once the sky is overcast much of the time, temperatures are considerably lower. On the other hand, because of the high humidity, bright sunny days after local showers seem very hot. In central, peninsular, and southeastern Thailand maximum temperatures seldom reach 100°F, while minimum temperatures are seldom lower than 65°F.

The range of temperatures is much greater in northern Thailand because of the greater distance from the sea, the increased elevation of the valleys, and the mountains, which cut off much of the wind. Houses have fireplaces for warmth; they are used nightly during the cooler weather, and warm clothing is desirable. Only on the highest mountains have frosts been reported.

The total annual rainfall varies from about 40 to 120 inches. In southern peninsular Thailand a long dry season seldom occurs. In this area the monsoon winds from the Bay of Bengal bring heavy rains to the western slopes during the months of May to September. The eastern coast of the peninsula receives most of its rain between October and January from the northeast trade winds which sweep in off the South China Sea and the Gulf of Siam. In southeastern Thailand the rainfall quantities and regime generally resemble those of peninsular Thailand.

Much of the rain which falls in central Thailand is from convectional showers and from squalls from the southwest. The average rainfall in this plain is about 40 inches, considerably less than the potential evapotranspiration. Around Bangkok gentle sea breezes are frequent during the summer months. During the almost rainless winter months, northeast breezes are common. Both in the western part of the central plain and in western Khorat there are pronounced rain shadows, with inadequate moisture for the growth of rice.

Rainfall uncertainty at Bangkok is indicated by the length of the rainy season, which varies from 174 to 236 days. As a result of seasonal extremes, the discharge of the Chao Phraya varies from a low of 4,000 cubic feet per second to a normal 54,000 cubic feet per second in the wet season, and a flood discharge of 95,000 cubic feet per second.

Since ancient times the civilization of the country has been founded on rice. It now supports the majority of the people, either with its production, milling, or export. The rice acreage amounts to 90 per cent of all cropland, several million acres in all. Although Thailand produces but 5 per cent of the world's rice, it is the second or third largest exporter. One or two million tons are shipped each year, and

Every waterway in Thailand provides its quota of fish. This fishing boat with its large net is on the Moon River near the town of Ubol. (*Courtesy United Nations*)

this export accounts for half of the nation's foreign income. While rice is dominant, soybeans, corn, castor beans, and cassava are of increasing importance. Silk is a reviving industry.

Farming methods are still primitive, but modern irrigation canals and mechanical pumps have been introduced, and tractors supplement water buffalo. The availability of water and its relation to river flood levels is often the key to settlement.

As many as a million people in the northern and western hill lands and in the Khorat Plateau still practice slash-and-burn agriculture, either moving their villages as needed or depending on shifting cultivation within a radius of a few miles. The area actually in crops may exceed a half million acres annually. Quick-

growing glutenous rice is the usual crop, maturing in four months to take advantage of the short rainy period. Lowland wet rice requires a constant supply of water, and many areas lack adequate amounts of summer rainfall in dry years, since it requires the equivalent of 70 inches of rain to balance evaporation. At times half the crop may be ruined by too much or too little water; even so, famine is rare. Only one crop is normally raised a year, except in the Chiangmai valley. Thailand has overspecialized in rice and depends on a fluctuating world market. The country is both underdeveloped and underdiversified. It must import cotton and other necessities, a large part of which might be grown locally.

Other cash crops hold an inferior position. Rubber and coconuts each account for several hundred thousand acres. Tobacco, cotton, corn, and beans are the chief upland or unirrigated field crops, in places based on slash-burn clearings.

Cultivated land is estimated at 20 per cent of the total area. Even in the delta around Bangkok only 40 per cent is utilized, so that expansion is probably possible, particularly for dry crops. This is one country where more mouths do not mean less food. Farms average 4 acres, but there are wide regional differences.

Water buffaloes are the principal draft animals in the wet-rice areas, with considerable numbers of bullocks in the drier farmlands. Work elephants are employed in the northern teak forests and in the Kra Isthmus.

Forest resources are still large, although the valuable teak has been considerably exploited. Seventy per cent of the country is covered by various types of forest, much of it slow-growing hardwood trees.

Rubber and tin stand next to rice as Thailand's second and third export products. Tin production is from the peninsula and amounts to one-tenth of the world total. Many types of mining are employed, from primitive shaft mines to hydraulic mining and the use of enormous dredges, some of them offshore, where they reclaim placer deposits. Tungsten is also produced.

The scarcity of fuel is a major obstacle to industrialization. There is no petroleum, and such coal as exists is lignite. Rice husks are a common fuel for power plants in Bangkok.

The railways, of meter gauge, radiate from Bangkok. One line leads west and south to Singapore; one line extends eastward to form a link with Cambodia; a branch penetrates the northeast, and another runs north to Chiangmai. While the railways total about 2,000 miles, there are only 1,000 miles of paved highways.

CENTRAL THAILAND

Within the country are four regions, each with its geographic personality: Central, Northern, Northeastern, and Southern Thailand. Ex-

cept for the last, all focus on the Chao Phraya valley. Three of the regions may be characterized by their export products. Central Thailand produces a surplus of rice; the North supplies teak; the South exports rubber and tin.

Central Thailand is the social, political, and economic heart of the country, with half of the people and the best rice land. Here, too, was the historic kingdom of Ayuthia. The region has been described as 68,000 square miles of almost unbroken monotonous scenery. All traces of the original forest have been removed, and the area is now a vast rice field. Here and there are small villages, often strung along rivers and canals. Everywhere rice dominates. "It leaps village boundaries, runs along roads and canals, and steals into the capital itself."

The region extends 250 miles from north to south and is half that in width. Through the middle extends the Chao Phraya–Klong Plain. The rainfall varies from 30 to 60 inches and is well distributed during the rice season. Most of Central Thailand is potentially arable, but only one-fifth is actually cultivated. Wet rice occupies 75 per cent of the cropland. This region accounts for more than half of the country's total cultivated area.

Most rice is sown broadcast after plowing the moist soil, rather than transplanted into paddies from seedbeds. During the rainy season the fields become deeply flooded, often to a depth of 10 or 12 feet; this rice is then called "floating rice." The utilized land per farm family is approximately 10 acres, twice that of any other region in Thailand.

On the southern edge of the mountains, 260 miles northwest of Bangkok, is Thailand's first large dam site, a multipurpose hydroelectric and irrigation project, TVA style. This is at Yanhee on a tributary of the Chao Phraya, where the 505-foot Bhumiphal dam will eventually produce 560,000 kilowatts of electricity, irrigate a half million acres of new rice land, and permit a dry-season second crop in now cultivated areas downstream.

Because of annual floods many of the people near the waterways live in compact villages along the natural levees. The rivers and canals are almost the only means of communication across the plain. Practically all houses in rural Central Thailand are elevated on poles. Considerable areas which are not easily flooded are left in wild jungle. Bullock carts are used in the dry season across areas where one must travel by boat during the rains.

Boats on the rivers and canals are the principal means of transportation in the Bangkok plain. Many houses float on pontoons along the river banks. Highway development in the Bangkok plain has been greatly retarded not only by the heavy clay soil, flooded for many months annually for rice growing, and the numerous rivers and canals which have to be bridged,

but by the absence of suitable surfacing materials nearby and by the government's reluctance to facilitate competition with any of the state-owned railways.

So large a portion of the area around Bangkok is now used to produce rice that most of the natural vegetation has been completely altered. Judging by the magnificent groups of towering dipterocarps growing about some of the older Buddhist temples along the river banks and a few relics of similar forests near the head of the plain, such forests probably once lined the rivers for much of the distance through the Bangkok plain. Nearer the sea, where the land is lower and brackish water comes in with the tides, mangroves are still

Many village homes are built on stilts as a protection against the annual floods. Those seen here are along the Menam Chao Phraya, north of Bangkok. (*Burton Holmes from Ewing Galloway*)

important. Back from the river channels, grasses so tall that "even a man on elephant back could not see out over them," comprised the principal type of natural vegetation. The lower slopes of the hills around the plain are still covered with forest which varies from a relatively luxuriant rain forest to low, open hardwood forests, depending upon the soil and rainfall conditions of the locality.

Since most of the rain comes with the southwest monsoon, between June and October, there are striking differences in the vegetation on the Bangkok plain between the dry rain shadow along the western side of the valley and the especially heavy rain area near the mountains along the border of the Khorat Pla-

teau. Toward the southeast and southwest, hills introduce a different landscape, with more forest and less rice. The hills to the east have heavy rainfall, but those to the west lie in a rain shadow and are drier than the plain.

Bangkok is Thailand's one important city, with a population of 1½ million. Whereas Thailand's population doubled in three decades, that of Bangkok quadrupled. The city lies 15 miles from the sea on the Menam Chao Phraya in the midst of a tidal flat intersected by numerous canals. It is sometimes known as the Oriental Venice, and also as the "City of the Angels." The city lies so near sea level that it seems scarcely afloat. Many streets were made by digging a canal alongside and using the ex-

The city of Bangkok lies close to sea level, and is intersected by many canals, or klong, along which venders deliver merchandise to shops which face the parallel streets. This is a view along Klong Padung. (*Courtesy United Nations*)

Modern Bangkok has become the aerial crossroads of Southeast Asia, in tune with all the world. This is Patpong Road. (*Courtesy Trans World Airlines*)

cavated dirt to raise the highway. Where these streets are to be widened, the canal is then filled in. The port extends along the river; near it are the larger commercial establishments; and a new port has been built some miles below the city. Since there is a troublesome bar at the mouth of the river, larger steamers anchor outside and transfer their cargo to lighters. About a thousand vessels call each year.

Modern Bangkok is laid out along spacious lines, with Western buildings and 300 Buddhist temples in colorful native architecture; elsewhere there are narrow streets lined with the shops of Chinese traders. The royal palace and associated buildings are in strikingly beautiful native design, with brilliantly colored tile roofs. Rice milling, teak sawmills, cement works, and factories for consumer goods indicate the chief

industries. Bangkok dominates the entire country and forms a powerful centripetal force. The city has miles of modern streets with modern homes, and its standard of living is one of the highest in Southeast Asia. The contrast of Bangkok with the little-changed countryside is striking.

NORTHERN THAILAND

Northern Thailand is a mountainous area between the Salween and the Mekong. A half dozen streams, tributaries of the Mekong or of the Chao Phraya, follow parallel courses through north–south valleys which lie at elevations of about 1,000 feet. Mountains rise steeply to heights of over 1½ miles. Many of the rivers are graded and have developed open valleys, where rice is grown on patches of alluvium. Elsewhere cultivation is of the migratory fire-cleared type. In parts of the Chiangmai valley where irrigation water is available, two crops of rice are raised. Cotton, tobacco, and opium are specialized crops. Less than one-tenth of the region is under cultivation.

The long dry season and the relatively low rainfall, little more than 35 inches annually, have been important factors in the development of the native vegetation. There are four important forest types: the more or less deciduous "monsoon" forests, of which teak is a component if the soils are sufficiently good; the evergreen forests, especially on the northern slopes and at higher elevations; limited forests on the highest ridges and peaks, in which pine and dwarf oaks are conspicuous; and relatively slow-growing open forests on intermediate slopes with poor sandy soils, where grow low trees similar to those much more extensively developed in the Khorat area.

This region covers 35,000 square miles, and has one-tenth of the total population. Many of the hill tribes are immigrants who arrived after the Thai, such as the Shans, Miao, Yao, Lissu, Muhso, and Kaw.

Teak is the distinctive export, but the quality is not quite so good as in Burma. Elephants are still used to move logs from the forests in the dry season.

The principal city is Chiangmai at the railhead, 410 miles or 20 hours north from Bangkok. Although this is the second city of Thailand, it has but 50,000 people. As a measure of the less-developed character of the North, Chiangmai is a city of oxcarts and handicrafts, in comparison with Bangkok with its autos and factories. Nearby is an airport for jet planes flying the direct route from Calcutta to Hong Kong.

NORTHEASTERN THAILAND

The landscape of the northeast has three components: extensive open forests which grade into dry scrub jungles on soils too in-fertile to be cultivated; alluvial lowlands with small diked rice fields; and grassy plains too deeply flooded after the rains and too dry at other seasons to be used for crops.

Most of the area is a flat to rolling region where erosion is so slight that the thoroughly leached soils have not been eroded and hence hold a low content of soluble minerals available as plant foods. Laterite is common. Some areas of favorable soil have a denser and better forest, often utilized for migratory caingin agriculture. Charcoal is an important product.

This region is known as the Khorat Plateau, from the name of the chief town. It lies east and north of the linear mountains, which rise abruptly to heights of 4,000 feet. The mountains represent igneous uplifts and perhaps faulting. The region as a whole is underlain by horizontal sandstones and shales, purplish-red in color. Elevations in the Khorat Plateau are under 600 feet, decreasing to the southeast.

The climate reflects the interior location, with greater seasonal variations than at Bangkok. Rainfall is erratic in time and uncertain in distribution, and the underlying sandstones are very permeable; agriculture is thus handicapped. During the winter dry season most of the region has a parched appearance; only after the rains does it become green. Rice occupies the bulk of the cropped area, but there is only a small surplus for export. Cattle and pigs are also shipped out of the region. Their presence accounts for the superior fertility of the soil near the villages. Small plots of tobacco, mulberry, and cotton are grown by many farmers.

The Mekong forms the eastern border of the country for 600 miles but because of the rapids in its course, trade moves overland to Bangkok.

Northeastern Thailand covers 62,000 square miles, one-third of the country, but the population represents less than one-fourth of the national total. Ten per cent of the land is under cultivation. Poor soils, inadequate rainfall, and relative isolation contribute toward the backwardness of the northeast; no other region presents such difficult problems.

Southeast Asia has a wide array of ethnic types. These Mussuh girls are from Chiangmai. (*Courtesy International Cooperation Administration*)

SOUTHERN THAILAND

Southern Thailand lies in the long Malay Peninsula. The region is nowhere more than 70 miles wide, and in places where it borders Burma, only 10 miles wide. This is an attractive region with palm-lined beaches, beautiful offshore islands, and verdure-clad mountains. In the south the people are of Malay types, Muslim in religion. The area is 28,000 square miles. Less than 10 per cent is cultivated, with about 4 acres per farm family. Elevations reach 4,520 feet, but in most areas summits are under 3,000 feet.

Proximity to the sea makes the climate pleasant, without excessive temperatures. The western side of the peninsula has its rainiest season between May and October; the eastern is wettest from October to February. As a result of this exposure to both monsoons, rainfall reaches about 100 inches a year and the humidity is uncomfortably high.

From the latitude of Bangkok south to the Isthmus of Kra, the international boundary between Burma and Thailand follows the crest of the mountains. The Isthmus of Kra is a relatively low divide between the Gulf of Siam and the Indian Ocean. South of this locality and most of the way to Singapore, the higher mountains are *en échelon*.

Between the many more or less separated ranges are a number of relatively low and wide valleys, through which pass railways and highways that make the crossing of the peninsula easy. Some of the river valleys have considerable areas of lowland plain. There are also coastal plains which have been formed more by degradation than from alluvial deposits.

Notable as monadnocks are the towering and sometimes fantastically shaped limestone hills which stand isolated in the plains, as islands off the coast, or in inland lakes. These hills are important because of the phosphatic bat guano found in the caves, and because they are the nesting place for the birds which build the edible nests, prized by Chinese as a basis for soup.

The granitic batholiths which form the cores of the main mountain ranges in peninsular Thailand are in some places tin-bearing. The very deep weathering and the subsequent erosion of the overlying rocks and of the granites themselves have liberated the tin ore, which is mined on an extensive scale by placer, hydraulic, shaft, and dredger methods.

The natural vegetation of the region may be divided as follows: tropical rain forest; evergreen forests on less rainy mountain slopes; mangrove swamps, especially in the muddy estuaries along the seacoasts; grassy plains here and there at low elevations; and fresh-water swamps. In the extreme northern part of the region is an extension of vegetation types from dry western-central Thailand. There are thus bamboo thorn scrub in the drier rain-shadow region and dwarf open hardwood forests on poor sandy soils along the lower slopes of the mountains, west of the thorn scrub.

As in all other regions of Thailand, rice is the most important and most generally raised crop. Yet relatively less of it is produced here than in other regions, for many of the people have other and easier ways to make a living. At times rice is even imported. Hevea rubber is produced in great quantities, a considerable part of it by natives who have only small plots. At least a million acres are now in rubber trees, and rubber ranks next to rice in export value. Tin-mining companies employ large numbers of laborers, and there are also individuals who wash tin on their own in the rivers. The long coast line provides ample opportunity for fishing; in normal times the export of fish to Singapore is considerable.

References on Thailand

See also the general references on Southeast Asia, Chapter 17.

Barton, Thomas F.: "Growing Rice in Thailand," *Jour. Geog.,* LIX (1960), 153–164.

Barton, Thomas F.: "Thailand's Rainfall Distribution by Geographic Regions," *Jour. Geog.,* LXI (1962), 110–118.

Blanchard, Wendell, and others: *Thailand,* New Haven, Conn.: Human Relations Area Files (1958).

Pendleton, Robert L.: "Laterite and Its Structural Uses in Thailand and Cambodia," *Geog. Rev.,* XXXI (1941), 177–202.

Pendleton, Robert L.: "Land Use in Northeastern Thailand," *Geog. Rev.,* XXXIII (1943), 15–41.

*Pendleton, Robert L.: *Thailand: Aspects of Landscape and Life,* New York: Amer. Geog. Soc. (1961).

22 Burma

*The Happy Land / Burmese Economy / Three Villages / The
Irrawaddy Valley / The Burma Mountains / The Shan Plateau /
The Tenasserim Coast / References on Burma*

THE HAPPY LAND

Few countries in Asia are so effectively isolated as Burma. Invading armies have rarely crossed her frontier, from the direction of either China or India, and only small groups have infiltrated through the encircling mountains. The British and the Japanese arrived by sea—the only open door. Unlike the other countries of the peninsula which have two or more river valleys or whose frontiers lie along level ground, Burma is focused on a single effective lowland, that of the Irrawaddy.

Burma is the second largest country of Southeast Asia, one-third the size of Indonesia, or the size of France or Texas. Its shape has been likened to that of a kite with a tail which extends 500 miles southward into the Malay Peninsula. From north to south, Burma extends 1,300 miles. This span in latitude, plus a vertical range of 3 miles, brings many environmental contrasts. One-fourth of the country lies outside the tropics.

Through decades of association with British India, Burma was once considered a part of the Indo-Pakistan realm, but its culture and

319

geography bear many resemblances to Thailand and the rest of Southeast Asia. The people are Mongols, not Aryans as in India; they are Buddhists rather than Hindus. Since monsoon conditions resemble those of India, many of the same crops are grown, but in place of food shortages and recurrent famines, Burma has surplus food for export.

Burma lies to one side of the main steamship routes and, in terms of modern exploitation, is an underdeveloped land with room for many million more people. But even though the population is growing rapidly, the farmers have a rice surplus.

Burmese history begins with the infiltration of tribal people from the north some 400 years B.C. About the same time, the Indians were establishing coastal trading posts. The Burmese themselves did not arrive until ten centuries later, concentrating their settlement in the central Irrawaddy valley, but never ruling the entire area that is now Burma. Following them came Shans, Kachins, and smaller groups, all appearing from the north. While racial ties are with China, cultural ties look to India. The country's history reached its golden age during the Pagan dynasty, 1084 to 1287, when the capital at Pagan was one of the greatest Buddhist cities in the world.

British penetration came in three waves: the First Burma War, 1824 to 1826, brought the conquest of the Arakan and Tenasserim coasts; the Second Burma War, 1852 to 1854, added the Irrawaddy delta; the remainder of the country was acquired piece by piece, ending with complete annexation in 1886. Since 1948 Burma has been a fully independent nation, entirely separate from the British Commonwealth.

The population numbers over 20 million and represents a remarkable growth, inasmuch as the census of 1931 numbered only 14.7 million. The people are divided among scores of racial groups. Three-quarters are Burmese, but there are over 1 million Karens, Shans, and Indians, about 500,000 Kachins and Shans, and about 250,000 Chinese, most of them artisans or merchants. A great variety of primitive people live in the mountains; in fact, few places on earth exhibit so much ethnic diversity. Though some are backward, none would be classed as primitive or aboriginal.

The Burmese are an attractive and intelligent people. The women are graceful and well dressed and live a free and open life. Scarcely a boy does not attend school except in the remoter areas, and literacy is higher than elsewhere in Southeast Asia. Yet while the core of Burma enjoys a measure of cultural unity, the country as a whole is marked by physical con-

Burma Data [1]

Area	261,789 square miles
Population	20,662,000 (1960 est.)
Rangoon (capital)	737,079
Mandalay	185,867
Primary and secondary pupils	1,922,149 (1960)
University (2) students	13,754 (1958–1959)
Rice	6,874,000 metric tons (1960)
Crude oil	555,000 " "
Tin	1,400 metric tons (1959)
Lead	19,500 " "
Zinc	11,000 " "
Electricity	365,000,000 kilowatthours (1959)

[1] *Britannica Book of the Year*, 1962.

Rice is Burma's great crop, with an annual surplus of several million tons for export through Rangoon. This is a view in the southern lowland. (*Courtesy International Co-operation Administration*)

trasts and ethnic regionalism. Only half of the area is dominated by Burmese culture.

Eighty-five per cent of the people are rural. The population density is less than 100 per square mile, so that even allowing for the large area of mountains, Burma appears underpopulated. Even in terms of population as related to cropland the density is under 500 per square mile. One writer has well described Burma as the "happiest land in Asia" because of this lack of population pressure.

BURMESE ECONOMY

Although the Burmese people are relatively poor, they are among the most contented in the world. They look forward to *Pyidawtha,*

their word for happy land, in the hope of developing a unified nation and a viable economy. Pyidawtha is thus the symbol of various development programs.

Burma's economy has rested too largely on rice, which in many years has provided the livelihood for four-fifths of the people and has contributed two-thirds of the country's export. The world needs all the surplus food which Burma can produce, but so long as the international economy is unstable or crop yields fluctuate in other countries, Burma's national income is subject to uncertainty.

The agricultural year begins in April when the low embankments around each field are repaired in preparation for the May rains. As soon as the rains arrive, the flooded ground is then plowed and harrowed, and seed rice is planted in small nursery plots. A month and a half later the seedlings are transplanted by hand. The harvest takes place in November and December, after which the grain is threshed on mud threshing floors by bullocks or water buffaloes.

The same crop is raised year after year without fertilization, and it has been suggested that "under present farming methods the soil is not managed but mined, with resulting continued degeneration and progressively declining yields."

In good years, Burma exports 3 million tons of rice, roughly half of her total yield. In this she leads the world, normally followed by Thailand and South Viet Nam, but in some years with the United States as the third-ranking exporter.

Ninety-five per cent of this rice is raised in the swamp lands of the delta, largely with natural irrigation as provided by the flood stage of the rivers. Burma has 2 million acres of irrigated land, much of it supplied by modern canals, but the bulk of this lies in the dry central area around Mandalay. Adequate water is available in the rivers, and if proper engineering works were constructed, several million acres of little-used terrace lands might be cultivated, and much larger areas which lie idle after the rice harvest might yield a crop during the dry season.

If, besides irrigation, improved farm methods and cheap fertilizers might be introduced and harmful insects and disease eliminated, Burma should be able to double its food output. It will be a long time before population outruns food supply. This day will someday arrive, and the nations which depend on Burmese rice to feed their own people should realize that the world may be approaching the situation where no nation has surplus food for export.

While the delta overspecializes in wet rice, the central area raises a variety of dry crops, such as sesamum and peanuts—both raised for their oil—millet, legumes, cotton, and tobacco

in addition to irrigated rice. The Burmese mountain areas are notorious for slash-and-burn or fire-cleared agriculture, known here as *taungya*. The chief crops are corn, beans, dry rice, and potatoes. As many as forty-five crops may be planted in a single field.

Small humped oxen and water buffaloes are the usual farm animals. Work elephants are still used, especially in the forest industries, but the number is declining.

The extent of land use in Burma is variously estimated, and some figures are misleading since they exclude remote areas. Forests cover roughly 60 per cent; arable land amounts to a little over 10 per cent; and unused but potentially arable land represents another 10 per cent. This leaves 20 per cent which is listed as "other," presumably village areas, water bodies, waste land, or unforested mountains. Culivated land averages nearly 1 acre per capita, and the area in rice exceeds 15 million acres.

Lumber is another major export. Burma has a wide variety of tropical trees, but the world market for them is largely undeveloped. These include magnificent tall dipterocarps of the tropical rain forests, many trees other than teak in the monsoon forests, and temperate forms from the uplands above 3,000 feet where frost is not uncommon. Prewar shipments from Rangoon amounted to 250,000 cubic tons of sawn lumber, most of it teak. In fact, Rangoon exports more wood than any other city in non-Soviet Asia.

Teak is Burma's main commercial lumber. Although teak also grows in most parts of Southeast Asia, Burma leads by far in production. Rangoon is thus the world's leading city for teak export. Teak grows in areas of modest seasonal rainfall in foothills up to 3,000 feet. Green teak logs are so heavy that they will not float; it is necessary to girdle the trees and wait several years until the wood has dried. The importance of teak lies in its strength, durability, freedom from shrinkage, and high resistance to fungus and insect attack. It is especially serviceable as deck planking on ships.

Bamboo is another forest product, someday perhaps usable for paper pulp. Some bamboos grow to heights of 60 feet.

Rubber has become important in the southern peninsula, subject to international quota regulations. This is one of the few examples of a plantation-style crop, so common elsewhere in Southeast Asia. Coconuts and tea are grown only in limited amounts.

Burma's mineral position is good, and exports make a substantial contribution to the economy.

Petroleum has been produced in the central Irrawaddy valley since 1887 and normally meets most of Burma's domestic needs with a surplus for export. The principal fields are at Yenangyaung, Chauk, and Singu, 200 miles north of Rangoon. Some of the crude oil is refined locally; some moves by pipeline to a refinery near Rangoon; and the rest is shipped by river. Natural gas now supplies a cement plant.

Coal, of lignite and subbituminous quality, appears to be poor and in short supply. The deposits are located in the Shan Plateau and along the Chindwin River, and are rather difficult of access.

Hydroelectricity holds considerable promise. Several projects are under consideration.

Lead and zinc are Burma's major minerals, with very rich deposits occurring together at the Bawdwin mines in the northern Shan states. This is one of the largest lead mines in the world. Reserves are large, and include associated silver and copper. The lead content of the ore averages 19 per cent, while that of zinc

More than a thousand elephants are involved regularly in Burma's teak industry in order to move logs in the forest areas to the rivers, and, as here, in the yards at Rangoon. (*Ewing Galloway*)

Burma leads the world in teak production, and the industry employs 100,000 men. These teak rafts are floating down a tributary of the Irrawaddy River, a journey of 900 miles, which requires three months to reach Rangoon. (*Courtesy United Nations*)

amounts to 12 per cent; copper averages 1 per cent and the silver content runs 15 ounces per ton.

Tungsten and tin occur in the southern Shan states at Mawchi, which prior to the Second World War was the world's leading tungsten mine and ranked third among underground tin mines. As with all Burmese production, the war brought widespread destruction. Tin and tungsten are also obtained near Tavoy and Mergui on the Tenasserim Coast where there are alluvial deposits.

In summary, lead, zinc, and tin are produced to the extent of several hundred tons a year; tungsten, antimony, copper, and nickel amount to a few tens of tons.

Burma has long been famous for its rubies

(among the finest in the world but now nearly gone), sapphires, lapis lazuli, jade, and amber.

Although Burma has 2,000 miles of meter-gauge railways and 10,000 miles of improved roads, the Irrawaddy and its associated rivers provide the chief highways. The only routes across the borders are the wartime Burma Road eastward to China, the Ledo Road north to Assam, and a route through the Shan states to Thailand; none are important, and all international traffic moves by sea.

The Burmese constitution of 1948 calls for a planned economy under which the state is charged with developing the economic interests of the people. Schemes have been developed for a welfare state called Pyidawtha, which would provide for industrial developments including a steel-products plant (although there is neither domestic ore nor coke) as well as factories based on local raw materials. Except for processing plants around Rangoon, industrialization is still in its infancy.

THREE VILLAGES

Burma is a land of agricultural villages, but conditions are far from uniform. Three sample studies by Robert Huke suggest something of the regional contrasts between the delta, the interior dry belt, and the northern valleys.[1]

The delta is the great granary of Burma, supplying 95 per cent of the country's export rice. Here live almost one-third of the population and here lies more than one-third of the cropland.

Tadagyi is a rural village in the heart of the delta, 65 miles southeast of Rangoon. This is only one of 1,000 settlements which dot the 10,000 square miles of the lower Irrawaddy and Sittang valleys. The village is surrounded by a sea of rice except where infertile laterite areas are covered by bamboo and second-growth timber.

Stretching as far as the eye can see is rice land. In the dry season, under the clear blue sky, this rice land lies brown and dusty, interrupted only by the fragile, lacy lines of green nipa palm bordering the meandering distributaries of the Irrawaddy. In the rainy season, these same fields lie sodden and green under the somber gray skies and are broken only by the now purposeful flow of the swollen channels.

The village lies on a low laterite block which rises a few tens of feet above flood levels. Tadagyi has thirty-two houses, half hidden amid palms, jackfruit, mango, and bananas.

A tiny meandering creek . . . flows lazily beneath an arch of palms, flowering vines and other jungle growth. The sun streams through a lace-

[1] I am indebted to Robert Huke for permission to quote and paraphrase from his field study entitled *Rice in Burma,* Syracuse University, Department of Geography (1953).

work of greenery, spotlighting orchids and other native blossoms.

Fields are irregular and range from a fraction of an acre to nearly 3 acres in size; all are diked to hold standing water, but since the rainfall of nearly 100 inches is adequate, no irrigation is needed. Where there is a slope, fields are smaller. Rice is planted in mid-June after the rains begin, and is transplanted in mid-July when the plant is 18 inches high. It takes about 56 woman-hours to transplant 200,000 stalks per acre. This means that an average farm of 8 acres grows 1½ million stalks of rice. Fortunately, three stalks are planted together at the same time. After the crop is harvested, by hand, in December, most fields lie fallow, although a few are used for raising vegetables. Sugar cane is a new crop. Irrigation would presumably enable a second crop to be widely grown.

The soil is relatively rich in organic matter. It is, however, very low in content of lime and available potash. In available phosphoric acid, which is essential to high yields of rice, it is very low.

Many of the families originally came from the Karen Hills, but there has been little change in the population for fifty years. No one is a large landowner; no one is poor. Most of the 158 people in the village have never traveled farther than the local market town of Myaungmya, 6 miles away. The houses are built of bamboo, and are raised about 6 feet above the ground. Roofs are thatched with broad palm leaves.

In contrast to the coastal delta, which receives abundant monsoon rain from the Bay of Bengal, interior Burma around Mandalay lies in the lee of mountains and has rain-shadow drought. Rice is widely grown but must be irrigated.

Huke begins his analysis of the adjoining villages of Bugun and Thayetkon as follows:

As one stands on the top of Mandalay Hill, 700 feet above the perfectly level riverine deposits of the Mandalay plain, the panorama of life in "the heart of Burma" is spread out like a multicolored, checkered tablecloth. Ten miles to the east, seemingly close enough to reach out and touch, and running north and south as far as the eye can see, lies the edge of the Shan Plateau. . . . Seven miles to the west the Sagaing Hills appear insignificant, but they, too, hold aloft more than their share of pagodas. . . .

The panorama is sliced in half by the Irrawaddy which comes into view from behind hills off to the north. . . . At the foot of our hill sprawls the hot, dirty city of Mandalay, partly veiled by the clouds of choking dust rising from her bustling streets.

As our primary interest lies in the study of agricultural villages, our gaze shifts from the broad panorama spread before us and focuses more closely on the carpet of paddy. Here the agricultural scene appears to be a duplication of the rice lands of the delta, a copy in miniature. The fields are smaller, the villages are smaller, and they are much closer together. In the villages the banana trees, the mango trees and the bamboos appear to compete for space with the tiny fragile houses. . . . The whole scene is woven together with dusty roads and weblike irrigation *chaungs.*

The villages of Bugon and Thayetkon are shoestring strips of houses along a main road, supplied with water by a canal.

Neither village is raised above the surrounding rice fields. From a distance they appear to be islands of trees in the midst of waving rice. . . . The dikes at the edge of the fields closest to the village keep the irrigation water out of the village, but there is little provision for draining away the

These farmers live in the small hamlet of Ba Hmwe Gon, 35 miles from Rangoon, where the Food and Agricultural Organization of the United Nations is introducing new methods of cultivation and marketing. (*Courtesy United Nations*)

rain water. During the monsoon it stands in the village paths and under the houses. . . . During the dry season the village paths are turned into ribbons of fine dust which rises in choking clouds behind every bullock cart and jumps up in little whirlwinds with every breath of air.

The two villages number 245 people in 51 houses, mostly of bamboo construction although several are built of teak. Roofs are generally of 4-inch straw thatch, although some are made of bamboo "shingles."

Field patterns around Bugon and Thayetkon differ from those of the village of Tadagyi since the land is flatter and fields are generally rectangular. Rice is grown on 86 per cent of the village farm lands, and most fields lie fallow for five or six months. There is little double cropping as such, but in some fields early maturing rice is transplanted in alternate rows so that the first crop matures several weeks earlier than the second. Although it is possible to raise a dry crop during the winter none of the local farmers do so.

The agricultural season is not dated by any month of the Western calendar or even according to the onset of the rains, which are fairly regular, but by the full moon of the seventh lunar month. By this time there is usually enough water in the canals, and on the day of the full moon water is admitted to the seed beds. After the fields have been soaked the ground is plowed; one man and a pair of bullocks can plow an acre in three days; harrowing requires two days more.

Harvesting occurs during the full moon of the twelfth lunar month, which commonly falls in the middle of December. Harvesting requires nine people per acre, and all of an individual's holdings are gathered during a single day so that there may be no dispute.

Most of Burma's cropland lies in the delta or in the Mandalay basin, but there is several million acres of potentially arable land in the northern valleys. Huke's third study centered on Mayan and Lajung in the Karen Hills—the former a Christian village, the latter a *Nat* or pagan settlement, where houses are built without windows so that spirits may not enter. These settlements lie 25 miles west of Myitkyina.

If one were to fly over the Kachin State in northern Burma one of the first things noticed would be that the topography is radically different from the topography in the delta or in the dry belt. Here, there are range after range of mountains and high hills. As one looked closer, it would be obvious that the village people do not farm in the valley bottoms, as might be expected, but rather they farm on the steep hillsides. Their *taungya* agriculture is known as "slash and burn."

To travel north or south from Mayan one must climb steep slopes covered by monsoon jungle. The area between its mixed hardwood and softwood giants is crowded beyond belief by an almost impenetrable tangle of brush, small trees, creepers, hanging vines and orchids, each one trying to choke its neighbor. To the explorer who tries to travel away from an established trail, a heavy *dah,* or sword, is indispensable. Travellers in such a jungle have no need to carry drinking water for any one of a number of hanging vines will supply a cool drink of sweet water when cut from the tree which supports it. Here in the jungle one is continually pressed in by the cool, damp, still air. To the person used to the noises of a city the barking deer, monkeys, birds and innumerable insects shatter the silence like fireworks in a cathedral.

If one travels . . . to the east or to the west, one finds himself . . . in the center of a narrow valley. Here the ground is level and in the lower places the jungle is replaced by a very dense tangle of canes, bamboos, elephant grass, and sugar cane. Again a path must be cut if one ventures away from the established trails.

Some of this vegetation represents second growth, where temporarily cultivated fields have been recaptured by nature. Many soils are so infertile that they are exhausted after two years of taungya cultivation, and several generations must pass before the land may again be cleared.

Both of these northern villages are small. Mayan has 40 homes and 250 people; most families depend on a taungya plot for their income. Lajung has 13 longhouses and 104 people.

No provision is made for smokestacks. . . . Twenty-four hours a day a cloud of brown smoke may be seen filtering through the roof of a long-house like mist rising from a river. . . . This continual smoking . . . changes the color of the bamboo . . . to a rich cherry red and at the same time produces long cobwebs of soot which hang like veils from all portions of the roof.

A small amount of irrigated rice is grown near each village, but most cultivation is from a dozen closely grouped hillside fire clearings several miles distant and of 3 to 30 acres in size. One taungya studied by Huke supported eight families and forty-six people, an average of two-thirds of an acre per person. Some slopes are as steep as 93 per cent. Where land is plentiful, fields are abandoned after the first crop; where used a second year, weeds are thick and difficult to clear; by the third year weeds become so thick that it is easier to clear the adjoining jungle. Erosion is also a problem on newly cleared land.

Taungya land is prepared in February, when the vegetation is completely cut over, including trees which may have a diameter of 4 feet. A month later the debris is burned. The field is then cleared, leaving only the stumps and larger logs and a veneer of ash. Planting then proceeds, even before the spring rains. In any given taungya there may be upwards of thirty-five different crops, including several varieties of dry rice, potatoes, beans, cucumbers, pumpkin, squash, sesamum, cotton, eggplant, tobacco, okra, peas, and tomatoes. These provide a nearly complete subsistence economy, with little surplus for sale.

THE IRRAWADDY VALLEY

The Irrawaddy valley and the adjoining Sittang lowland is the heart of Burma; it includes most of the agricultural land and population. During Tertiary times this was an arm of the sea, in which accumulated a great thickness of sediments, now veneered with the alluvium of the Irrawaddy and its associate, the Sittang. The region is 150 miles wide in the delta but narrows northward till it reaches Bhamo, 874 miles from the sea. Between the Irrawaddy and the Sittang lowland is the Pegu Range, which culminates in the 4,981-foot volcano of Mount Popa near the northern end.

The Irrawaddy River is the great unifier of Burma. The river is easily navigable by 300-foot vessels for 900 miles, with smaller boats continuing 100 miles farther to the point where two tributaries join to create the main river. Three defiles somewhat block navigation—near Mandalay, below Bhamo, and near Myitkyina—but ships are able to pass. The Chindwin, a major tributary, is navigable for 380 miles. The total length of commercially navigable waterways amounts to 4,000 miles.

The Irrawaddy rises in the snow-clad peaks of the far north, which reach to a height of 19,758 feet, and flows 1,350 miles south to the Indian Ocean. Parallel to its lower course is the 350-mile Sittang, at one time possibly a part of the Irrawaddy. The Sittang is also navigable, but there is a tidal bore in the funnel-shaped mouth.

The compound delta of the Irrawaddy and Sittang is Burma's rice bowl, based on the fertile alluvium and the abundant monsoon rainfall. The Irrawaddy lowland receives heavy rain from the southwest monsoon, reinforced by the funnel effect of the mountains on either side so that precipitation at interior stations reaches 125 inches. Sea-level stations receive 100 inches a year, chiefly from May till October; the rest of the year is relatively dry. Monthly temperatures vary only 10 degrees F from season to season, but are highest in the spring shortly before the rains. The heat and humidity are enervating for man, but good for vegetation.

Ten thousand square miles are in rice, and large areas might be added with simple irrigation. Since only 1 per cent of the delta is double-cropped, and since fertilizers or insecticides are seldom used and farm methods are out of date, rice yields per acre are only one-third those of Japan. With irrigation for a dry-season crop and other improvements, the area

The city of Rangoon has thousands of Buddhist pagodas; these are around the Shwe Dagon Temple. (*Ewing Galloway*)

might considerably increase its already large food output. The overconcentration on rice for export places the farmer at the mercy of fluctuating world prices. It has been estimated that the Chindwin valley contains 2½ million acres of potential farm land.

Fish, which form a common article of diet, are supplied from the rivers and many ponds. Fish nets may be found in almost every body of water.

The seaward margin of the delta ends in a maze of low islands on which are tidal mangrove forests not unlike the Sundarbans of the Ganges. Many trees rise to 100 feet. Extensive dike systems are necessary to keep out high tides.

Central Burma around Mandalay forms a separate subregion, much drier but densely populated and the center of historic Burma. It was the site of Pagan and six other ancient capitals.

This dry belt, lying in the lee of the mountains, receives less than 40 inches of rain, in places only 25 inches. In Koeppen terms, it has a *BS* or steppe climate. Millet, sesamum, peanuts, and cotton largely replace rice; and irrigation is generally necessary, unless dry-farming methods are employed where crops are grown one year in two or three. Crop failures sometimes bring famine conditions, although food is fortunately available from the delta.

Rangoon is Burma's one great city, with a population of nearly a million. Immigrants who were born in India make up an important fraction of the population and present a clash in culture. So, too, do the many Chinese who have lived in Burma for two generations without becoming citizens. The migrant character of Rangoon's population is shown by the high ratio of males to females.

The city lies 20 miles from the sea at the junction of several streams and near a southern spur of the Pegu Range. One of the famous sights is the great gold-faced Shwe Dagon pagoda, 370 feet high and the tallest Buddhist shrine in the world. Rangoon does not lie on the Irrawaddy itself but is connected with a navigable distributary through a canal.

Rangoon handles 85 per cent of Burma's foreign trade, and is the largest rice- and teak-shipping port on earth. Exports are rice and rice bran, teak and other timbers, metals and ores, hides and skins; in terms of value rice equals all other exports together. Imports comprise cotton goods, machinery, and miscellaneous manufactured articles. The city lies close to the steamship lanes connecting Europe with

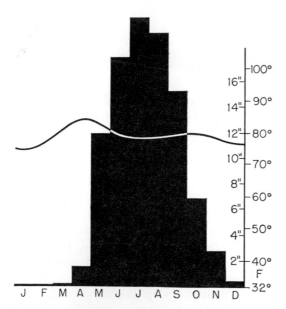

RANGOON. Elevation 18 feet, average temperature 81°F, annual precipitation 103 inches. The Irrawaddy delta receives the full impact of the monsoon.

Singapore, and it is on the main air route between Europe and Southeast Asia. The chief industries are the rice mills, and the primary business is commerce. Bassein is the principal port on the Irrawaddy River itself.

Mandalay, in the interior dry zone, is a former capital and the heart of inner Burma. The semiaridity is shown by the occasional dust storms. The city is reached by river steamer, by road, or by an eighteen-hour rail trip from Rangoon, 385 miles to the south. The population is approximately 250,000.

THE BURMA MOUNTAINS

Between the Irrawaddy and the Brahmaputra is a series of more or less parallel mountain ranges, little known geologically, wet and densely forested, and but sparsely populated. The northern part of the great arc lies partly within Assam, but two-thirds of the mountains are in Burma. The region includes the embayed Arakan coast and bordering Arakan Yoma Range in the south, and the Patkai, Kachin, and other hills, plus rugged mountains in the north where Burma borders Tibet.

The Burma Mountains form an effective barrier to travel. The numerous ridges are narrow but steep-sided and continuous, so that east–west travel is almost impossible. Though a few cart roads lead over difficult passes, there is no trade. In structural terms, a core of old crystalline rocks is flanked by closely folded sedimentaries on either side. Elevations reach 10,085 feet in Mount Victoria and 12,553 feet in Mount Sarametti on the Pakistan-Burma border. Earthquakes have repeatedly destroyed hundreds of villages.

British policy in India apparently sought to isolate the country by not developing external land communications. Burma has thus remained apart from Indian life, except as trade moved by sea. The absence of roads across the border made it impossible to reinforce Allied troops during the Japanese invasion and rendered the recapture of Burma especially difficult.

This region receives the full impact of the southwest monsoon off the Bay of Bengal; where this is augmented by orographic influences, precipitation becomes very heavy. The Arakan coast has a few stations that report 200 inches, and precipitation in the mountains is apparently 50 per cent greater, although no records are available. Half of the rain may fall in June and July. Soil erosion is serious where the forest cover has been removed.

Natural vegetation follows climate and altitude. Where rainfall exceeds 80 inches, there is a dense tropical evergreen rain forest with little agriculture or lumbering. Paths are mere tunnels through the forests. With 40 to 80 inches of rainfall and a longer dry period, the trees lose their leaves in the dry season. This is the home of many excellent types of trees, of which teak is the chief timber now exploited. Teak thrives best with 75 inches of rain and a temperature of 75°F. Burma has little natural grassland; where rainfall is under 40 inches the forest is replaced by scrub. It is not unusual to find frosts above 3,000 feet in the north.

Many areas are nearly uninhabited, and the few settlements are isolated. Traditional agriculture was a matter of clearing the forests by cutting the brush and girdling and burning the trees. In many localities the cleared areas have been replaced by bamboo thickets rather than by the original forest cover. The introduction of government forest preserves now restricts this waste. Corn, millet, and some rice are among the many crops. The development of large additional areas depends largely upon the control of malaria. As population increases, fire-cleared fields tend to be used more frequently, so that soils are depleted, erosion increases, and yields decline.

Jade and amber are secured in limited amounts.

The people of these mountains include a wide variety of non-Burmese races, some of them Nagas, Chins, and Kachins. So great is the diversity that "each village has its own language." Considerable areas have been classed as "non-administered," meaning that the government does not attempt to exercise jurisdiction. Slavery was permitted until early in the century, and some tribes in the far north are still warlike.

The most developed section is the Arakan coast, a discontinuous strip of coastal plain and small deltas with rocky peninsulas and many offshore islands. The area has many harbors but few ports. Akyab, the chief city, ranks next to Rangoon as a center for rice export. Most of the population live in the northern half of the coast near Akyab, but the entire coast accounts for only a million people. Fishing is important.

The Burma Mountains are so rainy, so hilly, and so malarial that their future appears limited. Development must await effective administration, education, transportation, markets for lumber, and agricultural planning.

THE SHAN PLATEAU

Eastern Burma is a plateau averaging 3,000 to 4,000 feet in elevation, sparsely inhabited by Shan tribesmen. The Shan Plateau resembles western Yunnan and northern Thailand in ethnic diversity, and many of its people have relatives across the borders. Since the elevation moderates the climate, this is a temperate land within the tropics. Part of the country is a dissected upland, but there are extensive areas in which agriculture might expand. Here and there are a few old lake basins, underlain by coal deposits.

The region is drained by the deep valley of the Salween River and to the east by the Mekong. The Salween flows as a mountain torrent in a canyon with such steep walls that villages may be 1,000 feet above the stream. The river rises 60 to 90 feet when in flood. The Salween measures 1,750 miles in length, and holds important hydroelectric potentials.

Beneath the Shan Plateau is a block of old gneiss, schist, and ancient marbles, sharply bounded along the Irrawaddy lowland by a 3,000-foot fault scarp. Unlike the Burma

Mountains with their folded structures, the Shan Plateau is an area of block faulting. Within this complex is one of the world's best sources of lapis lazuli. Rubies were once of importance, some among the finest in the world, but the production has declined greatly; sapphires and jade are also famous. Rich zinc, lead, and silver ores, with some copper and nickel, are mined at Bawdwin, where they occur in ancient intrusives. The mines at Bawdwin, which were worked by the Chinese in the fourteenth century, are one of the richest deposits of their type in the world. Only rock with 30 per cent lead and zinc combined is now considered to be ore.

Two meter-gauge railroads climb onto the Shan Plateau, the line to Shwenyaung and the important line to Lashio. At the start of the century, British and French interests were both seeking a rail route into southwestern China. The French line from Indochina to Yunnan was completed first, but on account of the formidable character of the topography on the Burma frontier, the British railway was not continued beyond Lashio. With the blockade of the China coast during the Second World War, China opened a spectacular automobile route from Kunming in Yunnan to Burma in 1939, with twin terminals at the railhead of Lashio and on the navigable Irrawaddy at Bhamo. This new back door to China and the projected parallel railway could be of increasing importance in peacetime trade with Europe.

THE TENASSERIM COAST

Burma projects 500 miles southward along the Malay peninsula in a strip averaging but 50 miles in width. This is the Tenasserim Coast, comparable to the Arakan lowland and mountains in its rugged configuration, numerous off-shore islands, and heavy monsoon rainfall. Despite the low latitude, temperatures rarely reach 100°F, and the annual monthly temperature range is less than 10 degrees F. The north–south alignment of the topography is shown in the course of the Tenasserim River, which follows a valley within 20 to 40 miles of the sea for 150 miles.

About two million people live in the Tenasserim area, many of them non-Burmese in race. The one city of importance is Moulmein in the north, where the Salween delta is virtually a continuation of the Irrawaddy delta lands. Elsewhere mountains prevail.

On the limited level land rice is the major crop. The long wet season with 200 inches of rain is favorable for rubber and coconut plantations.

Tungsten, tin, and antimony are important, and are produced at Tavoy and Mergui. Tungsten production began in 1910, and for a few years prior to the First World War Burma led the world; but since then she has commonly been second to China. The geology is that of old complex sediments, invaded by ore-bearing granitic intrusions.

References on Burma

See also the general references on Southeast Asia, Chapter 17.

Nigel, Cameron: "The Burma Road," *Geog. Mag.,* XXXIII (1960), 73–87.

*Spate, O. H. K.: "The Burmese Village," *Geog. Rev.,* XXXV (1945), 523–543.

Spate, O. H. K., and L. W. Trueblood: "Rangoon: A Study in Urban Geography," *Geog. Rev.,* XXXII (1942), 56–73.

Stamp, L. Dudley: "The Irrawaddy River," *Geog. Jour.,* XCV (1940), 329–356.

De Terra, Hellmut: "Component Geographic Factors of the Natural Regions of Burma," *Annals, Assn. Amer. Geogs.,* XXXIV (1944), 67–96.

23 Malaysia

The Malay Peninsula / People and Politics / Western Borneo /
References on Malaysia

THE MALAY PENINSULA

The term Malaysia refers to the several parts of the British Commonwealth in Southeast Asia: the former Federated and Unfederated States of the Federation of Malaya, the former Crown Colony of Singapore with its outports, and Sarawak, Brunei, and North Borneo. Malaysia thus includes two widely separated areas, the Malay Peninsula and Western Borneo. At their closest, the two halves are 350 miles apart; farther north the distance increases to 1,000 miles.

The Malay Peninsula has the area of Florida, but lies south of the latitude of Panama. The southern tip is only 2 degrees north of the equator; the northern end reaches 7 degrees north. The area's low latitude is suggested by the fact that throughout the year the length of day and night at Singapore varies by only nine minutes. Summer and winter are nonexistent; the only seasonal contrast lies in wind directions.

Malaya is mountainous, with a framework of north–south ranges *en échelon*. Elevations reach 7,186 feet, but much of the western peninsula is a low-lying plain from which mountains and hills rise abruptly. Where limestone is present, it may develop a karst landscape with precipitous cliffs.

333

At the beginning of the nineteenth century most of the Malay Peninsula was an uninhabited tropical rain forest, fringed with coastal mangrove swamps. Magnificent hardwood trees rose to heights of 100 feet. Year-round rainfall kept the landscape always green. The entire population numbered only about 250,000. The inhabitants were self-sufficient Malays, who carried on subsistence livelihood as coastal fishermen or as rice farmers along the river flood plains.

Three-quarters of interior Malaya is still in forest,

. . . one dense mass of jungle, so thick and so closely interlaced with thorny creepers that it is almost impossible to move a yard in any direction without previously cutting a *rentis,* or jungle path. Even traveling by river is difficult, for the river beds are full of snags and fallen timber: the smaller streams are generally covered by creepers from bank to bank, and the way has to be cut before a canoe can pass.[1]

[1] S. W. Kirby: "Johore in 1926," *Geog. Jour.,* LXXI (1928), 245.

Malaya lacks the rich history of its northern neighbors, and its modern development has been along other lines. Unlike Burma, Thailand, and the Indochina States, with their surplus of rice, Malaya no longer feeds itself. In fact, it is not even self-sufficient in lumber. These deficiencies reflect a labor shortage, due to several new export crops, chiefly rubber and coconuts. Along with the need for agricultural labor is the need for workers in the mining of tin, iron ore, and other metals. These new cash products, with their demand for a labor force which Malaya was not able to supply itself, led to the arrival of several million Chinese and Indians, so many that they outnumber the indigenous Malays. Buddhist temples and Hindu shrines dot the landscape alongside Muslim mosques.

Malaya has a maritime equatorial climate, characterized by high temperature and heavy rainfall. Temperatures generally exceed 80°F, and the annual range is only 4 degrees F. The day-to-night variation, however, may reach 20 degrees F.

Malaya Data [1]

Area	50,700 square miles
Population	6,909,000 (1960 est.)
Kuala Lumpur (capital)	316,230 (1957 census)
George Town	234,903
Primary and secondary pupils:	
Malay-language	459,618 (1959)
Chinese-language	416,284
Indian-language	54,759
English-language	276,161
University of Malaya students	1,923
Rubber	721,900 metric tons (1960)
Rice	903,000 " "
Copra	127,500 metric tons (1959)
Bauxite	388,000 " "
Tin	52,800 metric tons (1960)
Iron ore (60%)	5,736,000 " "
Cement	286,800 " "
Electricity	918,800,000 kilowatthours (1959)

[1] *Britannica Book of the Year,* 1962.

The annual rainfall everywhere is over 75 inches, and in places exceeds twice that figure. Averages may be deceiving, for while every month normally receives rain and the annual graphs appear evenly distributed, the rain comes in sharp concentrations, and dry spells when crops wither may occur erratically.

There is a tendency for each coast to have rainfall during the northeastern or southwestern monsoon, but the maximum fall may occur during the unstable transitional periods when local convectional thunderstorms or sharp line squalls yield torrential rain. As much as 4 inches may fall in an hour, or 15 inches in a day. Much of the water is thus lost through rapid runoff. On account of the high temperature, the losses from evaporation and transpiration amount to some 60 inches per year, so that the occasional dry spells may leave the ground parched. Crop yields may then drop to 25 per cent of normal.

Western Malaya is sheltered from the full effect of the southwest monsoon by the island of Sumatra, and thus receives less rain, while the east coast is wetter and more stormy when its monsoon is blowing. The west coast has five important harbors; the east has but one.

Rubber is Malaya's most valuable agricultural product. It occupies two-thirds of the cropland, accounts for nearly two-thirds of the country's export, and supplies one-third of the world's natural rubber. *Hevea brasiliensis* is a native of the Amazon forest, and was introduced into Singapore in 1877.

The rubber tree is remarkably tolerant of poor lateritic soils, provided there is good drainage and an appropriate climate with heavy rain, high humidity, and uniformly high temperatures. Suitable soil moisture and weather conditions are best found along the western foothills, and here *Hevea* is concentrated. Nearly 4 million acres of rain forest with its heterogeneous flora have been transformed into systematic monocrop orchards, quite unlike the original habitat of rubber in Brazil.

The development of high-yield rubber trees out of the original strains has called for extensive and costly experimentation. Since trees do not come into bearing until they are six or seven years old, the cost of clearing the dense forest and planting trees calls for a large capital investment and long-term planning—commitments which the native farmer is in no position to make.

Half of the production comes from estates of 1,000 acres and more, generally under foreign ownership. These corporations have high overhead expenses for research, foreign personnel, imported labor, access roads, and Western-style buildings. As a result of improvements, the best trees actually yield 1 to 2 tons of rubber per acre. To gather the latex requires one worker for each 6 acres. Several hundred thousand laborers on the plantations have come from South India.

The quality of plantation rubber is generally high, but so are production costs. Commercial production is in competition with small producers, both Malay and Chinese, who grow a few tens of acres of rubber as a side line with little overhead cost. In addition, rubber production has been plagued by wide fluctuations in price due to competition from Indonesia, which now leads the world, and from synthetic rubber.

Two other technical crops are significant: coconut products and palm oil, both grown for export and raised with Malay labor. The coco-

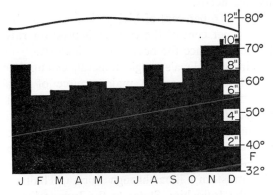

SINGAPORE. Elevation 33 feet, average temperature 81°F, annual precipitation 95 inches. Equatorial maritime conditions provide uniformity throughout the year.

Rubber latex is obtained by tapping the bark every other day on alternate sides of the tree. (*Courtesy British Information Services*)

nut palm and the oil palm differ somewhat in appearance; the former is tall, whereas the latter has branches fairly close to the ground so that the tree has a more compact and solid appearance. Both trees bear fruit throughout the year; both are generally grown on foreign-administered plantations. The white meat of the coconut is usually dried in the groves, and the copra is shipped to Singapore or Penang to be pressed for oil. Palm oil is prepared on the estates and shipped in liquid form; its production amounts to several tens of thousands of tons, slightly greater than that of coconut oil.

Rice is generally a subsistence crop, grown most widely in coastal areas of the north and west, where cash income from rubber or tin is unavailable. Almost all wet rice is raised within 50 feet of sea level. These reclaimed swamp lands provide Malaya's only treeless landscapes. Malaya produces but one-third of its rice needs.

Only 16 per cent of Malaya is cultivated, but only 4 per cent of the country is used for raising food; hence the necessity for imports.

Tin is Malaya's magic mineral, essential to world industry and a major source of local wealth. Tin is one of those uncommon metals whose distribution is highly localized. While it is found in Bolivia, in central Africa, and elsewhere, the bulk of the world's supply is produced in an oval zone which extends from southwestern China through Burma, Thailand, and the Indochina States to the Indonesian islands of Banka and Billiton south of the equator. Malaya lies in the center of this metallogenic zone. Tin has been produced since the fifteenth century, largely by Chinese, but the big development dates from the discovery of rich deposits about 1870.

Malayan tin accounts for one-third of the world's supply, and its sale represents nearly one-fourth of the country's exports. The metal originates in and around the deep-seated granitic intrusions which here and there underlie the peninsula, especially near the contact with adjacent limestones and other sediments.

The principal mineral is cassiterite, the oxide which contains about 75 per cent tin. Some tin is mined underground in veins or lodes, but most of the production is obtained from placer deposits, where the cassiterite, heavier than most minerals, has been concentrated by present or former streams.

Alluvial tin deposits are worked by either of two methods, both of which involve separation by water, much as placer gold is mined elsewhere. The simplest method involves shooting a jet of water into old gravels, which are then separated as the water flows over the steps of a sluice. Operational costs are relatively low, and most hydraulic mining is in the hands of the Chinese. A more expensive method, largely financed by European capital, involves the use of large floating dredges which create their own lake as they gradually eat their way into old alluvial gravels, dumping the waste gravels behind them. Good ore-bearing gravels may contain a pound of tin per cubic yard. Many workable deposits contain only 0.00015 tin.

Most tin areas lie close to the inner margin of the western plains, often near the well-drained soils used for raising rubber. The area from Singapore to Penang is thus known as the tin and rubber belt, especially in the Kinta valley of Perak and near Kuala Lumpur in Selangor. Where the alluvium is thin it may be worked by hydraulic methods; where thicker and deeper, dredges are necessary. Less labor is called for than with rubber production, and the workers are characteristically Chinese rather than Indian.

The economy of Malayan tin is related to changing world needs, growing production elsewhere, and the approaching exhaustion of known deposits in the peninsula. Most mining methods leave the landscape covered with scars, and the costs of rehabilitation enforced by modern legislation represent an added expense. Many streams have become badly overloaded by the addition of sediment from placer operations; some towns downstream have been buried, and rice fields have had to be abandoned.

Other metals include iron and aluminum ores (in large production), some gold, and modest amounts of low-grade manganese and tungsten. The chief iron mineral is high-grade hematite, averaging 50 to 65 per cent metal, which is mined in Johore and Trengganu along the east coast. The annual production amounts to several million tons, almost entirely for use in Japan. Since the east coast lacks good harbors, shipment is difficult.

Bauxite, the ore of aluminum, is produced in Johore for refining in Japan, Taiwan, and Australia. The output amounts to several hundred thousand tons a year.

Coal is of low grade, and suffers in competi-

Singapore Data [1]

Area	225 square miles
Population	1,687,300 (1961 est.)
Chinese	73%
Malays	13%
Indians	8%
Singapore City	953,500 (1958 est.)
Primary and secondary pupils	353,562 (1960)
University (2) students	3,305

[1] *Britannica Book of the Year*, 1962.

tion with cheap petroleum imported from Indonesia. The chief mine is in Selangor on the west coast.

To an unusual extent, the economy of the Malay Peninsula rests on the world demand for its two principal exports, rubber and tin.

PEOPLE AND POLITICS

The peninsula of Malaya is both a bridge and a barrier. Along its shores have moved peoples from Asia to Australia, and routes around or across it have linked India and China. Western Borneo has had less contact with the outside world, but its coast forms a ladder from Indonesia to the Philippines. Malaya is both an avenue and an obstacle—a peninsula but with many of the characteristics of an island. Location is thus a basic factor in Malayan geography, more permanent than internal assets like rubber or tin.

The British Empire was fortunate in having statesmen of great vision. Among them was Sir Stamford Raffles, who foresaw the strategic importance of the Strait of Malacca and secured the island of Singapore for Great Britain in 1819. Malacca and Penang had already been taken by the British, the former from the Dutch in 1795. British Malaya, before the 1940s, included the four Federated States of Perak, Negri Sembilan, Selangor, and Pahang, and the five Unfederated States of Johore, Kedah, Kelantan, Perlis, and Trengganu. When these states became in 1947 the independent Federation of Malaya, Singapore, including the outposts of Penang and Malacca, remained under British control as a Crown Colony. It became an independent state, within the Commonwealth, in 1959.

Through the Strait of Malacca passes all the shipping between Europe and Eastern Asia; here meet the Pacific and Indian realms. Singapore is the crossroads of the East, 75 miles north of the equator. The island measures some

Singapore is one of the world's busiest transit ports; it commands the Strait of Malacca, gateway between the Indian and Pacific Oceans. Five million tons of cargo are handled each year. (*Courtesy Caltex*)

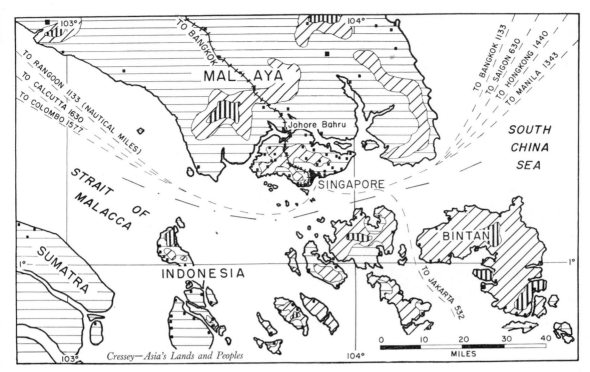

The island of Singapore commands the Strait of Malacca, gateway between the Indian and Pacific Oceans. The island was secured for Britain by Sir Stamford Raffles in 1819 and is one of the key points along the lifeline of the Commonwealth.

24 by 14 miles and is separated from the mainland by a channel a mile wide. A causeway crosses the channel and facilitates the linking of Singapore by rail with Bangkok. The city lies at the extreme south, with the British naval base in the north. Singapore's entrepôt trade amounts to several billion dollars a year. Commerce rather than industry provides the main occupation, and Singapore is the great trade center of the realm. With its magnificent harbor, it is one of the world's busiest ports of call; it is thus a logical center for the collection, grading, and export of many tropical products. Among them are rubber, spices, gums, resins, fibers, and minerals. The city is the major entrepôt of the Asiatic tropics for bazaar goods and machinery, and also for banking and engineering services. Its population numbers about two million, three-quarters of whom are Chinese.

Despite its importance, the future of Singapore is in many ways uncertain. As we have previously indicated in the discussion of Thailand, the air age has brought major changes in the accessibility and importance of different localities. For many through travelers the airport at Bangkok has replaced the docks of Singapore. As an airport, Singapore is now chiefly a transit point for Australia. Singapore exists by reason of trade, and if it were ever effectively detached from the Federation of Malaya its prosperity might suffer seriously. On the other hand, the peninsula is not so dependent upon Singapore. It has alternate ports at George Town on the island of Penang and at Port Swettenham, which serves the capital of Kuala Lumpur. Although Singapore has been the cultural as well as the commercial center, Kuala Lumpur is fast becoming a competitor, since it lies in the middle of the tin and rubber belt.

The future of the Malay Peninsula, both in-

Rail services lead north from Singapore to Bangkok. This is the "Golden Blowpipe" express train in the state of Kelantan. (*Courtesy Federation of Malaya*)

ternally and in its relation to the Commonwealth, is related to its complex population. In the Federation of Malaya, Malays outnumber Indians, Chinese, or Indonesians, though probably not all aliens together. Since many of these outsiders have retained their original citizenship and loyalties, the Malays themselves feel

a natural concern about the influence of the unassimilated element upon the future of the region. The separate island of Singapore has a million Chinese, and if union with the peninsula is in question, their vote might alter its political character. Unlike the refugee Chinese in Hong Kong, who are strongly anti-Communist, some

North Borneo Data [1]

Area	29,388 square miles
Population	454,328 (1960 census)
Jesselton (capital)	21,714

[1] *Britannica Book of the Year*, 1962.

Brunei Data [1]

Area	2,226 square miles
Population	83,877 (1960 census)
Petroleum	4,505,000 long tons (1960)

[1] *Britannica Book of the Year*, 1962.

of the second-generation Chinese in Singapore have sympathies with Mainland China.

One solution for the racial, economic, and political problems of the Federation versus Singapore lies in a larger grouping to include the various parts of British Borneo, where most people are Malays, under the overall name of Malaysia. This will dilute the political influence of the Chinese but effectively reinstates Singapore as the political and commercial center.

Yet a political Malaysia faces problems of internal unity. Only a few roads cross the Malay Peninsula to link the east and west coasts, and there is little historic unity among the several states. Western Borneo is merely a coastal fringe, linked only by sea routes. Whether there can be coherence across 1,000 miles of sea between Malaya and Borneo is quite a different question. Religion is a divisive factor, for most Malays are Muslims, while Chinese tend to be Buddhists, and Indians are Hindus.

The peninsula lacks a natural focus, although rubber and tin center on Kuala Lumpur. All the best ports are along the west coast. One unifying asset is the 1,000-mile network of railways, a heritage from British rule. Another is the large export surplus, which helps to give Malaya one of the highest standards of living of any country in Southeast Asia. Very little of Borneo is as well developed as Malaya.

WESTERN BORNEO

Western Borneo (formerly British Borneo), although too often overlooked, forms an important part of the Southeast Asian realm. It includes the states of Sarawak, Brunei, and North Borneo, which cover 78,864 square miles, an area considerably larger than Java. Their population, however, is less than 2 million. Physical conditions resemble those of adjoining Indonesian Borneo, but British control produced a different economy.

During the nineteenth century Sarawak had a unique development as the personal property of the sovereign Brooke family, the British head of which became the hereditary rajah. North Borneo also had a brief period under an American rajah, J. W. Torrey, but then passed under the control of a British chartered company, later to become a Crown Colony. Brunei was originally a sultanate, later administered as one of the Straits Settlements. The present sultan traces his descent from the fif-

Pineapples are grown throughout Malaya, especially on areas of peat soil. Johore is the leading exporter. (*Courtesy Federation of Malaya*)

Sarawak Data[1]

Area	48,250 square miles
Population	744,391 (1960 census)
Kuching (capital)	50,000
Petroleum	4,574,000 long tons (1960)

[1] *Britannica Book of the Year*, 1962.

Fishing is an important Malaysian industry, thanks to a coast line of 1,200 miles. This fisherman is from Perak. (*Courtesy Federation of Malaya*)

teenth century, and Brunei was once a powerful native kingdom. It was visited by Magellan in 1521 who was much impressed by the wealth of the court; at that time the royal palace was guarded by fifty-six cannon.

The area has always been closely associated with Singapore, which serves as its main trade center, especially for its rubber, copra, pepper, and gold. Petroleum is the major export, and production may come to rival that of Sumatra. The three states of Western Borneo have never fed themselves and depend on imports for much of their rice.

Western Borneo has many of the characteristics of an undeveloped tropical land, with an uncertain future. Much of the interior is an uncleared and unsurveyed forest, backed by mountains, where primitive aborigines engage

in hunting, fishing, and migratory agriculture. The coast is fringed with impenetrable swamps of mangrove or nipa palm, where scattered Malays engage in fishing or raise rice. Only a small percentage of the area has been developed for systematic cultivation. Transport facilities are everywhere so poor that coastal shipping and shallow rivers provide the principal avenues of communication. The island of Labuan is the chief entrepôt.

The numerous aboriginal tribes are generally grouped as Dyaks, which is merely a term for inland or mountain people, although some live near the coast. For the most part their cultivation of the land is of the ladang type. Malay people are found along the coast and in the larger settlements; all of them are Muslims; some have Arab blood. Chinese are numerous, perhaps accounting for one-fifth of the population. Many are engaged in trade or find work in the oil and gold fields. A few Indians, originally from Madras, live in the towns.

Rainfall is generally above 100 inches, and there is no dry season; the mean temperature is near 80°F throughout the year. As a result, the vegetation is that of a tall, luxuriant evergreen rain forest. In well-drained areas the taller trees reach 150 to 200 feet, and climbing plants, such as rattans, grow in profusion. It has been said that a monkey could travel across Borneo from end to end without ever touching the ground.

A British traveler has vividly described the vegetation.[2]

The jungle of Borneo, when first seen from the deck of a ship, stretches smooth and unbroken along the distant shore, for all the world like a green ice cap. It is as dangerous as an ice cap, and as empty, and as vast. It rises from the coast in tier after tier, climbing the precipitous slopes of the Crocker Range, which runs down the west coast some twenty miles inland, and then spreads scarcely without interruption over the tangled mass of hills, mountains, and valleys that stretch across to the distant Sulu and Celebes Sea. North Borneo is as big as Ireland; it is virtually all jungle. . . .

The jungle view was breathtaking, panoramas of mountains packed with thick foliage, tremendous trees themselves embraced passionately by

[2] K. G. Tregonning: *North Borneo,* London: Her Majesty's Stationery Office (1960), 5, 48.

fern and creeper. At times [the road] turned high on some ridge, above a pulsating valley, and at others sweeping down to some minute clearing of smoothly planted *padi,* and again climbing, pushing through the jungle that hung over the road; apart from the road the jungle seemed untouched, as if it had stood there inviolate; truly a virgin jungle.

Much of the life of natives in the small clearings involves an unending attempt to prevent the natural vegetation from reoccupying cleared land, for the jungle invades every clearing as soon as it has a chance. Above 3,000 feet the rain forest is replaced by smaller trees covered by a thick blanket of moss, a product of the drizzling rain and mist. While lumber is not yet an important export, several million acres of commercial timber are considered possibly accessible to the coast. Many of these trees are very hard and durable.

The highest peak in all Southeast Asia is Kinabalu, 13,455 feet. Although the rainfall is heavy at times, the enervating humidity of the coast gives way at elevation to pleasant sunny days where one can move without perspiring and blankets are needed at night.

The most important crop is rice, with the acreage in wet rice increasing because of government restrictions on ladang cultivation with its dry rice. Sago replaces rice as the standard diet in some areas. Many other tropical crops are grown, including corn, cassava, coconuts, sugar cane, coffee, pepper, and rubber.

References on Malaysia

See also general references on Southeast Asia, Chapter 17.

Chapman, F. Spencer: "The Chinese in Malaya," *Geog. Mag.,* XXIII (1951), 401–411.

Dale, W. L.: "The Rainfall of Malaya," *Jour. of Tropical Geog.,* XIII (1959), 23–37.

*Dobby, E. H. G.: "Singapore: Town and Country," *Geog. Rev.,* XXX (1940), 84–109.

Dobby, E. H. G.: "Settlement Patterns in Malaya," *Geog. Rev.,* XXXII (1942), 211–232.

Dobby, E. H. G.: "The Kalantan Delta," *Geog. Rev.,* XLI (1951), 226–255.

Dobby, E. H. G.: "The North Kedah Plain: A Study in the Environment of Pioneering for Rice Production," *Econ. Geog.,* XXVII (1951), 287–315.

Fisher, C. A.: "The Railway Geography of British Malaya," *Scottish Geog. Mag.,* LXIV (1948), 123–136.

Fisher, C. A.: "The Problem of Malayan Unity in Its Geographical Setting," in R. W. Steel and C. A. Fisher (eds.): *Geographical Essays on British Tropical Lands,* London: G. Philip (1956), 271–344.

*Ginsburg, Norton S., and Chester F. Roberts: *Malaya,* Seattle: University of Washington Press (1958).

Harris, George L., and others: *North Borneo, Brunei, Sarawak,* New Haven: Human Relations Area Files (1956).

Journal of Tropical Geography (Kuala Lumpur).

Kahin, George: "The State of North Borneo, 1881–1946," *Far Eastern Quarterly,* VII (1947), 43–65.

Leach, D. L.: "The Survey of Sarawak," *Geog. Jour.,* C (1942), 98–106.

Ooi, J. B.: "Tin Mining Landscapes of Kinta," *Malayan Jour. of Tropical Geog.* (1955).

Roberts, Chester (ed.): *Malaya,* New Haven, Conn.: Human Relations Area Files (1955).

Spencer, Joseph E.: "Seasonality in the Tropics: The Supply of Fruit to Singapore," *Geog. Rev.,* XLIX (1959), 475–484.

Spencer, Joseph E.: "The Cultural Factor in 'Underdevelopment': The Case of Malaya," in *Essays on Geography and Economic Development,* Chicago: The University of Chicago Press (1960), 35–48.

Stead, Ronald: "The 'New Villages' in Malaya," *Geog. Mag.,* XXVII (1955), 642–652.

Swayne, J. C.: "Sarawak," *Scottish Geog. Mag.,* LVIII (1942), 59–63.

24 Indonesia

People and History / Climate and Crops / The Geological Base / Java / The Outer Islands / References on Indonesia

PEOPLE AND HISTORY

When the Dutch government took over Java in 1796, the population of the island numbered 3½ million and appeared to have been more or less stationary for centuries. When the Dutch left in 1949 the population had grown to nearly 55 million, with a density of over 1,000 per square mile for the island as a whole and even three to four times that figure in terms of cultivated land alone.

What is more, already overcrowded Java is growing at the rate of a million a year. The island accounts for two-thirds of the population of the Republic of Indonesia, but since Java covers less than one-tenth of the area of Indonesia as a whole, one may wonder whether these tropical islands may someday come to have several hundred million people. Small wonder that Ellsworth Huntington has written of "Java, the Despair of Malthus." And yet the land supports these people in reasonable comfort; few parts of Asia have such attractive and cheerful people.

Indonesia is much the largest of the states in Southeast Asia, covering two-thirds of the area of the entire realm. Both Sumatra and the Indonesian part of Borneo are as large as Thailand. The 3,000 islands equal the size of the United States east of the Mississippi, and in overall

345

Indonesia's population has grown so rapidly that Ellsworth Huntington once called Java "the despair of Malthus." While the man-land pressure is serious, the people are remarkably prosperous and cheerful. This is a new immigrant village in southern Sumatra. (*Courtesy International Cooperation Administration*)

distance they exceed the breadth of the United States. From east to west Indonesia measures 3,000 miles; from north to south the distance is nearly half that figure. Nowhere is there an obvious core area, though Java serves as such.

The discovery in Java of the remains of very early man, *Pithecanthropus erectus,* makes it clear that Indonesia has been inhabited for several hundred thousand years. Among the earliest representatives of modern man were the Negritos, some of whom still survive in the eastern islands. Then came Caucasoid people such as the Papuans, followed by Mongoloids,

and later by Malays. Some of the earliest people may even have migrated overland from mainland Asia since there was dry-land connection during glacial times when the sea level was lower.

By the first century Indian traders came to the coasts of Sumatra, Java, and Borneo, their infiltration resulting in several local states with an Indianized and either Buddhist or Hindu culture. In places conflict arose between coastal trading states and interior agricultural areas. The most important of these local sea-oriented states was that of Sri Vijaya in southern Sumatra, which became dominant from the seventh to the twelfth centuries, later to be replaced by the Javanese state of Madjapahit, where better soils led to better productivity. Neither state left much record.

Chinese traders appeared about the same time as the Indians, but did not make many permanent settlements until after the thirteenth century. These contacts were primarily economic, whereas Indian influences included cultural penetration.

Arab merchants came to Indonesian waters early in the Christian era, and Islam arrived by the thirteenth century, some of the missionaries coming from the Hadhramaut in southern Arabia. Muslim contacts penetrated as far as the Philippines by 1480. Islam thus came into conflict with Buddhism and gradually became the dominant Malay culture. Although far from the Arab world, Indonesia is one of the largest Islamic states, and sends thousands of pilgrims to Mecca.

The Portuguese were the first European traders. But their search for spices and conquest resulted in difficulties with the local Muslim states, and the island of Timor is their only remaining souvenir. The Dutch East India Company arrived by the end of the sixteenth century and developed early associations with Chinese merchants, especially at Batavia, now Jakarta. In 1796 the company surrendered its charter, and the islands became a political colony of the Netherlands, except for a period of British ownership from 1803 until 1816.

What is now Indonesia had never been a single native state. When the Dutch took control, they found diversity in race, religion, settlement density, agriculture, prosperity, and culture. Java was by far the most developed section; the eastern archipelago and the interior of the larger islands were little known. Most of the people could be called Malays in a broad sense, but there were many Chinese and aboriginal peoples. About 250 languages were

Indonesia Data [1]

Area	575,893 square miles [2]
Population	92,600,000 (1960 est.) [3]
Jakarta (capital)	2,081,200 (1958 est.)
Surabaya	1,135,300
Bandoeng	951,900
Semarang	444,800
Surakarta	380,843 (1956 est.)
Makassar	357,400 (1957 est.)
Medan	342,200 (1958 est.)
Palembang	337,300
Jogjakarta	289,400 (1957 est.)
Primary and secondary pupils	7,959,981
University (6) students	41,000
Rice	13,500,000 metric tons (1960)
Rubber	575,100 " "
Sugar, raw	810,000 " "
Copra	526,000 metric tons (1959)
Crude oil	18,216,000 " "
Tin	22,920 " "
Bauxite	387,000 " "
Electricity	966,724,000 kilowatthours (1958)

[1] *Britannica Book of the Year*, 1962.
[2] For Western Irian, formerly Netherlands New Guinea, add 160,618 square miles.
[3] For Western Irian add 715,661 people.

spoken in the islands, grouped into Indonesian, Melanesian, and Polynesian types.

In spite of the many difficulties they faced, the Dutch achieved one of the best colonial administrations of any Western power. In no other Asian colony were Europeans content to settle down for their lives, still loyal to their homeland but making the colony their permanent residence. Racial prejudice was nonexistent, and children of mixed parentage were given full European status. Dutch energy developed excellent agricultural research and raised crops such as sugar cane to a high level of efficiency. While 2.400 estates were developed in unoccupied areas, native farmers were forbidden to sell their land to outsiders, including Dutch and Chinese. Thus Indonesia never developed a large class of absentee landlords. Elementary education became widespread, especially in Java, as did good roads and public health. What was lacking was preparation for political freedom.

During the twentieth century Indian influence has declined, but the number of Chinese, largely small merchants in the larger cities, has increased to 1½ million. The unwillingness of many Chinese, now second- and third-generation residents, to accept Indonesian citizenship has been an occasion for trouble.

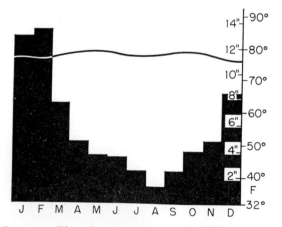

JAKARTA. Elevation 26 feet, average temperature 80°F, annual precipitation 71 inches. Northwestern Java lies south of the equator and receives most of its rain from the Asiatic monsoon.

Indonesian independence in 1949 brought further problems: the heritage of Japanese occupation from 1942 to 1945; resentment by the Outer Islands of domination by Java; Dutch unwillingness to turn over Western New Guinea, known to the Indonesians as Western Irian, which the Dutch regarded as ethnically distinct and not an integral part of the Netherlands Indies; and major changes in international trade due to fluctuating prices for rubber, tin, or sugar. Whereas the Netherlands Indies balanced its budget through large exports, many of these have now declined, leaving Indonesia with a trade deficit.

Cultural contrasts range from the European civilization of the coastal cities to aboriginal conditions in the remote interiors where, until recent decades, the people were headhunters.

CLIMATE AND CROPS

Since all Indonesia lies within 11 degrees of the equator and none of the islands is large enough to modify conditions appreciably, the climate is fundamentally maritime equatorial. Temperatures are consistently high, though not excessive, and the humidity remains high. The combination of hot nights and high humidity makes lowland climates very enervating. Many people who can afford to take a holiday spend a few weeks each year in the cooler mountains.

Temperature is largely a matter of elevation rather than of season, for the duration of sunlight on the longest and shortest days of the year differs by less than an hour. In Jakarta at sea level, with a yearly average of 79°F, the warmest and coolest monthly averages are within 2 degrees. In contrast, Bandoeng at 2,395 feet has a delightful climate with a yearly average of 71°F, while Tosari at 5,888 feet averages 61°F, and Gede at 9,914 feet has 48°F. No station has ever recorded freezing temperatures. Frost is rare and occurs only on high, sheltered plateaus. Heavy showers or the onset of sea breezes may bring a drop of 9 degrees. Temperature seasons scarcely exist.

Coconut products form an important export from several of the Indonesian islands. The white meat is extracted and dried in order to obtain coconut oil. (*Courtesy Indonesian Information Service*)

The islands lie between the two monsoon centers of Asia and Australia with their alternating high and low pressures. To these pressure differences is added the shift of the northeast and southeast trade-wind belts, recurving to their right or left where they cross the equator, and centering on the intertropical convergence zone. From December to March the air flows out of Asia; from May to September the wind blows in the opposite direction.

Rainfall is everywhere abundant and in many places very heavy. Stations with less than 40 inches and a noticeable dry season are found only in the Lesser Sunda Islands. In January the combined Asiatic outblowing monsoon and trade winds are relatively rainless at sea level but yield heavy rain on mountain slopes or after having crossed the equator and re-curved as northwest winds. In Java this combination of winds is known as the west monsoon. Conditions are reversed in July when air masses originate over Australia.

Many mountain sides receive over 100 inches of rain, with relatively less humid rain-shadow conditions in their lee. Local convectional showers are important at all seasons, usually related to powerful updrafts due to convergence conditions. Thunderstorms are numerous on mountain slopes near the equator, with a world record of 322 thunderstorm days a year at Bogor (Buitenzorg), south of Jakarta.

While the heavy rainfall and high temperatures tend to impoverish the soil, another factor leads to relative fertility. This is the chemical character of many lava flows and ash deposits, high in soluble mineral nutrients. This composition of volcanic material accounts for the successful agriculture of Java and the limited prospects on the other islands, where volcanic action is absent or where the underlying magma is acidic rather than basic in composition. Fertilization is generally necessary for high yields.

Indonesia has long held a unique place in tropical agriculture because of the variety and excellence of its products. The area was first known to Europe for its spices, later on for its quinine, indigo, tea, coffee, rubber, copra, palm oil, kapok, sisal, tobacco, and sugar. During the Dutch period these crops were grown for export, and prior to the Second World War about 10 million acres out of a total cultivated area of 40 million were planted to crops for overseas sale. Some of these were grown on large estates, but production by small farmers was also important. These agricultural products accounted for two-thirds of the total value of exports. In agriculture, as in other matters, conditions in Java are quite distinct from those in the Outer Islands, both in the kinds of crops and in the intensity of land use.

Present-day agriculture is of three types. Sedentary subsistence cultivation includes irrigated rice fields, known here as *sawahs*. Rice provides the bulk of the food supply and is the product of some of the most intensive land use to be found anywhere, especially on the terraced mountain sides in Java. In a few favored areas one crop succeeds another the year round, so that there is always a harvest; famines are unknown. Other subsistence food crops include corn, usually grown as an upland crop or as an unirrigated crop on idle rice fields; sweet potatoes; manioc, in part raised for making tapioca; peanuts; and soybeans.

In earlier days—and still to a considerable extent in the interior of the larger islands—shifting cultivation is the rule. This process of fire clearing, widespread throughout Southeast Asia, is here known as ladang, and provides the chief food for several million people. In the Outer Islands, ladang cultivation may represent 90 per cent of the agricultural area, with a total planting of some 20 million acres each year.

The chief crops in shifting agriculture are dry rice, corn, sweet potatoes, bananas, taros, and manioc. Since cleared fields can be used for only a few years before weeds and the forest take over, no more than one-tenth or one-twentieth of the land can be in production at any one time. If the process appears wasteful, the poverty of the soil must be recognized. The rapid growth of population has led to more and more intensive land use, so that ladang cultivation is on the decline. Vast areas of tropical rain forest await development, but to convert such land to normal agriculture usually involves a heavy capital investment for clearing, irrigation, fertilizers, transport, and public services.

The high development of export crops by the Dutch was based on agricultural research and good management. While the bulk of the production was obtained from large estates, chiefly on the Outer Islands, small-scale native output came to contribute two-fifths of the total. Pepper and spices were the earliest cash crops, although they never involved large acreages. Independence has brought a decrease in the number of large specialized farms and a major decline in the export of their products.

Sugar has lost much of its former importance, but rubber has taken its place in export significance since Indonesia supplies one-third of the world's crude rubber. Quinine, pepper, kapok, and vegetable oils contribute to world trade. Since world prices fluctuate widely, agriculture has had its periods of prosperity and collapse.

THE GEOLOGICAL BASE

One of the world's most active seismic and volcanic areas encircles the Sunda Platform, bordering Sumatra, Java, and the Lesser Sunda Islands, and circling west of New Guinea to the Philippines. Although earthquakes of major violence are uncommon in Indonesia, an average of 500 minor tremors are recorded each year. The major danger is from submarine quakes, which give rise to great sea waves, erroneously called tidal waves but properly known by their Japanese name of tsunami, which may advance over coastal lowlands and cause great loss of life.

Several hundred volcanoes are present in the Indonesian arc, of which 71 have erupted since the year 1600, especially in Java and Sumatra. Scores of others are classed as dormant, where activity is confined to steam and gas vents or to boiling springs known as solfataras. It is rarely safe to assume that a volcano is really dead until enough time has elapsed for erosion to have eliminated the visible cone. Volcanic eruptions have cost the lives of many thousands of people, not so much from lava flows as from ash fall and mud flows, and in places from hot clouds of dust. Volcanic cones exceed 10,000 feet in elevation on a half dozen islands. In addition to the usual craters, there are many supercraters known as cauldera, usually due to the collapse of a mountain top as the underlying support is withdrawn.

While volcanic activity may be very destructive, a beneficial dividend accrues through the weathering of certain types of lava and ash into fertile soils. Sulfur is a volcanic by-product, and the many hot springs are useful. Possibly power may be produced by tapping underground heat.

Volcanic activity may be classed as quiet where lava pours out with relatively little violence and builds a broad cone, or as explosive where tremendous steam pressures blow lava skyward, breaking it into ash fragments which pile up in a steep cone at the angle of rest. Most Indonesian volcanoes are of the latter type.

The classic example of a violent explosion is found in the eruption of Krakatoa in 1883—probably the greatest activity of its kind in recorded history, though the eruption of Tam-

The East Indian arc is one of the most active volcanic areas on earth. This is a view of the Tenger cauldera in eastern Java, with the steaming Bromo crater in the center. (*Courtesy Indonesian Information Service*)

boro in 1815 may have been of equal violence.

Krakatoa was an island in the Sunda Strait, midway between Java and Sumatra. After two hundred years of inactivity, the volcano burst into violent eruption, and two-thirds of the island disappeared. Some of the fine ejected material was thrown to a height of 17 miles and carried completely around the world, producing brilliant sunsets for two years. The nearby Sunda Sea was covered with pumice, and a rain of ashes fell over southern Sumatra and western Java. The sound was heard in Singapore and Australia, and the barometric wave was recorded in Amsterdam. The greatest damage was caused by a violent tsunami, which reached a height of 118 feet. Pouring inland as far as 6 miles, it drowned 36,000 people.

For forty-four years Krakatoa remained quiet, and the ash-covered remnants became clothed with vegetation. Then in 1927 activity resumed, and a new cone was built up where the sea had been 1,000 feet deep. This ash island is known as Anak Krakatoa, the "child of Krakatoa."

Volcanoes with large crater lakes may prove especially dangerous when rising lava ejects the water and covers the slopes with boiling mud flows. One such flow from Keloet covered 50 square miles in forty-five minutes, and killed 5,000 people. To limit the recurrence of such a catastrophe, tunnels have been dug through the crater rim to siphon off the lake. Measurements of water and fumarole temperatures now provide warning to nearby villages.

The volcano Batoer on the island of Bali has had seven lava flows in a century; in one eruption 21 million cubic feet of lava were poured out in seven weeks.

Mineral resources have been important since early in the Christian era, when tin, gold, and petroleum were sought by Arab and Indian traders. Geological studies are far from complete, but there is some suggestion of considerable wealth.

Oil is produced on Sumatra near Palembang and Djambi in the south, and at Medan in the north. Borneo has fields at Balikpapan and Tarakan. Petroleum also occurs on Java and Ceram. While oil production is modest in world terms, Indonesia is one of the largest sources between Iran and California.

Tin is a major mineral, and alluvial placer deposits on the islands of Bangka, Billiton, and Singkep make Indonesia the world's second- or third-largest producer. Bauxite is mined on Bintan, near Singapore; sulfur and manganese are produced on Java; and nickel occurs in Celebes. Iron ore is present in abundance, but there is no suitable coke for smelting. Low-grade coal is available for power in central Sumatra, western Java, and eastern Borneo.

There are several ways to regionalize the islands. In geological terms, one may describe the western archipelago as the Greater Sunda Islands, including the large units of Borneo, Celebes, and most of Java and Sumatra, which make up the old land mass of the Sunda Platform; in contrast, the eastern archipelago, made up of smaller islands of complex structure and separated by deep seas, is sometimes known as the Lesser Sunda Islands; farther east are islands such as the Moluccas and New Guinea, which are related to the old Sahul Platform adjoining Australia.

Structurally, the old stable platforms are bordered by young fold mountains with volcanic belts, so that one may differentiate between the outer folded arc with its volcanoes and earthquakes and the inner and more stable areas.

In political and economic terms it is common to speak of Java, with its dense population, and the Outer Islands, sparsely inhabited. This is the order here followed.

JAVA

Nowhere in the tropics, of either the Old World or the New, is there a land like Java. Its population increase is almost without parallel, as is the intensity of its land use. The combination of luxuriant vegetation, picturesque volcanoes, cheerful people, active countryside, and intelligent development makes Java an unusually attractive island. Arable land is so close

Java is so densely populated that every available square foot must be put into production. Terraced rice fields, or sawah, dominate every hillside. (*Courtesy International Cooperation Administration*)

to the maximum that no more than a small additional percentage can be made suitable for agriculture. Rice fields already climb the slopes of volcanoes wherever land can be terraced and irrigated.

As we have already indicated, Java has long been the leading island of Indonesia, and the Dutch made it the center of their colonial empire. The island has a length of 600 miles and lies farther from the equator than other parts of Indonesia, its position giving a touch of seasonality. The small island of Madura, an eastern structural extension, is usually included in Javanese statistics.

The century and a half of Dutch rule brought many improvements, including the large-scale management of water, an excellent network of roads and railways, and extensive agricultural research.

Along the northern shore is a low coastal plain of alluvium, across which the silt-laden rivers follow diked channels. This is intensively devoted to rice or sugar cane. Farther south lies a zone of low hills where the soils are less fertile, usually derived from marl and limestone. The central mountain backbone has numerous volcanoes, rising above a base of folded sedimentary rocks. Eighty-five peaks exceed

6,000 feet in height, and the highest volcano reaches 12,200 feet. Here and there are intermontane basins, nearly level, which are covered with rice sawahs. A hilly coastal zone parallels the south shore, with but little level land.

The original forest mantle is preserved only on the higher slopes, no more than enough to control runoff. Teak is the chief commercial tree in the lowlands.

Rain comes chiefly with the northwest monsoon, though convectional showers occur at all seasons. Most of the lowlands have 60 to 100 inches, and only in the extreme northeast is the amount under 40 inches. One mountain station reports nearly 400 inches a year.

A prodigious amount of work has gone into irrigation, chiefly for rice but also for sugar cane and other crops. Irrigated land accounts for about half of the farm area. Half of the land is double-cropped, and it seems scarcely possible to increase the farm area. Whereas elsewhere in Asia it is usually necessary to use great care to prevent erosion where water flows from one terrace level to another, Javanese soils are so nonerosive that little is needed except a few stones or a broken crock to line the spillways.

Rice and corn account for two-thirds of the acreage. Corn, peanuts, and manioc, or cassava, are raised as second crops after the rice harvest on drained sawahs, or where irrigation is not available. Both early- and late-maturing rice are raised, with the harvest in 70 to 140 days, usually in May or June at the beginning of the relatively dry season. As rice is grown the year round in rainy western Java, one may see side by side bright green seedbeds, flooded fields glistening like fragments of broken mirrors on the hillsides, freshly planted fields, all shades of green in growing fields, ripe brown rice, and elsewhere the harvest in process. Thus the same plot may yield two crops of rice and another crop within the year. Although both acreage and production have been increasing, Java is no longer able to feed itself and must import rice from the Outer Islands or abroad.

Corn is usually grown on less fertile land and without irrigation. The chief root crop is cassava, with a large export to the United States for the preparation of tapioca. Both sweet and white potatoes are grown. Peanuts and soybeans are other food crops.

Fish supply an important item in the diet and are raised in ponds throughout the island, both inland and along the seashore. In some places, the sawahs are reflooded after the rice harvest, and fish become a secondary "crop."

In Java rubber is grown at elevations of 300 to 1,500 feet, while in Sumatra most plantings are below 300 feet. This planting on high levels is due to the lack of available lowlands not already in cultivation.

Sugar was one of the best-known exports from Java, and the most important until 1930, when the production reached 3 million tons and cane was grown on a half million acres. The decline of sugar production since that time is an example of the serious effect of world economic conditions upon tropical products. Sugar cane is harvested thirteen or fourteen months after planting, and is rotated with other crops so that the same land is planted to cane once in three years. No second or ratoon crop is grown. Extensive research enabled the Dutch to develop some of the most productive varieties of cane in the world, now also raised in Hawaii, Cuba, and Louisiana, where the cooler climate requires a growing season up to twenty-two months. The average yield per acre in Java is three times that in the Philippine Islands.

Quinine is a unique product, an alkaloid made from the bark of the cinchona tree. This is the most widely used remedy for malaria. Seeds were brought to Java from South America in 1854. Most cinchona is grown at an elevation of 5,000 feet in western Java on fertile porous soils, rich in organic matter. Here, as with sugar, the yield has been greatly increased through research. Although once a government monopoly, cinchona is now raised chiefly on private plantations.

Java has had a tradition of progress for more than a thousand years. During the eighth and ninth centuries the people were Buddhists and later on Hindus. Among their architectural achievements is a giant stupa or monument known as the Borobudur in central Java. The ornamentation of the four sculptured terraces is particularly rich, comparable in artistry to the ruins at Angkor in Cambodia. With the arrival of Islam, this monument was covered with earth and trees to prevent its desecration and was unearthed only a century ago.

Three ethnographic groups of Malays inhabit the island: the Sundanese in the west, the Javanese in the center, and the Madurese in the east. Population pressures have been serious since the beginning of the century. Solutions are thought to lie in further intensification of agriculture, in industry (which may hold limited promise), and in emigration to the Outer Islands. All solutions call for large capital investments.

Java is noted as the place where remains have been found of very early man. The discovery of *Pithecanthropus erectus* at Trinil in 1891 was followed by the finding of three additional skulls by 1940. *Pithecanthropus* is of approximately the same early Pleistocene age as *Sinanthropus* in China; possibly no other human fossil material is so old.

In Java there are a half dozen cities with over 250,000 people. Jakarta, formerly Batavia, founded in 1619, is the capital and chief seaport, with a population of 2 million. It has had a phenomenal growth since independence. It really comprises four towns: the artificial port of Tandjoengpriok, 6 miles away, the old town of Batavia, the adjoining settlement of Djatinegara, and the new section known as Weltevreden. Because of the oppressive heat, many government offices have been moved to Bogor, formerly Buitenzorg, in the foothills, home of the famous botanical gardens; and some bureaus have even been located at Bandoeng in the mountains. Jakarta is the great commercial center of Indonesia, 532 nautical miles from Singapore.

Surabaya is the second city and port, with over a million people. Surabaya is a modern city and the port for the trade of eastern Java with the islands beyond.

Semarang is the port of north central Java. Bandoeng, Surakarta, and Jogjakarta are interior towns, each with several hundred thousand people.

THE OUTER ISLANDS

The Outer Islands include the large islands of Sumatra, whose Indonesian name is Andalas; Borneo, or Kalimantan; Celebes, or Sulawesi; and Western New Guinea, or Western Irian, plus hundreds of smaller islands. Although they contain nine-tenths of the total area of Indonesia, they account for only one-third of the population. In trade the Outer Islands surpass Java in the value of exports. Rubber is by far the most important crop, with the east coast of Sumatra leading in acreage. Prior to the Second World War there were several hundred estates, each thousands of acres in extent. Dutch, American, British, Belgian, and French capital was invested.

The undeveloped character of these islands has already been referred to. In part, this reflects infertile soils, swampy coastal areas which make approach difficult, and the inaccessibility of the interior. The original population was sparse, and many of the people have remained backward with little tradition of past glory. Dutch control in several of the larger islands did not become effective until the beginning of the twentieth century.

Colonization of these islands from overcrowded Java has been a definite government policy for several decades. Where plantations had acquired and developed new land, the problem of securing laborers was relatively simple; but where groups of colonists are now to be settled on new land, much preliminary work is required by the government. The Javanese are wet-rice farmers, and irrigation systems are not easy for the individual pioneer to arrange. Migratory ladang cultivation offers no attractions for the immigrant.

Sumatra was a major center for large foreign

Indonesia's Outer Islands account for nine-tenths of the area but only one-third of the population. Large sections remain little touched by outside influences, as in this village in Sumatra. (*Courtesy Indonesian Information Service*)

estates. Since Java offered no room for new plantations, Sumatra has developed tobacco, rubber, palm oil, and sisal on a large scale, along with tea and coffee. Oil has become a major export, and low-grade coal supplies Java. Sumatra's proximity to Singapore has tended to orient it toward the Malay Peninsula rather than toward Java. The principal cities are Medan and its port of Belawan-Deli in the northern rubber area, the oil center of Palembang in the south, and Padang on the west coast.

Borneo is the world's second-largest island, next to Greenland in area. The northeastern coast, which makes up Western Borneo, has been considered in the previous chapter. Much

of the island remains uncleared forest, and the lowlands are so poorly drained that there is little cultivation. Subsistence agriculture is based on rice, corn, and cassava, commonly in ladang clearings.

Celebes is also empty but has a relatively dense population in the northern peninsula, where there is a large Christian community around Mendao. Many of the coastal people in Celebes make their living from fishing or copra. The chief city is Makassar in the south.

Western New Guinea, known to the Indonesians as Western Irian, was the last remnant of Dutch sovereignty in Southeast Asia, dating from the seventeenth century. The area measures 160,618 square miles and has a population of 715,661. The people are Papuans rather than Malays.

Portuguese interest in the Spice Islands dates from the sixteenth century, but their sole remaining possession is the eastern half of the island of Timor, with an area of 7,450 square miles. As elsewhere in the easternmost islands, the fauna and flora have an Australian character. There is a distinct dry season and, consequently, some savanna country. The population numbers a half million.

One mile east of Java lies the island of Bali, which despite its nearness to the larger island has developed a culture and charm of its own. Nowhere else in Indonesia are the people so attractive or cheerful, or are native arts and crafts so well developed. Most of the people are Hindus rather than Muslims. The eastern part of the island is dominated by Mount Agung or Bali Peak which is 10,499 feet high. Most of the people live on coastal plains and terraced slopes. Every square inch of rice land is used to the limit.

The people of Indonesia vary widely in culture. Those in the west belong to Malay groups; those to the east are Papuans. Some tribes, such as the Kubus of interior Sumatra and the Dayaks of Borneo, represent low-level ethnographic groups; others are as advanced in civilization as the inhabitants of Java, notably the people of Bali and Lombok directly east of Java, who engage in comparable intensive agriculture.

References on Indonesia

See also the general references on Southeast Asia, Chapter 17.

Broek, Jan O. M.: "The Economic Development of the Outer Provinces of the Netherlands Indies," *Geog. Rev.*, XXX (1940), 187–200.

Fryer, D. W.: "Recovery of the Sugar Industry in Indonesia," *Econ. Geog.*, XXXIII (1957), 171–181.

Harrison, Tom: "Innermost Borneo; Ten Years' Exploration and Research," *Geog. Jour.*, CXXV (1959), 299–311.

Harrison, Tom: "Explorations in Central Borneo," *Geog. Jour.*, CXIV (1949), 129–150.

Hart, G. H. C.: "Recent Development in the Netherlands-Indies," *Geog. Jour.*, XCIX (1942), 81–102.

Schneeberger, Werner F.: "The Kerayan-Kalabit Highland of Central Northeast Borneo," *Geog. Rev.*, XXXV (1945), 544–562.

Van der Kroef, Justus M.: "Indonesia's Economic Future," *Pacific Affairs*, XXXII (1959), 46–72.

25 The Philippines

A Historical Preface / The Physical Base / Crops and Minerals / Luzon / The Visayan Islands / Mindanao / References on the Philippines

A HISTORICAL PREFACE

An explanation of the geography of the Philippine Islands should be preceded by a glimpse of their history. In no other part of Southeast Asia has European penetration had the same effects. Magellan reached the islands in 1521, and Spain took possession in 1565. Although the people of the islands at that time spoke diverse languages, they were already knit together in culture, and the Filipinos had an extensive trade with China and other parts of the Orient.

Trans-Pacific trade dates from 1564, when the first of the famed Manila galleons sailed from the Philippines for Acapulco in Mexico. In addition to the products of the Philippines such as cigars, the galleons carried silk, porcelain, and embroidery from China; spices from the East Indies; drugs, ivory, camphor, and teak from Malaya; and gems from India. In return came European merchandise and Mexican silver dollars for the China trade, widely current in East Asia until the 1930s.

This trans-Pacific trade continued until 1815, and within the span of 2½ centuries, more than

358

a thousand of these rich galleons moved out of the Orient. From Acapulco their cargo was carried over the "China Road" to Mexico City and thence to Europe.

Westbound, these ships followed the trade winds across the Pacific. On their eastbound trip the Spanish took advantage of the prevailing westerlies and followed a great-circle course north of the Hawaiian Islands. This brought them along the California coast, where British privateers—among them Sir Francis Drake—lay in wait for some of the most tempting and romantic prizes ever set before a freebooter. As a protection for these galleons, the Spanish developed ports like San Diego. California thus first gained significance from its relative proximity to Asia.

Spanish interests centered in trade and Chris-

tianity. A unique heritage from Spanish rule in the Philippines is the large proportion (90 per cent) of Christians among the people. Most are Roman Catholic. A little Spanish is still spoken among the wealthy class, for three centuries of colonial rule have left a deep impress. In some particulars this is but a surface covering for the basic Malay culture.

In 1898 Admiral Dewey won the Battle of Manila Bay and introduced a period of American control which has resulted in a veneer of Anglo-Saxon civilization. English is used in the larger cities and by the younger generation, but smaller towns and rural settlements have been less affected. American rule has been unique in the history of European imperialism. Elsewhere colonies have been justified solely for their benefits to the mother country, notably

Many Filipino farmhouses are built on poles in order to protect them against flood and to provide shelter for animals underneath. The sliding shutters reflect the tropical climate. Rice, coconut, and bananas are characteristic crops. (*Fenno Jacobs from Three Lions*)

so with the French. The American position, in strong contrast, has been well stated by United States Secretary of State Elihu Root, in his instructions to the commission that set up a civilian government:

In all forms of government and administrative provisions which they are authorized to prescribe, the commission should bear in mind that the government they are establishing is designed not for our satisfaction or for the expression of our political views, but for the happiness, peace and prosperity of the people of the Philippine Islands, and the measures adopted should be made to conform to their customs, their habits and even their prejudices to the fullest extent consistent with the accomplishment of the indispensable requisites of just and effective government.

A striking illustration of American geographic illiteracy in 1898 is shown in the treaty with Spain by which the United States bought the islands for 20 million dollars. The commissioners had no suitable map and hence incorrectly defined the boundary of what they wished to secure. This resulted in uncertainty concerning a 150-mile string of islands next to Formosa in the north, and the omission of the Sulu Archipelago in the south. A subsequent payment of $100,000 was necessary to include the latter, and two other treaties were necessary before all the Philippines were transferred.

The United States also neglected to take over the Caroline, Marshall, and Mariana Islands, then Spanish. These later came into German hands and were transferred to Japan after the First World War. It was these islands that gave Japan defense in depth during the Second World War and made her defeat so costly. In 1898 they might have been secured at little or no cost.

With American control came free access to the world's richest market. Sugar, copra and coconut oil, abacá or Manila hemp, and tobacco were shipped to the United States in large amounts without the tariff restrictions imposed on goods from adjoining tropical lands. This trade enriched the average Filipino and provided funds for education and public works, but it did not compel agriculture to be efficient. As a result, the yield of sugar per acre was only one-third that of nearby Java.

The American administration of the Philippines was seriously negligent in its lack of an adequate policy for scientific agriculture and forestry, in contrast to the strong support of research elsewhere by Dutch, French, and British governments. Since the islands became in-

Philippine Data [1]

Area	115,707 square miles
Population	27,455,799 (1960 census)
Manila	1,145,723
City of Quezon (capital)	397,374
City of Cebu	259,194
Davao	231,833
Primary and secondary pupils	4,441,350 (1958)
Rice	3,740,000 metric tons (1960)
Corn	1,165,000 " "
Copper	44,630 " "
Chromite	738,555 " "
Iron ore	1,143,874 " "
Gold	408,400 fine ounces (1960)
Silver	527,214 " "

[1] *Britannica Book of the Year*, 1962.

dependent, Philippine products have found it difficult to compete in the general world market. This disadvantage has resulted in agitation for continued economic reciprocity with the United States.

Independence finally came to the Republic of the Philippines on July 4, 1946. Never before had a Western power voluntarily given up its richest colony. An attractive economic future potentially awaits the Philippine Islands. They have fertile soil, numerous minerals, a good location, and room for four times the present population. But many problems must be solved before the Philippines become one of the ranking nations of Southeastern Asia. Preferential treaty relations with the United States end in 1974. If the Philippines have difficulty in selling their sugar and other exports outside the American market, government finances may be seriously impaired. In considering their continued relations with the United States we should remember that the islands are far removed from North America. As seen on a globe, the great-circle route from Seattle to Manila clearly passes near Alaska and directly through Tokyo, rather than straight across the Pacific. Japan is thus becoming an important trade area for the Philippines.

Although the detailed ethnographic background is uncertain, the various people of the Philippines, except for minor tribes, are essentially Mongoloids with a Malaysian culture. They include those who speak various languages or dialects, such as Visayan, Tagalog, and Ilocano, but they are all related as a racial group. Others are the Muslims or Moros, the Negritos, and the "pagan" Igorots, among whom are such groups as the Ifugao and the Bontoc. No less than eighty-seven different dialects are spoken. Tagalog has been proclaimed the national language, but it is used by only one-fourth of the people; English and Spanish still have official status.

Rural settlement types vary from those of shifting agriculture, where there are few permanent habitations, through scattered homesteads, to native villages known as barrios, and nucleated sugar haciendas. The barrios often have a shoestring pattern where adjacent villages are strung along a country road for miles; whereas larger towns focus on the church and market.

The population growth has indeed been phenomenal—among the highest in the world, although a part of the apparent increase may reflect the inaccuracy of earlier census data. When the Spanish arrived in the mid-sixteenth century, the population may have numbered 500,000. In 1800 the islands had about 1½ million people. When America took over in 1898 the number had grown to 7½ million, but when the control of the United States ended forty-eight years later the total was nearly 19 million. By 1960 the population numbered 27½ million, an eighteenfold increase in a century and a half.

While the increase is impressive, the population problem to date has been one of maldistribution rather than overall congestion. Portions of the larger cities are particularly overcrowded. Mindanao and other islands still have large underdeveloped areas. Will the Philippines duplicate Japan or Java? Or is this another Sumatra where poor soils limit agriculture?

Prior to the Second World War there were almost a million people of Chinese ancestry in the islands, more than 100,000 of whom retained Chinese citizenship. Intermarriage has been widespread. As elsewhere, merchants of Chinese ancestry control much of the retail trade, though they are now partly Filipinized.

THE PHYSICAL BASE

If the 7,100 islands of the Philippines were in the New World, they would extend from the latitude of Cuba to the Guianas in South America, a distance equal to that from upper Lake Michigan to the Gulf of Mexico. From the northernmost island one may see the mountains of Taiwan; from the southernmost one can easily look across to Borneo.

Two-thirds of the area is in Luzon and

Mindanao, which cover 40,814 and 36,906 square miles, respectively. Among other islands of importance are Mindoro, Panay, Negros, Cebu, Bohol, Leyte, and Samar, all of them part of the central Visayan group, and Palawan to the west. Only one-third of the islands are important enough to have recognized names, and only one-seventh are inhabited.

Extensive areas are mountainous, and there is probably more level land in interior valleys than on coastal plains. The mountain system of the Philippines is a succession of folds, fault blocks, and volcanic ranges with a north–south trend. In the central area many of the synclinal basins are below sea level and account for the embayed and insular character of the archipelago. There are at least 20 active volcanic craters. One of the most symmetrical cones in the world is that of Mount Mayon in Luzon. The highest elevation is Mount Apo in Mindanao, 9,450 feet. Earthquakes are frequent, but have seldom been destructive, partly because of the more or less flexible type of house construction. Like the islands of Indonesia and Japan, the Philippines are mountains in the process of rising from the sea, with most formations of Cenozoic age. To the southeast is one

of the greatest depths in the ocean, the Mindanao Deep, at 34,400 feet.

Rainfall seasons rather than temperature differences determine the climatic regions of the islands. Only in the extreme north is there a noticeably cooler season. Along the west coast the dry season lasts from November till mid-March, with temperatures in the lower 70s, and continues until mid-June with considerably warmer days though temperatures rarely reach 100°F. The rainy season lasts from June through October and is accompanied by cloudy weather and high relative humidity. This rainfall regime is modified where mountains lie in the path of moisture-bearing winds. The east coasts have a fall and winter maximum but no dry season in summer. In the south, rain is distributed throughout the year. Interior valleys more or less surrounded by mountains are much drier than the coasts. Conditions are everywhere suitable for crops of one type or another, although irrigation may be necessary for a few months.

No part of Asia experiences so many or such destructive typhoons; about twenty cross the islands each year. They rarely visit Mindanao, but the central and northern islands feel the violence of these storms from April to December. Typhoons first appear in the vicinity of the Caroline, Marshall, and Mariana Islands and move west and then north. Their high winds and torrential rainfall bring serious destruction to coconut plantations, fields of sugar cane and abacá, and the irrigation arrangements for rice fields. Shipping likewise suffers.

Forests cover half of the Philippine area. Mangroves grow along the low coasts; tropical rain forests once covered the plains and lower mountains; pine forests grow at higher elevations; and moss-clothed forests cover the highest mountains where clouds commonly shroud the summits. Excellent tropical hardwoods are present in abundance, and there is a considerable export, especially of lauan, often termed Philippine mahogany. Much of the best timber is relatively inaccessible, but is rapidly being exploited. Plantings of true mahogany grow to

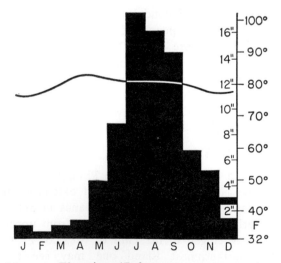

MANILA. Elevation 47 feet, average temperature 81°F, annual precipitation 82 inches. This rainfall graph is the reverse of that for Jakarta in the previous chapter.

Mount Mayon on the island of Luzon is the world's most perfect volcanic cone. It rises to 7,943 feet above the city of Legaspi. (*Courtesy Pan American World Airways*)

a diameter of 20 inches in twenty years. Cogonal savannas have rank grasses which grow to heights of 3 or 4 feet, and occasionally are as tall as 6 feet, with a thick cover, and appear to result from abandoned clearings. These artificial or man-induced grasslands have come to occupy one-fifth of the Philippines.

One-fourth of the land is in farms, but only two-thirds of this area is actually cropped. The potentially arable land is placed at somewhat over half of the total.

CROPS AND MINERALS

Agriculture is characterized by subsistence rice, and by export sugar, coconut products, abacá or Manila hemp, and tobacco. There are few plantations larger than 500 acres, for the Filipinos have discouraged foreign investments.

Rice and tobacco are the usual crops in the fertile valleys. Coconuts are grown on the sandy coastal plains and up the hillsides to elevations of 2,000 feet. Abacá is raised on the moist eastern slopes, especially in Mindanao and southeastern Luzon. Corn and sweet potatoes occupy the drier and unirrigated soils. Rubber production is not important, although there are plantations in Mindanao. Pineapples are canned on the same island and have come to be a large export industry.

In terms of area involved, the ten leading crops, in order, are rice, coconut, corn, abacá, bananas, sugar cane, sweet potatoes, manioc, tobacco, and mango.

Cultivated land is concentrated in central and southern Luzon, southern Panay, Cebu, western Negros, and Leyte, where more than half of the area is in crops. In most of Mindanao, Palawan, and the northern mountains of Luzon, cropland averages less than 10 per cent. The fact that only one-tenth of the farm land appears to be double-cropped is an indication that no land shortage exists. Only one-fourth of all the farm land receives supplementary irrigation water.

Rice is raised on nearly half of the total crop area. Four methods of cultivation are used: flooding fields in which the rice is transplanted from seedbeds; the *sabog* method of broadcast sowing on wet or flooded fields; *secano* cultivation, which is the growing of dry upland rice on plowed fields; and the planting of caingin rice in fire-cleared forest openings, where the individual seeds are placed in small holes made by a stick or other sharp-pointed tool.

Corn is the second great food crop, generally raised on drier land. It accounts for some 15 per cent of the crop area. On Cebu and Bohol, where the soils are derived from coral formations and are largely unirrigable, corn almost entirely replaces rice.

The acreage in coconut palms, amounting to almost 15 per cent, is comparable to that of corn. Production occurs along the shores of most islands except in northeastern Luzon where typhoons are too destructive. The area southeast of Manila has been called one of the largest artificial forests in the world, with 150 million coconut trees. Ground-water supply and elevation are as important as rainfall and soil in determining the location for coconut cultivation. Thus coastal plains are suitable, even though sandy, since ground water from the hilly interior here comes near the surface. Trees begin to bear at the age of six or seven years and continue for forty to sixty years. Unfortunately, the cadang-cadang disease has become an increasingly serious threat to the coconut groves.

The Philippines have usually led the world in the export of coconut oil and are second to Indonesia in copra. Shipments of copra and coconut oil normally amount to a million tons a year. To make copra, the coconut meat is dried in the sun, or over a fire made from the outer husk.

The chief use of coconut oil, one of the principal vegetable oils of commerce, is in soap and margarine. Some steamers on the run from the United States start with enough fuel oil for the round trip; when they reach Manila, half of their tanks are empty. These are then cleaned and filled with coconut oil as cargo for the return trip.

Aside from providing oil and copra for export, the tree supplies food, clothing, and shelter.

Sugar production had a spectacular rise prior to the Second World War when nearly a million tons where shipped annually to the United States. From 2 per cent of the world's total, the islands' share rose to 16 per cent, with forty-four "centrals" or modern steam sugar mills producing centrifugal sugar. Cane is raised on large areas by wealthy landowners and sold to the refining companies, whereas in Java the entire process is in the hands of the same concern; hence, in part, the difference in yields. The volcanic soils of Negros and central Luzon provide ideal conditions, with just the right length of dry season. Yields are lower than in some countries, but partly because of better fertilization, they have increased considerably.

The importance of sugar as a cash crop is shown in the fact that it accounts for over half of all exports. When the islands gained independence, they were given preferred access for sugar to the American market until 1974. Without the quota arrangements, Philippine sugar cannot compete on the world market. Since the industry has been a major source of tax revenue, the political results of removal of support may be serious.

Abacá is one of the unique crops of the Philippines, grown nowhere else so extensively. Abacá, which belongs to the banana family, has fibers 8 to 10 feet in length. This fiber is very strong and elastic and exceptionally resistant to salt water; hence its use for marine cordage. The trade name is Manila hemp. It is chiefly grown on Mindanao and in southern Luzon, where there is a wet tropical climate without strong winds. The production around Davao was originally developed by the Japanese. Another fiber is Philippine sisal.

Tobacco was one of the chief products under Spanish rule but now accounts for only 2 per cent of the crop area. The principal district for tobacco is the Cagayan valley in northern Luzon.

The Philippines are able to produce at least small quantities of such crops as cotton, cassava, coffee, fruits, forest products, kapok, and rubber. But these are the very items of which surplus supplies are available elsewhere.

Too much of the agriculture is designed for export markets; export crops occupy one-third of the agricultural land. It has been estimated that half of the population obtain their liveli-hood from coconut products, sugar, abacá, to-bacco, and embroidery. As a result, the islands do not feed themselves, and an important part of the imports are foodstuffs, particularly of American-style foods. If the market for the present export crops is curtailed, a considerable period of American preferential tariffs may be necessary in order to forestall economic distress.

The mining industry has had a spectacular growth. Prior to the Second World War, the Philippines produced more gold than Alaska or any American state except California, with an output of a half million ounces. Silver is usually associated with gold in equal amounts by weight. Most of the yield is from the Benguet district near Baguio in northern Luzon.

Iron-ore production has developed rapidly, with 1 million metric tons a year shipped to

The Philippines supply much of the world's marine cordage, made from Manila hemp, or abacá. Mindanao and southern Luzon lead in production. (*Ewing Galloway*)

Japan. Camarines Norte in eastern Luzon, the island of Samar, and Surigao in eastern Mindanao are the areas of production; Surigao has an estimated reserve of a billion tons. The latter are lateritic ores with an iron content of 48 per cent, low silica, sulfur, and phosphorus, but unfortunately, too much nickel, chrome, and aluminum. The ores are easily mined and are near tidewater.

Chromium was not discovered until 1935. Since then, the Philippines have come to rank fifth with 10 per cent of the world output. The Zambales deposit in western Luzon is one of the largest in the world, with 10 million tons of ore, much of it averaging 50 per cent chromium oxide. Manganese is very extensive but of medium quality. Shipments to the United States started in 1935. Copper, lead, and zinc are present, but not in sufficient quantities to make export attractive.

Petroleum is lacking, and coal is negligible. The coal is lignite of Oligocene age and not suitable for smelting purposes. Unfortunately there appears to be no basis for a domestic metallurgical industry; coke must be imported or the ores exported. In fact, it is doubtful that the Philippines can soon develop heavy industry. The metals are present, but suitable coal and oil are lacking, and there are few large hydroelectric sites.

Communications in this island world have always presented a problem. Shipping has long been important. The American occupation brought the beginnings of a good highway network, interisland steamers, and air services. While facilities are still inadequate, these communications have helped the Philippines to avoid excessive sectionalism.

The islands enjoyed a considerable measure of postwar prosperity. This was in part due to large American payments for war damage and a continuation of preferential markets, but was also attributable to the basic assets of the area.

LUZON

Within the Philippines are many divergent environments and types of land utilization. In

Manila lies on both sides of the Pasig River. The veneer of American and Spanish culture is here thicker than in provincial towns. (*Ewing Galloway*)

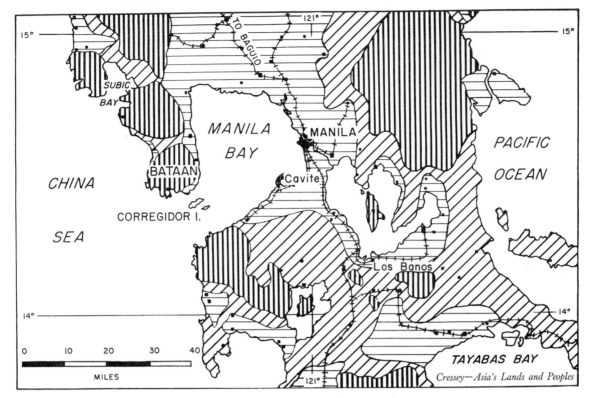

Manila is the metropolitan center for the Philippines, with a population four times that of its nearest rival. Plains are shown in horizontal lines; hills are represented by diagonal lines; mountains are ruled vertically.

general, the landscape pattern is finely cut, as are many of the regional subdivisions. An analysis of geographic regions should consider the climatic contrasts between the east and west coasts, the distribution of coconuts and abacá, and topography. The simplest scheme is to deal separately with Luzon, the Visayan Islands in the center, and Mindanao. This threefold regionalization omits the Sulu archipelago in the south and Palawan to the west, steppingstones to Borneo.

Luzon is the largest, best known, and most important of the islands. Even here wide contrasts exist between the highly developed central agricultural plains and the less changed lands in the mountains. Primitive Negritos using bows and arrows live only 50 miles from Manila.

Two mountain ranges extend into northern Luzon. Between them is the Cagayan valley, one of the most important agricultural areas in the Philippines. The subregion looks northward and is cut off from Manila by rough terrain. Its rich river-bank soils have made it the leading tobacco district. Because of the intermontane position, there is a considerable dry period in every year.

West of the Cagayan valley lies the forested Mountain Province. The elevation averages 4,000 feet, so that the climate is temperate. Here is the highest peak in Luzon, Mount Pulog, which rises to 9,400 feet. The highland city of Baguio has become the principal mountain resort of the islands, frequented during the hot, dry season from mid-March through May. Within the province are the Bontoc and Banaue

Few terraced lands anywhere are more spectacular than the Igorot and Ifugao areas of northern Luzon, where flooded fields follow the contour, tier upon tier. Such terracing is uncommon elsewhere in the Philippines. (*Fenno Jacobs from Three Lions*)

areas, famous for the rice terraces of the Igorots and Ifugao, which cling to the steep, rainy side of the valleys. Here too is the major gold-mining district of the islands. The northeast coast of Luzon is also mountainous and backward. Northwest Luzon holds the densely populated Ilocano coastal area.

Most of the cropland of Luzon lies in the central lowland around Manila Bay and northward to Lingayen Gulf; here half of the land is under cultivation. Rice is the great crop; coconuts are grown in the southern part and sugar cane in the north.

Along the west coast is the rugged and densely forested Zambales area, which terminates to the south in the Bataan peninsula and the island of Corregidor.

The southern peninsulas of Luzon are a mixture of mountains, volcanoes, and interior plains. The commercial crops are coconuts and abacá.

Manila is the chief city of the Philippines, with a population in the metropolitan area of well over two million. This is the homeland of the Tagalog people. The city is situated on the delta of the Pasig River where it enters the broad but shallow Manila Bay. The bay provides one of the world's finest harbors, and the modern port has been developed behind break-waters at one side of the river, with an extensive area built up by dredged mud from the harbor. Interisland vessels dock along the river. An old walled city known as Intramuros is a relic of Spanish days, affording a contrast to the conspicuous penetration of American cultural forms. Manila's chief industries relate to the export and import trades, and to shipping. Large-scale industrialization has developed in the suburbs.

Despite its importance as an entrepôt in the Philippines and for American trade, Manila does not duplicate the regional commerce of British Hong Kong or Singapore. In terms of American influence in the Pacific, the Philippines represent the end of the line.

THE VISAYAN ISLANDS

Although the numerous Visayan islands have but half the area of Luzon, their population is nearly as large. In several districts over 50 per cent of the land is cultivated, and population densities are higher than anywhere else in the Philippines. Mountains and plains in the Visayan islands are roughly in the proportion of 2 to 1.

Harvesting time on an upland farm. Only the head of the grain is cut. Stalks are left to dry, and then are cut or burned. (*Courtesy: Caltex*)

The small island of Cebu dominates the Visayans. The black-clay coral soil of the island is mostly incapable of irrigation and too dry for rice, so that corn is the staple food, and coconuts the export. The climate is healthy and drier than elsewhere; the rainfall is about 40 inches; and the people are very industrious. Cebu has the densest population of any province in the Philippines, and its port, the City of Cebu, ranks next to metropolitan Manila. The adjoining island of Negros has fertile volcanic soils which have helped it to become the major sugar producer.

While English, Spanish, and Tagalog are the official languages of the country, the dialect spoken by the largest percentage of people is Visayan.

Agricultural conditions on the island of Cebu have been described by a soils technologist, Robert Pendleton.[1]

Long before we reached the harbor, it was clear why the Cebuanos' main food is corn in place of rice; the very shallow soil offers little opportunity for the raising of lowland rice. Once

[1] Robert L. Pendleton: "Glimpses of Hinterlands," *The Philippine Agriculturist*, XXIII, no. 10 (1935), 829–830.

ashore and out into the suburbs back of the city, the austerity of the conditions was still better realized. While the porous coral limestone which covers more or less deeply the older and more compact geological formations of much of the island does weather into a heavy black rich soil, the land slopes so steeply that certainly a good deal of the rainfall must run off the surface, while the limestone is so porous that much of the water which soaks into the soil cannot be retained there but percolates to great depths. This means it is often impossible in many places in the uplands to obtain even domestic supplies of water from wells.

In the course of the trip across the island, via Camp 7, to Toledo, we were repeatedly amazed at the steepness of fields cultivated to annual crops. It was, therefore, not difficult to believe that a farmer near Cebu fell *off* his field, breaking a leg.

The thinness of the soil, and the limestone make it impractical to terrace the fields. The black, granular soil even in the dry state naturally very easily works down the slopes, and the corn stalks laid across the slope do not retard erosion very much. Soil erosion is naturally a very serious problem, and in Cebu in numbers of places, there is no longer any soil at all on the limestone. It is fortunate that trees including mangoes seem to thrive on these steep soils, with their roots going deep down into the cracks and crevices of the rocks.

MINDANAO

Much of Mindanao is undeveloped and poorly mapped, and the sparse population of the interior is in sharp contrast to that of Luzon. The island is frequently referred to as a land of promise, the frontier of the Philippines, but large areas are ill suited to colonization.

Most of the people live along the coast and near the few towns, although land not too steep to plow is most abundant inland. Extensive plains with relatively extensive swamps occur

This is the Moro fishing village of Palang on the island of Jolo. (*Courtesy Standard Oil Company of New Jersey*)

in Cotabato and the Agusan valley on either side of the north–south mountain axis. Settlement possibilities include upland areas from 1,000 to 5,000 feet above sea level, climatically suitable for Europeans. Soils in the vicinity of the numerous volcanoes have been enriched by falls of ash so that their fertility is good. Alluvial soils are also rich, but elsewhere leaching has markedly reduced the fertility.

The extensive forests provide large and excellent timber reserves, except where they have been burned over by caingin cultivation and replaced by wiry cogon grass. These grasslands supply the food for a considerable cattle industry. Iron ore, gold, and some coal are the mineral resources now in production.

Abacá and ramie fibers were once extensively cultivated by the Japanese around Davao in the south, but production has declined. Rubber is grown in limited amounts near Zamboanga. Bananas and excellent pineapples for export are raised. Copra forms an important export.

References on the Philippines

See also the general references on Southeast Asia, Chapter 17.

Cutshall, Alden: "Mineral Resources of the Philippine Islands," *Scientific Monthly,* LIV (1942), 295–302.

McIntyre, Wallace E.: "The Retail Pattern of Manila," *Geog. Rev.,* XLV (1955), 66–80.

Pendleton, Robert L.: "Land Utilization and Agriculture of Mindanao, Philippine Islands," *Geog. Rev.,* XXXII (1942), 180–210.

Spencer, Joseph E.: "Abacá and the Philippines," *Econ. Geog.,* XXVII (1951), 95–106.

*Spencer, Joseph E.: *Land and People in the Philippines,* Berkeley, Calif.: University of California Press (1952).

Spencer, Joseph E.: "The Cities of the Philippines," *Jour. Geog.,* LVII (1958), 288–294.

*Ullman, Edward L.: "Trade Centers and Tributary Areas of the Philippines," *Geog. Rev.,* L (1960), 203–218.

Wernstedt, Frederick L.: "Cebu: Focus of Philippine Interisland Trade," *Econ. Geog.,* XXXII (1956), 336–346.

THE SOUTH ASIAN REALM

Monsoon Asia reaches its climax in India, Pakistan, and Ceylon, with its alternation of moisture and aridity, of lush vegetation and withered fields; all seasons are warm. Population presses on the limited resource potentials.

"The bulk of the village population gets only the most meager living in terms of food, clothing, and shelter. Urban factory labor lives no better, possibly worse. Without seeing Indians in their villages, towns, and cities, it is difficult for a Westerner to visualize the extent and effect of their poverty. And if the average American visitor wants to remain sensitive to the conditions in which the masses of the people live, it is well for him not to stay in the country long. Very quickly the want, the disease, the discomfort, the misery, become only accepted facts." (W. Norman Brown: *The United States and India and Pakistan,* Cambridge, Mass.: Harvard University Press (1953), 15. Quoted by permission.)

Bullocks in Bengal. (*Cecil Beaton, courtesy British Information Services*)

26 The Subcontinent

Cultural Contributions / Historical Developments / International Relations / Population Problems / References on South Asia

CULTURAL CONTRIBUTIONS

South Asia has produced one of the world's rich cultures. India's heritage is comparable with that of China or Greece. Indian literature is one of the world's oldest and richest, and architecture and the fine arts date back to the third millennium B.C. Few buildings in the world are more magnificent than the Taj Mahal in Agra.

The fact that the West may be unaware of the better qualities of Indian culture should not blind our eyes to its importance. To an extent unknown elsewhere, Hindu life revolves around philosophy and religion, around man's relation to the universe. Systematic introspection has been practiced in India for centuries. Certain attitudes of mind and ethical ideals are peculiar to India; one of them is intellectual tolerance. To each person only a facet of truth is visible, just as different views of a diamond reveal different colors. We see the universe only in terms that our minds are capable of understanding; hence no one is wholly right, and no one is wholly wrong.

Hinduism's unique qualities may have kept its point of view from wider acceptance by other civilizations. The exaltation of the quiet life has prevented it from dealing with obvious evils about it. Poverty and disease which impress Westerners carry a different meaning in India. In a conversation between the author and a wealthy landlord about the economic welfare of his tenants, he remarked, "If my tenants have spiritual happiness, nothing else matters."

Other parts of the world have developed more active philosophies, but in a hectic world the West should increasingly look with tolerance and interest upon Indian concepts of peace. The philosopher, Will Durant, has summarized the things we might gain by a more receptive attitude.[1]

As invention, industry and trade bind the continents together, or as they fling us into conflict with Asia, we shall study its civilizations more closely, and shall absorb, even in enmity, some of

[1] Will Durant: *The Story of Civilization,* New York: Simon and Schuster (1935), 633. Quoted by permission.

The Ajanta caves, near Hyderabad in south central India, date from the second century B.C. to the seventh century; the caves number thirty in all. This is the main entrance. (*Courtesy Indian State Railways*)

its ways and thoughts. Perhaps, in return for conquest, arrogance and spoliation, India will teach us the tolerance and gentleness of the mature mind, the quiet content of the unacquisitive soul, the calm of the understanding spirit, and a unifying, pacifying love for all living things.

Indian civilization is a continuous and mature stream. The present century of dramatic change should involve not a hasty discarding of the traditional, but rather a modifying of the inherited to meet the needs of the modern world. India's culture is bound to persist, and we need increasingly to understand the wealth of its human and environmental resources. To this task geography provides the preface.

The origins of Hinduism predate its arrival in India, long before the Christian era. It has always been an amorphous religion without clear theology, and with so many variations that it has been able to attract different people. In its philosophical aspect, sometimes called Brahmanism, it involves rituals and symbolism which represent truth and right and their opposites, and the nature of the soul and its reunion with the supreme being.

Hinduism, rather than race or language, forms the most solid basis for national consciousness in India. Caste is Hinduism's most obvious symbol, with some 2,300 divisions of people and their associated social and economic taboos. Brahmans are at the top; at the bottom are the 50 million noncaste or "untouchables." Some of the latter have been able to acquire considerable wealth and political power, but they are the exceptions. Urban life no longer makes it possible for one group to avoid physical contact or even the shadow of another, but caste remains a firm restriction in marriage. Gandhi did a great deal to reduce the importance of caste, and social differences are outlawed in the Indian constitution, but the system is still a rigorous factor in much of life, especially in towns and rural areas.

Among the aspects of Hinduism which have geographic significance is the reverence for cattle, of which there are 200 million in India. Many are emaciated; few find enough food or are strong enough to work all day; and their sheer numbers reduce the available acreage of food for man.

Alongside Hindu culture are many other social and religious philosophies, for the subcontinent is quite as diverse as Western Europe, possibly more so. Few generalizations can apply to India as a whole; much less to India, Pakistan, Nepal, and Ceylon. Ten million people are Christians; the faith was brought to India in the first century. Another 6 million are Sikhs. There are nine major religions and as many as two hundred languages or dialects, twenty of which are spoken by a million people each. Although Buddhism originated here, only traces remain, chiefly in Nepal, on the south slope of the Himalaya, and in the island of Ceylon.

Muslims in the realm number 100 million, largely but not entirely in Pakistan. Whereas Hinduism was built on a caste-oriented society, Islam is democratic and without social stratification. Muslims of the subcontinent look to Mecca for their spiritual inspiration, although their interpretation of its significance may not be exactly that of the Arabs. While Islam reached India shortly after the death of Mohammed, its political impact dates from around 1000, when Afghan conquerors overran the north.

Amid the contrasts and confusion of the realm one must be careful to give proper values to the many aspects of Indian and Pakistanian life. No single volume or observation gained from a casual tour can embrace them all. Why is this land so confusing? Why are the realities of poverty in such contrast to the material resources and the spiritual achievements?

Some of these contrasts have been described by Vera Anstey.[2]

India must not be judged by its great ports and other industrial areas. These latter are the scene of striking anachronisms, symptomatic of the direct impingement of the modern on the medieval.

[2] Vera Anstey: *The Economic Development of India,* London: Longmans (1929), 1–2. Quoted by permission.

There are two Delhis, the old crowded city shown here and the new administrative center around the capital. (*Courtesy Ford Foundation*)

In Bombay, for instance, the motorcar—driven possibly by a Parsee lady—dodges in and out between foot-passengers and bullock-carts; the latest product of the universities jostles with the fakir, and broad and beautiful streets look out to the narrow alleys of an Eastern bazaar. In a few moments one may pass from the luxurious dancing hall of the Taj Mahal Hotel to dimly lighted back-streets whose pavements are covered with the sleeping figures of the inhabitants of the chawls, i.e., working-class dwellings, or from the operating theater of an up-to-date hospital to the haunts of emaciated, disabled beggars, who drag their possibly self-mutilated limbs through the noisome dust and dirt of the gutters. Mechanical inventions and the materialistic outlook have begun to leaven India, but it is necessary to realize the immense size and importance of what still remains unleavened. The crumbling of the authority of caste, the loosened bands of religion, the adoption of the Western "economic" outlook, and acceptance of Western methods and ideals have as yet affected only a tiny percentage of the people. The masses undoubtedly still live in the material surroundings and retain the social outlook of medievalism.

The two centuries of British occupation have left a veneer of European culture, including the widespread use of English—the only language generally understood. Beneath the imposed political unity remain diverse loyalties of race, religion, and tradition. Their strength was evidenced by the explosive separation of India

Some of the ancient history of the Subcontinent has been revealed by the archaeological excavations at Taxila near Rawalpindi in the northwest. This was a Buddhist monastery. (*Courtesy Pakistan Consulate General, New York City*)

and Pakistan, and they still influence the continued provincial changes within each country.

India, Pakistan, Ceylon, and the Himalayan countries form an isolated subcontinent, a realm as large and populous as Western Europe. So far as effective communications are concerned, the Himalaya might as well be the Arctic Ocean; in fact aerial access would be easier if the mountains were replaced by a frozen sea. The long seacoast is, for the most part, harborless. Not a railroad crosses the borders of the realm, and no more than three or four roads.

Few other parts of Asia are so detached or culturally isolated. The claim of the realm to be a subcontinent is quite as justified as that of Europe. Since the peninsula as a whole can no longer be termed Indian, it is here referred to as Indo-Pakistan, or Pak-India. Taken together with adjacent countries, it forms the South Asian realm.

HISTORICAL DEVELOPMENTS

Most of our knowledge of early India comes from the dry northwest. Archaeological research in the upper Indus valley indicates that settlement dates back to at least 5000 B.C. Following early Stone Age developments came a bronze culture centering in farming villages. Still earlier, there were dark-skinned people akin to early Negroid stocks of Africa and Melanesia, some of whom still live as aborigines in the central part of the peninsula.

Two of the famous later sites in the Indus valley were Taxila, near Rawalpindi, and Mohenjo-Daro, near Karachi, both apparently occupied by city-building Dravidian people. About the same time, pastoral and agricultural Aryan people spread into the Ganges valley. Out of the mixing of these two groups came the development of Hindu civilization, with the main culture hearth in the Indo-Gangetic

Plain, understandably known as Hindustan.

The Dravidians, the Aryans, and all subsequent invaders poured into South Asia from the northwest, entering through various gaps in the mountains such as the Khyber and Bolan Passes. During the past three thousand years these peoples have included Persian strains, Greeks following the conquests of Alexander, and various peoples from the direction of Afghanistan, such as the Moguls.

Successive waves of immigrants have pushed across Pak-India to the south and east, generally forming a gradual intermixture with the previous inhabitants but sometimes surrounding and isolating them. While many people have moved on to Southeast Asia, the chief migration out of northwest India was that of the gypsies, who appear to have left about the year 1000.

John Brush has described the advance of Islam into South Asia as follows: [3]

The spread of Islam into the subcontinent may be likened to a flowing of a tide from the northwest, its depth still discernible until 1947 in terms of percentage distribution of adherents. The highest percentage of Moslems (virtually 100 per cent) is found today in Afghanistan and Baluchistan. The tide flooded the Sind and Punjab plains (50 to 90 per cent) and passed through the eastern Punjab gap, a strip of land bounded on the north by the Himalaya and on the south by the Thar desert (25–50 per cent), and flowed with diminishing force down the Ganges valley (10–15 per cent) or turned southward across the Vindhya hills into the Dekkan (10–15 per cent). The delta

[3] John E. Brush, in Norton Ginsburg (ed.): *The Pattern of Asia*, Englewood Cliffs, N.J.: Prentice-Hall (1958), 477–478. Quoted by permission.

The towering Gaya Temple is one of the holiest shrines of Buddhism, for here Gautama Buddha experienced his enlightenment. It is near Patna, in Bihar. (*Courtesy Indian State Railways*)

region of Bengal stands out with its anomalous preponderance of Moslems (50–80 per cent) at a great distance from the source of the tide.

While Muslims are a religious rather than a racial group, those in West Pakistan represent relatively late immigrants who brought Islam with them, whereas the Muslims of East Pakistan are earlier inhabitants, once Buddhist and Hindu, who were converted to Islam a few centuries ago. In Quaker terms, the inhabitants of West and East Pakistan might be described as "birthright" and "convinced" Muslims, respectively. Herein lie some basic problems of political unity. West Pakistan speaks Urdu; the East uses Bengali.

The bulk of North India and Pakistan is now occupied by Aryan people, speaking Indo-European languages related to Sanskrit, such as Hindi or Urdu; the southern third of the peninsula is inhabited by Dravidians and mixed groups, who use Telegu or Tamil. Those in the north tend to have light brown skins, reflecting their Caucasoid background; on the other hand, people in the south may be nearly black, showing their descent from an early Negroid stock.

Among the earliest recorded events is the invasion of Alexander the Great, who passed down the Indus valley in 327 B.C. In A.D. 1001, Delhi was captured by Mahmud of Ghazni in Afghanistan, and Muslim rule continued until 1398, when the Mongol conqueror, Tamerlane, sacked Delhi. His descendant, Baber, was the first of the great Mogul rulers, whose brilliant period continued until 1707.

European contacts began with the arrival of Vasco da Gama's three small Portuguese vessels at Calicut in 1498 and continued under the Dutch, French, and English. In 1757 the British East India Company acquired control over the province of Bengal, to which other areas were later added.

Prior to independence and the separation of India and Pakistan in 1948, India was made up of the 12 provinces of British India and some 548 princely states. The former comprised two-thirds of the country; the latter were a miscel-

laneous group ranging in size down to 1 square mile. The name India could be used only as a general term, for there was no single sovereign government. Small Portuguese and French possessions along the coasts also remained as souvenirs of earlier conquests.

The political pattern of preindependence India represented a crystallization of the chaos that England found, and produced, when the East India Company carried on its operations in the seventeenth and eighteenth centuries. The Mogul dynasty reached its peak under Akbar, who ruled from 1560 to 1605. Even then the southern peninsula was divided among independent Muslim and Hindu states. The collapse of the dynasty was due as much to internal as to external factors.

The British came originally for trade rather than conquest. As warehouses were established along the coast, the East India Company entered into political relations with whoever ruled the region. When civil difficulties arose, the British found it necessary to employ police to guard their possessions, and from this they expanded to militia, which were used to aid their political favorites. Successive events, in part accidental, in part manipulated, gave the East India Company and its militarily supported native rulers increased political control. In places this expansion was piecemeal, the frontier advancing as it was expedient to quell disturbances in bordering territory; elsewhere whole provinces were transferred to British administration, either under their official Mogul governor or under rebellious leaders.

The pattern was changed from flux to fixation by Warren Hastings in 1817 to 1818. In some areas, widespread consolidation of petty kingdoms had just occurred; elsewhere territorial chaos was still the rule. After the Sepoy Rebellion, in 1858, control of British India was transferred from the East India Company to the British crown, and Queen Victoria became Empress of India in 1877. Since the British advanced from the sea, modern political geography has been quite unlike that of ancient times when invaders came from the northwest.

The South Asian realm includes three republics—India, Pakistan, and Ceylon, all members of the British Commonwealth—and three kingdoms—Nepal, Bhutan, and Sikkim, the last two being under Indian protection. Between India and Pakistan lies the disputed area of Kashmir. Specific problems of each country are considered in later chapters.

INTERNATIONAL RELATIONS

Although foreign contacts have often played an important role in Indian history, few areas of Asia have developed in greater isolation. On all sides the subcontinent is bordered by effective barriers: almost impassable mountains, thick tropical forests or the complete absence of vegetation, and harborless seacoasts which are either clifflike or fringed with sand bars and coral.

On the landward side no invasion has ever reached Hindustan from the north. Few passes cross the 1,500-mile-long Himalaya, and all are closed by snow for months. Although invading armies never conquered India from this frontier, Tibeto-Chinese culture did spill down the slopes, and as a result, much of the south face of the Himalaya follows Lama Buddhism rather than Hinduism. The significant cultural limit lies along the Terai swamp belt at the base of the mountains rather than along their crest.

The northeastern frontier, though lower than the Himalaya, is almost as impenetrable. In place of the east–west parallel ranges in the north, here structures extend roughly north–south for 600 miles. The topography is much less rugged than the ranges which culminate in Mount Everest, but the wet monsoon moves up each linear valley giving it a dense forest. The combination of ridge and jungle has given India a secure protection on the side of Burma. As an overland commercial neighbor, China did not exist.

The northwest border, now along West Pakistan, is different. Aridity replaces humidity, and while the topography remains rugged, there is no barrier of snow or forest. Two easy gateways lead through the Sulaiman and Kirthar Ranges—the Khyber and Bolan Passes—but in the 1,000-mile frontier there are hundreds of camel trails. Vigorous migratory people occupied nearby Afghanistan and the countries beyond; time after time they burst into what is now West Pakistan and northern India. This was the avenue for the Aryan invaders five millenniums ago and for the Dravidians before them.

India's isolation by sea has been even more striking. No significant contacts for trade or culture were made before the arrival of European merchants in the seventeenth century. Arab sailors used the seasonal monsoon winds to link Bombay and Zanzibar, and Malay seamen came to the east coast, but few Indians ever developed a seafaring tradition.

The coast line of India and Pakistan, which measures some 3,500 miles, is almost devoid of natural harbors or sheltering islands. Strong winds create rough seas, and many ports are without shelter, so that ships must anchor several miles offshore and transfer freight into lighters, later to be carried through the surf by porters.

The west coast has alternating rock walls and sand bars, and the few river mouths are unusable. Karachi was merely a shallow lagoon until protected by a breakwater. Bombay (meaning "good bay" in Portuguese) is the only first-class harbor. Farther south a line of barrier beaches and lagoons provide only very shallow harbors, as at Calicut. Goa is an exception, but its former Portuguese ownership cut it off from the interior.

The east coast is little better, for it is lined with mangrove swamps and coral reefs. Madras is the main port, but the city lies on a straight coast line and the harbor is entirely dependent on breakwaters. The deltas along the mouths of the Ganges and Brahmaputra are bordered by shallow water far into the sea and have extensive swamps on the landward side. Calcutta, up the Hooghly River, though somewhat more fortunate, depends upon continuous dredging for its harbor. East Pakistan has developed a port at Chalna, south of Khulna, but only at great expense. Not until the shore swings southward along the Arakan coast is there the possibility of a good harbor, as at Chittagong.

None of these ports were developed by Indians seeking foreign contacts; instead, they grew in response to outside markets or foreigners seeking raw materials. Pre-British India never looked seaward, nor did any significant culture reach it across the water.

Even more than China, India developed in economic isolation. Both countries were self-sufficient; both were surrounded by inferior peoples; neither country had more than a few who ventured far; neither was prepared for the tidal wave of European materialism.

While the physical geography of the realm remains constant, many international relations have now changed. The Republic of India is today among the great powers: second in numbers, sixth in area, and fifth in gross national product. British control has gone, although the Commonwealth remains, but new contacts have developed overseas and over the mountains. American financial and technical aid counters Soviet Communistic ideologic penetration. Pakistan is smaller than India but her population places her in the top half dozen nations. The new nation is conscious of its place in the greater Muslim world.

South Asia may lie on the other side of the world from the United States, but jet planes make it accessible within hours. From New York eastward to Bombay is about the same distance as from San Francisco westward to Calcutta; yet for both journeys ships must make long detours so that the airline distance of 8,000 miles becomes a distance by sea of nearly 10,000 miles. Equally short is the air route across the Arctic, for the great-circle course which links the centers of population in each country lies directly over the pole.

Where overland travel from Moscow or Peking to Delhi was once impractical, planes now fly directly. Trans-border roads and railways, however, are for the far future, and heavy commerce will continue to move around the periphery of Asia by water. Intellectually, the Himalaya no longer isolate India and Pakistan on the north, and the ocean has ceased to be a cultural frontier.

For two centuries, South Asia has been a British satellite. A veneer of language and government tradition remains, but increasingly the several countries are developing their own orientation. Their self-sufficiency may considerably alter international trade, particularly as Commonwealth ties diminish.

The Indian Ocean was once essentially a British lake, economically tributary to the United Kingdom. From Cape Town to Singapore, British trade in British ships bound for British ports dominated all activity. The only important exception was the Netherlands Indies. India and Pakistan are now the most significant of lands bordering this ocean, both in population and productivity. It may be a half century before industrial developments make the countries economically self-sufficient and the center of a commercial sphere of their own. When that time comes, the realm should be one of the half dozen major economic units of the world.

The early trade of India was limited by inadequate internal communications and the difficult routes to Europe either around Africa by sea or overland via Iran. Muslins and gems were traded for gold. The Suez Canal changed part of the picture in 1869, when bulky agricultural products of low value could reach Europe. Until 1931 India was the world's greatest market for the precious metals. Most of them were hoarded and taken out of circulation. Lyde states that, since the days of the Roman Empire, India has consumed 60 per cent of the world's gold production and 40 per cent of its silver.[4]

Two trade avenues led outward from pre-British India, neither very significant. One crossed the northwestern frontier to inner Asia and China; the other contact was provided by

[4] L. W. Lyde: *The Continent of Asia,* New York: St Martin's Press (1933), 473.

The Municipal Building in Bombay is a souvenir of British rule. The city, with its fine port, serves as India's chief gateway to Europe. (*Courtesy American President Lines*)

Arab sailors who traded along the coasts westward to Africa and eastward sometimes as far as Canton. It is a commentary on India's isolation that her most important export to China was not goods but a religion, Buddhism, which traveled with the lightest of baggage.

Throughout the British period, India normally exported more than she brought in. Imports were predominantly consumers' goods such as cotton textiles and machinery, while exports consisted of agricultural commodities and mineral raw materials such as cotton, jute, tea, oil seeds, leather, and manganese. India was the standard example of an underdeveloped country with raw material exports and manufactured imports.

Since the industrialization which followed the Second World War, foreign trade has undergone a marked change. The individual purchasing power of the peasant is low, but the aggregate bulk is so large that India and Pakistan now rank as one of the major foreign trade areas. India now imports producers' goods such as tools, metals, chemicals, crude oil, and raw materials, as well as grains, to such an extent that the balance of trade tends to be unfavorable. Great Britain continues to lead in Indian and Pakistan foreign trade, closely followed by the United States.

The greatest transit port of the South Asian realm is Colombo in Ceylon, point of call for thousands of boats traveling from Suez to Singapore. In the number of ships, Colombo handles as many as all the several ports of India and Pakistan together, although most of the vessels take on or discharge very little cargo. Bombay and Calcutta are rivals for first place among Indian ports. Bombay usually leads in value of cargo, import tonnage, and number of ships; Calcutta is ahead in export tonnage. Karachi in Pakistan is the third port in South Asia, followed by Madras.

India and Pakistan will produce an increasingly large share of their own industrial needs, and this will alter present international relations. One may question, however, whether the overland neighbors will outweigh those across the seas. As internal prosperity increases, purchasing power will rise, and a rich subcontinent will be a better world customer than a poor India or Pakistan.

POPULATION PROBLEMS

Well over 600 million people live in South Asia; in numbers they are second only to the teeming millions of China, more than all the people of Europe combined—one person out of every five on earth. In terms of total area, this means an average in excess of 300 people per square mile; in terms of food-producing cropland, the density in many areas exceeds 2,000 to each square mile, and in places the rural population may reach twice that figure. Both figures are far above the world average.

The growth of the population is impressive. Toward the end of the sixteenth century, the population of India was approximately 100 million; by the first census of 1872 the number rose to 206 million. The population in 1941, including both British India and the Indian States, was 389 million. By 1961 the combined population of India and Pakistan had risen to 532 million. Such totals must be viewed against careful statements early in the century that the area was saturated with people and that population would soon become stabilized. While the population of South Asia is behind that of China, both are indeed phenomena.

India's rate of population growth amounted to 21.5 per cent in the decade 1951 to 1961, as compared with 13.3 per cent in the previous ten years. This large increase in the rate of growth apparently reflects the availability of public health services and sanitation, and a general rise in prosperity. As O. H. K. Spate has pointed out,[5]

It seems broadly true that social customs practically place a premium on reproduction, so that when better times do come the flow of births is as overwhelming as is mortality in bad years; there is thus a close, direct correspondence between harvests and mortality.

Half of the people live in the northern lowland, which occupies but one-fifth of the area. In the lower Ganges valley, population densities exceed 2,000 per square mile, while parts of the desert and delta jungles are essentially empty. Only one-fifth of the total number of people live in cities of 5,000 or over, for India and Pakistan are the most rural of all large countries in the world. Literacy is under 20 per cent, with the largest percentages in Bengal and Madras.

Two factors guide population distributions: level alluvium and adequate water. Densities are high in the rice lands of the Ganges lowland and along many coasts. The Indus lowland has fair soil but is too dry for agriculture except where irrigated. The emptiest areas are the arid lands of the northwest and the higher mountains.

If one appreciates land-man adjustments, one may infer physical features from a study of the rural population map, or one may judge the carrying capacity of an area if one understands its terrain, soil, and climate. In a long-settled realm like South Asia, population is in close conformity with environmental potentials; only as technology changes are distributions apt to be rearranged.

Apparently, one of India's and Pakistan's greatest problems, like China's and Japan's, is agricultural overpopulation. Strenuous efforts

[5] O. H. K. Spate: *India and Pakistan,* New York: Dutton (1954), 99. Quoted by permission.

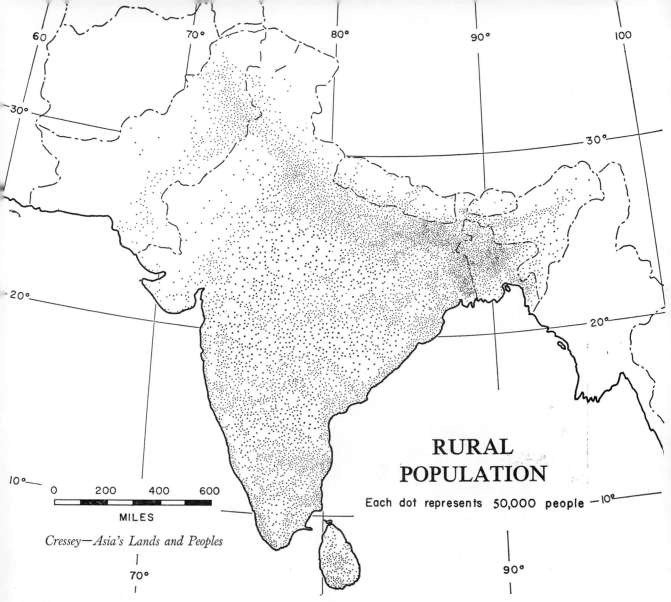

RURAL
POPULATION

Each dot represents 50,000 people

MILES

0   200   400   600

Cressey—Asia's Lands and Peoples

India, Pakistan, Nepal, and Ceylon account for 600 million people, one-fifth of all mankind. To understand the pattern of settlement is to understand the physical environment and land-use development.

have been made to increase the food supply, but population grows at about the same rate. Famines and disease once took a tremendous toll, but in the twentieth century, railways and efficient grain distribution under government supervision have gone a long way toward eliminating starvation.

The rural landscape is dominated by small villages. In predivision India, settlements with less than 500 people numbered 450,000, and

there were 200,000 more villages with populations under 5,000. Such villages accounted for 80 per cent of the total population, and for the most part were connected by trails rather than roads.

In many places these settlements are tied to the water supply; elsewhere they represent the need for defense, as is shown either by an enclosing wall or by the closely packed houses with blank outer walls. Within each village

Most of the north is inhabited by Aryan people, in contrast to the Dravidians of the south. This man is from Rajasthan. (*Courtesy Trans World Airlines*)

there may be separate quarters for the various castes. Many settlement patterns are linear, extending along higher ground on natural levees or on the edge of a bluff, or following a line of springs at the base of a hill. Elsewhere an area of unproductive laterite amid good soil may be the site of a village.

Where villages have occupied the same site for centuries, the gradual accumulation of debris has built a low mound. In areas subject to flooding this becomes a security asset so that other sites are less attractive.

House characteristics vary from region to region. Some areas have mud walls and thatch roofs; elsewhere brick or wood is used with tile roofs. Protection from heat may be as important as shelter from rain. Courtyards are invariably present. Most villages have their local reservoir or tank which supplies water for man

and animals during the dry season. These tanks are focal points for community gossip.

Until the mid-twentieth century little change was possible in village life. Today most villages have a radio; many are visited by an occasional mobile movie unit driven in over a new road; most have a primary school; some have a weekly clinic; a local agricultural adviser is nearby. A sense of nationalism is in the air. All these things are transforming many villages, but their sheer number, the weight of tradition, and the limited environmental potentials mean that change presents problems. Even the wisest of central governments faces sober difficulties.

The restrictions of language and religion divide people into isolated cultural communities which make government and business difficult. In social, linguistic, and political structure, the subcontinent is quite as complex as anything the peninsula of Europe has ever known; national coherence is thus very difficult.

The differences among people are in part ethnographic. The higher castes tend to have fairer skin, higher foreheads, and rounder faces. Aryans, who represent the latest invasions, in general are lighter and have thin noses; Dravidians are dark-skinned and broad-nosed. The class stratification of Hindu society has been a serious barrier to modernization.

The major cultural clash in the twentieth century has been between the Hindus, who represent two-thirds of the combined population, and the Muslims, who comprise one-fifth. Each religion gives to India and to Pakistan, respectively, its principal cultural and religious unity, but there is no common language, race, or history in either land.

Conflict between the various communal groups has long been a political factor. In post-division India, Hindus account for 85 per cent of the population, and the 40 million Muslims represent 10 per cent. Within Pakistan the percentages are about reversed.

The creation of two sovereign states in South Asia, India and Pakistan, raises a unique problem since the physical geography of the land south of the Himalaya suggests that it should be a single political unit. The idea of a separate Muslim nation was scarcely given serious consideration prior to 1940 and is only the nationalistic expression of a religious minority. Under British rule the various social communities enjoyed relative security, but the Muslims felt that they could not be sure of tolerance under a government ruled by a Hindu

This girl from Rajasthan is wearing a colorful sari and is bedecked with ornate jewelry. (*Courtesy Trans World Airlines*)

majority. When the boundary between West Pakistan and the Indian Union was decided, religious tensions became so acute that some five million people on each side of the border migrated to either Hindu or Muslim areas.

The boundaries between India and Pakistan were designed to give the latter those contiguous areas where Muslims exceed Hindus. Religious groups are so intermixed that any line is apt to wind irregularly across railways, trade areas, and minor civil boundaries. Merely to say that there are more followers of Islam on one side of a line and more Hindus on the other overlooks the fact that such a frontier cuts directly across the core area of other groups, such as the Sikhs.

References on South Asia

The standard volume is O. H. K. Spate: *India and Pakistan*. Excellent material may be found in the chapters by John E. Brush in Norton S. Ginsburg (ed.): *The Pattern of Asia*.

See also general references for Asia, Chapter 1.

Azevedo, Carlos de: "Goa, Damao and Diu," *Geog. Mag.*, XXVII (1954), 53–67.

Bowser, Earl: "The Land of the Indos," *Canadian Geog. Jour.*, LVII (1958), 50–61.

*Brush, John E.: "South Asia," in Norton Ginsburg (ed.): *The Pattern of Asia*, Englewood Cliffs, N.J.: Prentice-Hall (1958).

*Champion, H. G.: "A Preliminary Survey of the Forest Types of India and Burma," *Indian Forest Records*, I, no. 1 (1936).

Davies, C. Collin: *An Historical Atlas of the Indian Peninsula*, Fair Lawn, N.J.: Oxford University Press (1953).

*Fawcett, C. B.: *A Political Geography of the British Empire*, Boston: Ginn (1933).

Fowler, F. J.: "Some Problems of Water Distribution between East and West Punjab," *Geog. Rev.*, XL (1950), 583–599.

Geddes, Arthur: "The Alluvial Morphology of the Indo-Gangetic Plain," *Transactions and Papers* (1960), 253–276.

Karan, Pradyumna P.: "Sikkim and Bhutan," *Jour. Geog.*, LX (1960), 58–66.

*Karan, Pradyumna P.: *Nepal: A Cultural and Physical Geography*, Lexington, Ky.: University of Kentucky Press (1960).

Learmonth, A. T. A.: "Medical Geography in India and Pakistan," *Geog. Jour.*, CXXVII (1961), 10–26.

Learmonth, A. T. A., and A. M. Learmonth: "Aspects of Village Life in Indo-Pakistan," *Geography*, XL (1955), 145–160.

Mason, Kenneth: "The Himalayas as a Barrier to Modern Communications," *Geog. Jour.*, LXXXVI (1936), 1–16.

Mayfield, Robert C.: "A Geographic Study of the Kashmir Issue," *Geog. Rev.*, XLV (1955), 181–196.

*Panjabi, R. M., and others: "India and Pakistan, 1947–1957," *Geog. Mag.*, XXX (1957), 161–208.

Spate, O. H. K.: "Geographical Aspects of the Pakistan Scheme," *Geog. Jour.*, XLVI (1943), 125–136.

Spate, O. H. K.: "The Partition of the Punjab and of Bengal," *Geog. Jour.*, CX (1947), 201–222.

Spate, O. H. K.: "The Partition of India and the Prospects of Pakistan," *Geog. Rev.*, XXXVIII (1948), 5–29.

*Spate, O. H. K.: *India and Pakistan*, 2d ed., New York: Dutton (1957).

Trewartha, Glenn T., and James L. Verber: "Regionalism in Factory Industry in India-Pakistan," *Econ. Geog.*, XXVII (1951), 283–286.

27 Indo-Pakistan
Land and Resources

The Land Base / Monsoon Climate / River Problems / Natural Vegetation / Soils

THE LAND BASE

Extraordinary physical contrasts characterize the South Asian realm. It contains one of the wettest spots on earth as well as one of the driest; the highest and largest of all mountain ranges border vast river lowlands; dense rain forests contrast with lifeless deserts; the problem of agriculture is in one area too much water, in another, too little. Unlike the pattern of microscopic detail in Japan, the topographic features in South Asia group themselves into simple major units. Local contrasts exist but are subordinate.

This land has charm and glamour, but it also has poverty and problems. The cultural landscape everywhere reflects the intensity of man's quest for livelihood in a land of uncertain rainfall. Wherever the environment permits, crops are grown to the limit. Here is Monsoon Asia at its climax, with a seasonal rhythm of rainfall which affects all man's activities. Although the average rainfall is generally abundant, its effectiveness is restricted by high thermal energy and high evapotranspiration. Surprisingly large parts of the subcontinent are semiarid and even desert.

The entire realm embraces 1,743,782 square miles, roughly half of the area of the United States. From the borders of Iran eastward to the frontier of Burma is about 2,000 miles; from the southern tip of the peninsula to northern Kashmir is 2,000 miles; midway between north and south lies the Tropic of Cancer. Despite this great size and extent, all the area south of the mountain wall is essentially tropical.

Within South Asia are three entirely different physical areas, unlike in geological history, surface configuration, and potential utilization. These are the mountain wall of the Himalaya and other encircling ranges; the lowland plains drained by the Indus, Ganges, and Brahmaputra Rivers; and the dissected plateau in the peninsula to the south, with its extension in Ceylon.

In the whole of peninsular India there is scarcely a single marine fossil, except in marginal strips that show local sea invasions. Much of the country is underlain by a basement complex of highly metamorphic schist and gneiss, with some granitic intrusions. Preserved within long troughs or depressions among these crystallines are altered sediments, now phyllites, slates, and marbles. From the latter is secured beautiful building stone, such as the marble used in the Taj Mahal. All these are Archeozoic in age. Overlying them, and apparently Proterozoic, are great thicknesses of limestone, shale, and sandstone. Despite their great antiquity, these sediments are undisturbed and testify to the stability of much of India since Pre-Cambrian times. Thus the peninsula is one of the great positive areas of Asia, a massif which has remained undeformed and above sea level.

Near the close of the Paleozoic era, sandstones and shales accumulated in fresh-water basins. Along with these, beds of coal were formed, especially in the northeast. Permian glacial evidence in latitude 17°N, and in the Salt Range, latitude 33°N, presents unsolved problems, for the tillite in the latter area contains boulders whose sources lay 750 miles to the south.

The latest important episode in peninsular geology began in the Cretaceous era and continued into the Tertiary, when enormous lava flows buried much of the western area. Despite much erosion around the margins, the area still covered is 200,000 square miles. The maximum thickness is unknown, but near Bombay the exposures are at least 6,000 feet thick. Separate layers of these fissure flows are from 6 to 90 feet thick. Basalt and andesite are typical, with rhyolite in some places. Associated ash and tuff are present, as well as interbedded sediments. These horizontal flows are responsible for many flat-topped hills and dissected escarpments.

No satisfactory term describes the area south of the Indus and Ganges lowland. Not all of it is actually peninsular, nor is it all a dissected plateau. The term Deccan is variously used; by some it is restricted to the area of lava flows in the west; by others the term is applied to all the upland south of the Satpura Range, to be described later; again it may embrace the entire area south of the Indo-Gangetic lowland. It will here be used for the triangular-plateau part of the peninsula, as bounded on the north by the Satpura line.

Escarpments border each side of the Deccan. On the west are the Western Ghats with elevations of a half mile and more. These one-sided mountains rise abruptly from the Arabian Sea but descend gradually to the plateau on the east. The steep-sided valleys facing the ocean are in the same stage of development as the much deeper valleys of the Himalaya, suggesting that the elevation of the Western Ghats was simultaneous with the uplift of the great mountain wall of Tibet. The Eastern Ghats are a discontinuous line of hills which mark the inner margin of the coastal plain, farther inland than the western escarpment; most elevations are

Peninsular India drops off abruptly to the Arabian Sea in a great escarpment known as the Western Ghats. This is the railway from Bombay to Poona; alongside it penstocks carry water for generating electricity. (*Courtesy Indian State Railways*)

under 3,000 feet. These bordering mountains meet in the south to form the Nilgiri Hills, with their continuation in the Cardamon Hills at the tip of the Deccan.

The Deccan slopes eastward, so that the three main rivers have their source in the Western Ghats. From south to north these are the Cauvery, Kistna, and Godavari. Where they cross the Eastern Ghats the valleys are narrow and the current swift; elsewhere the rivers are near local base level and flow through broad open valleys in late maturity. The most noticeable topographic features are the flat-topped hills and scarped edges of the lava flows or horizontal sandstones. Otherwise structure does not notably influence the configuration of surface features.

The northern margin of the Deccan is less definite. The principal break is the Satpura Range, a line of uplands between the westward-flowing Narbada and Tapti Rivers. This elevation continues eastward into the Maikala Range and the uplands of Chota Nagpur. North and south of the Satpura Range are the Vindhya and Ajanta Ranges, so that the northern edge of the Deccan is a threefold zone.

Besides the Deccan there are two other hilly sections in the peninsular upland: Malwa in the northwest and Oriya in the east. The drainage of the former is north to the Ganges. Malwa is limited on the west by the worn-down Aravalli Range which nearly reaches Delhi. Oriya includes the rugged hills and valleys in the basin of the Mahanadi River, including the Chota Nagpur uplands. Although close to Calcutta and well supplied with coal and iron, Oriya is

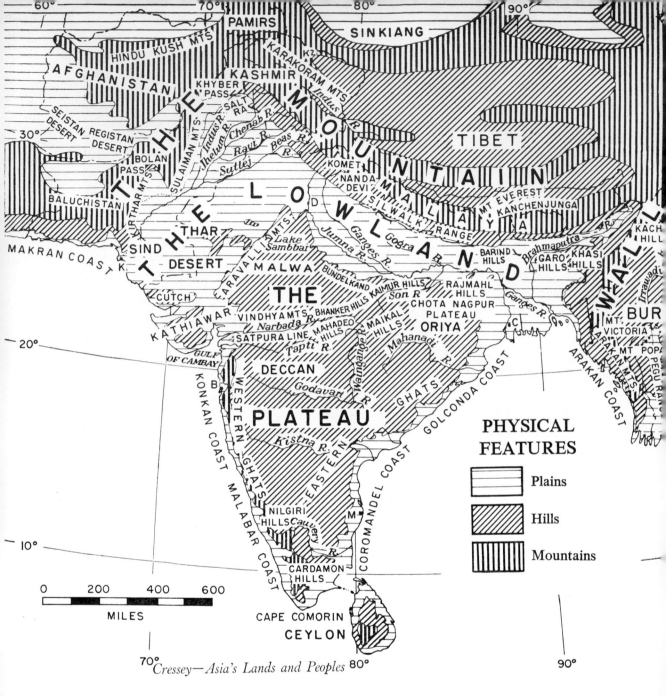

South Asia has three major physical divisions: the mountain wall dominated by the Himalaya; the lowland drained by the Indus, Ganges, and Brahmaputra; and the hilly plateau in the peninsula, bordered by the Western and Eastern Ghats.

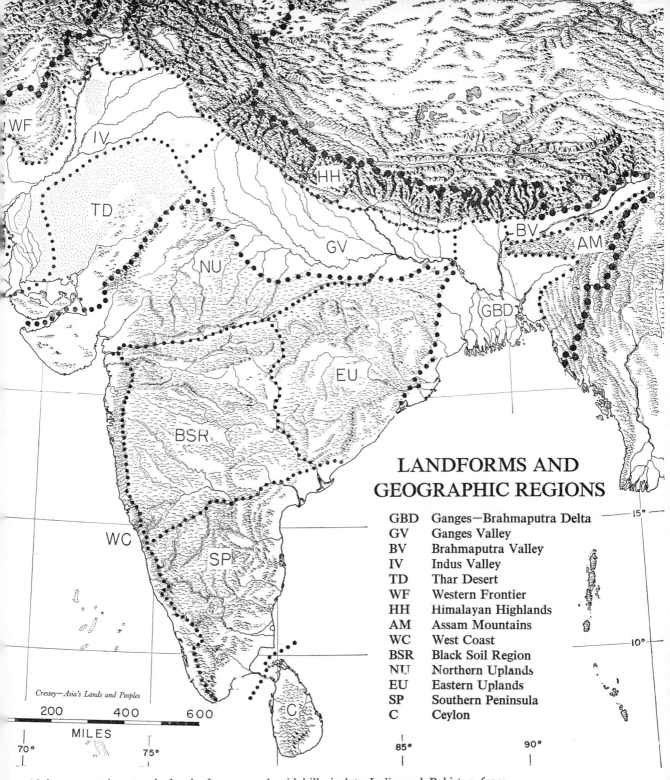

LANDFORMS AND
GEOGRAPHIC REGIONS

GBD	Ganges—Brahmaputra Delta
GV	Ganges Valley
BV	Brahmaputra Valley
IV	Indus Valley
TD	Thar Desert
WF	Western Frontier
HH	Himalayan Highlands
AM	Assam Mountains
WC	West Coast
BSR	Black Soil Region
NU	Northern Uplands
EU	Eastern Uplands
SP	Southern Peninsula
C	Ceylon

Cressey—Asia's Lands and Peoples

Alpine mountains, tropical rain forests, and arid hills isolate India and Pakistan from
the rest of the continent, and the limited number of good harbors reduces contacts by
sea. (*Base map by Erwin Raisz*)

THE LAND BASE   393

one of the least populous and most backward areas south of the mountains.

Coastal plains border both the Arabian Sea and the Bay of Bengal. On the west, level land is narrow and discontinuous, for in places the Ghats come to the sea as cliffs. The east-coast plain continues from the Ganges to Cape Comorin, and around Ceylon. The width is 75 miles or less, and conditions of land use and settlement somewhat resemble those in the Ganges delta. South of Bombay the littoral is known as the Konkan and Malabar Coasts; on the east, reading counterclockwise from opposite Ceylon and northward, are the Coromandel and Golconda Coasts.

Both the eastern and western margins of peninsular India are almost devoid of natural harbors. Bare rock walls alternate with mangrove swamps and straight beaches. River mouths are particularly unsatisfactory. At many smaller ports it is necessary for steamers to discharge cargo into lighters several miles offshore. The few port cities owe their importance to access to their hinterland rather than to natural harbor advantages.

Between the peninsular plateau and the Himalayan mountain wall lies the Indo-Gangetic lowland. Most of it is a great alluvial plain but it includes the erosional surface of the Thar Desert in the west. This is the heart of Indian life and history. Here are the greatest rivers, the Ganges and Brahmaputra in the east and the Indus in the west. The Ganges delta lies in the old province of Bengal, now divided between India and Pakistan; the Brahmaputra flows across Assam. The three rivers and most of their tributaries rise amid the snow-covered ranges to the north. Since their flow does not depend entirely upon the summer monsoon, they never run dry and are thus of great value for irrigation in the plains. In contrast, the rivers in the peninsula are fed only by the summer rain and are often nearly dry during the winter.

Few areas of flat alluvium are so extensive. Scarcely a hill or mound is to be seen. Nearly 1,000 miles from its mouth, the Ganges is only 500 feet above sea level. Deposits of sand and clay extend to depths of thousands of feet, and few pebbles are found on the surface. The only distinction is between the older and slightly higher alluvium with lime concretions and alkaline soils, and the newer alluvium at the present stream levels without nodules.

In the northwest, the plain of the Indus and the adjoining Thar Desert is 300 to 400 miles wide; along the Ganges the width is 150 to 200 miles. Where the plain is narrowest lies Delhi, the natural gateway between the humid rice lands to the east and the drier wheat country of the Punjab. Although the two areas are topographically similar, the eastern half of the lowland with its greater precipitation has five times the population of the west.

Two regional names are used in the Indus valley; the lower portion is the Sind and that near the mountains is the Punjab. The latter derives its name from the fact that it is drained by five tributaries of the Indus: the Jhelum, Chenab, Ravi, Beas, and Sutlej. Pakistan and India both share the Indus and the Ganges lowlands. In the former the boundary crosses several main rivers and irrigation canals, with serious complications for agriculture. In the latter the boundary cuts through the delta, leaving several mouths of the Ganges in each country.

The ancient geography of southern Asia was once very unlike the present. Where now rise the Himalaya was once a long sea that extended westward to Europe. This ancient Mediterranean, known as Tethys, occupied a subsiding geosyncline which received vast quantities of marine deposits from the Cambrian to the mid-Cenozoic eras. From the end of the Eocene into the late Pliocene, this trough of sediments was subjected to powerful compression from the north against the resistant old land of the peninsula. Most of the orogeny took place in the Miocene; the sea was obliterated, and the towering Himalaya took its place. Beds that were once horizontal are now powerfully faulted, folded, and overturned on a grand scale, and flank a central igneous core. Structure guides topography, with linear ranges following the direction of folding.

Fringing the main rampart, which extends 1,500 miles from the Indus to the Brahmaputra, are lower mountains, known as foothills even though they rise to 5,000 feet. The chief of these are the Siwaliks, which give their name to the great system of ancient river deposits of which they are composed. These beds resemble those now accumulating in the Indo-Gangetic lowland and are from 16,000 to 20,000 feet in thickness. The Miocene and Pliocene fauna is famous for its variety of mammalian remains. Apparently these beds accumulated as ancient alluvial fans in a foredeep, much as did the present sediments of the Ganges and Indus. North of the Siwaliks are still other deformed geosynclines.

Occasional earthquakes in Assam and the Punjab indicate that movement still continues.

To the northwest, north, and northeast the mountains rise abruptly from the plain. From one end to another the rampart is continuous, although a variety of ranges marks both ends. The chief mountains in the west are the Sulaiman and Kirthar Ranges, which extend from the Makran coast toward the Pamirs. No single name can be given the Assam mountains next to Burma in the east, nor is their structural relation to the Himalaya entirely clear. The general trend is north–south, but there is a western offshoot in the Khasi Hills. The main range is the Himalaya, but behind it lie other ranges, including the Karakoram in the west. In this inner range rises K^2, the second-highest mountain on earth, 28,250 feet. In the eastern Himalaya is Mount Everest, 29,028 feet.

West of the mountain wall are Baluchistan

Arid mountains border the Indo-Pakistan realm on the northwest. These are the roads through the Khyber Pass. (*Courtesy Consulate General of Pakistan, New York City*)

and Kashmir; beyond them are Iran and Afghanistan. On the southern slopes are Nepal, Bhutan, and Sikkim, while to the north is China. Few passes cross the front ranges; north to Tibet are several passes near Darjeeling and there are others from the Punjab. From Kashmir several passes connect with Chinese Sinkiang, including the 18,317-foot Karakoram Pass, and the main trail by way of Gilgit.

MONSOON CLIMATE

Although South Asia provides the classic example of a monsoon climate, with seasonal to-and-fro winds supposedly due to the alternate heating of land and sea, the actual mechanics of circulation are quite different. It has been well said that while every schoolboy understands the monsoon, the official meteorological departments are still in doubt as to its origin.

Nowhere else are so many people so intimately dependent upon rainfall rhythms; the whole prosperity of India and Pakistan is tied up with the eccentricities of its seasonal winds. Other lands have their climatic personality, but in few is it so prominent or meaningful. Alternately the realm is lush and green, or a dreary brown; supersaturated atmosphere gives way to extreme aridity. Seasonality thus dominates all life. Within the realm there are the widest contrasts in the amount of rainfall, ranging from excessive precipitation to almost zero.

The conventional explanation has been that the monsoon circulation is the result of thermal relations between land and sea. Thus a heated subcontinent would mean that the air is expanding, rising, and overflowing, with resulting low pressure above the land and high pressures on the encircling sea. Surface winds would thus blow landward during the summer and bring rain from the sea. Winter outblowing air would be dry.

This oversimplification is not quite true. We now know that the circulation is independent of temperatures and pressures in central Asia because of the Himalaya barrier. Furthermore,

heat alone is not a sufficient explanation. The realm is hotter in May before the summer monsoon than in July when the circulation is at its height; temperatures also remain high after the end of the monsoon. If heat and low pressure alone were the answer, the area of heaviest rainfall would correspond with rising air, whereas the hottest area is actually the driest. The monsoon fluctuates from year to year, but the highest summer temperatures are correlated with years of low precipitation.

South Asia lies within the latitude of the trade winds, and if the earth were all water or all land, there would be a steady circulation from the subtropical high with its descending air to lower pressure and rising air at the thermal equator. In the Northern Hemisphere the equatorward winds are turned to their right, according to Ferrel's law, and become northeast and progressively easterly winds as they approach the low-pressure doldrums; south of the equator are the southeast trades.

Since the axis of the earth is tilted, the vertical rays of the sun shift $23\frac{1}{2}$ degrees with the season, alternately toward the respective pole, causing the thermal equator to move with them, though to a lesser degree. Thus the trade-wind belts migrate north and south. If this were all, the northeast trades over the subcontinent would shift southward in the winter, bringing their associated subtropical high pressure and dry air with them. In summer the humid southeast trades would cross the geographical equator and invade the peninsula. Apparently the monsoons represent a modification of these conditions.

As the sun advances northward in summer, an elongated low-pressure area develops along the Indo-Gangetic lowland, oriented WNW–ESE. Inflowing trade-wind air masses from the southwest converge toward this trough, and some encircle it from the east, making it a modified intertropical convergence zone. The westward turning of the monsoon from the Bay of Bengal is apparently related to this low-pressure trough rather than to the physical barrier of the Himalaya, per se.

The cause for the sudden arrival or "burst" of the monsoon in June is not fully understood. In part, it may be related to the final disappearance of high-level westerly jet streams which shift north of Tibet at this season. In part, the abrupt beginning of the monsoon is related to the disappearance of the temporarily restraining influence of local high-pressure areas over the Arabian Sea and the Bay of Bengal. In any event, the southeast trade winds abruptly rush north to join the low-pressure belt over northern India. This change occurs with such suddenness that the monsoon is said to break or burst. During July, the mean monsoon velocity at Bombay is 14 miles per hour.

As the southeast trades cross the geographical equator, the rotation of the earth turns them to their right, and they become the southwest monsoon. The summer monsoon is therefore an accentuated and diverted trade wind shifted from the Southern to the Northern Hemisphere. One arm of the monsoon from the Arabian Sea strikes the western mountainous coast of the peninsula of India nearly at right angles. Over the Bay of Bengal the movement is more from the south, but upon reaching the mountains of eastern India the circulation is deflected upward over the Khasi Hills and to the right and left, up the Brahmaputra and Ganges valleys.

Since the southern trade winds have crossed several thousand miles of warm Indian Ocean, they arrive over India and Pakistan with a high moisture content. However, the land is even warmer than the sea, so that sufficient cooling for condensation requires some local mechanism. Thus steady winds usually bring fair weather. Rain may result from several causes. The first is orographic, admirably illustrated by the heavy rainfall on the Western Ghats and the eastern Himalaya. Within the plateau, convectional storms account for some of the rain. This is also true over the Ganges valley, but here a third cause of rising air is produced by the crowding and convergence of air streams next to the mountains.

It is also clear that the monsoon is not a steady current, for within it there are surges or pulsations which bring rain. At other times there are small depressions within the monsoon circulation, some due to high-level conditions, while others are related to wind shear within the monsoon.

Just before the monsoon breaks, the instability of the frontal atmosphere develops local thundershowers on land and tropical typhoons in the Arabian Sea and the Bay of Bengal that bring what are often known as the mango rains, since this fruit is just maturing. Similar storms continue, but with less intensity, throughout the period of the southern monsoon and yield considerable rain. Typhoons are especially active at the end of the summer, when their onshore winds may develop the so-called tidal waves that inundate east-coast deltas. The sea may rise 10 to 30 feet in a half hour, as in 1876 when 200,000 people were drowned at Bakarganj near the head of the Bay of Bengal. On October 7, 1937, a storm wave 40 feet high, accompanying a hurricane, swept up the mouth of the Hooghly River causing the loss of some 300,000 lives.

The monsoon arrives in Ceylon, at Travancore, and the tip of Burma by the beginning of June, and reaches Bombay about June 5. The Bengal branch arrives in Calcutta by June 15 and progresses up the Ganges valley to the Punjab by the end of June. The southerly monsoon continues until mid-September in the Punjab, mid-October in Bombay, late October in Calcutta, and early November in the south. In Calcutta the monsoon proper lasts from June 15 to September 15, with intermittent showers and high humidity through October. By that time the sun has shifted southward beyond the geographical equator, although the thermal equator lags behind it. The mechanics necessary for pulling the southeast trade winds into the peninsula are no longer present, so that the southerly winds gradually weaken and withdraw before the developing northeast trades.

Variations in the arrival, duration, distribution, and intensity of the monsoon are of profound importance but have largely eluded explanation. There appear to be interesting correlations between such items as pressures over the Australian deserts and subsequent Indian rainfall. Other studies show parallelism between Indian drought and low Nile floods due to diminished Ethiopian rainfall. There may also be correlations with outbursts of Antarctic air and with the path of high-level jet streams.

During winter months, monsoon wind directions are reversed. Northwest winds move down the Ganges valley and turn south and southwestward over the peninsula. These appear to be modified northeast trade winds. Their velocity is but half that of the summer monsoon. Normal winter subtropical high pressure over the Tropic of Cancer is augmented by local anticyclonic conditions in West Pakistan. The winter monsoon blows from October to the end of February and is responsible for India's cool season.

The winter monsoon air is descending and directed seaward, so that it is dry and rainless over India and Pakistan. Since Ceylon receives the northern monsoon off the ocean, its highlands have ample rain. The Madras coast also has winter rain, either from typhoons or the northeast monsoon which strikes the Madras coast obliquely from the Bay of Bengal.

From December to March the northwest has a procession of weak cyclonic storms and cool fronts which move across the Punjab from Iran. These shallow depressions bring modified polar continental air masses and draw in moist air from the Arabian Sea, which results in a few inches of rain for the wheat fields of the upper Indus. The total rainfall is low but significant. Much of the Karakoram snow cover is derived from this circulation. Winter is a dry season of clear skies except in the northwest and extreme southeast, where winter is slightly rainy.

Since air travel has called for increased information as to winds aloft, something is now known of the thickness of the monsoons. In June, southwesterly winds prevail up to 5,000 feet, above which the wind is from the northwest, veering to the northeast over the peninsula. In July and August the monsoon thickens

to 12,000 feet, but throughout the summer, east winds prevail aloft. The northerly monsoon is 10,000 feet thick in October, with strong west winds aloft all during the winter, usually with jet streams. At no season does monsoon circulation cross the mountain wall.

The South Asian realm has the widest possible variations in rainfall. The heaviest precipitation is orographic, as on the slopes of the Western Ghats, the Assam Hills, or the southern Himalaya. In each of these localities the amount exceeds 200 inches. The wettest spot is Cherrapunji in the Khasi Hills of Assam. This station stands at the edge of the hills where great masses of air crowd against the 4,000-foot cliffs. The average rainfall is 425 inches, most of it concentrated in half of the year.[1] Annual totals at Cherrapunji vary from 283 inches in 1908 to a record of 905 inches in 1861. The rainfall in the single month of July, 1861, reached 366 inches. Some localities in the Western Ghats may be as wet.

Some of the rainfall on the lowlands is associated with weak cyclonic storms that move westward from the Bay of Bengal. One inch may fall in ten minutes, and 40 inches has been recorded in twenty-four hours. The rainy season is not continuous, and there may be days or weeks of clear skies in the drier areas. Parts of the Sind have almost no rainfall, and yet Doorbaji, with an annual average of 5 inches, once received 34 inches in two days.

Rain shadows are pronounced. Thus in the Deccan, southern Madras, and across the Himalaya in Tibet the yearly total drops to 20 inches or less. When the winds move downslope, foehn warming and evaporation occur.

Not only is the monsoon eccentric in the total amount of precipitation, but variations in its beginning or end or concentration may be even more serious. When periods of lessened rainfall or other irregularities occur two years in succession, widespread disaster may result.

[1] The world's heaviest known rainfall is on the slopes of Mount Waialeale in the Hawaiian Islands in the path of the trade winds, where the average is 460 inches.

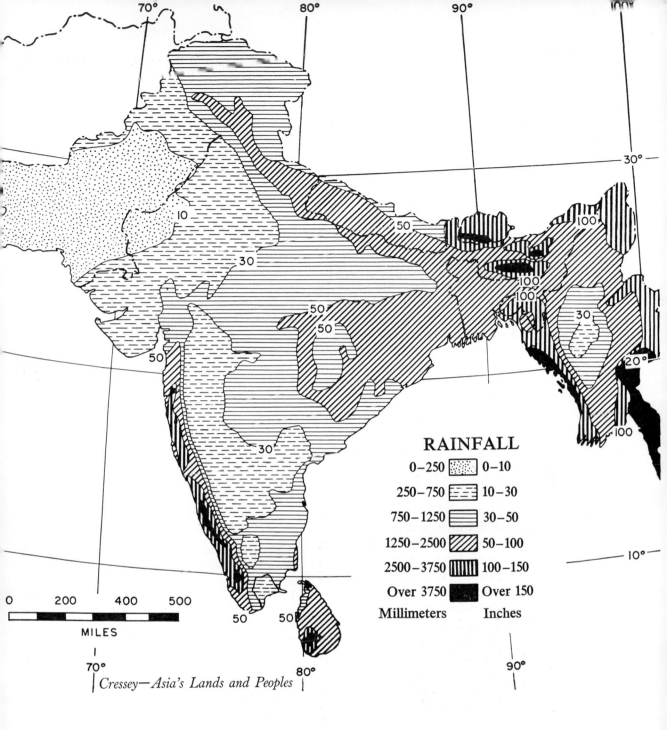

RAINFALL

0–250	![dotted]	0–10
250–750	![light dash]	10–30
750–1250	![dash]	30–50
1250–2500	![diagonal]	50–100
2500–3750	![vertical]	100–150
Over 3750	![black]	Over 150
Millimeters		Inches

Cressey—Asia's Lands and Peoples

Precipitation ranges from 400 inches near the head of the Bay of Bengal and along the Western Ghats to 5 inches in the Thar Desert of the northwest. This is a monsoon land, par excellence, so that for half of the year much of the subcontinent is virtually arid. (*Modified from H. G. Champion: Indian Forest Records, and E. K. Cook: Geography of Ceylon*)

India and Pakistan have three seasons. The arrival of the monsoon in June inaugurates the wet season. This is really India's spring, for nature then comes to life. Despite the high sun, the ocean air and cloud cover keep the day temperature in the nineties. The heat increases from south to north as the winds lose their effect. Humidity is high, but breezes make it bearable. In Bombay, June to September temperatures average 82°F for day and night, while in Calcutta the figure is 84°F.

Conditions are even more unpleasant just after the rains, for the humidity is high, and although the thermometer is lower sensible temperatures increase. During the rainy period, it is difficult to dry one's clothing except over a fire. Furniture put together with glue is apt to come apart. Books and shoes mildew overnight.

Following the cessation of the rains, temperatures decrease, and the cool, dry season extends from late November, or December in the south, through February. Light frosts occur in the Ganges valley, and the clear skies make the climate attractive to the European, although poorly clad Indians may complain bitterly of the cold.

The hot season begins in March. Temperatures rise to 100°F or more in the daytime, although the nights are cooler. The sun is nearly vertical in April and May, and the air is relatively still. All work is suspended at midday, for heat and glare are intense as the molten sun shines from a cloudless sky. Dust storms and tornadoes are locally destructive.

Despite marked variations in rainfall, the climate of the realm is essentially a unit. Although only half of the country is actually within the tropics, the mountain wall is so effective a barrier in keeping out Siberian air that the north is 3 to 5 degrees F warmer than corresponding latitudes in the United States. Some areas are much wetter than others, and the extreme northwest and southeast have year-round rain, but the general climatic mechanism is uniform.

It seems a mistake to divide the realm climatically, as is done by Koeppen, into an *Aw* type of climate in the south and a *Cw* type in north; both areas are really tropical, with dry winters. India and East Pakistan are humid, and the contrast between them and the desert and steppe of West Pakistan—*BS* and *BW*—is valid.

As the average annual rainfall varies from place to place and as it becomes more concentrated in one season, variations in the amount from year to year increase. Where the normal total is under 20 inches, no agriculture is attempted without irrigation, and rainfall fluctuations are expected and planned for. Where the total exceeds 80 inches, there is almost always a surplus of moisture, even in dry years. Forty inches of rain is normally adequate, but when it fails, famine is threatened. Thus the most seriously affected areas are those where there is usually just enough water. In most of the realm evapotranspiration amounts to some 30 inches, and only the precipitation above that figure has meaning for agriculture.

Long experience with rainfall fluctuations has brought population distribution into close agreement with climatic possibilities, but so great is the pressure of people that too many have occupied the marginal lands where drought is certain to recur.

A vivid description of the monsoon has been presented by Khushwant Singh.[2]

To know India and her peoples, one has to know the monsoon. It is not enough to read about it in books, or see it on the cinema screen, or hear someone talk about it. It has to be a personal experience because nothing short of living through it can fully convey all it means to a people for whom it is not only the source of life, but also their most exciting impact with nature. . . . It is preceded by desolation; it brings with it the hopes of Spring; it has the fullness of summer and the fulfillment of autumn all in one.

Those who mean to experience it should come to India some time in March or April. The flowers are on their way out and the trees begin to lose their foliage. . . . For the next three months the

[2] Khushwant Singh: *I Shall Not Hear the Nightingale,* New York: Grove Press (1959), 101–103. Quoted by permission.

sky becomes a flat and colorless gray without a wisp of a cloud anywhere. People suffer great agony. Sweat comes out of every pore and the clothes stick to the body. . . . The thirst is unquenchable, no matter how much one drinks. The nights are spent shadowboxing in the dark trying to catch mosquitoes and slapping oneself in an attempt to squash those hummings near one's ears. . . . When the cool breeze of the morning starts blowing, one dozes off and dreams of a paradise with ice cool streams running through lush green valleys. Just then the sun comes up strong and hot and smacks one in the face. Another day begins with its heat and its glare and its dust.

After living through all this for ninety days or more, one's mind becomes barren and bereft of hope. It is then that the monsoon makes its spectacular entry. Dense masses of dark clouds sweep across the heavens like a celestial army with black banners. The deep roll of thunder sounds like the beating of a billion drums. Crooked shafts of silver zigzag in lightning flashes against the black sky. Then comes the rain itself. First it falls in fat drops; the earth rises to meet them. . . . Then it comes in torrents. . . . Where there was nothing, there is everything: green grass, snakes, centipedes, worms, and millions of insects.

It is not surprising that much of India's art, music, and literature is concerned with the monsoon. Innumerable paintings depict people on roof tops looking eagerly at the dark clouds billowing out from over the horizon with flocks of herons flying in front. . . .

An Indian's attitude to clouds and rain remains fundamentally different from that of the European. To the one, clouds are symbols of hope; to the other, those of despair. . . . An Indian, when the rains come, runs out into the streets shouting with joy and lets himself be soaked to the skin.

The lower Ganges divides into a series of distributaries long before it reaches the Bay of Bengal. This aerial view near Kalikapur is at 23° 45′ N and 89° 55′ E. (*Courtesy United States Air Force*)

Much of the Indus valley is dry, either a desert or seasonally arid. This water hole is 2 miles east of Karachi in the Thar Desert. (*Courtesy Indian State Railways*)

RIVER PROBLEMS

South Asia has two categories of rivers: those which depend on seasonal rainfall and thus greatly diminish in flow during the dry season, and those which rise in high mountains where year-round moisture is available. The former flow through the peninsula; the latter lie in the Himalaya or in the extreme south of India and in Ceylon where both monsoons bring rain. Both types experience floods, often disastrous, but they differ in their minimum flow.

The three great Himalayan river systems are the Indus or Sindhu, with the five Punjab tributaries: Jhelum, Chenab, Ravi, Sutlej, and Beas; the Ganges or Ganga, fed by the Jumna, Gogra, Rapti, and Gandak; and the Brahmaputra, known across Tibet as the Tsangpo.

All these northern rivers rise in snow-crowned peaks and are already big streams when they emerge onto the Indo-Gangetic plain. The sources of several of them lie north of the main range, across which the rivers flow

in tremendous gorges. Though the volume may vary widely, there is always a dependable flow. The main rivers were once navigable across their lowlands, but so much water is now withdrawn for irrigation that river travel by steamer is no longer possible.

The rivers of peninsular India are fed only during the four months of monsoon rains; in winter they become almost dry or so nearly so as to be useless for irrigation. Some of the rivers flow through well-incised valleys, leaving little room for a flood plain and making it difficult to divert irrigation water onto the adjoining uplands.

Three groups may be recognized. Two main rivers drain west to the Arabian Sea: the Narbada and the Tapti. Four rivers flow eastward to the Bay of Bengal: the Mahanadi, the Godavari and its tributary the Wainganga, the Kistna or Krishna, and the Cauvery; all four rise in the Western Ghats and flow eastward across the peninsula. In addition, a few small rivers, such as the Son, drain north to the Ganges valley.

Most rivers are shallow, and in all India only 1,500 miles of waterways are navigable for powered boats.

Life in the subcontinent has always been vitally related to water. Few areas receive the right amount of rain at the right time. This calls for irrigation both with wet crops like rice and with dry grains like wheat. Because of the seasonal character of the rainfall and the irregularities of the monsoon, irrigation has become highly developed, supplying water to one-fourth of the agricultural area. Supplies are obtained from shallow wells, reservoirs, and canals which are supplied from rivers.

About 15 million acres are irrigated by wells, chiefly in the Ganges valley, the Punjab, Madras, and Bombay. Of the many devices used to lift the water, the most common is a leather bag at the end of a rope which runs over a pulley above the well and is pulled by a pair of oxen. The oxen usually walk down an incline when the well is deep. Another device is the Persian water wheel, used with earthen jars attached to an endless belt which dip into the well from the rim of the wheel; here again oxen are used. Still more simply, water is lifted by manual labor by means of a long pivoted lever. Since well water is difficult to secure, it is used sparingly and only on high-value crops.

The construction of reservoirs, usually known as tanks, goes back to very ancient times. Some are shallow ponds dug to catch rain water; others are made by a dam across a stream. Some tanks cover many square miles; others cover less than an acre. South India is the most characteristic region for reservoirs. Except in the Indus lowland, they are a conspicuous feature of the landscape. In Madras there are tanks known to be 1,100 years old. About 10 million acres are irrigated in this manner.

Almost every village in the Deccan has its tank, perhaps the gift of some former rich resident. To it come the cattle for water; in it are washed the clothes and vegetables; into it is dumped the refuse; from it are obtained fish; and the water is often the only source for domestic use. Toward the end of the dry season when the pond shrinks to a fraction of its normal size, the odors become intolerable. Small wonder that cholera, malaria, and other diseases have been widespread. Since these ponds are often covered with a scum of algae, one American has humorously referred to them as the Village Green.

India and Pakistan have the longest mileage of modern irrigation canals in the world, nearly 100,000 miles in all. Most of these are in the northwest, where engineering skill has turned the wastelands of the Punjab and Sind into a great oasis, which produces wheat and cotton in what was formerly an empty desert. Developments in the upper Ganges valley are equally impressive. Canal irrigation in the peninsular plateau must depend on stored seasonal rain, but the rivers of the northern lowland are fed by melting snows and do not run dry. The Punjab has long been famed for the diversion weirs across its streams near the mountains; these take irrigation water from the rivers so that the interstream areas, or doabs, are made available for wheat growing. The total area served by canals in the two countries amounts to nearly 50 million acres.

One of the great contributions of the British period was the introduction of hydrologic engineering. Low dams, known as barrages, raised many river levels so that canal systems might receive water at all seasons. Thousands of miles of main canals were constructed, and the resulting irrigation system was the most extensive in the world. It provided the Ganges valley with dependable water, and enabled several tens of millions of people to settle on previously empty areas along the Indus.

Egypt has long been famed for its Aswan dam, but it was the lessons learned on the Indus that made modern Egyptian irrigation possible. The mile-long Sukkur or Lloyd Barrage on the lower Indus irrigates an area in the Sind larger than the whole of cultivated Egypt.

Along the east coast it has been customary to construct diversion canals at the head of the deltas in order to bring water to the areas between the streams. Such canals usually operate only when the river is in flood stage. A large irrigation project on the Cauvery River stores water for 1.3 million acres and generates considerable electric power. On the west coast a canal even runs under the Western Ghats to bring irrigation water eastward from the wet coastal slopes to the drier interior near Tinnevelly.

The possibilities of diverting normal river flow into irrigation canals have been about exhausted. Future plans thus call for high dams and large storage reservoirs which will accumulate flood flow for use during the dry season. These projects have held an important place in the successive five-year plans in both India and Pakistan. While primarily designed for irrigation, such reservoirs also provide a site for hydroelectricity, and their controlled flow reduces flood dangers.

South Asia has a combined runoff of 1.3 billion acre-feet; in other words, the water would cover this area to a depth of 1 foot if it were feasible so to spread it. The Ganges and Brahmaputra contribute half of the total, followed by the Indus. None of the rivers in the peninsula begin to compare in volume with these Himalaya-fed giants; the Godavari and

Mahanadi, which are the two largest, have barely one-fifth of the flow of the Ganges.

In 1951, prior to the first Five-Year Plan, only 7 per cent of the river flow was utilized; a decade later at the end of the second plan the new projects had raised the total to 13 per cent. Ultimate plans, for the far future, count on using as much as 33 per cent of the runoff.

Numerous irrigation projects in India involve a million acres or more, chiefly in the Punjab and Uttar Pradesh areas of the north and the Orissa and Andhra Pradesh areas along the east coast. Other important developments are the Bhakra-Nangal Project in the Punjab, the Damodar Valley Project in the heavy industry area of Bengal and Bihar northwest of Calcutta, and the Hirkund Project on the Mahanadi River in Orissa.

The Bhakra-Nangal Project is the largest of of the multipurpose developments in India. It lies on the Sutlej River where that stream leaves the mountains and involves two dams, 740 and 90 feet high, four power houses, two 50-foot diversion tunnels, each a half mile long, and a vast network of canals and electric transmission lines. The electric capacity is 604,000 kilowatts. Several million acres in the Punjab and Rajasthan receive dependable water.

Water Resources in South Asia [1]

(in million acre-feet)

River system	Average flow	Utilization		
		Pre-1951	Plan 1	Plan 2
Indus	168	8.0	11.0	1.2
Ganges	400	38.0	21.5	14.5
Brahmaputra	300	2.3	—	—
Godavari	84	12.0	1.0	1.5
Mahanadi	84	3.1	10.5	0.2
Kistna	50	9.0	15.6	2.6
Narbada	32	0.2	—	10.1
Tapti	17	0.2	0.7	3.5
Cauvery	12	8.0	1.3	0.6
Total, with other rivers	1,356	88.0	61.6	34.2
Percentage utilization	100%	7%	11%	13%

[1] Indian Ministry of Information and Broadcasting: *India: A Reference Manual*, Delhi.

The Damodar Valley Project is designed to curb the turbulent river through the construction of four storage dams. More than a million acres are irrigated; and some of the 1,550 miles of canals are navigable, thus linking the Raniganj coal fields with the Hooghly River and Calcutta. Hydroelectricity supplements thermal electricity, based on local coal, with a total capacity of a million kilowatts. This power supplies the steel works at Jamshedpur, the Burnpur copper mines, the coal mines of Bengal and Bihar, cement works and engineering plants at Asansol, and the city of Calcutta.

The Hirkund Project involves a very large earth dam, 3 miles long and 200 feet high, which stores 6,600,000 acre-feet of water for supplemental irrigation in the Mahanadi delta. The reservoir measures 288 square miles in area. Installed electric capacity amounts to 232,500 kilowatts.

Scores of other reservoir and canal projects have been completed or are under way, many of large dimensions. Some are primarily for irrigation; some concern flood control. One of the problems associated with lowland storage is that the rate of evaporation is so high that large shallow reservoirs may lose an important part of their storage before it is used. The problem is not so great with upland storage in the Himalaya. In both areas, silt accumulation is rapid.

Development projects in Pakistan are no less important, though there are marked differences between the humid east, where the problem is one of floods, and the arid west, where irrigation is imperative.

Two river projects have been developed in East Pakistan. Near the port of Chittagong the Hernafuli reservoir will develop 120,000 kilowatts of electricity, and along the lower Ganges irrigation water will be pumped into the Kobadak River to make possible a second and third crop on 2 million acres.

West Pakistan holds more hydrologic possibilities, notably at the Warsak dam on the Kabul River, where both electricity and irrigation are involved. The Indus valley has long been noted for elaborate irrigation works in the Punjab; these may be greatly enlarged when reservoirs are someday built along the edge of the mountains.

The boundary between India and West Pakistan was based solely on religious considerations, and as a result it cut across several rivers and canals, with disrupting effects on irrigation. Political agreements have resolved the water rights of the two countries, but extensive canal changes were involved.

NATURAL VEGETATION

South Asia has a rich and diversified flora, but little of it is distinctive. About one-fifth of the realm is officially classed as forest, but much of this is in the Himalaya, the Assam Hills, or other inaccessible areas, or includes open or stunted scrub.

Almost every type of climax cover is represented. Most vegetation reflects monsoon alternations of rainfall. There are some differences between north and south, but resemblances are far more important. Many hill lands are periodically burned to ensure a better crop of grass for grazing. Where cultivation has been allowed to lapse, extensive tracts have grown up to jungle and bamboo thickets. Few areas of untouched virgin forest remain, for countless generations have cut over most areas, giving rise to an artificial savanna with scattered acacias and euphorbia. Within the settled regions commercial timber is so scarce that farm buildings are usually built of mud.

Throughout India, Pakistan, Nepal, and Ceylon altitude is more important than latitude in determining floristic regions. The Himalayan zone is especially interesting, for within a horizontal distance of 60 miles are reproduced essentially all the vegetation types found in a 3,000-mile traverse of North America from the tip of Florida to Labrador. On the lower slopes of the Himalaya, dense tropical forests pass at successively higher elevations into pine, oak and maple, birch and fir, mountain meadows, and bare rock.

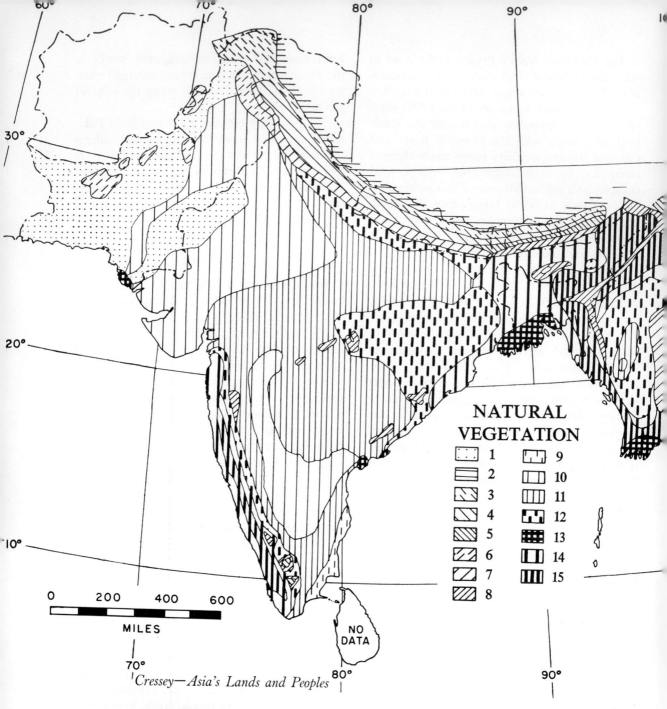

NATURAL VEGETATION

1	9
2	10
3	11
4	12
5	13
6	14
7	15
8	

NO DATA

0 200 400 600

MILES

Cressey—Asia's Lands and Peoples

The forms of natural vegetation reflect climate and elevations. (*After H. G. Champion: Indian Forest Records*)

1. Desert
2. Alpine
3. Dry alpine
4. Dry temperate
5. Wet temperate
6. Subtropical dry forest
7. Subtropical pine forest
8. Subtropical wet forest
9. Tropical dry evergreen
10. Tropical thorn forest
11. Tropical dry deciduous
12. Tropical moist deciduous (monsoon)
13. Tropical tidal
14. Tropical semievergreen
15. Tropical wet evergreen

Much of the peninsula is by nature a great monsoon forest land of teak, banyan, palms, and bamboo. Planted trees such as the mango replace part of the original cover. The Indo-Gangetic Plain is so extensively cultivated that portions are now nearly treeless, and certainly without any trace of the original vegetation.

The major factors in the distribution of forest types are climatic. Soil, drainage, exposure, and history are locally significant but do not alter the general picture. The pattern of natural vegetation thus reflects the distribution of rainfall, and at the same time forecasts possibilities of agricultural utilization.

Four major forest types are defined by Champion.[3] These are the tropical forests with six associations based largely on moisture; the subtropical forests with three types from wet to dry; the temperate forests, which have but two moisture associations; and two alpine forms. There are, in addition, tidal forests, the steppe, and the desert. Where rainfall exceeds 80 inches there is an evergreen rain forest. With 40 to 80 inches and with alternate wet and dry seasons, forests are of the deciduous monsoon type. Twenty to forty inches of rainfall produces dry forest and scrub; with less than 20 inches there is low bush or desert.

The Indus valley and Baluchistan have the sparsest vegetation, partly true desert and partly marginal steppe. The Thar Desert is actually somewhat more humid than areas nearer the Indus which are now irrigated. Only specialized xerophytic forms can survive the aridity and extremely high temperatures.

Alpine vegetation of stunted trees and rhododendron prevails between 9,000 and 11,500 feet. Larch and birch are the principal trees. Xerophytic plants requiring but 10 inches of rainfall live at even higher elevations. Mountain meadows with buttercups and primroses grow up to 18,000 feet.

Temperate mountain forests are restricted by temperature requirements to higher eleva-

[3] Champion, H. G.: "Preliminary Survey of the Forest Types of India and Burma," *Indian Forest Records*, new series I, no. 1 (1936).

tions. Rainfall may be 60 to 250 inches. There are considerable floristic differences between the main area in the Himalaya and the mountain summits at the southern end of the peninsula. As elevations increase, the wet evergreen forests of laurel, oak, and chestnut, but without conifers, change to moist temperate forests with pine and beautiful Himalayan cedar. Trees may be as high as 150 feet. These forests, comparable to those of the temperate zone in Europe and North America, flourish at altitudes ranging from 5,000 to 11,000 feet. The dry temperate forest is present on the inner ranges of the Himalaya where rainfall is under 40 inches. Winter snow covers the ground to a depth of 7 feet at 6,000 feet elevation, 14 feet at 8,000 feet, and 18 feet at 10,000 feet.

Subtropical mountain forests are found on the Nilgiri and Cardamon Hills, the higher mountains of the Assam frontier, the Himalayan foothills, and in Baluchistan. Those in the south and northeast are of the wet type. Along the central Himalaya pine forests prevail, while in the northwest are subtropical dry forests. The subtropical wet forests have average temperatures of 65 to 75°F and a wide range of rainfall, always in excess of 65 inches and up to that of Cherrapunji. Trees generally rise 70 to 100 feet with a shrubby undergrowth and many vines. Elevations range from 3,000 to 6,000 feet. Oaks and chestnuts are usually present. Subtropical pine forests characteristically have a pure stand of hard pine. The rainfall is 40 to 50 inches, and the formation extends continuously on the southern slopes of the Siwalik Range. Annual fires, started by natives to drive out wild animals, or in order that the ash may fertilize the soil, prevent the development of undergrowth but favor the growth of grass for grazing. Dry evergreen subtropical forest is found in the Punjab foothills and elsewhere in the northwest.

Special conditions of winter rain along the Madras coast and in Ceylon account for the tropical dry evergreen forests. Hard-leaved trees predominate, 30 to 40 feet high.

Thorn forests with acacia, mimosa, and eu-

No mountain barrier is more imposing than the Himalaya. Here Kanchenjunga towers above the Siwalik foothills, with the resort city of Darjeeling in the left foreground. (*Ewing Galloway*)

phorbia growing 15 to 30 feet high are found in the drier Deccan and around the Thar Desert, where the rainfall is from 10 to 30 inches. This is an area with little carry-over of moisture so that the soil becomes hard and baked during the dry season. Grazing replaces agriculture.

Tropical dry deciduous forests have a continuous but uneven canopy. Many of the same species present in the moist forests also grow here but are reduced to 50 feet in height. Single species cover wide areas. The lower rainfall limit is 30 inches, and the undergrowth is drought-resistant, or xerophytic. There is a striking contrast between the entirely leafless period with exposed soil, and the luxuriant growth after the rains.

The tropical moist deciduous forest is more open and has purer stands. Trees reach 100 feet in height, with a bamboo undergrowth. Climb-

ing vines are large and abundant. This is the representative monsoon forest, adjusted to periodic drought, although the term may also be applied to drier groups. During the rainless period the trees lose most of their leaves and the country has a parched appearance. Drought becomes apparent in March and April rather than in the cooler season, and new leaves may arrive before the monsoon rains. Mean temperatures average above 75°F, and the rainfall is 60 to 80 inches with a dry season of four to six months. These forests are the typical home of the important teak tree. A variant of this type is the sal forest, which flourishes with rainfall down to 40 inches; the sal tree also furnishes a valuable commercial timber. Soil variations produce local subsidiary types, among them impenetrable thickets of bamboo.

The Ganges, Mahanadi, and other east-coast

rivers meet the sea in low delta plains, threaded with distributaries. Large areas are flooded with each high tide. Salt water covers the sea margins of such deltas, but river flood water inundates the interior areas. In such situations there are tropical tidal forests, as in the Sundarbans southeast of Calcutta. Dense stands of mangroves rising to 100 feet are characteristic along tidal channels.

Tropical semievergreen forests border the evergreen types on the lowlands, where rainfall is somewhat less or where the soil is porous. The forest is dense and from 80 to 120 feet tall. Evergreens predominate in the lower canopy with deciduous varieties rising above them.

The tropical wet evergreen forest is composed of numerous broad-leaf species without local dominants. Many trees are 150 feet tall, often with straight trunks for 100 feet. The canopy is very dense and is laced together by vines. Owing to the dense shade, ground vegetation is nearly absent, or there may be an undergrowth of canes. Temperature means are near 80°F, and the rainfall is 80 inches or even 120 inches for optimum conditions, so that this is a true rain forest. The longer the dry season, the heavier must be the total rainfall. These forests reach their greatest development in Ceylon, Assam, the foothills of the eastern Himalaya, and the Western Ghats.

The term jungle properly refers to rank growth of brush, vines, and tall grass, often growing on abandoned land, and not to a dense rain forest as the word is sometimes incorrectly used. It may also be applied to tropical deciduous forests.

Two other types of vegetation deserve com-

The Terai swamps mark the border between the Indo-Gangetic lowland and Nepal. These hunters are seeking tigers. (*Ewing Galloway*)

ment, bamboo and palms. Bamboo is a grass, but may grow to heights of 50 feet and reach a diameter of 3 inches. Here as elsewhere in Monsoon Asia, bamboo finds a wide use for houses and scaffolding, furniture, implements, fodder, fuel, and for making paper. Clumps of bamboo are found around many villages, and the output numbers hundreds of millions of stems a year.

Palms are as varied as bamboo, and more widespread since they are present in both dry and saline areas. Coconut palms border most coasts. While the wood has little structural value, palm fiber, or coir, is used for ropes and mats, and several varieties of palms supply material for intoxicating beverages. Fuel is another byproduct.

SOILS

Though only the beginnings of soil surveys have been made, we can recognize four major soil types in Indo-Pakistan: alluvial soils of the Indo-Gangetic plain, some with steppe or desert characteristics; the black *regur* soils of the Deccan; the red soils of the southern and eastern peninsula; and the soils with lateritic characteristics.

The older Pleistocene alluvium, often referred to as the diluvium, is reddish-brown in color with lime concretions from one to four inches in diameter which are known as kunkur. This soil is the *bhangar,* in contrast to the modern alluvium or *khadar.* Present-day alluvial soils are more sandy and seldom contain concretions. The modern deltas and flood plains of the Ganges, Indus, and smaller rivers exemplify the newer alluvium, while the older alluvium occupies interstream areas with elevations up to 180 feet above the rivers. Both bhangar and khadar are fertile, but the water table is lower in the former, and its higher elevation makes it more difficult to irrigate. Rajasthan and the Thar Desert are covered with soils that show steppe and desert features including a veneer of wind-blown loess. Some of these grassland soils extend well down the

Ganges valley into regions now naturally covered with forest.

These various alluvial soils cover 300,000 square miles, and provide livelihood for nearly half the people of South Asia.

The black soils, or regur, range from deep black to brown and gray. The upper horizon is 3 to 6 feet thick, and has a high content of clay, which gives it water-holding capacity and unusual stickiness. The soils have a fairly large iron and aluminum content, adequate lime and magnesium, and some organic matter. In some respects, these tropical black soils are similar to temperate chernozems, but their organic content is very low. They differ from lateritic soils in that the latter develop with heavier rainfall and a forest cover, while regur requires a steppe environment. Most of the regur overlies basaltic lava flows. It was once assumed that the distinctive color resulted from the weathering of this rock, but typical regur is also known to overlie metamorphic rocks. The nature of the coloring matter is still uncertain but is in part both a mineral constituent and organic carbon. These soils spread over the interior of the peninsula east of Bombay.

Red-soil types grade from black to brown. They are usually deficient in organic matter but contain lime and magnesia. Iron and aluminum compounds are abundant. Such tropical soils cover large areas in Madras, Mysore, Orissa, Bihar, and the eastern interior.

Laterite was first described in India, and is a geological formation, rather than a true soil, developed as a residual product exclusively on flat surfaces, often of peneplain characteristics. The underlying bedrock may be of various types, usually crystalline. As a result of long-continued tropical leaching, laterite is a rock of porous and slaglike structure, unequally permeated with iron oxides and varying in color from reddish brown to yellow. White kaolinized spots may occur. Silica has been almost removed by leaching. Iron and aluminum oxides are abundant, often forming 90 per cent of the whole, so that the respective laterites become an iron or aluminum ore.

Development of such laterite may have required one or more geologic epochs, possibly since the Eocene. Laterite is properly to be regarded as a geological formation, even though formed near the surface, and not as a true soil. Where freshly exposed it may be easily quarried; on exposure to the air it becomes rock hard. Since it is already the end product of weathering, it is indefinitely durable, as shown in ancient buildings.

Where modern soils develop on these laterites, they are termed lateritic. Since the parent material is already highly weathered, environmental factors can modify it but slightly. Two types of lateritic soils may be distinguished: those formed at upper levels on original laterite, and those developed at low levels or on slopes over redeposited laterite. True lateritic soils are confined to relatively small areas in Ceylon, northeastern Madras, the Western Ghats, and Chota Nagpur. High temperature, abundant rainfall, and tropical forest cover are conditioning factors.

This summary omits the bog and coastal soils, the extensive area of saline and alkaline types in the deserts of the northwest, and areas of bare rock. Vertical zonations introduce many soil types on the slopes of the Himalaya. Mountain soils are likewise present in the Vindhya and Satpura Ranges, the Nilgiri and Cardamon Hills, and central Ceylon.

It is important to emphasize the fact that, although variations occur, tropical soils are of limited fertility. With high temperatures and heavy rainfall, plus variations in the height of the water table due to the monsoon, leaching and oxidation are far more active than in temperate lands. While the lush vegetation may yield large amounts of organic material, most of it decays so quickly that little is converted into humus. Tropical rain forests produce as much as 100 tons of organic matter per acre, but the rate of destruction exceeds the supply, so that sterile sandy soil with little humus or soluble mineral plant food lies directly on the surface.

Heavy rainfall results in rapid erosion, especially where hillsides have been cleared for cultivation. Runoff may be so rapid that slope soils seem virtually arid. The best soils thus tend to be in valley bottoms where fresh alluvium accumulates.

28 Indo-Pakistan People and Livelihood

Agriculture / Industry and Resources / Communications /
Planned Economy

AGRICULTURE

The soil provides the basis for livelihood in most of South Asia. Two-thirds of the people in India and Pakistan are farmers, as are a smaller fraction in Ceylon. The world of the average farmer ends at his horizon. His interest is centered in the village where he lives except for an occasional journey of a few miles to a bazaar or fair. Within this circle life follows a routine round of simple, stereotyped activ-

ities. With an eye on the sky for the monsoon and with his hands in the earth for food, man lives close to nature.

The agricultural landscape changes with the season and from north to south, but south of the Himalaya and east of the Thar Desert it all has a characteristic touch. The foliage is tropical and luxuriant; cultivated fields are tiny and of irregular shape as the result of generations of repeated subdivision; and livestock is abundant. The poverty of the people and the mud-and-straw houses reflect the marginal livelihood of the overcrowded land.

India, Pakistan, and Ceylon are lands of villages, more than 650,000 in number. Most of them are located away from paved roads or railways and are but little affected by the tides of nationalism that sweep the cities. Each settlement is nearly self-sufficient, with its own artisans, carpenters, and blacksmiths who furnish all needed tools. A shop or two supply the few material wants, and a temple or mosque cares for the religious needs. Traditional practices still suffice, and the high percentage of illiteracy makes changes difficult. Outside markets for farm produce are limited, so that increased labor brings few rewards. Recurrent years of poor crops pile up indebtedness to the local moneylender.

Despite extensive government efforts for agricultural improvement, the sheer magnitude of the reform problem means that for most farmers cultivation is still rudimentary. Plows are simple, iron-tipped sticks which stir but do not overturn the soil. In most areas they are light enough to be carried to the fields on the farmer's back, but in the sticky black soils of the Deccan the plows are heavier and require up to six yoke of oxen. Crops are reaped with a sickle, threshed by the feet of cattle, and winnowed in the wind. The mattock is used in place of a spade.

Some progress has been made in consolidating scattered holdings, though many farmers with no more than 3 or 4 acres in all till one or two dozen farm plots. Considerable acreages, especially of irrigated wheat and cotton, are now sown with improved seeds. Each area has its agricultural research stations.

The national income needs desperately to be raised, but there is little hope of improvement in the near future through mining, lumbering, fishing, animal husbandry, or industry. Agriculture must remain the dominant occupation. The cultivated area has risen gradually during each decade, but population increases as fast. Additional areas may be double-cropped as water becomes available, and yields may be increased through better seed selection and farm management. Present yields are much below world averages.

Fertilization would materially increase the harvest, but farmers are too poor to purchase commercial preparations. Unfortunately for the future, India does not appear to have abun-

Since other domestic fuel is lacking, cakes of cow dung are widely used for cooking. (*Courtesy Paul F. Cressey*)

dant phosphates or other raw materials for the manufacture of mineral fertilizers. The large number of farm animals suggests the availability of manure, but in the absence of other fuel for domestic needs, some of the cattle and buffalo dung is made into cakes and burned. Compost piles are used, and to a limited extent, legumes are plowed under for green fertilizer. Rotation and fallowing are common practices, and the interplanting of legumes and grains also helps to maintain fertility.

Land which is reported as arable, including that used for tree crops, in India, Pakistan, Nepal, and Ceylon amounts to 475 million acres, of which some 300 million acres are actually sown each year. The rest of the arable land is so infertile or so dry that it must lie fallow in alternate years. Since the total area of South Asia amounts to 1,110 million acres, less than one-third is agriculturally productive. It amounts to only ½ acre per capita.

Rice is the leading crop, covering about 25 per cent of the crop area. Sorghums and millets such as jowar, bajra, and raggee together account for 30 per cent. Wheat covers 10 per cent. Oil seeds and cotton each represent 7 per cent of the crop area.

Forests occupy 150 million acres, many of them in peripheral areas such as Assam, Nepal, or Ceylon. Wasteland and other unproductive areas, including the Thar Desert, measure 450 million acres. Permanent pastures, all of them quite poor, account for 30 million acres. This gives a total of 630 million acres without any

agricultural use, more than half of the area of South Asia.

Rice is the staple crop in all the wetter areas, but it is too expensive for the poorer classes who live on sorghums and millet. Rice culture follows the rainfall lines. Where the rainfall exceeds 80 inches, rice is dominant; with 40 to 80 inches it is still important; under 40 inches it is grown only with irrigation. The principal areas are the lower Ganges and the east-coast deltas. The total area is about 110 million acres. Two crops a year are grown near Madras, but elsewhere one crop is the rule, succeeded by a fallow period or a period of legume raising. Imports of several million tons a year are essential, chiefly from Rangoon.

Some rice is sown broadcast, but transplanting is customary. An acre of seedlings will suffice for six to ten times the field area, and the young rice is ready to be transplanted after four to five weeks in seedbeds. Unhusked rice is known as paddy, and the flooded fields where it is grown are commonly called paddy fields.

Three varieties of millets and sorghums are widespread, occupying some 125 million acres. Jowar sorghum is comparable to Chinese kaoliang and looks like American broom corn in the field. It grows 8 to 12 feet tall and resembles corn, except that it has a cluster of grain at the top. Jowar is the most widespread of the sorghums, grown chiefly in Malwa and the western Deccan, where the rainfall is 20 to 40 inches. It is usually a summer crop but may be raised in the winter in the south. Jowar is grown for

Land Use in South Asia [1]

(in thousand hectares)

	Total area	Arable land incl. fallow and orchards	Irrigated land	Forest and wood-lands
India	328,888	159,662	22,534	51,030
Pakistan	94,625	24,825	10,051	2,562
Ceylon	6,561	1,523	255	3,546
Nepal	14,080	3,894	—	4,532
All South Asia	444,154	189,904	32,840	61,670

[1] United Nations, Food and Agricultural Organization: *Production Yearbook*, 1960.

Bananas are widely grown, as is shown in this scene in Mirzapur, North India. (*Courtesy Ford Foundation*)

both food and fodder. Bajra millet is more tolerant and hence can be planted on poorer soils; it is not so tall. It has much the same regional distribution as jowar, although in any particular area it takes the poorer sites. Both of these sorghums are rotated with cotton. Raggee millet requires a rice climate but will grow on poorer soils; its locale is the southern Deccan.

Wheat is the third crop of India and Pakistan, grown principally in the Punjab and on the Malwa Plateau. The crop area is about 40 million acres. Nearly half of this is irrigated, for wheat is planted after the summer rains and otherwise depends upon stored ground moisture and the scanty precipitation from winter cyclonic storms. New irrigation projects in the Sind and the Punjab have materially increased wheat production. The yield per acre is low, but India with Pakistan ranks fourth in world acreage. In some years Karachi has an export surplus.

Other food crops are barley, millet, corn, legumes, sugar cane, and many vegetables. Barley competes with wheat but is crowded onto the poorer soils in the drier interior. In the absence of a meat diet, legumes are significant. Gram, or chick-pea, accounts for 25 million acres. It is always a winter crop and provides a valuable rotation for soil fertility. The acreage of sugar cane is the largest in the world, but the yield per acre is so low that imports are necessary. Cane is raised in the Ganges lowland, with the best yields in the central valley. Great improvements are possible in varieties of cane and in cultivation practices.

Cotton is grown very widely; the black soil zone with under 50 inches of rainfall in the Deccan behind Bombay leads in the total of 25 million acres. The acreage in India and Pakistan exceeds that of the United States, but the production is less than half, and Indian yields per acre are among the lowest in the

world; Pakistan does a little better. The fiber is coarse and too short for the best cloth. Most of the raw cotton is used by Indian mills, but some cotton is still spun in the homes. One of the complaints of Indian nationalists was that modern European-style industry displaced the old household looms which provided work for the slack season and offered a modicum of income. Factory-made cloth is better, but the peasant has little cash with which to buy it.

Oil seeds include sesame, linseed from flax grown for its oil rather than its fiber, rape, mustard, and castor bean. Peanuts were not reported prior to 1911, but by 1960 were grown on 15 million acres. They now form the chief vegetable-oil export and make this realm the leading world source. Many parts of the plateau share in the production, chiefly the drier areas. Indian linseed once dominated the world market but has been surpassed by the Argentine product. Coconut oil is an important export from the west coast and from Ceylon.

Jute is the coarse fiber used for making burlap and gunny sacks. Pakistan with India supplies three-fourths of the world's yield, grown on 3,500,000 acres about evenly divided between the two countries. One area dominates production, the wet delta lands of Bengal, where fall floods inundate wide areas and make it necessary to cut the crop under 3 or 4 feet of water. After the plant is gathered, it is soaked or retted until the fiber is loosened. At the time of the partition of India, the jute was grown in what is now Pakistan while the mills for processing jute and the export facilities were concentrated across the border in Calcutta. Each country now has its own jute-growing area and mills.

Tea was introduced from China about 1850, although it is now known that some varieties are indigenous in Assam. The hills of central Ceylon form the largest single area, followed by the Brahmaputra valley of India and the district south of the Khasi Hills in eastern Pakistan. Tea is also grown near Darjeeling and elsewhere in the Himalaya foothills, and in the Cardamon and Nilgiri Hills at the extreme end of the peninsula.

Some of the earliest exports of India were her spices, such as curry, chilies, pepper, ginger, nutmeg, and cloves. Coffee and cinchona (for quinine) are raised in the southernmost hills, and tobacco grows in the foothills of the Himalaya. Indian indigo was known to the Greeks and Romans, but the synthetic dye has nearly eliminated the native product.

Tropical fruits exist in wide variety. The cultivated mango has a delicious flavor—though a Westerner may have to learn to like it—and in the summer is the chief fruit for the poorer classes. Other fruits are pumeloes, limes and other citrus fruits, custard apples, bananas, guava, and papaya. In the northwest apples, peaches, and pears are raised.

Crop seasons are divided between the summer-planted and autumn-harvested *kharif* crops, and the winter-grown rabi crops. The distinction is not entirely seasonal, since kharif crops may be grown in the far south during the winter, thanks to its rain. The planting of summer kharif crops is delayed until after the first monsoon rains; if these arrive unusually late, difficulty follows. The chief winter rabi crops are wheat, barley, oats, and legumes; typical kharif crops are early rice, grain sorghums, most cotton, and jute.

India and Pakistan are credited with a quarter of the world's cattle, but they are certainly the poorest quarter. Humped cows or oxen and water buffalo are found everywhere, with camels in the dry northwest and a few elephants in the wetter east. Hindus hold the cow in religious esteem, and since the taking of life is forbidden, the animals are never killed no matter how feeble or diseased they may be. Working bullocks must be fed, but cows are usually left to pick up what they can find. Millions of useless cattle compete for food urgently needed for work animals. Muslims, on the other hand, have no taboos with respect to cattle.

Hybrid corn offers promise of greatly increased yields, here grown in North India. (*Courtesy International Cooperation Administration*)

India and Pakistan have a quarter of the world's cattle, but many are poorly fed and unable to do hard farm work. These bullocks are plowing a rice field at Ghandigram. (*Courtesy Indian Consulate, New York City*)

Hindu India provides a contrast to China in its source of farm power. In India oxen or buffaloes do the work; in China human labor is more depended upon. Not all the draft animals in India are efficient, but their abundance is significant. In both countries rural mechanization is in its infancy.

The dairy industry is but little developed, and water buffalo milk is preferred to cow's milk since it is richer in fat. A few areas specialize in cattle breeding, with fine strains in Gujarat and Nellore. Good pasture is limited.

Hindus and many Muslims eat no meat, but hides constitute a valuable export.

The soil directly supports two-thirds of the people, and indirectly all but a small fraction. The northern lowland is more congested than the plateau, but the concentration of people represents available food possibilities rather than relative prosperity. Probably each region in South Asia is filled to its capacity. As population increases, the pressure for food becomes more acute. Since harvests depend on rain and since agriculture supplies most of the national

income, it may well be said that the government's budget is a gamble against the monsoon.

Many problems account for the serious status of agriculture and make the solution uncertain. Economic factors of poor land and staggering debt combine with low market prices. Religious prohibitions against the elimination of unproductive livestock as well as the avoidance of a meat diet are serious barriers. Lack of fertilizer is especially unfortunate in a land of poor tropical soils, naturally low in organic matter because of the rapid oxidation in a warm, moist climate.

Behind all these problems lies the tremendous total of some 600 million people. With such numbers and with such social and political problems, the best agricultural plans are difficult to put in operation.

India's history has been punctuated at frequent intervals by disastrous famines, during the worst of which tens of millions have died and wide tracts of country have been desolated. Pestilence follows famine. In 1769 to 1770, 10

million people or one-third of the population, perished in the Bengal famine. From 1369 to 1407, a famine devastated the Deccan and so reduced the population that land went out of cultivation for years.

In the famine of 1899 to 1900, 475,000 square miles were affected. At this time the rainfall over most of India was extremely low; in several localities practically no rain fell. Thus a great fodder shortage resulted, and cattle died by the million. Although actual deaths from starvation were low, the extensive outbreaks of cholera and malaria raised death rates tremendously.

Famines arise when large groups fail to produce enough food for their own needs and lack means of obtaining it from other sources. Should this disaster recur, relief may necessitate close cooperation between India and Pakistan. What will happen if East Bengal has another famine such as that experienced by all Bengal in 1943? Will West Pakistan be able to furnish food? Will ships be available to transport this food? How much will India be expected to do to alleviate such a situation? If the Deccan area has another widespread famine, will Pakistan furnish surplus food? Close understanding between India and Pakistan is obviously essential.

INDUSTRY AND RESOURCES

Five primary activities contribute to the wealth of a nation: agriculture, animal husbandry, fishing, forestry, and mining. Only the first has been of major significance in India and Pakistan. Secondary production involves the manufacture of primary materials, but South Asian industry is restricted to the products of agriculture and the few mines. The arrival of a significant industrial era for India has long been forecast, but its appearance is gradual and its future problematical. Despite the limited extent of modernization, the sheer bulk of production is so great that India and Pakistan rank as one of the major industrial areas of the world.

Long before the arrival of Europeans, certain arts and crafts were considerably developed. Few countries have matched Indian textile skills in cotton, wool, and silk. Cotton cloth, woven from long-staple varieties of cotton, was prized by the Greeks. Artistic temple and household vessels were made of copper and brass. Superior steel was exported several centuries before Christ, some of it to be worked into "Damascus" swords. When the British arrived, they eagerly sought the muslin from Dacca, the carpets and shawls from Kashmir, the marble inlay from Agra, dyes such as indigo, and a variety of spices.

To medieval Europe India was synonymous with gold and precious stones. Pliny referred to Indian gold in A.D. 77. Ancient India knew the arts of smelting and made use of iron, copper, and bronze. Primitive slag heaps are widespread. Yet it is now evident that the concentration of material wealth in the hands of a few did not imply rich mineral resources. Thus many of the gold placers now worked yield such a low return that only the cheapest labor can operate them. Production figures reflect human poverty rather than intrinsic mineral wealth.

Village handicrafts provide simple household pottery, iron plows, sickles and hoes for agriculture, coarse cotton cloth, vegetable oils, and leather. There are wide contrasts between the luxury items produced for the wealthy or for export and the simple peasant needs. The lack of an intermediate market and the cost of transport restrict traditional industry to the village and its requirements.

Modern technology and the march of world events are profoundly altering all this. Whether the result was deliberately planned or not, British rule effectively destroyed many Indian crafts and turned the country into an exporter of raw materials and an importer of manufactured goods.

The mineral production of India is strikingly concentrated in the uplands 200 miles west of Calcutta. Coal, iron ore, limestone, and manganese are in fair proximity; out of these has grown a large iron and steel industry. Elsewhere mineral deposits are widely scattered. Pakistan is not an important producer. Geological studies make it clear that India, Pakistan, and Ceylon have a considerable variety of minerals, but in terms of both area and population, the known reserves appear quite low. The major exceptions are iron ore, manganese, and mica. Only a fraction of 1 per cent of the people are engaged in mining.

India's coal reserves down to a depth of 2,000 feet are estimated at 66 billion tons. Most of this is good bituminous coal of Permo-Carboniferous age in the Damodar valley in Bengal and Bihar, and in the valleys of the Mahanadi and Godavari. These occurrences are down-faulted remains of fresh-water basins. One seam in the Bokaro field is 126 feet thick. The fact that only 2 billion tons are suitable for metallurgical coke may be a serious industrial handicap; high-quality reserves may be exhausted in a few decades. Largely undeveloped Tertiary lignite or subbituminous reserves are present in Assam and the Punjab. Pakistan's coal is limited and of poor quality.

Production in 1960 exceeded 50 million tons in India and reached almost 1 million tons in Pakistan. The supply is barely adequate for the needs of transportation, factories, and smelting, so that the west coast sometimes imports South African coal. Household consumption accounts for only a small part of the total.

Ninety per cent of the coal is produced in the Chota Nagpur Plateau of Bengal and Bihar, where many beds are exceptionally thick. The principal mines are at Raniganj, Jharia, Karanpura, and Bokaro.

Petroleum appears to be entirely lacking in the Ganges lowland and the plateau, but there is a small output of oil and gas in West Pakistand, the Punjab, Assam, and East Pakistan.

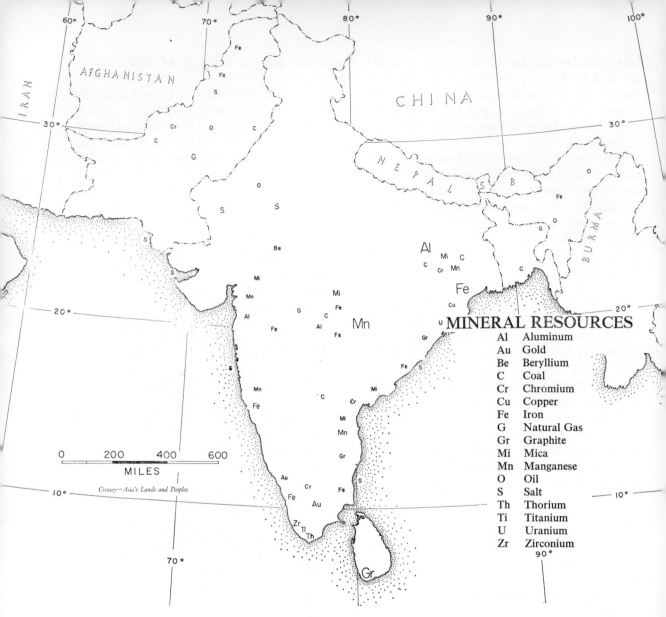

India is abundantly supplied with iron ore and with manganese but is seriously deficient in coal and oil. This map is limited to resources in production.

Natural gas is especially important in Pakistan because of its shortage of coal.

Hydroelectricity is of increasing importance in connection with the comprehensive river projects. One of the early installations was in the Western Ghats near Bombay, where pipes descend 1,725 feet and develop a pressure of 750 pounds per square inch against the turbines. Electric power is also developed on the Jhelum in Kashmir, the Cauvery in Madras, and elsewhere. The hydroelectric potential of South Asia has been roughly estimated as 500 million kilowatts, but only 2 per cent of this has been developed.

All these sources of power may be enlarged, but the total power resources appear modest in world or even Asian terms, and their distribution is highly regional, so that heavy transport charges are involved where coal must be used at a distance from the mines. In the absence of coal, hydroelectricity has an important future, but the seasonal rainfall necessitates expensive reservoirs in all installations south of the Himalaya. Much of South Asia has no nearby source of industrial power.

The wide distribution of the native iron industry suggests, quite rightly, a similarly extensive occurrence of iron ore. But some old mines are not of modern economic significance. At the time of Alexander the Great, 326 B.C., India was as familiar with iron and steel as was Greece. King Ashoka's column of wrought iron dates from the third or fourth century.

Hematite ore of exceptionally high quality is present in the northeastern plateau, chiefly in the Singhbhum district in Bihar and Orissa. The chief outcrop is a range 40 miles long, which is mined cheaply by open-cut methods. The ore is associated with banded jasper, and the average iron content is from 60 to 70 per cent, the latter representing the theoretical maximum. Both quality and tonnage are better than those of the ores near Lake Superior, with conservative estimates of 1 billion tons of "actual" ore and another 1 or 2 billion tons of "potential" ore. This iron belt is by far the largest and best reserve in all Asia, with the possible exception of some in the Soviet Union.

Iron ore is widely distributed in Mysore; hematite schist and limonite are mined in the Baba Budan Hills. Other high-grade ores are present near Goa, within 4 miles of a harbor. Gwalior has several ore deposits, but they are remote from coal. Lateritic ores with 30 per cent iron are widespread in the peninsula.

One of the largest iron ore bodies of the world may lie in the Salem district southwest of Madras. The ore is a rich magnetite but is not suited for modern blast-furnace treatment, and there is no nearby coal. Similar magnetite ores in Archean rocks are found widely in the plateau but are not commercially workable.

India clearly has fabulous reserves of iron ore, much of it of exceptionally high grade. Reserves should last for millenniums, rather than centuries, but the necessary coal is quite limited.

Steel is produced at several major centers, all in the Chota Nagpur Hills a few hundred miles west of Calcutta, where coal and iron ore lie in close proximity. The oldest plant is at Jamshedpur, built in 1911 with private Indian capital but using American engineers and equipment. About 1960 new plants came into operation at Bhilai in Madhya Pradesh, built by the Soviet Union; at Durgapur in Bengal, constructed with United Kingdom assistance; and at Rourkela in Orissa, with German engineering but entirely Indian capital. Each of these four plants had an initial capacity of about one million tons of steel a year; Jamshedpur now has more than doubled this output. Steel is also made at Asansol and Kulti. Blast furnaces making pig iron but without steel processing are present in the southern peninsula at Bhadravati, and elsewhere. Whereas South Asia was an importer of iron and steel products until 1960, these new plants may provide a surplus for export. Pakistan lacks suitable raw materials for a steel industry.

The largest steel plant is that of the Tata Iron and Steel Company, Ltd., at Jamshedpur, 155 miles west of Calcutta, one of the largest single mills in the British Commonwealth. Rich 60 to 70 per cent hematite ore comes 45 miles from Gurumaishini in the Singhbhum district; coal is brought 110 miles from Jharia; and dolomite flux is transported 40 miles. Manganese is nearby. Assembly costs are less than half of those in the United States or England, and the Tata plant is one of the cheapest producers of pig iron in the world. Steel costs are higher since there is little scrap for melting. To produce 1 ton of pig iron at Jamshedpur requires 1½ tons of iron ore, 1⅔ tons of coking coal, and ½ ton of dolomite flux.

India ranks second to the Soviet Union as a producer of manganese. Production of this ferroalloy fluctuates with the world output of steel, in which process it is used to remove oxygen and sulfur, or in some cases as a toughening alloy. India's reserves amount to 110 million tons, and the output is about 1 million tons a year. Deposits are widely scattered, with the largest reserves in Madhya Pradesh and Bombay. Deposits of manganese represent residual concentrations from long-continued weathering of basic rocks. The local steel industry uses one-tenth of the supply; most of the rest goes to England, France, and the United States.

Aluminum was not produced until 1939, when a plant was opened in Bengal. Copper ores from the Singhbhum district are smelted at Mandhandar in Bihar. There is little refining of other metals. Suitable raw materials for cement are widespread, but transportation costs for coal are so high that imported cement is used along the west coast of India and in Pakistan.

Chemicals are an essential part of modern industry and are so interdependent that the absence of one link may handicap many others. Most of the raw materials are available in India or Pakistan, but they are seldom near to both power and markets. Supplies of sulfuric acid are produced in India from imported materials; Pakistan has large amounts of sulfur.

The import and export of gold bullion has little relation to production or actual use. It represents rather speculation and the movement of wealth. In the nineteenth century, India was one of the largest buyers of gold and silver in the world. When Great Britain went off the gold standard in 1931, shipments of gold from India exceeded 1 billion dollars in eight years. There is a prosperous mining area in Mysore and numerous native operations elsewhere which report no statistics. The annual production amounts to several hundred thousand ounces.

Two characteristic minerals are sheet mica and graphite. Over three-quarters of the world's sheet mica comes from India. Excellent supplies in Bihar and Madras, plus cheap labor, make split sheets of muscovite available at low prices. Trimmed sheets are produced up to 80 square inches. Ceylon has long been noted for natural graphite, but artificial graphite has reduced the demand.

Sulfur and chromite are of some importance in Pakistan. Salt is mined in the Salt Range of Pakistan, and is evaporated from sea water along the coasts of Bombay and Madras.

The resource picture for India may be summarized in the table below.

Among the industries based on agricultural raw materials, the most important are textiles, manufactured chiefly in cotton mills around Bombay and jute mills near Calcutta. A part of Bombay's leadership in textiles is due to the initiative of Parsi industrialists, but the localization also reflects the concentration of cotton growing on the black regur soils of the Dec-

India's Mineral Sufficiency

Surplus for export	Adequate for present needs	Apparently inadequate
Aluminum	Chromium	Lead
Beryl	Coal	Nitrates
Gypsum	Copper	Petroleum
Iron	Glass sand	Phosphates
Manganese	Gold	Sulfur
Mica	Nickel	Zinc
Salt		
Thorium		
Titanium		
Zirconium		

Mica is one of India's distinctive minerals, mined in large sheets or "books" in the ancient rocks of the peninsula. (*Courtesy Government of India Information Services*)

can. Short-staple varieties of cotton predominate here, with improved long-staple cotton on the irrigated lands of the Indus. The growth of cotton was stimulated when the American Civil War cut off imported supplies, and the first successful mill started operations in 1853.

Jute production goes back a century. It is the cheapest of all fibers, the material being used for gunny sacks, burlap, coarse carpets, and cordage. The industry was highly centralized in Calcutta; in fact that city still dominates the world market. But following partition, Pakistan has developed its own mills. Jute production employs nearly as many workers as all the cotton mills together.

A similar concentration characterizes the other agricultural industries. Leather prepara-

tion is centered in Madras province on account of the availability of suitable bark for tanning purposes. Excellent cowhides as well as goatskins and sheepskins are exported to Europe and the United States. Hides and skins rank high in the export trade.

Sugar factories must lie close to the cane, so that Uttar Pradesh, Bihar, and Orissa lead in sugar mills.

The chief paper mills are close to the Calcutta market and to coal, but their raw material is sabi grass which comes 900 miles down the Ganges. At another mill, bamboo is used for pulp. This appears the most desirable material for future paper making, provided that the power may be secured cheaply. Lac, a resin secreted by an insect, is used in shellac and sealing wax, in lithographic ink, and as a stiffener in hats. Bengal and the central Ganges valley lead in its production. Neither India nor Pakistan has good kaolin for a high-grade pottery industry.

The countries of South Asia enjoy natural advantages with respect to competing imports. On the other hand, the chief markets are the coastal seaports accessible to foreign merchandise; and for interior industries the rail freight to the seaboard may equalize the seaborne charges from overseas. There are few shortages of essentials for basic industry. Coal, iron, and many other minerals are adequate for present needs, although probably not for a vast expansion comparable to that of Europe or perhaps of China.

One of the major problems in the future of industry is geographic. The essential raw materials are concentrated in a few localities, in many instances away from power and/or markets. Vast consuming areas are either without raw materials, as is true in the northern lowland, or do not have the power to develop what they possess. Bombay has hydroelectric power, a market, and a port, but no minerals. Calcutta has both port and market, and within 200 miles has the best association of coal and iron ore; it would seem to be the most promising area for heavy industry.

The bulk of the present industry is made up of consumers' goods rather than of machines or tools or producers' goods. It may be a long while before India or Pakistan becomes a great primary manufacturing region.

COMMUNICATIONS

Transportation has long presented a problem in India. Since Europeans approached South Asia from the sea, coastwise shipping was developed before modern internal communications. Unfortunately, the country has few good harbors. Coral reefs, delta shoals, and monsoon winds make it necessary at many ports for vessels to discharge cargo into lighters several miles offshore. There are few natural harbors

and several of those along the peninsula are cut off from their hinterland by mountain barriers.

Internal communications have been equally unsatisfactory. Rivers are alternately in flood or reduced to a mere trickle, so that few are navigable. The alluvial plains are entirely without road-making materials, and local travel is difficult during the muddy season. Neighboring villages are often cut off from each other during the rains, so that trade is limited.

Railway construction began in 1853. Unfortunately, several rail gauges have been used; as a result, passengers must sometimes change cars, and freight must break bulk en route. Half the mileage is in the Indian broad gauge, 5 feet 6 inches as compared with the United States standard of 4 feet 8½ inches. Two unconnected regions of meter gauge occur in the north and in the south. Narrow-gauge feeder or hill lines have tracks that are either 2 feet 6 inches or 2 feet.

In 1960 the railway total of India amounted to 35,000 miles as compared with 7,000 miles in Pakistan. In length of railway lines, India ranks fourth in the world, following the United States, the Soviet Union, and France.

When railways were first laid out they naturally radiated from Calcutta and Bombay, and to a lesser extent from the ports of Madras and Karachi. From Bombay, the chief western gateway, the distance north to Delhi is 861 miles. Another route, northeast from Bombay via Jubbulpore and Allahabad, is the main line to Calcutta, 1,223 miles or 40 hours away. A third route runs through the cotton area to Nagpur (at the center of India), and another provides connections with Madras, 794 miles to the southeast.

Four main railway lines radiate from Calcutta: north and east into Assam; northwest to the coal fields and up the Ganges valley 950 miles to Delhi; west to the important rail center of Nagpur in the central Deccan; and southwest along the coast to Madras, 1,030 miles or 37 hours distant. Madras is the focus of railway lines north to Vizagapatam, south to the port for Ceylon, and for two lines into the southern Deccan. Nagpur lies at the intersection of the commercial hinterlands of Madras, Calcutta, and Bombay. The trade boundary between the two latter ports continues north to Delhi. Thus each of the three seaports has approximately the same tributary area.

There is still no line connecting Burma with India. The island of Ceylon is only 22 miles from India, and there are intervening islands and sand bars, known as Adam's Bridge, which might make railway construction feasible.

Pakistan's railway pattern is the result of what was left over after partition. West Pakistan has a rail system which leads north from Karachi, but the boundary through the Punjab pays no attention to the established network and winds irregularly across important railways. East Pakistan has lines which were built to serve Calcutta, but traffic has been disrupted by the political frontier; a narrow-gauge line leads southeast to Chittagong, the only natural harbor. Proposals to link up the West Pakistan system with Europe involve the politically undesirable route through Afghanistan to Soviet Middle Asia or a line by way of the deserts of Iran.

The present rail net provides adequate coverage for most of the realm. The closest spacing follows the concentration of population in the Ganges valley. The sparsely inhabited areas of Baluchistan, the Thar Desert and western Rajasthan, the eastern Deccan, and Chota Nagpur in the northeast of the plateau have correspondingly low rail mileage. The Western Ghats fringe the sea so closely that no coastal railway extends south from Bombay. The Himalaya impose an abrupt barrier, although mountain lines reach the summer resorts or hill stations of Simla north of Delhi and Darjeeling north of Calcutta. Nepal and Bhutan are without railways.

The Pak-Indian realm has four major automobile highways, which follow a framework that dates back to the remote past. The most famous is the Grand Trunk Road, from the Khyber Pass via Delhi to Calcutta. The others connect Calcutta with Madras, Madras with Bombay, and Bombay with Delhi. It has proved difficult to provide a satisfactory system of improved automobile roads; in many areas they cost almost as much as railways. Only part of the Grand Trunk highway is paved; elsewhere water-bound macadam is the rule. Numerous rivers are unbridged, and sections of many important roads are liable to be inundated.

The lack of good roads has long been a handicap to trade, social coherence, and political unity, and no well-developed transportation by river, canal, or coastwise vessels has been developed to compensate for it. The country has never had an important north–south highway extending from the Indo-Gangetic lowlands into the peninsula; Jubbulpore commands the best gap. Cultural stagnation and regional isolation have been inevitable. Each invading monarchy has found India relatively easy to subdue but difficult to organize.

PLANNED ECONOMY

South Asia is eager to modernize. India and Pakistan are in the midst of ambitious plans, partly governmental, partly private, which are designed to improve all segments of the economy. While competition with China is not a direct objective, it is nevertheless clear that much of Asia is watching the relative progress of India and China with their contrasting procedures. In few other countries is the competition between Communism and democracy so critical.

India's first Five-Year Plan began in 1952. This and the successive plans were designed to raise the standard of living and provide for a richer and more varied life, specifically for "the most effective and balanced utilization of the country's resources." With population increasing at a rate of about 2 per cent a year, such goals can be achieved only through an even more rapid rise in the overall rate of production, so that the announced goal for the gross national product has been around 5 per cent per year.

Tractors are used on experimental farms, but the initial cost and the expense of fuel and upkeep seem to make them impractical for widespread adoption. This is an example of land reclamation in Madhya Pradesh. (*Courtesy Ford Foundation*)

Such increased production is no small task, especially in view of the limited capital available. The first plan encountered many difficulties. Shortages were universal; there was rarely enough food, and crop failures led to frequent famine; housing and sanitation were incredibly bad for millions; industry was developing but was not yet able to supply the nation's needs; and the government itself had growing pains.

The successive Indian plans have included allocations to agriculture and community development, irrigation and power, village and small industries, heavy industry and mining, transport and communications, and social services. These projects have involved a combina-

tion of private and public investment, with modest assistance from overseas sources.

Pakistan began its first Five-Year Plan in 1955, and the country's program was no less ambitious than that of India. For example, the second plan, ending in 1965, was designed to raise the gross national product by 20 per cent in five years, to increase the per capita income by 10 per cent, to raise food production 21 per cent, and to increase industrial production by 47 per cent. Here, as in India, such gains are meaningless unless population increases can be slowed down.

The official goals of both the first and second plans in Pakistan were "a standard of living for all the people as high as can be achieved with the resources available to it; education of all in accordance with their talents; victory over disease; adequate facilities for transport and communications . . . and evolution of the national culture in literature, art and science."

To finance the foreign exchange aspect of such development, Pakistan looks to the export of jute, cotton, tea, wool, and hides and skins, plus loans and grants.

The basic problem in both countries is the same: to locate and evaluate the undeveloped resources and to plan on their wise development. In a real sense, such an assessment is also the function of this volume. Geography deals with inventory and location; wise planning can-not take place without an awareness of "how much of what is where."

All of Asia is in the midst of dramatic transformation, and no one should visualize India, Pakistan, Ceylon, or even Nepal in terms of what may have been true a decade ago. The question is not of change, but of its rate and of the limitations to its effectiveness.

On the basis of known assets, South Asia has an impressive future—provided that population does not continue to explode. Even with the birth rate under control, it does not appear likely that India or Pakistan can ever match the industrial strength of Western Europe, Anglo-America, or the Soviet Union, and probably not that of China.

29 Regions of North India

*Indian Prospects / The Ganges Valley / The Brahmaputra Valley /
The Assam Mountains / The Himalayan Highlands / References
on India*

INDIAN PROSPECTS

The sovereign democratic Republic of India, officially known to Indians as Bharat, occupies three-quarters of South Asia, no less than 1.2 million square miles. While India is much smaller than China or the Soviet Union, its relative size tends to be belittled by map projections such as the Mercator which reduce the importance of areas near the equator.

India finds itself confronted with baffling internal problems at the very time when international tensions thrust it onto the world scene.

Americans who fail to appreciate India's struggle for domestic unity and desire for unaligned international status should refer to the similar period in their own history when the original colonies were reluctant to transfer sovereignty and when "no entangling alliances" was the rule. At the same time, the United States should recognize its geopolitical stake in Indian prosperity. If democracy and capitalism fail to yield a better life in India, and that soon, and if China demonstrates rapid material progress, the consequences in the developing nations of Asia and Africa may be very far-reaching.

India certainly aspires to international stature, in the Commonwealth, in the area of the Indian Ocean, and in United Nations affairs. But until her own house is in order and she can show a far higher agricultural and industrial development, she will lack the ability to carry much weight. Given a few decades of peace and development, India may rank as one of the great world powers.

Whereas the subcontinent's harborless coast was an effective international frontier in the days of sail, the Arabian Sea and the Bay of Bengal now provide a highway to the outside world. The Himalaya remain as a surface barrier, but already airlines link Delhi with Moscow. What was once a world apart is becoming a vital part of the international community.

Problems of expanding population are no less serious than the rapidly expanding economy. As O. H. K. Spate has well said, India needs more fertility in her fields and less fertility in her homes. Without a real net increase in productivity, disaster may follow.

Among India's internal problems has been that of reorganizing the 560 political units which it inherited from British days. These ranged from quasi-independent kingdoms and British provinces, thousands of square miles in extent and counting tens of millions of people, to a tiny estate of only 1 square mile and a population of 96. Some of the native states had been split into dozens of noncontiguous pieces. The allegiance of Kashmir is still a matter of dispute with Pakistan; it remains the only In-

The Political Divisions of India [1]

Division	Capital city	Area, square miles	Population, 1961 census
States			
Andhra Pradesh	Hyderabad	106,052	35,977,999
Assam	Shillong	84,899	11,860,059
Bihar	Patna	67,198	46,457,942
Gujarat	Ahmedabad	72,137	20,621,283
Jammu and Kashmir	Srinagar	86,024	—
Kerala	Trivandrum	15,003	16,875,199
Madhya Pradesh	Bhopal	171,210	32,394,375
Madras	Madras	50,132	33,650,917
Maharashtra	Bombay	118,903	39,504,294
Mysore	Bangalore	74,122	23,547,081
Orissa	Bhubaneswar	60,162	17,565,645
Punjab	Chandigarh	47,084	20,298,151
Rajasthan	Jaipur	132,150	20,146,173
Uttar Pradesh	Lucknow	113,452	73,752,914
West Bengal	Calcutta	33,928	34,967,634
Union Territories			
Delhi		573	2,644,058
Himachal Pradesh		10,880	1,348,982
Manipur		8,628	—
Tripura		4,036	1,141,492
Andaman and Nicobar Islands		3,215	63,438
Laccadive and other islands		11	24,108
North East Frontier Agency		—	—
Naga Hills		—	—
Republic of India	Delhi	1,259,797	432,840,844

[1] *Statesman's Yearbook,* 1961. To these totals must be added former Portuguese Goa, 1,619 square miles, population 637,591 (1950).

Since many provincial names have been changed since the independence of India and Pakistan, it may be helpful to have this map of traditional areas; some were British states; some were sovereign native states, of which there were once more than 500.

dian state with a Muslim majority. The new India is a federation of sixteen states, with residual powers vested in the central government in Delhi.

Four of the states in northern India are dominantly Hindi in language. They are Uttar Pradesh, the northern province, which is a new name for the former United Province; Madhya Pradesh, the central province; Bihar; and the Punjab, which includes the eastern part of the old British Punjab. Uttar Pradesh leads all the states in population. Three states in the west which use Indo-Aryan languages are Maharashtra, Gujarat, and Rajasthan; the languages are Gujarati and Marathi. Maharashtra ranks third in area and third in population; arid

The complex political divisions of India reflect the confusion which attended the collapse of the Mogul dynasty, the imposition of British rule following the penetration of the British East India Company, and the expression of nationalism and communal feelings following independence.

Rajasthan is second in area but toward the bottom in population. Three small eastern states, also speaking Indo-Aryan languages, are Assam, West Bengal, and Orissa. Nagaland is a new state on the Burma frontier, created in 1961.

Dravidian languages prevail in four southern states: Telegu is spoken in Andhra Pradesh;

Kanarese, in Mysore; Tamil, in Kerala and Madras.

The sixteenth state is Jammu and Kashmir. Since it continues in dispute with Pakistan, a paragraph on its recent history may be appropriate at this point. During the period of British domination, some of the various princely states had Muslim rulers as holdovers from the Mogul empire; others had Hindu rulers. When the region became independent, the theory was that the respective rulers would decide whether to join India or Pakistan. Thus the Maharajah of Hyderabad, deep in the peninsula, refused to join India, even though his subjects were overwhelmingly Hindu, and military coercion was necessary. The population of Kashmir is strongly Muslim, but its ruler was a Hindu who decided to join India.

In addition to the provinces, India has a number of territories such as the federal capital district at Delhi; the former Punjab hill country in Himachal Pradesh; hill lands next to Assam known as Manipur and Tripura; island groups such as the Andamans; and the North East Frontier Agency. Bhutan and Sikkim are small Himalayan states under Indian oversight. Nepal is completely independent.

No less real are the environmental and human contrasts which make India so diverse. Such coherence as India possesses derives from propinquity and physical boundaries, and from Hindu culture, rather than from a sense of national loyalty. Europe is no more diverse or difficult to unite than South Asia. To understand India, we must examine its land, climate, and people, and must see them state by state and region by region.

The preceding three chapters have dealt with South Asia as a whole; the realm will now be broken down into geographic regions. Within the South Asian realm are many diverse environments, here grouped into two geographic provinces and sixteen regions. Since these subdivisions deal primarily with visible elements of the landscape, they largely ignore the political frontiers. Nations impose tariff barriers and influence the movement of commodities, and thus have an inescapable bearing on human geography. Man cannot alter the patterns of rain and surface and soil; and only with difficulty can he change the cultural landscape.

Five of these geographic regions are in the Indo-Gangetic lowland and three in the encircling mountains. Those which are largely in India will be described in this chapter, while those largely in Pakistan will be considered in that chapter. Five regions are in the plateau to the south, plus Ceylon, and form the geographic province of South India.

The regions to be considered within North India are the Ganges valley, the Brahmaputra valley, the Himalayan highlands, and the Assam Mountains.

THE GANGES VALLEY

The Ganges rises in the snow-crowned Himalaya and flows 1,500 miles through the Hindustan lowland. Along its banks are the classical cities of Hindu history. The Ganges landscape typifies the agricultural regime and population density made possible by the monsoon.

The region is sharply bounded by hills to the north and south, but grades imperceptibly east and west where rainfall changes bring transitions in crops. Within the area lie most of Uttar Pradesh and the northern half of Bihar, a total of about 120,000 square miles and some 125 million people. The Ganges delta forms a separate geographic region, but since it lies largely within Pakistan, its features are described in the chapter on that country.

Beneath the valley is an accumulation of sand and clay to unplumbed depths, ancient alluvial deposits spread by Tertiary and Quaternary rivers in a vast geosyncline. The relief is

CALCUTTA. Elevation 21 feet, average temperature 80°F, annual precipitation 63 inches. Rainfall is concentrated during the summer monsoon.

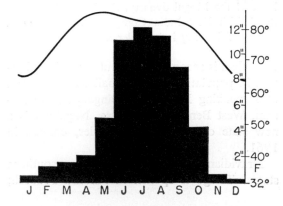

almost featureless, with an elevation of only 700 feet at Delhi. The Ganges has two main tributaries: the Jumna which joins it from the west and south, and the Gogra from the north.

The rivers carry great quantities of silt in their flood stage, and its accumulation has built extensive natural levees, often capped by artificial embankments. When these are overtopped by flood, widespread inundation results; at times a new channel is formed and lakes or swamps are developed along the old course. Between the valleys, higher ground prevents flooding. The present flood plain or alluvial levels are called the khadar; the older surfaces, the bhangar.

The soils of these areas of older and higher alluvium contain calcium carbonate nodules known as kunkur which are used for making lime or surfacing roads. Capillary action during the dry winter brings water to the surface, where its evaporation concentrates soluble salts

CHERRAPUNJI. (Right) Elevation 4,309 feet, average temperature 64°F, annual precipitation 425 inches. This hill station in Assam is India's wettest. Since rainfall is so great, the scale of this graph differs from the others.

DELHI. (Below) Elevation 714 feet, average temperature 77°F, annual precipitation 25 inches. As the monsoon advances up the Ganges valley, rainfall becomes progressively less.

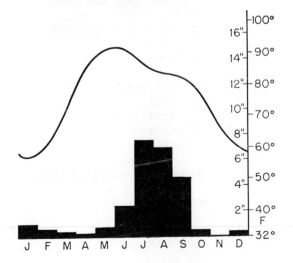

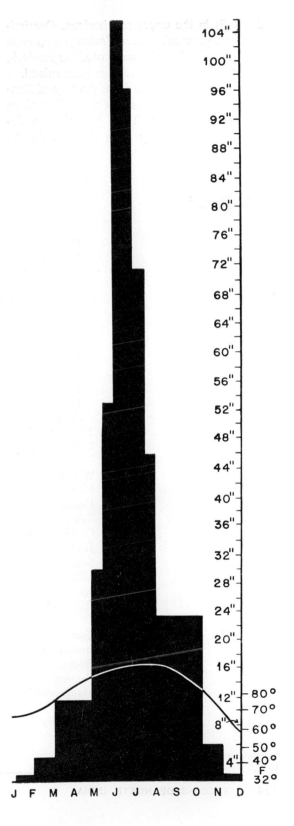

and alkalis in the upper soil horizon. Overirrigation and poor subsurface drainage aggravate the situation in the drier parts of Uttar Pradesh, where 3 million acres have thus been ruined.

The summer monsoon from the Bay of Bengal is turned to the west up the valley along the mountain barrier. Thus precipitation decreases westward away from the sea. At the same time, maximum summer temperatures are everywhere high. Patna in Bihar has 47 inches of rain and maximum temperatures of 114°F. For Allahabad to the west the figures are 42 inches and 117°F; Cawnpore (Kanpur) has 32 inches and 117°F; Agra has 27 inches and has reached 117°F; Delhi near the western edge receives only 25 inches and has a temperature

India Data [1]

Area (with Goa)	1,261,602 square miles
Population (with Goa)	437,073,429 (1961 census, incomplete)
Bombay	4,146,491
Calcutta	2,926,498
Madras	1,725,216
Hyderabad	1,252,337
Gujarat	1,149,852
Cawnpore (Kanpur)	947,793
Delhi	914,790
Bangalore	907,627
Poona	721,134
Lucknow	662,196
Nagpur	643,186
Benares (Banaras)	573,558
Howrah	514,090
Agra	509,108
Primary and secondary pupils	35,380,485 (1957–1958)
University (37) students	858,846
Wheat	9,890,000 metric tons (1960)
Rice	52,185,000
Peanuts	4,424,000
Tea	324,000 metric tons (1959)
Cotton, fiber	682,000
Jute	731,000 metric tons (1960)
Sugar, raw	2,925,000
Millet	7,474,000 metric tons (1959)
Sorghum	7,992,000
Rapeseed	1,054,000
Coal	52,616,000 metric tons (1960)
Iron ore (65%)	11,524,000
Steel	3,178,000
Cement	7,836,000
Manganese (metal)	516,000
Electricity	16,146,000,000 kilowatt hours (1960)
Cattle	158,651,000 (1956)

[1] *Britannica Book of the Year,* 1962.

maximum of 115°F. Maximum temperatures come in May, except in the west where June may be hotter.

The rainfall occurs during the growing season and is normally adequate, but in drier seasons irrigation is available from wells and canals which distribute river water. Irrigation is regularly used for such crops as cotton and sugar cane. Cultivated land exceeds 70 per cent of the total, and double cropping is common.

The Ganges valley grows almost every kind of crop produced in the South Asian realm. Summer rice in the east interfingers with winter wheat in the west, although both crops are grown throughout. Jowar, bajra, barley, sugar cane, oil seeds, and corn are widely distributed. Cotton is raised in the west. The region leads in the production of sugar cane and lac. It also leads in the density of cattle. Some writers divide the valley into upper and middle subregions, for the two extremes differ in crop combinations, irrigation practices, natural vegetation, and soil, but there is only a gradational change between the dominance of such wet or dry crops as rice and wheat and their respective climates.

The chief cities are Patna, Benares (Banaras), Allahabad, and Cawnpore (Kanpur) on the Ganges, Agra and Delhi on the Jumna, and Lucknow, all of them with populations of a half million or more. Patna is the modernized capital of Bihar, celebrated for its rice. Benares is a sacred city for both Hindus and Buddhists, and its history goes back long before the Christian era. The many pilgrims provide a market for fine craft work. Benares is reached by river steamers and has the first railway bridge built over the Ganges above Sara, north of Calcutta. Allahabad is a commercial center at the junction of the Jumna and the Ganges. Cawnpore is the most important industrial city of northern India, a creation of the modern cotton, wool,

The Ganges is Hinduism's sacred river, and Benares is its most famous city. Flights of stairs or ghats line the river for miles; here pilgrims come to bathe, and here they hope to be cremated after death. The Golden Temple is at center. (*Ewing Galloway*)

Much of the agriculture in the upper Ganges valley depends on irrigation canals. Where the current is sufficiently swift, water wheels are turned, which thereby lift water for the adjoining fields. (*William Simmons, courtesy Ford Foundation*)

leather, oil-seed, and sugar industries. Agra is the site of the exquisite Taj Mahal. The third-largest city in the region is Lucknow, capital of Uttar Pradesh.

The position of Delhi is unique in both site and situation. It lies on the Jumna and was at the head of navigation until irrigation withdrawals reduced the flow of the river. Here was the place where water travel from the east changed to overland routes westward to the Punjab. Immediately west of the city is the Ridge, northernmost continuation of the Aravalli Range. Several low hills are within the city. Delhi commands the narrowest gap between the Ganges and Indus valleys; communications farther south are blocked by the Thar Desert, while to the north rise the Himalaya. From Delhi to Hardwar, where the Ganges leaves the mountains, is just over 100 miles. Delhi's strategic location is thus a logical place for the political control of both the dry west and the wet eastern Hindu part. Delhi is 950 miles from Calcutta, and 861 and 940 miles from Bombay and Karachi, respectively. Railways lead in a half dozen directions. At least six other capitals had been built on the site before the British moved the government of India here from Calcutta in 1912. In 1947 it be-

came the capital of the new India, with the government offices in a Western-style section known as New Delhi. Metropolitan Delhi numbers 1½ million people. The hill station of Simla, at an elevation of 7,116 feet in the mountains to the north, is the hot-weather capital.

Although Calcutta lies in the geographic region known as the Ganges delta, largely within Pakistan, rather than in what is here described as the Ganges valley, it may appropriately be discussed at this point. The city is the chief gateway to the Ganges lowland and dominates the eastern half of India. The population of Greater Calcutta, including the suburb of Howrah across the river, is about 5 million, making it one of the largest cities in the British Commonwealth of Nations.

Calcutta lies on the outside of a bend on the eastern bank of the Hooghly River, 120 miles from the point where ships take on a pilot outside the mouth. The port extends for 20 miles along the river and has a depth of 28 feet. Spring tides average 11 feet and keep the shifting channel of the Hooghly scoured; otherwise silting would block the river, since it is no longer an important distributary of the Ganges. Dredging is necessary.

The location of Calcutta is significant. The Hooghly provides deep water; no other rivers block railway access to the west; canals bring raw jute from the east; coal and iron are nearby; the city is built on a natural levee which permits drainage away from the city into other streams; and in the economic hinterland live 250 million people. Calcutta is around the corner from Europe but closer to the markets of East and Southeast Asia. As a result of these geographic advantages, Calcutta is one of the leading ports of the Orient, handling more than 10 million tons of cargo a year.

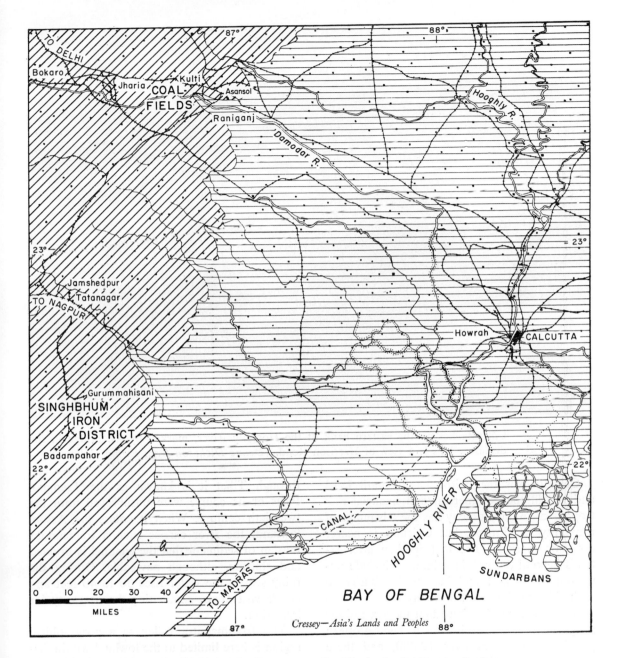

Calcutta lies up the Hooghly River, the westernmost distributary in the Ganges-Brahma-putra delta. One hundred and fifty miles to the west are India's major sources of coal and iron ore. Level land is shown by horizontal lines, hills by diagonal lines, and mari-time dikes by lines of dots. The scale is similar to that of other city maps in this volume.

Calcutta lies on the eastern bank of the Hooghly River, marked by the bridge in the distance. This is a view of Harrison Road. (*Deane Dickason from Ewing Galloway*)

Calcutta was the British capital until 1912 and is still the commercial and financial metropolis of India. Bombay has the advantage of proximity to Europe, but Calcutta is nearer domestic markets. The metropolitan area extends beyond the political limits to include numerous residential and industrial suburbs on both sides of the river. So many male workers have come from elsewhere that the sex ratio is roughly two men to each woman. The European population numbers over 10,000, and there are at least twice that number of Anglo-Indians.

THE BRAHMAPUTRA VALLEY

The Brahmaputra is even longer than the Ganges, and for the first half of its 1,800-mile course it flows eastward parallel to the latter but behind the mountains. In this section through Tibet it is known as the Tsangpo. Parts of its course were unsurveyed until the twentieth century. When it enters the Assam lowland, the river carries such a tremendous burden of sediment that the channel is braided and shifting, although navigable. During the rainy season the water rises 30 to 40 feet and floods vast areas, eliminating the necessity for irrigation.

The Brahmaputra valley as a geographical region is here limited to the lowland within Assam, all of it in India but connected either by a narrow-gauge railroad corridor north of East Pakistan or by uncertain transit rights across Pakistan. The region faces the Ganges delta on the west, but on the other three sides is hemmed in by mountain walls, lofty to the north and east but low to the south. The Brahmaputra valley is thus in contrast to the Ganges valley, where there is access from three sides. The valley is some 500 miles long but nowhere much more than 50 miles wide, one of the smallest of all South Asian regions.

The Garo and Khasi Hills on the south partly keep out the monsoon rains, but a strong current moves eastward up the valley and gives an average rainfall in excess of 80 inches. Where the monsoon crosses the hills from the south, there are dry foehn effects on the north slopes.

Rice throughout, jute in the west, and tea in the foothills are the chief crops. Assam is one of the world's leading producers of tea for export, with Calcutta as the normal port. The valley still contains large forests of teak and sal. Elephant ivory and rhinoceros horn are secured in the forest zones. Large areas of land are unused, partly jungle marsh along the river banks, so that cropland is generally under 20 per cent.

Assam is different from the rest of the South Asian realm in race and history. Many primitive tribes live here. Assam forms a separate cultural area in which some conditions resemble those of Burma. Unlike the congestion in the Ganges valley, population densities average but 150 per square mile; hence there is a large migration into Assam, especially for seasonal labor in the tea plantations.

Lignite and oil are obtained in the bordering hills. River steamers carry most of the freight, although there are narrow-gauge railways. No bridge spans the Brahmaputra.

These women are from Assam in the Brahmaputra valley. Many ethnic types are similar to those in northern Burma and Thailand. (*Courtesy Indian State Railways*)

THE ASSAM MOUNTAINS

The Assam Mountain region includes the east–west Garo and Khasi Hills and the north–south ranges near the Burma border. The lowlands of Assam have already been considered. Although the area is small, the rainfall is noteworthy, and the scarcity of roads into Burma makes this an effective barrier for the eastern frontier.

The Assam Mountains receive the full force of the monsoon from the Bay of Bengal, and the rainfall is especially heavy where the winds are forced to rise over mountains. The second-heaviest rainfall station in the world is at Cherrapunji, where the average total precipitation is 425 inches. This station lies at 4,309 feet next to the steep southern face of the Khasi Hills. In contrast, Shillong, at 4,920 feet but within the mountains and back from the edge of the range, receives but 84 inches of rain, while Sylhet in the lowlands to the south has 157 inches.

Natural vegetation reflects the rainfall in a dense tropical rain forest. There is little farming or lumbering in the wetter areas. Agriculture is limited to fire clearings, where the ash supplies fertilization, and to the few areas of alluvium along the streams. Corn, millet, and rice are grown.

THE HIMALAYAN HIGHLANDS

Himalayan structure and topography are complex, increasingly so toward the west. In general, there are three parallel zones. The Outer Himalaya include the mile-high Siwaliks with a series of Appalachian-type anticlines and synclines, dissected into a series of escarpments and dip slopes and separated by linear valleys called duns. At the southern limit is a great overthrust directed from the north. The Lesser Himalaya, in the middle, rise 7,000 to 15,000 feet and are marked by recumbent folds and strong thrusting. On the north is the Great Himalaya Range with an average crest line of 20,000 feet. Its geological structures are im-perfectly known but appear to resemble Scottish Highland faults rather than Alpine nappes. Igneous intrusions make the structure complex.

The Himalayan highlands present many geological problems, not the least of which are the river systems. The Indus and the Brahmaputra, which rise near each other in the area of the Manasarowar Lakes in Tibet, flow in opposite directions and cross the mountains 1,500 miles apart. Numerous rivers with headwaters on the north slopes, such as the Sutlej which rises in the same lake region, break through the ranges at right angles in antecedent valleys, the rivers being older than the mountains.

Some of these valleys are the deepest canyons on earth.

The most remarkable example is the Indus Valley in Gilgit Agency where at one place the river flows through a narrow defile, between enormous precipices nearly 20,000 feet in altitude, while the bed of the valley is only 3,000 feet above its level at Haiderabad (the head of its delta). This gives to the gorge the stupendous depth of 17,000 feet, yet the fact that every inch of this chasm is carved by the river is clear from the fact that small patches or "terraces" of river gravel and sand beds are observed at various elevations.[1]

It is but 12 miles from the Indus to the peak of Nanga Parbat, 26,629 feet high. At a point on the Kali Gandaki River, where the stream is at 9,000 feet, nearby elevations on either side rise to 26,810 and 26,504 feet. The Sutlej and Brahmaputra have comparable gorges. The

[1] Wadia, D. N., *The Geology of India,* New York: St Martin's Press (1954), 19.

Nepal Data [1]

Area	54,362 square miles
Population	9,180,000 (1960 est.)
Katmandu (capital)	105,247 (1954 census)
Primary and secondary pupils	144,782 (1960)

[1] *Britannica Book of the Year,* 1962.

youthful character of these valleys is indicated by their gradients. For example, the Brahmaputra descends 7,200 feet in 25 miles through the main range. Few of these chasms can be traversed so that access to Tibet is over lofty divides, snow-blocked for many months.

Pleistocene glaciers have left enormous heaps of moraine at elevations of 6,000 feet and lower. Although the peninsula was not glaciated in that era, parallel climatic changes brought widespread alterations in the fauna and flora.

The giant peaks are in the Great Himalaya: Nanga Parbat in Kashmir; Nanda Devi in Uttar Pradesh, 25,645 feet; Mount Everest in Nepal, 29,028 feet; and Kanchenjunga, 28,146 feet. While Mount Everest, known to the Tibetans as Chomolungma, or Goddess Mother of the Land, is the most famous, its peak is less impressive than some others, for example, its neighbor Makalu with its 11,000-foot cliffs.

Between the Punjab and Chinese Sinkiang is a complex of mountains, the whitest, snowiest, iciest ranges outside of polar regions. In the midst of them lies the Karakoram Pass with an elevation of 18,317 feet. This name has been variously applied to some of the snowy mountains, but it is now recognized that the Karakoram Pass is not in the Karakoram Range. The range lies between the Indus and Shaksgam Rivers and includes the world's second highest peak, K², with an elevation of 28,250. Within this area are numerous glaciers 30 and 40 miles long.

Within the Himalaya and the Karakoram area there are 50 summits over 25,000 feet high, of which only a few have been climbed. Mount Everest stands supreme, both because of its height and the difficulty of ascent. Early attempts to climb it involved an approach from the north just before the arrival of the monsoon. It was finally conquered from the south in 1953.

Between the Indo-Gangetic Plain and the Himalayan highlands is a narrow belt of swamps and wet forests, continuous for most of the distance except in the drier west. In the east this forested strip is known as the duars; elsewhere it is the Terai. Where the Terai has not been drained, this marginal zone has a sparse population. These swamps, rather than the mountains, form the northern limits of cultural India. North of the Terai lie the first foothills, actually mile-high mountains but termed hills because of what lies beyond.

Vegetation limits are influenced by rainfall as well as altitude, the heaviest precipitation being in the east. Dense subtropical forests extend to an elevation of 6,000 feet. Deciduous forests are typical between 5,000 and 11,000 feet, and in this zone are the hill stations of Darjeeling, 7,431 feet, and Simla, farther west, 7,224 feet. The former has 123 inches of rain, while the latter has but 62 inches. Coniferous trees are present from 9,000 to 12,000 feet. Here the air has lost most of its moisture, and rainfall is under 40 inches. Rhododendron grows from 9,000 to 13,500 feet, while stunted alpine growths, seldom over 2 feet in height, prevail above this, according to exposure. Beyond is barren rock and snow. On the south slopes the snow line descends to 14,000 feet in the east and 19,000 feet in the west. On the dry Tibetan side snow-line elevations are higher. The highest level of cultivation is near 12,000 feet, with some summer pasture a few thousand feet higher.

Bhutan Data [1]

Area	19,305 square miles
Population	670,000 (1960 est.)

[1] *Britannica Book of the Year*, 1962.

Sikkim Data [1]

Area	2,744 square miles
Population	161,080 (1961 census)
Gangtok (capital)	7,000

[1] *Britannica Book of the Year*, 1962.

The foothills of the Himalaya introduce a very different environment and culture from the plains of Hindustan. These porters are crossing a stream in Nepal. (*Courtesy United Nations*)

Between the Outer and Lesser Himalaya and north of the Punjab is the famed Vale of Kashmir in the Jhelum valley. At an elevation of 5,250 feet lies Srinagar, surrounded by cultivated fields and glorious mountains. Nearly 2 million people live in an area 20 by 80 miles. The inhabitants of Kashmir are noted for their art and industry. Shawls made of goat's wool, carpets, woolen cloth, and wood carving are world famous. Houseboat trips on the Jhelum and the Dal Lake provide some of the most beautiful views in the world.

The independent kingdom of Nepal lies on the south slopes of the Himalaya, between the icy crest line through Mount Everest and the tropical Terai swamps at the base. Although Nepal has a population of nearly 10 million, it plays but a small part in international affairs.

An automobile road now leads to the capital at Katmandu.

Nepal is sacred to both Buddhists and Hindus; to the former as the birthplace of Gautama Buddha, to the latter since important tributaries of the Ganges rise in Nepal. The people are of mixed Mongol origin, the best known of whom are the Gurkhas, famed for their skill as soldiers in the British army.

The country extends along the Himalaya for 500 miles and has a width of 100 to 150 miles. The wide range in altitude brings corresponding contrasts in the landscape. Few small countries are so diverse. Several longitudinal river valleys in the Siwalik Range provide ribbons of agricultural land, notably the old lake bed, some 15 by 25 miles in area, at a height of 4,500 feet, which surrounds the capital. The least representative part of Nepal, but also the most productive, lies in the marshy but fertile Terai, famed for its forests and wild animals and now partly cleared.

Farther east, and occupying a similar position, is the semi-independent state of Bhutan, under Indian protection. Sikkim is another dependency, with its capital at Gangtok.

References on India

A wide variety of material may be found in the *Geog. Rev. of India* (Calcutta) and the *Indian Geog. Jour.* (Madras).

See also general references on South Asia, Chapter 26.

Ahmad, Enayat: "The Rural Population of Bihar," *Geog. Rev.*, LI (1961), 253–276.

Behre, Charles H., Jr.: "India's Mineral Wealth and Political Future," *Foreign Affairs,* XXII (1943), 78–93.

*Brown, J. Coggin, and A. K. Dey: *India's Mineral Wealth,* 3d ed., Fair Lawn, N.J.: Oxford University Press (1955).

Brush, John E.: "Divided India," *Jour. Geog.*, XLVI (1948), 209–219.

Brush, John E.: "The Distribution of Religious Communities in India," *Annals, Assn. Amer. Geogs.*, XXXIX (1949), 81–98.

Brush, John E.: "The Iron and Steel Industry in India," *Geog. Rev.*, XLII (1952), 37–55.

Caroe, Sir Olaf: "The Geography and Ethnics of India's Northern Frontiers," *Geog. Jour.*, CXXVI (1960), 298–309.

Gorrie, R. MacLagan: "Soil and Water Conservation in the Punjab," *Geog. Rev.*, XXVIII (1938), 20–31.

Grant, W. J.: "Delhi, the Flower of India," *Geog. Mag.*, XII (1940), 132–145.

Hoffman, L. A.: "India: Main Population Concentrations," *Geog. Jour.*, CXI (1948), 89–100.

Kapp, K. William: "River Valley Projects in India," *Economic Development and Cultural Change,* VIII (1959), 24–47.

Karan, Pradyumna P.: "Economic Regions of the Chota Nagpur, Bihar, India," *Econ. Geog.*, XXIX (1953), 216–250.

Karan, Pradyumna P.: "Iron Mining Industry in Singhbhum-Mayerbhanj Region of India," *Econ. Geog.*, XXXIII (1957), 349–361.

Karan, Pradyumna P.: "Locational Pattern of the New Centers of the Iron and Steel Industry," *Jour. Geog.*, LVI (1957), 366–374.

Karan, Pradyumna P., and William M. Jenkins: "Geography of Manufacturing in India," *Econ. Geog.*, XXXV (1959), 269–278.

Kirk, William: "The Cotton and Jute Industries of India," *Scottish Geog. Mag.*, LXXII (1956), 38–52.

Kirk, William: "The Sino-Indian Frontier Dispute," *Scottish Geog. Mag.*, LXXVI (1960), 3–13.

Orchard, John E.: "Industrialization in Japan, China Mainland, and India: Some World Implications," *Annals, Assn. Amer. Geogs.*, L (1960), 193–215.

Panjabi, R. M.: "Chandigarh: India's Newest City," *Geog. Mag.*, XXXI (1958), 401–414.

Russell, Sir E. John: "India's People and Their Food," *Geog.*, XXXVII (1952), 125–141.

Spate, O. H. K.: "The Indian Village," *Geog.*, XXXVII (1952), 142–152.

Subrahmanyam, V. P.: "The Water Balance of India according to Thornwaite's Concept of Potential Evapotranspiration," *Annals, Assn. Amer. Geogs.*, XLVI (1956), 300–311.

Wadia, D. N.: *The Geology of India,* New York: St Martin's Press (1954).

Wiley, S. C.: "Kashmir," *Canadian Geog. Jour.*, LXII (1961), 22–31.

30 Regions of South India

*The West Coast / The Black Soil Plateau / The Northern Uplands /
The Eastern Uplands / The Southern Peninsula*

The contrasts between the northern and southern geographic provinces of India are largely matters of surface configuration. Rainfall is slightly lower in the southern farm lands, and crops are therefore different. Many of the inhabitants are Dravidians rather than Aryans like the peoples of the north. Hindu religion predominates, with only small areas of Muslims. None of these contrasts are at all comparable to the striking differences between North and South China.

Within peninsular India are five major regions: the west coast, the black soil plateau, the northern uplands, the eastern uplands, and

the southern peninsula; nearby Ceylon adds a sixth.

THE WEST COAST

The west-coast region is a narrow strip of lowland and escarpment extending from Cape Comarin at the tip of the peninsula to the Gulf of Cambay, a thousand miles to the north. Little uniformity or coherence can be expected in such an attenuated area; yet certain factors entitle the region to be considered as a unit.

The Arabian Sea is bordered by fault escarpments on three sides, perhaps as recent as the

Pliocene; these mark the margins of a down-dropped block. One of these dislocations forms the Western Ghats at the edge of the Deccan Plateau. Viewed from the sea, these are 3,000-foot mountains; seen from the east they are a line of hills. The topographic contrast seen in this asymmetrical divide is striking; youthful canyons on the west are actively gnawing into eastward-draining open valleys in late maturity.

The northern half of the escarpment is cut in horizontal lava flows, so that slopes have a step-like development. Farther south, granitic rocks prevail, and the land forms are more rounded.

Toward the south, the Eastern and Western Ghats meet in the Nilgiri Hills, which rise to 8,700 feet. South of them is the 800-foot Palghat Gap, and farther south are the high Cardamon Hills.

The Western Ghats receive the full effect of the summer monsoon off the Arabian Sea. Throughout most of the region, precipitation at sea-level stations exceeds 100 inches, diminishing to the north. Bombay has only 71 inches and southern Gujarat but 40 inches. As the moist winds rise over the mountains, rainfall increases to 200 and even 300 inches at hill stations. In the basin of the hydroelectric installation near Bombay, as much as 540 inches has been recorded in 90 days.

In the extreme north are the only westward-flowing rivers of importance in the entire peninsula, the Narbada and Tapti. South of these valleys the Western Ghats present a barrier which is crossed by only three railways until the Palghat Gap is reached. Along the Konkan coast in the north the mountains come close to the sea and restrict level land to discontinuous strips a few miles in width. Farther south the

Canals play an important role in the coastal plains of South India. This is a scene near Quilon. (*Courtesy India State Railways*)

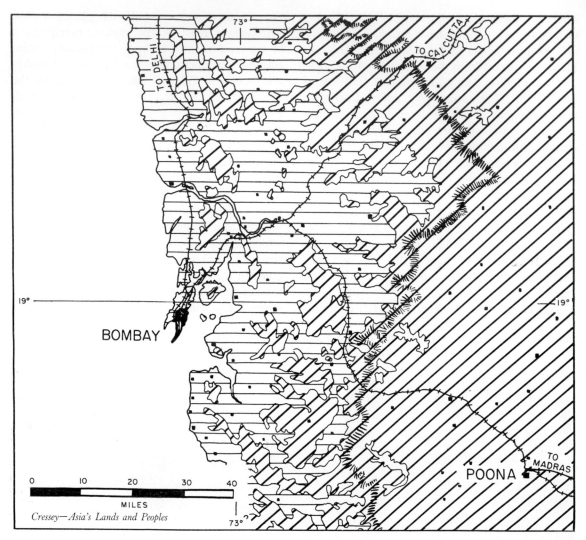

Bombay, with its excellent natural harbor, is India's main seaport along the west coast. Level land extends only a few tens of miles to the base of the Western Ghats.

Malabar Coast widens to 70 miles. Barrier beaches with sand dunes and lagoons fringed with mangrove swamps are characteristic.

In general there are three linear subregions: a sandy coastal strip intensively used for coconut palms; a cultivated zone of alluvium, half of it planted in rice; and the heavily forested mountain slopes. Large supplies of bamboo, teak, ebony, and sandalwood are rafted down the turbulent rivers in flood stage. Despite the extensive area of unproductive land, the population density reaches 500 per square mile.

Overland communications are limited and have always tended to isolate the region from the interior. Access to the sea is not much easier, for harbors are few, and most navigation must be suspended for three months at the height of the monsoon. Trade dates back to early times when Arab merchants made regular voyages to Zanzibar and the African coast, trading back and forth as the monsoons allowed. Most of the Indian sailors or lascars employed on British boats traveling to Asia come from this region. Coastal fishing is important.

Several special products are obtained here. The oldest and most famous are pepper, ginger, and other spices. Copra and coconut oil form important exports. This is the only area in India where coir, the fiber from coconut husks, is commercially produced. Coffee acreage has declined but is replaced by tea. Rubber production is gradually expanding. Quinine is produced in the Nilgiri Hills at altitudes over 3,000 feet and is sold at low prices in order to check malaria.

Bombay is the leading natural harbor, not only for the west coast but for much of India. The city lies on a peninsula which protects a large bay, sheltered at all seasons. Behind the city two passes give access to the interior for railway lines. Hydroelectric power is available from the nearby Western Ghats and is supplemented by coal brought from Calcutta by boat. The hinterland grows cotton, the country's most important commercial crop and the basis of the city's chief industry. Bombay's development coincides with the completion of rail connections in 1861, just in time to profit from the cotton shortage that arose during the American Civil War. After this emergency passed, the opening of the Suez Canal in 1869 established Bombay as the principal western gateway to India. Although slightly second to Calcutta as a port, Bombay is of major importance for communications with Europe. The city is the center of native finance and industrial management, whereas Calcutta was long dominated by British capital.

The population of Bombay is more than 4 million and growing rapidly. The city is particularly congested, and high labor costs are driving cotton mills to the interior. Social contrasts are striking. On the one hand, Bombay has some of the worst industrial slums in the

The Marine Drive in Bombay is lined with modern apartment houses, in contrast to slum conditions elsewhere in the city. (*Courtesy India Government Tourist Office*)

world; on the other hand, there are splendid boulevards. Wealthy Indian merchants live in Bombay. There is a constant flow of factory workers back and forth to their family homes in the villages, so that the ratio of men to women in Bombay, as in Calcutta, is almost 2 to 1. Linguistic and racial groupings are said to be more heterogeneous than those in New York City. In public places caste is an almost forgotten phenomenon, but in some family aspects it remains rigid. Housing conditions are so serious that one-third of the population lives in single rooms occupied by six persons or more.

The second most important port on the west coast is the former Portuguese colony of Goa with its excellent harbor, terminus for the only

rail line across the Ghats between Bombay and the Palghat Pass. Other cities of historic interest are Trivandrum, Calicut (Kozhikode) and Cochin, the latter having a newly developed port that rivals Madras on the east coast.

THE BLACK SOIL PLATEAU

The most distinctive and one of the most puzzling soils of peninsular India is the black regur soil of the western Deccan. In color, clay content, abundance of lime, and fertility it somewhat resembles the chernozems of temperate grasslands, but it is low in organic matter, and the color is not a result of carbonaceous material. The black color may be due to dark mineral constituents. The distribution of

Harvest is a hand operation; grain is usually carried to the family threshing floor. (*Courtesy Indian Consulate, New York City*)

This woman is carrying rocks with which to build a road in Bombay. (*Courtesy Standard Oil Company of New Jersey*)

black soil is more or less coextensive with the great flows of basalt, and it was once regarded as a normal product of weathering *in situ*. It is now clear that representative regur is also found on metamorphic rocks and alluvium, and that not all areas underlain by lava have typical black soil.

Black soil is best developed on level to undulating upland or valley areas where soil-forming processes have reached maturity. On slopes where erosion intervenes, the color is more reddish and the soil more sandy. Where mature, the regur is a heavy clay, high in calcium carbonate, iron oxides, and alumina, but low in humus. Even without fertilizers it produces excellent crops, and the texture is especially favorable for the retention of summer moisture for winter cultivation.

The best environmental conditions for regur appear to be 20 to 40 inches of rainfall, concentrated in a brief wet season, with high temperatures at other times of the year. Natural vegetation is of the dry savanna type. Only a part of the geographic region has fully developed deep black soil; elsewhere it is reddish-black and more sandy.

Most of the black soil plateau is underlain by great fissure eruptions of basaltic lava, poured out at various dates between the late Cretaceous and early Eocene eras. Despite erosion, more than 200,000 square miles are still covered. The term "trap," as sometimes applied to the area, is used in the Swedish meaning of stairs or steps, referring to the surface form of the outcrops, rather than in the geologic sense, referring to the rock itself. To avoid confusion it is better to describe the material as basalt and the topography as a scarped tableland.

Individual flows are a few tens of feet in thickness and may be separated by ash or sedimentary layers. Columnar jointing is so well developed that the water table is at considerable depths, often beyond the reach of the native wells. The material is a uniform augite basalt, grayish green to purple or red in color. There is a maximum thickness of 6,000 feet in the west, but the flows thin rapidly in all directions. No trace remains of ancient volcanoes, and the material appears to be entirely derived from fissures.

The black soil region is limited on the west by the crest of the Western Ghats with their heavier rainfall, although basalt locally reaches the sea. The geographic boundary on the north is near the Narbada valley, which in turn is bounded on the south by the Satpura and Mahadeo Hills and on the north by the Vindhya Range. Eastward and southward the limits of the region are not so clear. In general, the region reaches the Waingange valley along the 80th meridian, and extends to the southern limits of former Bombay and Hyderabad, thus into Mysore and Andhra Pradesh. Within the area is all of Maharashtra and the western half of Madhya Pradesh. Two westward-flowing rivers drain the north: the Narbada and Tapti; farther south the Godavari and Kistna flow to the east.

Throughout the region, the grain sorghum known as jowar is the dominant food crop, both for man and beast. It is grown on the black soil and accommodates itself to rainfall variations. Bajra millet replaces jowar as a supplementary food crop on lighter soils. Legumes are often interplanted. These are summer crops and are rotated with wheat and linseed, which will grow during the dry winter season. Rice is seldom raised.

Cotton is the chief commercial crop, but conditions are not too favorable. The short rainy period requires that quick-maturing short-staple varieties be grown. Planting occurs as soon as the rains moisten the ground in June, and the growing season is somewhat lengthened by irrigation. Fortunately, the regur soils retain moisture into the maturing period. American varieties do not do well here, although they are suitable in the Indus valley. Most of the fiber is under 1 inch in length. The chief areas are the deep black soils of the Tapti and upper Godavari valleys.

The interior Deccan is a traditional famine zone. It lies in the rain shadow of the Western Ghats, so that rainfall is from 20 to 40 inches, with a variability of 25 per cent. Not only does the total vary, but the duration and intensity fluctuate. When it does rain, an average of ½ inch per day is common. Since the surface regur soil is tight, much of the water runs off. The fortunate moisture-retaining capacity of the soil does not necessitate so much irrigation as elsewhere. Artificial ponds, known as tanks, are widespread, and numerous large reservoirs, many of them modern engineering works, store rainfall in the areas of heavier precipitation near the Western Ghats.

Until the introduction of railways and an export market for cotton, wheat, and linseed, the Deccan remained backward and isolated. Few of the invasions into India from the northwestern passes effectively penetrated the Vindhya mountains and forests. Cultural conditions changed but little for centuries, and in the absence of stimulating intercourse, there was little progress. Each village was self-sufficient. The blacksmith, carpenter, and potter worked for

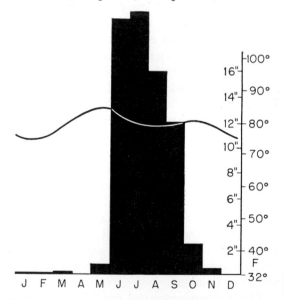

BOMBAY. Elevation 37 feet, average temperature 81°F, annual precipitation 71 inches. The abrupt arrival of the summer monsoon is obvious.

the village as a whole and were paid by the village at harvest time. There were few outside products and little money with which to buy them.

Population densities average 250 per square mile, with as much as 10 acres per farm family. Most of the people are Marathas, whose distribution closely corresponds with the extent of the lava flows. Several cities are outstanding. Hyderabad is the capital city for Andhra Pradesh; Poona lies on the upland southeast from Bombay; near the edge of the eastern uplands is the important rail center of Nagpur. The populations of Poona and Nagpur exceed ½ million each; Hyderabad has more than 1 million people. Other cities serve as local commercial towns. The area of the region approximates 170,000 square miles, and the population exceeds 40 million.

THE NORTHERN UPLANDS

The northern uplands form a triangular region in the northwest corner of the plateau, within the curve of the Indo-Gangetic Plain. The region is well bounded but somewhat complex internally. Two exposures of Archean gneiss buttress either end, the ancient Aravalli Range in the west and the Bundelkhand massif

in the east. On the south are the Vindhya and Kaimur Ranges. The Ganges lowland borders the north as far eastward as the Son River. In the southwest, the peninsula of Kathiawar forms a subregion. In political terms, the northern uplands include eastern Rajasthan, Gujarat, as well as parts of Madhya Pradesh.

The geology and resulting surface are equally varied. Overlying the Archean complex are early Paleozoic formations, while burying both in the southern half is an extension of Deccan basalt flows with some black soils. This lava area is the Malwa Plateau. Elevations rise from the Ganges lowland to 2,500 and 4,000 feet in the bold Vindhya escarpment overlooking the Narbada valley. Portions of the Aravalli Range reach 5,000 feet.

Rainfall decreases from 40 inches in the east, which is under the influence of the Ganges valley monsoon, to 20 inches in the west, where the Arabian Sea monsoon is dominant. High temperatures reduce the agricultural effectiveness of this precipitation. Wheat, jowar, and cotton are grown. Population is sparse for India, and there are substantial areas in forest or otherwise not in cultivation.

The state of Gujarat in the west is a drier continuation of the west coast, with some rice but more millet and cotton. Central Kathiawar has forest-clad hills that contain India's only

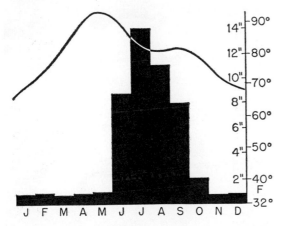

NAGPUR. Elevation 1,025 feet, average temperature 81°F, annual precipitation 49 inches. This station is representative of interior South India.

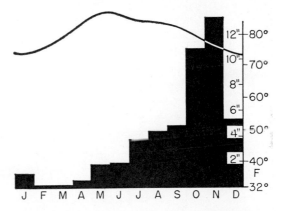

MADRAS. Elevation 51 feet, average temperature 89°F, annual precipitation 50 inches. The southeastern coast receives most of its rain from the winter monsoon.

lions; elsewhere the Kathiawar peninsula is dry and barren.

The region has two cities of interest. Ahmadabad is a highly industrialized city, second to Bombay in cotton milling. It has quadrupled in size since 1900. In the extreme east is the rail center of Jubbulpore, which commands the gap for a railroad southward through the Satpura Range, as well as a route westward to Bombay via the Narbada valley. It is also a cotton-manufacturing center.

THE EASTERN UPLANDS

No part of India south of the mountain wall is so badly dissected and so unusable for agriculture as the eastern uplands. Monsoon jungle and primitive tribes here go together. Fortu- nately the region has very great mineral wealth.

The eastern uplands lie in parts of Bihar and Orissa and the eastern part of Madhya Pradesh. Like the northern uplands, they are surrounded on two sides by the lowland of the north. Along the north are the Maikal and Mahadeo Hills, a continuation of the Satpura Range; westward the area merges with the black soil region. The southern limit is less well defined but is drawn near the Godavari River, excluding the delta. Between the Eastern Ghats and the sea is a narrow coastal plain, which may be included in the area for convenience. There is little need to consider a separate east-coast region, since it is less distinctive than the western coast.

Over large areas cultivated land drops below 10 per cent, and nowhere is it much more than 50 per cent. This absence of cultivation is not

Most of India's heavy industry centers near the coal fields west of Calcutta. This scene is in a tinplate mill. (*Courtesy Government of India Information Services*)

due to inadequate or fluctuating rainfall, for the precipitation is from 40 to 60 inches and is as dependable as anywhere in the country. Most hillsides are still in forest and too steep for cultivation, even if cleared. Rice and raggee millet are the dominant crops, but irrigation is difficult on account of the extent of valley dissection. Only locally is it possible to divert river water to irrigate interstream areas. Wheat, cotton, jowar, and bajra are absent. Corn, oil seeds, and legumes are grown for local consumption.

Within the region are practically all the Permo-Carboniferous rocks of the peninsula, and they contain excellent bituminous coal. The principal fields are in Bihar, Hyderabad, and Madhya Pradesh. Reserves in the Raniganj, Jharia, Bokaro, and Karanpura fields account for the bulk of India's coal, particularly that of coking quality. The nearby iron range of Singhbhum has provided a basis for spectacular metallurgical developments in Jamshedpur and nearby steel centers. Mica and manganese deposits are extensive.

The eastern coast is as poorly supplied with harbors as the western. A railroad from Nagpur over the Eastern Ghats to Vizagapatam has made this city an important port with the best harbor on the entire east coast. Shipments of manganese ore are important. The backward nature of the eastern uplands is suggested by the absence of any city with 100,000 people.

THE SOUTHERN PENINSULA

The southern peninsula has high temperatures and high humidity throughout the year. There is never a cool season except in the highlands, so that the terms summer and winter become meaningless. The temperature rarely exceeds 100°F, but the climate is enervating and fully tropical. Palm trees flourish. Most of the area is sheltered from the southwest monsoon by the Western Ghats, but beginning in October there are three months of heavy rain brought by tropical hurricanes off the Bay of Bengal during the period of the "retreating"

monsoon. The annual rainfall declines westward from 50 inches at Madras to half that figure in the rain shadow of the Western Ghats, but there higher and cooler elevations increase the rainfall effectiveness. The area receives a little moisture from the northeast monsoon winds in winter.

Within the geographic region are three topographic subregions: the Carnatic coastal plains and deltas of the Godavari, Kistna, and Cauvery Rivers; a succession of low hills which form the Eastern Ghats; and the tableland of Mysore in the west. Population densities vary accordingly, from an average of 500 per square mile and a maximum of four times that figure along the coast to 200 per square mile in the northwest plateaus. The total population is about 60 million in an area of 125,000 square miles.

This is one of the most progressive parts of all India. The people speak Tamil and Telegu, and are unusually literate; a majority of the people in Madras province are able to read and write. Hindus comprise 85 per cent of the total, and there are only a few Muslims. Many cultural contrasts set off this southern region from the rest of India, such as the bright-colored clothes and the temple architecture.

Rice and raggee millet are the staple crops, the former where fields may be flooded, the latter on drier upland soils. Rice cultivation is more difficult than dry-crop cultivation because irrigation is imperative. Since rainfall is uncertain, the southern peninsula has often been a famine zone. Precipitation records indicate that in the stations where the average is 25 to 30 inches per year, 11 to 13 out of 50 years are dry, and 6 to 8 years have severe drought. With 30 to 40 inches, 7 to 11 years are dry, of which 2 to 5 have serious drought. Where the rainfall exceeds 40 inches in the northern Deccan, only 4 to 7 years in 50 are dry, of which less than 2 are severely dry. Tanks and wells are widely used.

The total irrigated area in Madras province covers 7,500,000 acres. A considerable part of this irrigation is the result of modern engineering works. In the Cauvery delta, 1 million acres have long had an uncertain supply from local irrigation canals. With the building of a huge dam upstream at Mettur, this area now has dependable water and 300,000 additional acres are available for raising rice.

Cotton is grown on 2 million acres, partly for export. An important cash crop is peanuts, raised for their oil, especially in the area northwest of Madras. Sugar cane, coconuts, and tobacco are also grown. Teak and sandalwood come from the higher hills in the west. Commercial crops are not so important as in the black soil region.

Laterite, widespread in South India, reaches its climax in the south. Where fully developed, it is a brick-red porous geological formation, high in hydrated oxides of iron and aluminum, and low in clay and silica. Extreme compositions range from limonite to bauxite. Underlying bedrock is apparently less important as a

determining factor than a rainfall of more than 50 inches, a wet and dry season, the absence of erosion, and tropical vegetation. The development of true residual laterite may require a time as long as that since the Eocene. When freshly quarried, laterite may be cut with a shovel, but on exposure to the air it becomes indurated and makes a good building material. The word is from the Latin meaning "a brick." Laterite is equally well developed on the high basalt hills of Bombay and in the low areas of Madras. The term laterite should be restricted to the residual bricklike product of long-continued weathering on a peneplain; it is a geological formation, not a soil. From this parent material may later be developed a lateritic soil. Older buried laterites are found at various horizons in the stratigraphic column. The agricultural value is low.

Madras is India's third city and her third port, with a population of 2 million. The site

This is the village of Nagerkoil, south of Trivandrum in Kerala province, one of the most prosperous and progressive parts of India. (*Courtesy Indian State Railways*)

Hindu temples rise above the city of Srirangam in Madras province. Pilgrims travel here to worship at the temple of Vishnu. (*Courtesy Indian State Railways*)

has nothing to recommend it and was chosen accidentally when an English ship unloaded cargo on an open sandy beach. The present harbor is an artificial enclosure about a half mile square. The business of the hinterland calls for some port, and in the absence of possible competition, Madras has grown. The vicinity lacks coal or important industrial minerals, but hydroelectric power is brought from the Western Ghats.

The city of Madras has long had foreign contacts, and has a sentimental interest for Americans in that both Cornwallis and Elihu Yale were governors. In the days of the Yankee clippers these sailing vessels sometimes carried ice as ballast around Cape Horn, with apples in refrigeration; and an old icehouse still stands on the beach at Madras. The hinterland is one of the most advanced parts of the Indo-Paki-

stan realm. A larger number of people speak English in Madras than elsewhere, and the city is more Europeanized. Madras and Travancore resemble Canton in their progressiveness.

Leather preparation is a significant industry, with the bark of the avaram shrub used for tanning. Sheepskins are exported in tanned form; goatskins commonly are dried and untanned. Cowhide is shipped in both forms. Hides and skins account for half of the outgoing trade of Madras, with peanut oil representing about 15 per cent. Raw cotton and tobacco are also shipped. The number of cotton mills are declining within the city, but those that remain are among the largest and best. Cotton mills are important throughout Madras province.

Bangalore, Mysore, and Madura lie in the upland interior, and their elevation gives them a healthy and pleasant aspect.

31 Pakistan

Political Backgrounds / Economic Potentials / The Ganges-Brahmaputra Delta / The Indus Valley / The Thar Desert / The Western Frontier / References on Pakistan

POLITICAL BACKGROUNDS

Although Pakistan has been referred to repeatedly in the previous chapters, this nation of 100 million people deserves separate consideration. Pakistan is a federal Islamic republic within the British Commonwealth of Nations. It consists of two provinces: East Pakistan with 15 per cent of the area and 55 per cent of the population, and West Pakistan with the bulk of the area and less than half of the population. The federal capital is in West Pakistan at Islamabad (Anantnag) near Rawalpindi.

Pakistan is a coined word in which *P* stands for Punjab, *A* for Afghanistan (parts of which it was once hoped might be included) or perhaps for the Afghans as people, *K* for Kashmir (still a part of India), *I* for Islam, *S* for Sind, with *tan* from the last syllable of Baluchistan. In Urdu, *pak* stands for spiritual purity, and *stan* means land. During the predivision agitation for Muslim recognition, consideration was also given to the formation of an Islamic state in Bengal and Assam, to be known as Bangistan, and in the Hyderabad Deccan under the title of Osmanistan. The present East Pakistan is made up of eastern Bengal and part of former Assam. West Pakistan takes in the former provinces of Punjab, Sind, Baluchistan, and the North-West Frontier.

Islam came to the subcontinent as a political force in the days of the Mogul empire. Since their base was in the northwest, it was here that Islam became most developed, but Muslim groups arose throughout the country. This was especially true where large blocks of low-caste or noncaste Hindus became Muslims through mass conversion.

During the British period, the overall Muslim-Hindu ratio was roughly 1:4. Though occasional friction between these and other religious communities was held in check by the government, deep-seated animosity was obvi- ous. Tens of millions of people belong to faiths other than Hindu or Muslim. With the approach of independence, the scattered Muslim communities felt that as a minority group they might experience political repression. Out of this grew the agitation for a nation of their own.

Unfortunately, no coherent area or clear boundary was possible, since Muslims are everywhere intermingled with Hindus. East and West Pakistan arc merely areas where Muslims are more numerous than Hindus, though not necessarily forming a majority. The high tensions and enormous mass migrations which accompanied partition led to the death of several hundred thousand people of both faiths.

Within present-day Pakistan, Muslims constitute 85 per cent of the population, but there

Pakistan Data [1]

Area:	
West Pakistan	300,839 square miles
East Pakistan	55,134 "
Total	355,973 "

Population:	
West Pakistan	40,815,000 (1961 census)
East Pakistan	50,844,000
Total	91,659,000
Karachi	1,916,000
Lahore (capital West Pakistan)	1,297,000
Dacca (capital East Pakistan)	558,000
Hyderabad	434,000
Lyallpur	426,000
Chittagong	363,000
Rawalpindi (national capital)	343,000
Primary and secondary pupils	5,892,500 (1960)
University (6) students	22,686

Rice	13,744,000 metric tons (1960)
Wheat	3,938,000 "
Jute	1,021,000 "
Cotton fiber	306,000 "
Cottonseed	589,000 "
Tea	25,400 metric tons (1959)
Coal	831,600 metric tons (1960)
Oil	290,400 "
Cement	1,140,000 "

Electricity	950,610,000 kilowatthours (1957)

[1] *Britannica Book of the Year*, 1962.

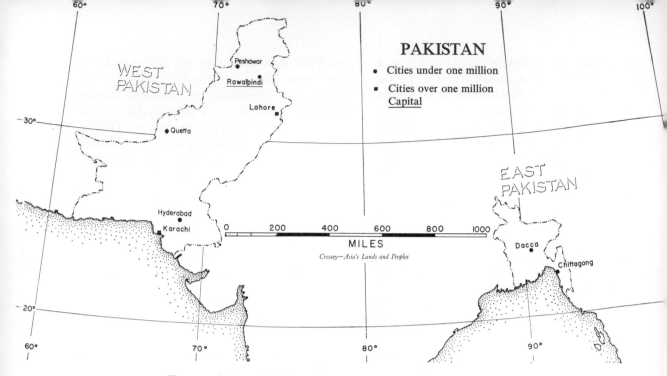

The two halves of Pakistan are 1,000 miles apart, connected only by sea around Ceylon or across India. Whereas much of West Pakistan is a semidesert, watered by the Indus, East Pakistan is an overwet delta with different people, crops, and economy.

are 10 million Hindus, a half million Christians, large numbers of Sikhs, and many others. Urdu is spoken in the west and Bengali in the east. These tongues, with English, are the official languages.

During the early agitation for a Muslim state, it was hoped that all, or the eastern part, of Afghanistan might be included. Ethnic Afghans or Pushtuns live on both sides of the border, with as many or more in Pakistan as in Afghanistan. The present boundary, along the Durand line, is an artificial frontier which represented the extent of British control. Since the boundary remains unchanged, there is agitation for a new ethnic state under the name of Pushtunistan. To the Afghans, this should be carved out of Pakistan, extending eastward to the Indus; to the Pakistani, any new state should lie beyond their frontier within Afghanistan.

The partition of India and Pakistan and the division of the latter into two very disparate units, unfortunate from most geographic viewpoints, represents a return to the fractionalization which has so often characterized the sub-

continent. Only under British control was there a real approach to unity.

When the subcontinent became independent in 1947, only a part of India was under actual British ownership; the rest was made up of native states, large and small. The heads of these semisovereign areas were either the descendants of rulers appointed by the Moguls and thus usually Muslims; or they were the descendants of rebels against Mogul rule who arose during its declining decades, often Hindus. Where given a chance, Muslim rulers naturally desired that their state should become part of Pakistan, even though the majority of their subjects might be Hindus.

One problem arose in Kashmir where, although the majority of the people were Muslims, the ruler was a Hindu who preferred union with India and opened the boundary to Indian troops. Since a plebiscite would presumably favor union with Pakistan, India was unwilling to conduct a vote, and the Kashmir problem became a major cause for disagreement.

One glance at the map shows the difficulty

of administering East and West Pakistan as parts of a united country, 1,000 miles apart and linked only by a long sea route or transit rights across a not-always-friendly neighbor. It should also be noted that Assam in northeastern India is almost as detached from the balance of its country.

The two parts are quite unlike. West Pakistan is culturally allied to the core of the Muslim world, but many of the people in East Pakistan are former low-caste Hindus. In West Pakistan the population density approximates 100 per square mile, while East Pakistan has nearly 1,000 people in a similar area.

Since the eastern and western provinces have such basic differences in environment and economics, political friction is inevitable. Should this ever lead to separation, either province would be quite unable to exert military or other force. While West Pakistan might be able to carry on alone, East Pakistan would experience great difficulty in any attempt at independence.

ECONOMIC POTENTIALS

The agricultural problems of East and West Pakistan are diametrically different. The East has too much rain, so that drainage is more important than irrigation. Almost the entire West has too little rain, so that irrigation is imperative. In East Pakistan the Ganges and Brahmaputra deltas have a maze of distributaries with widespread swamps, whereas the Indus valley is a land of tributary rivers with intervening desert. East Pakistan, in the Ganges-Brahmaputra delta, is a congested rice land with a food deficiency. West Pakistan in the dry Indus valley has a surplus of wheat which once supplied other parts of India, but which now, because of Pakistan's desire for foreign exchange, is shipped abroad. The raw cotton of the Indus valley was formerly processed in what is now India.

East Pakistan is the world's leading producer of jute, but most of the original mills were outside the country in Calcutta. In like manner the free movement of Assam's tea to Calcutta is blocked by the location of East Pakistan. West Pakistan is the fortunate heir of British engineering, especially in the Punjab where a vast network of modern canals brought water to 10 million acres. The country likewise inherited the best army, for most of the British Indian troops were recruited from the northwest.

Neither part of Pakistan appears well endowed with mineral assets. Poor coal, in thin seams and high in ash and sulfur, is mined in the Salt Range and near Quetta, both in West Pakistan. Some lignite is available in East Pakistan. Small amounts of oil are produced near Attock, along the Indus, and supplies of natural gas have been developed in both provinces. The Sui gas field in Baluchistan may be of importance, and the Sylhet area in East Pakistan appears promising. In the absence of adequate fuel supplies, West Pakistan may turn to the hydroelectric potentials of the Himalaya; hence the importance of Kashmir.

Chromite is the chief metallic mineral which occurs in large amounts, with a modest production in Baluchistan. Some antimony is mined in the western Himalaya. The only iron ores are of low grade and without economic value in the absence of coking coal. Rock salt in very large amounts occurs in the Salt Range, and salt is produced in interior lakes and along the shore near Karachi.

In short, Pakistan has a limited raw-material base for modern heavy industry. In its place the country should look forward to the processing of agricultural products such as leather, jute, cotton, and food. None of these industries were well developed at the time of partition, for what is now Pakistan was chiefly concerned with primary production for export, or in the case of jute, for processing in Calcutta. Industry had developed elsewhere, and Karachi was little more than a transit port with none of the fabrication which developed around Bombay or Calcutta.

One of the major problems in East Pakistan is that of a suitable seaport. Chittagong is off-center and served only by a narrow-gauge line. None of the many mouths of the Ganges and

Cotton is a major crop in the irrigated Indus valley in West Pakistan. This is a village market. (*Courtesy International Cooperation Administration*)

Brahmaputra east of Calcutta provide a suitable harbor, but port developments are under way at Chalna, south of Dacca.

Few of the items produced in one province can justify the cost of shipment to the other. Most traffic must move by sea, for the cost of rail freight across India is too high. To move cement, for example, from the Salt Range kilns to Dacca involves a rail haul of 750 miles to Karachi, transshipment, an ocean voyage of 3,000 miles, another transshipment, and then 100 miles overland to Dacca.

The economic difficulties of East Pakistan appear more critical than those of the more diversified West. Jute is the great export crop, now processed by new mills within the country rather than at Calcutta as formerly. Should world demand for jute decline or production increase within India, Pakistan's national budget would be directly affected and the East might become a major liability for the West.

This is the more serious since the West Pakistani often look down on their fellow religionists in the East, whose language, tradition, and backgrounds are different.

Pakistan launched its second Five-Year Plan in 1960 with the goal of self-sufficiency in food supply, a 50 per cent increase in industry, and a 20 per cent rise in the national income. Allowing for the anticipated increase in population, this should result in a 10 per cent gain in per capita living standards.

By geography and by history, Pakistan and India are complementary. Without reasonably free trade neither country can easily reach its full stature. Political separation based on communal distrust defies all the facts of economics. The solution of the Indus water problem and the agreement on transit rights in 1960 represented a major step in cooperation.

Every facet of geography argues for close cooperation between India and Pakistan. If one is to regard the other as a foreign country with restrictive customs formalities, it will be a high price to pay for Hindu and Muslim religious nationalism. Whatever the success of Pakistan, it should be borne in mind that the basic problems of this part of the world are not to be solved by political means alone.

THE GANGES-BRAHMAPUTRA DELTA

Within Pakistan lie four of the fourteen geographic regions which make up the South Asian realm. In East Pakistan there is the Ganges-Brahmaputra delta, which spreads westward across the border into India. In West Pakistan lie the Indus valley and the Thar Desert, both largely within the political limits, plus the western frontier.

The Ganges and Brahmaputra delta lies astride the Indo-Pakistan boundary, and it is impractical to describe it separately for each nation. No other area in either country is more homogeneous in land forms, climate, utilization, race, or language. Muslims are more numerous in East Pakistan, and Hindus predominate across the border in India, but the difference is religious rather than racial. Two-thirds of the region lies in East Pakistan, but it also includes West Bengal, the Mahanadi delta, and part of Orissa in India.

From the bay of Bengal to the Himalaya is 350 miles. In an east–west direction the region narrows to 140 miles between the Garo and Rajmahal Hills and widens to 300 miles in the latitude of Calcutta. The total area for the region is 90,000 square miles, twice the size of New York State.

On most sides, the delta is clearly limited by hills or the sea. To the southwest, the Chilka Lake at the southern edge of the Mahanadi delta is a historic boundary. On the northeast and northwest, the main valleys of the Ganges and Brahmaputra are set off by slight climatic differences.

Within this delta plain live nearly 100 million people. Nowhere else in this subcontinent, and in few other places in Asia, are there so

many per square mile. The average is close to 1,000, and in some rural areas that figure is trebled. In contrast, the Mississippi delta has 60 per square mile. Despite the presence of Calcutta, the rural population makes up 90 per cent of the whole. Bengali is the language spoken by nine out of ten people, both Muslim and Hindu.

This region is the flood plain of the two great river systems of the northeast. Large areas are inundated by the October and November floods, and hundreds of thousands of people have been drowned in these months. Countless natural distributaries and artificial canals intersect the plain, especially near the coast. The old delta in the west is less apt to be flooded than the new and actively growing delta in the east. In the eighteenth century the Ganges and Brahmaputra had separate mouths, and changes are still frequent. The seaward margin of the Ganges delta, known as the Sundarbans, is intricately divided by tidal channels and covered with mangrove forest. Conditions in the Mahanadi delta to the southwest are similar. Between the Ganges and the Mahanadi deltas are coastal sand dunes.

Three sections around the margins are slightly higher: next to Chota Nagpur in the west, the Barind Hills in the north, and the Surma valley to the east. Each upland is covered with scrub jungle and the hilltops are little used.

The climate of the Ganges and Brahmaputra delta is excellent for rice and jute but the combination of high temperature and humidity makes it ill-suited for man. The monsoon breaks in mid-June, bringing copious rain from a warm sea, and provides some coolness and relief after the sultry spring. September and October have intermittent showers and are very trying, as temperatures rise and the humidity is still high; at this season those who can afford it leave the delta for the hill station of Darjeeling, as they do also from mid-March until the break of the monsoon. The winter cool period is short. Rainfall amounts to 50 inches in the Mahanadi delta and increases eastward

East Pakistan is a land green with rice, jute, and sugar cane. This view is at Kushtia. (*Courtesy International Cooperation Administration*)

with 63 inches in Calcutta, 74 inches in Dacca, and 157 inches at Sylhet. Despite the almost complete absence of winter rain, the ground is so moist that the landscape remains green throughout the year. Malaria is especially serious here.

Rice covers 85 per cent of the cultivated land, some 30 million acres in all. Dry crops such as wheat or millet are absent, but vegetables and oil seeds are grown. Jute is the great cash crop, especially on the new delta to the east, where each flood brings a layer of fertilizing silt. Jute tolerates acid soils that are deficient in lime, and the crop covers 2 million acres; 80 per cent of the predivision yield was in Pakistan, but jute is now raised in Indian Bengal.

The chief city in East Pakistan is Dacca,

capital of the Eastern Province, with a population of a half million. This is the new center of the jute industry, for which an export center has been developed to the south. At the far eastern end of the delta is the port of Chittagong.

Calcutta once dominated the region, but its influence is now limited to the Indian part. The city has been described in the chapter on the regions of North India.

THE INDUS VALLEY

The western Indo-Gangetic lowland includes the plains and low hills from the Aravalli Range west to the Sulaiman Mountains, and from the Salt Range and Siwaliks south to the Arabian Sea. Much of it is the alluvial valley of the

Indus, but the southeastern half lies in the Thar Desert, where there are erosional and aeolian land forms rather than a river-deposited surface. Each half forms a geographic region, both of them largely within Pakistan.

The tributaries of the Indus extend east to west along the base of the Himalaya for 400 miles, and the main river flows south across the plain for 600 miles before reaching the sea. About 140,000 square miles are included within the region, with a population of some 50 million. Two distinct subregions are present: the Punjab in the north, with two-thirds of the area and nine-tenths of the people; and the Sind, south of the constriction made by the Sulaiman Mountains and the Thar Desert.

The word Punjab is of Persian origin and refers to the area drained by the five chief tributaries of the Indus: the Jhelum, Chenab, Ravi, Beas, and Sutlej. Each rises in the Himalaya and follows a shifting course across vast alluvial fans until it joins the Indus halfway to the sea. Since the Outer Himalayan or Siwalik Mountains are composed of easily eroded sedimentary rocks, each river is overloaded with debris, whose deposition en route across the plain continually raises the stream beds. This aggradation has built the bed of the lower Indus 70 feet above the surrounding country. Irrigation by diversion canals is made easy, but flood hazards are acute when the dikes break.

Each of the rivers frequently changes its course, often by tens of miles. In the third century B.C., the course of the Indus was 80 miles

Water is raised from the Indus by an endless chain of earthen jars, lifted as a bullock operates a gear arrangement. The Lloyd Barrage in the distance raises the level so that irrigation canals may be diverted. (*Courtesy International Cooperation Administration*)

THE INDUS VALLEY   463

to the east of the present channel, and it emp-
tied into the Rann of Cutch. The Jumna, now
a Ganges tributary, once flowed to the west,
and several hundred miles of abandoned river
channels through the Thar Desert may represent its old course. Dead cities date back to
3000 B.C.

Interstream areas are known in India as
doabs, originally from the country between the
Ganges and the Jumna. In many places these
remnants of old alluvial fans are slightly higher
and the sediments are mid-Pleistocene rather
than Recent. Differences between older and
younger alluvium as referred to in the Ganges
valley are more emphasized here, such as the
presence of lime nodules or kunkur in the older
areas.

Three surfaces may be recognized: the modern deltas, the newer alluvium or khadar, and
the older alluvium or bhangar. The material of
each is essentially similar, and the topographic
differences are only gradational. Part of the
contrast may relate to glacial epochs in the
Himalaya; part of it may merely represent normal stream planation.

The Indus valley is hot. Jacobabad in the
northern Sind has June temperatures consistently reaching 120°F, with a maximum of
127°F; the monthly day-and-night mean is
98°F; [1] rainfall is but 4 inches per year. The
eastern Punjab is somewhat more humid, with
precipitation up to 20 inches. Winters are cool,
with frost in the north.

During the winter small cyclonic storms
crossing West Pakistan from Iran produce a
little rain, but most of the limited precipitation
is in the summer. The Indus valley is exposed
to both arms of the monsoon; but the one which
moves up the Ganges is nearly dry upon arrival, while the Arabian Sea division is rainless
since it here moves nearly overland from Iran
and Arabia.

Irrigation is essential for successful agriculture in most of the Indus valley, although some
crops may be grown without it in the north

[1] The highest official air temperature on earth has
been recorded at Azizia in northern Africa, 136.4°F.

where rainfall is higher or ground water is available from the hills. Canals are an ancient development but were greatly expanded by the
British. Half of the total mileage in the entire
realm is in the Indus valley. Each of the major
streams has its system of distributaries, with
their inverted dendritic pattern. It is unfortunate that the boundary between Pakistan and
India cuts diagonally across several of these
rivers and canals. Should more water be diverted upstream, less land can be irrigated farther down. The problems that follow irrigation
of dry lands are shown by the fact that almost
as much money is required to get rid of surplus
water due to subsoil saturation as is spent on
irrigation supply.

Wheat is the most important crop, but only
half is irrigated. Yields in the Punjab are
slightly above the Indo-Pakistan average. Barley and oil seeds are other spring-harvested
crops; millet and corn are autumn crops. Cotton is an important cash crop on irrigated land
during the summer.

Colonization started in 1886, and the 1891
population density of 7 per square mile in the
Punjab has now risen to nearly 1,000. The
people of the Punjab are predominantly Muslims. The Punjabi are tall and well built and
have a long tradition. Many Punjabi travel
throughout Pakistan and India as salesmen or

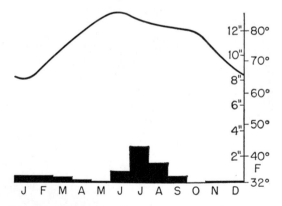

KARACHI. Elevation 13 feet, average temperature
78°F, annual precipitation 8 inches. West Pakistan has a desert climate with only a trace of the
monsoon.

as moneylenders, for the uncertainties of the monsoon and the general lack of capital often make it necessary for farmers to borrow money.

Among the various peoples of the Punjab are the Sikhs, with a religion somewhat intermediate between that of the Hindus and Muslims. The men are tall, have a splendid physique, and make good soldiers; they once served as policemen in British cities throughout Eastern Asia. Although they number but one-eighth of the people in the Punjab, they own one-fourth of the irrigated land. The division of their homeland by the Indian-Pakistan frontier is one of the many cultural problems created by the artificial political boundary.

The chief cities within Pakistan are Lahore, Hyderabad, and Karachi. In East Punjab, and hence in India, is Amritsar. Karachi is Pakistan's leading port and ranks fourth in the subcontinent. It ships wheat and raw cotton, but its humidity is too low for cotton mills. The city was developed during the twentieth century as an outlet for the northwest, and has experienced marked growth. Until 1960 it was Pakistan's capital. Since Karachi is 200 miles closer to Aden than is Bombay, it is the nearest port to Europe in South Asia. It is also an important station for air services. The population rose from 375,000 in 1947 before partition to 2 million by 1960. Whereas Hindus once made up half of the population, they now number but 2 per cent.

THE THAR DESERT

Between the Indus valley and the Aravalli Range at the edge of the peninsular plateau is an arid region, nearly empty in its northern

West Pakistan is dry, and many villages resemble this settlement at Rahimyar Khan. Walls of pounded earth and flat roofs reflect the climate. (*Courtesy International Co-operation Administration*)

THE THAR DESERT 465

and more desert area, and only sparsely inhabited in the south near the sea. This includes a large Indian area in western Rajasthan and northern Gujerat. In the north is the Thar Desert proper; in the south is Cutch. The desert corresponds with the former political area of the Sind.

The summer aridity of the Thar Desert presents several problems. Low pressures and proximity to the sea would suggest rain, but instead the skies are cloudless. Winds from the east are dry since the monsoon has lost all its moisture coming up the Ganges valley, and on the north and west are mountain barriers that keep out surface winds. From the south, winds enter the Sind with a relative humidity of 80 per cent, but high surface temperatures reduce this figure to 55 per cent in the interior. A convectional rise to 3,000 feet would give rain, but before this elevation is reached, surface air mixes with dry air masses from the west so that cloud formation is prevented. Thus the sun, directly overhead, shines without interruption and heats the surface, still further lowering the relative humidity. Summer pressures are low.

The rainfall is generally under 10 inches and, since there is little possibility of developing irrigation, most of the area is a desolate waste, covered with shifting sands or scattered brush. Older rock hills project above the undulating surface. Camel caravans link the few oases. While pasturage is limited, livestock herding is a major source of livelihood.

Here and there are shallow playa lakes. The most important is Lake Sambhar, which covers 90 square miles with a maximum depth of 4 feet after occasional rains; at other seasons it is a dry salt flat.

The Rann of Cutch, to the south, was an arm of the sea in early historic times but is now nearly filled with sediments, alternately wet and dry with the seasons. From its salt-incrusted surface and from sea spray, the southern monsoon annually carries 130,000 tons of salt into Rajasthan.

In 1819, 2,000 square miles in the western

Rann sank 12 to 15 feet, while a nearby area of 600 square miles rose several feet.

THE WESTERN FRONTIER

Northwestern Pakistan is not only a place, it is a problem. Nowhere else did the British Empire have a land frontier of such pressing military significance. Through these mountains came all previous invasions of India; beyond them today is the Communist Soviet Union and the restless Mohammedan world.

West of the Indus tower the 11,000-foot Sulaiman and the 7,000-foot Kirthar Ranges. What lies in their immediate hinterland is not so significant as the fact that they are a rampart bounding Pakistan on the west. This 600-mile length of mountain wall has about the same length as the boundary next to Burma, but in the east there are climatic as well as topographic barriers to penetration. The history of the two frontiers is entirely different. Pakistan is now the guardian of this boundary for India.

Six significant routes lead westward: the Khyber Pass to Kabul in Afghanistan, the important Bolan Pass to Quetta in Baluchistan, the arid Makran coastal strip, and the lesser Gumal, Kurram, and Tochi Passes. These are paths of history. In addition there are 350 trails usable by camels. All these tend to be one-way roads in terms of warfare, easy for the descent of warlike tribesmen who wish to raid the plains but difficult to penetrate and police. Road building has become the key to the pacification of this frontier.

From Istanbul to the Indus, Southwest Asia has a succession of high arid plateaus, surrounded by mountains. Anatolia is the westernmost; Baluchistan the easternmost. Nowhere in this succession is there much rain, but such precipitation as occurs follows the Mediterranean sequence of winter rain, which occurs with the displaced belt of cyclonic storms, and summer drought due to subtropical high pressure. The Sulaiman Mountains mark the boundary between winter-Mediterranean and summer-monsoon rainfall regimes.

Much of Baluchistan is nomad country, too dry for cultivation without irrigation and lacking in adequate sources of water for canals. (*Courtesy International Cooperation Administration*)

In topography, climate, race, and ways of livelihood, Baluchistan might properly be grouped with the Southwestern Asia realm, but in trade and history it is not so related. The geographic region of the western frontier as here considered includes Baluchistan, most of the former North-West Frontier Province, and part of the Punjab behind the Salt Range. The area is some 170,000 square miles, and population densities range from nearly zero in some deserts and mountains to 10 per square mile for Baluchistan as a whole, 200 for the former North-West Frontier Province; and several hundred per square mile in the fertile valleys of the Punjab.

Climatic conditions improve from south to north, although level land unfortunately diminishes. Quetta with 9 inches of rain represents the mean. Thus the Makran coast is a desolate desert strip where people and their cattle alike subsist on fish. Baluchistan is a land of interior drainage and withering rivers which descend from barren, mile-high mountains; great gravel fans testify to the aridity of the country. Into them, Persian-style horizontal wells known as *qanats* or *karez* have been dug for water to irrigate lower flood plains. Sorghum is the chief grain, with some wheat and barley. Excellent fruits are raised everywhere. In the areas of partially rain-fed agriculture of the Punjab, wheat leads and is followed by millet, barley, and corn.

This is the land of the nomadic pastoralist rather than the settled farmer. Transhumance is common; as summer comes the shepherds move their flocks and herds to the cooler mountain slopes; in the winter they descend to the lowlands or even to the Sind. Thousands of nomads migrate back and forth between central Afghanistan and the Indus valley each year.

The Salt Range has long attracted geological attention. At its base are immense beds of Eocene salt, and the overthrust structure reveals an excellent stratigraphic record.

The three most important cities are Quetta, the center of Baluchistan; the former arsenal and military post of Rawalpindi, the traditional gate to Kashmir, near the site of the new national capital at Islamabad (Anantnag); and Peshawar on the railway to the Khyber Pass.

References on Pakistan

Additional information may be found in the *Oriental Geographer* (Dacca) and the *Pakistan Geog. Rev.* (Lahore).

See also general references on South Asia, Chapter 26.

Ahmad, Nafis: "Industrial Development in East Bengal (East Pakistan)," *Econ. Geog.,* XXVI (1950), 183–195.

Ahmad, Nafis: "The Pattern of Rural Settlement in East Pakistan," *Geog. Rev.,* XLVI (1956), 388–398.

*Ahmad, Nafis: *The Economic Geography of East Pakistan,* Fair Lawn, N.J.: Oxford University Press (1958).

Elwin, Verrier: "The North-East Frontier Agency of India," *Geog. Mag.,* XXIX (1956), 405–416.

Fergusson, F. F.: "Famine and Water Supply in Western Rajputana," *Geog. Jour.,* XCIII (1939), 39–53.

Gulick, Luther H., Jr.: "Irrigation Systems of the Former Sind Province, West Pakistan," *Geog. Rev.,* LIII (1963), 79–99.

Hodges, R. C.: "Indus Water for Pakistan," *Canadian Geog. Jour.,* LXI (1960), 97–105.

Johnson, B. L. C.: "Crop Association Regions in East Pakistan," *Geography,* XLIII (1958), 86–103.

Stephens, Ian: "Bahawalpur," *Geog. Mag.,* XXVII (1954), 328–338.

32 Ceylon

Tropical Island / Regional Contrasts / References on Ceylon

TROPICAL ISLAND

The island of Ceylon has long been a port of call halfway across the Indian Ocean for ships between the East and the West. Chinese junks here met Arab vessels 2,000 years ago, and trade between the Orient and Europe by this route supplemented the overland commerce through central Asia. Ceylon is shown on Ptolemy's maps of the second century after Christ, and it was visited by the Chinese Buddhist pilgrim Fa Hsien in the fourth century. In the thirteenth century, Marco Polo on his way home described Ceylon as "the best island of its size in the world."

Ceylon's location made it a colonial prize.

The Portuguese came in 1505; a century and a half later the Dutch took over but were replaced by the British in 1795. The island became a British Crown Colony in 1802 and a republic within the Commonwealth in 1948. As a part of South Asia, Ceylon has shared in its history, but as an island it has been distinct.

While still a stopping point on Great Britain's lifeline to Australia, independent Ceylon has felt free to decide her own foreign policies, as in the matter of trading rubber for rice with Communist China. The development of aviation has changed Ceylon's essential location since the great east–west airlines cross India and Pakistan far to the north and leave the island to one side. Along with Suez, Aden, and

469

Singapore, Colombo is now somewhat on a side road. On the other hand, the island's stature has grown with the creation of the multinational Colombo Plan for economic development around the Indian Ocean.

To the Ceylonese, their country is known as Lanka, its historic Brahman name, rather than by the Portuguese name of Zelan. To Europeans, Ceylon is the pearl of the Orient.

Geologically, Ceylon is a slightly detached part of the Western Ghats, separated by a submerged gap comparable to that of Palghat. The strait is 22 miles wide, full of sand banks and low islands, and through it there is only one navigable passage. In its physical geography Ceylon somewhat resembles South India, with increased emphasis on low latitude and with a marked cultural individuality.

The core of the island is a mass of Pre-Cambrian crystalline rocks which form a central mountain area, rising to 8,292 feet. Encircling these hills and mountains are lowlands and a coastal plain. Mineral resources in the interior include graphite, gem stones such as sapphires and rubies, and iron ore, for which there is no coal.

As Ceylon is nearly on the equator, the temperature is uniform throughout the year, and since the island is surrounded by the sea, temperatures never exceed 96°F. Thus Colombo has monthly averages between 78 and 82°F for the year. Both monsoons bring rain; in summer to the southwest side of the island and in winter to the northeast. On the slopes precipitation amounts to 100 or 200 inches, and the total everywhere exceeds 50 inches, except in the extreme southeast and northwest where there are no hills to lift and cool the monsoon winds. In general, Ceylon is influenced by the southwest monsoon from late May until September, and receives the northeast monsoon from November until January. The former is the stronger of the two. The climatic division between the east and west coasts, conditioned by seasonal rains, is as geographically important as the topographic difference based on altitude.

Within an area of 25,332 square miles, the population exceeds 10 million. Two-thirds of the people are Buddhist Singhalese. The others include Hindu Tamils, a Dravidian group from South India, along with some Arabs and Malays. Political action centers around these ethnic groups. In size and location, Ceylon finds some parallel in Hawaii or Cuba.

Only one-fifth of the land is productive, although as much as half might be cultivated. The presence of this undeveloped agricultural land is a major asset, for Ceylon's population has been growing very rapidly. Unlike India, Ceylon has an extensive amount of plantation or estate agriculture. A dependable tropical climate prevents distress. The rice production

Ceylon Data [1]

Area	25,332 square miles
Population	9,651,000 (1959 est.)
Colombo (capital)	426,127 (1953 census)
Primary and secondary pupils	2,117,988 (1959)
University of Ceylon	3,177 (1959)
Rice	737,000 metric tons (1959)
Tea	187,396 " "
Rubber	98,400 metric tons (1960)
Copra	224,100 metric tons (1959–60)
Cement	89,700 metric tons (1960)
Electricity	297,700,000 kilowatthours (1960)

[1] *Britannica Book of the Year*, 1962.

The Far East's most beautiful haven of catamarans—the Mt. Lavinia Beach, near Colombo. Ceylon's tropical beaches are among the loveliest in the world. (*Photo by Ewing Galloway, New York*)

does not meet more than half of the local needs, but the export of commercial crops pays for imported food.

Around the sandy coast are extensive coconut plantations; hence copra is a large export. Rice is grown on the plains, and its acreage is nearly as large as that in coconuts. Other lowland crops are cinnamon, cloves, and citronella oil. Ceylon is a typical tropical island, with hot but not oppressive temperatures which favor agriculture.

The interior hills were once covered with splendid forests, of which only small areas remain. Many forests have been cleared by fire to secure suitable soils for raising coffee. This crop has now declined and is replaced by tea. Tea is Ceylon's most valuable export. It is superior to most of the Assam product, and there is a large export to England and the United States. Rubber is grown below 2,000 feet and exceeds tea in acreage. Cacao and quinine are also produced. Some of the mountain people carry on migratory cultivation in fire clearings. The mountain core in Ceylon has always had greater economic significance than the lowlands.

Colombo is the chief city and the leading port of the Indian Ocean; its population numbers a half million. The harbor is partly artificial but is adequate for the extensive transit

Bamboo grows to giant size on Ceylon. (*Courtesy J. W. Beardsley*)

traffic. Kandy in the hills is an important center for Buddhism, which has entirely disappeared from India. On the east coast is the splendid natural harbor of Trincomalee, once the chief British naval base in the Indian Ocean.

REGIONAL CONTRASTS

Distinct environmental and human contrasts divide Ceylon into three geographic subregions. One is the wet coastal lowland in the southwest; another is dominated by the interior hills and mountains; the third comprises the dry northern half of the island. Climatic conditions reflect monsoon circulation, exposure, and soils.

The lowland wet zone lies along the southwest coast in the Colombo area. Part of the region is an alluvial coastal plain with 70 to 100 inches of rain. Here rice occupies the marshy areas, with coconut, tea, rubber, and most settlements on the slightly higher lands between the rivers. Cash crops such as coconut products or rubber are often so profitable that rice culture is neglected. In some of the ridge country where elevations reach 3,000 feet and rainfall amounts to 200 inches a year, there are remnants of the original tropical rain forest. In climate and crops, conditions in southwest Ceylon somewhat resemble those in Travancore and Cochin in Southwest India.

Colombo, with its exposed position at sea level, receives rain at all seasons, with maxima in May and October during each intermonsoon period. Stations at higher elevations have their heaviest rain during the summer southwest monsoon. While the island experiences considerable variability, serious drought is uncommon in the wet zone, for the soil stores enough moisture for a considerable carry-over. While rainfall is normally sufficient to keep rice fields flooded, irrigation is commonly available. Flood control is more important than water shortage.

Mature soils tend to be lateritic, red in color and low in humus, lime, and phosphorus. Immature alluvium is usually more fertile.

The wet zone is the home of the lowland Singhalese, and was the center of a kingdom dating from 1235. Arab and European influences were also concentrated here. This is now the most densely populated area, and has the most intensive agricultural utilization.

The hills of central Ceylon around Kandy have a diverse topography which reflects their complex geology and erosional history. Elevations reach 8,281 feet, and some of the country is quite scenic. While rainfall amounts to 100 inches and more, even higher than in the lowlands, temperatures are moderated by altitude. Thus at 6,000 feet the mean daily reading

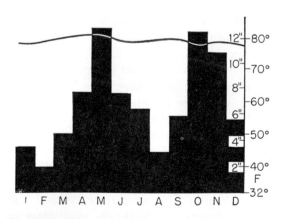

COLOMBO. Elevation 24 feet, average temperature 81°F, annual precipitation 93 inches. Ceylon receives rain as the doldrums move north and south.

Colombo is always a port of call for vessels bound directly from Aden to Singapore. This is the custom house. (*Palmer, Courtesy American President Lines*)

is around 60°F. Remarkable terracing for rice characterizes some slopes, in places with serious erosion. Much of the region is so thickly populated that densities of 1,000 per square mile are recorded, even in the very hilly sections.

The city of Kandy, an ancient capital, lies in a basin area between 1,000 and 2,000 feet in elevation. This is the home of the upland Singhalese. Because of its isolation, the region remained relatively empty and undeveloped until captured by the British in 1815; traditional cultures remain. This is the seat of the University of Ceylon.

This hill country is an important area for tea estates, especially above 3,000 feet elevation. Small shifting areas of fire-cleared fields are devoted to millet, corn, or dry rice; this method of cultivation, known as chena, is similar to that practiced in many forest areas of South and East Asia. Fields are abandoned after a year or two because of the growth of weeds.

The lowland dry zone, which covers the northern and eastern half of Ceylon, has a landscape quite unlike the rest of the island. The surface is possibly an old peneplain. While the northeast monsoon brings 50 inches of rain, the high rate of evapotranspiration reduces its value, and there is a pronounced dry period from February to October. Settlement is sparse. Much of the interior is a plain covered by a dense jungle and underlain by laterite. Some dry areas have a thorn-scrub or savanna-grassland cover.

In the extreme north lies the Jaffna Peninsula with some fertile soils developed on lime-

Although Ceylon is well suited for raising rice, so much of the agricultural land is devoted to rubber, tea, coconuts, or other export crops that the island does not feed itself. This view is between Colombo and Kandy. (*Courtesy Trans World Airlines*)

stone. Surface water is so limited that agriculture depends on wells. This is a Tamil area, with densities of 1,000 people per square mile, and it makes periodic demands for political autonomy. While rainfall is excessive during the northeast monsoon in November and December, the southwest monsoon is nearly dry. Somewhat more humid conditions prevail on the east coast.

Two thousand years ago, northern Ceylon was the site of a flourishing civilization which dated back to 500 B.C., shown by the remains of a highly developed irrigation system later abandoned. Agricultural redevelopment is now under way. No coconuts, tea, or rubber flourish in this dry area. Rice is the chief crop, but there is inadequate water for irrigation. Considerable migratory chena cultivation is carried on.

References on Ceylon

See also general references on South Asia, Chapter 26.

*Cook, Elsie K.: *Ceylon: Its Geography, Its Resources and Its People,* New York: St Martin's Press (1951).

Farmer, B. H.: "Agriculture in Ceylon," *Geog. Rev.,* XL (1950), 42–66.

Farmer, B. H.: "Problems of Land Use in the Dry Zone of Ceylon," *Geog. Jour.,* CXX (1954), 21–33.

Farmer, B. H.: "Rainfall and Water Supply in the Dry Zone of Ceylon," in R. W. Steel and C. A. Fisher (eds.): *Geographical Essays on British Tropical Lands*, London: George Philip & Son (1956), 227–268.

MacFadden, C. H.: "The Gal Oya Valley: Ceylon's Little TVA," *Geog. Rev.*, XLIV (1954), 271–281.

McCune, Shannon: "The Land of Ceylon," *Jour. Geog.*, XLVI (1947), 83–91.

McCune, Shannon: "Man's Activities in Ceylon," *Jour. Geog.*, XLVI (1947), 147–159.

Meddegoda, P. N.: "Reclaiming the Dry Zone of Ceylon," *Geog. Jour.*, CXX (1954), 271–281.

Wikkramatileke, R.: "Ella Village: An Example of Rural Settlement and Agricultural Trends in Highland Ceylon," *Econ. Geog.*, XXVIII (1952), 355–363.

Wikkramatileke, R.: "Problems of Land Use Mapping in the Tropics: An Example from Ceylon," *Geography*, XLIV (1959), 79–95.

THE SOUTHWEST ASIAN REALM

Four colors dominate the landscape of Southwest Asia: the brown of the desert, the white of the snow-crowned mountains, the green of the agricultural land, and the black of the oil fields. Much of the area is a dry land, where life depends on the wise management of the available water. For millenniums this realm has been a contest zone because of its crossroads location.

"Baghdad is a great city which used to be the seat of the Calif of all the Saracens in the world, just as Rome is the seat of the Pope of all the Christians. A very great river flows through the city, and by this you can descend to the Sea of India. There is a great traffic of merchants with their goods this way; they descend some eighteen days from Baghdad, and then come to a certain city called Kisi, where they enter the Sea of India. There is also on the river, as you go from Baghdad to Kisi, a great city called Basra, surrounded by woods, in which grow the best dates in the world." (*The Book of Ser Marco Polo,* translated by Henry Yule, London: John Murray, 1871.)

Date palm in Bahrein. (*Courtesy Caltex*)

33 Southwestern Mountains, Deserts, and Oases

Asian Crossroads / Mediterranean Climate / Mountain Pattern / Desert Areas / The Fertile Crescent / Irrigation Agriculture / References on Southwest Asia

ASIAN CROSSROADS

The following chapters on Southwest Asia are built around three ideas: the crossroads character of the realm, the role of water in its economy, and the way in which man is changing the landscape.

One major asset of the area is its strategic position between Europe, Africa, and the bulk of Asia. Since the beginnings of history its people have served as middlemen at the crossroads of civilization.

Most of Southwest Asia is dry, and if the area did not have high mountains to extract moisture from passing winds and preserve it in the form of snow until summer, much of the area would be a desert. Man's survival has depended upon his skill in managing water.

Man has lived here for at least a hundred centuries, and during this time he has made many changes in land use and in means of livelihood. With the introduction of modern techniques, and thanks to fabulous royalties from oil developments, dramatic transformations are under way. The coming decades may be quite different from the past.

The crossroads character of Southwest Asia is evident today when we examine the sea routes through Suez and the Bosporus, or the air lanes from Europe to Asia which pass over Beirut, or the continuing search for an overland route to India, whether from the Soviet Union across Afghanistan or from Turkey through Iran. Here is where Europe, Africa, and Asia meet; few places on earth have such a focal position.

Location rather than intrinsic assets makes the realm significant. The population is scattered and contributes little to world trade. Aside from truly vast reserves of oil, the mineral assets are modest and the industrial prospects limited. Nor is there here a potential surplus of food or other export products.

For the most part this is a poor area. Yet every world conqueror since Alexander the Great has had his eye on Southwest Asia. The Mongols under Genghiz Khan and Tamerlane stormed across the realm. The Crusaders came from the west, followed by the modern states of Europe: witness the Kaiser's dream of a Berlin-to-Baghdad railway.

Not only has this realm been a magnet, but

The ancient fortress of Rumeli Hisar near Istanbul commands the eastern entrance to the Bosporus. Snow occasionally falls on Istanbul. (*Courtesy Turkish Information Office*)

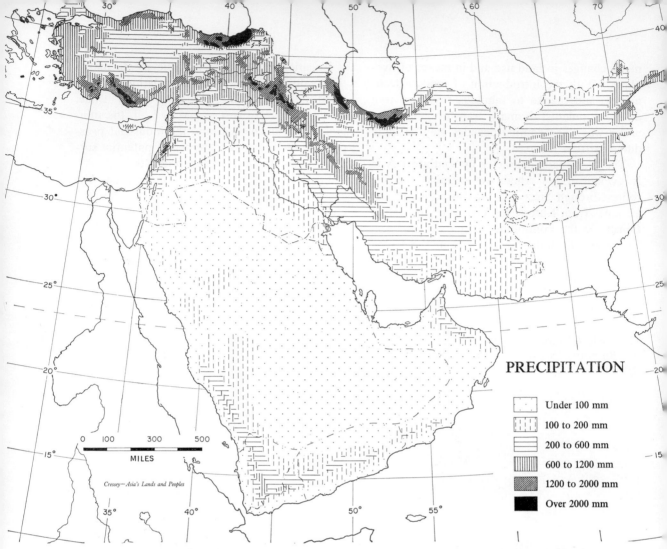

PRECIPITATION

Under 100 mm
100 to 200 mm
200 to 600 mm
600 to 1200 mm
1200 to 2000 mm
Over 2000 mm

Cressey—Asia's Lands and Peoples

Most of Southwest Asia is dry; only a few areas receive enough rainfall for normal agriculture. While mountain slopes facing the Black and Caspian Seas may have 100 inches of precipitation, much of Arabia has only 5 inches. (*Based on maps by Douglas Carter and Edgar Rosenen, Laboratory of Climatology*)

it has also been an explosive center of political power. Babylon and Assyria spread across a half million square miles, their conquests reaching a climax some seven centuries before Christ. A century later the Persian Empire covered 2 million square miles. During the seventh and eighth centuries the Arab empires, centered on Damascus and Baghdad, reached from Turkestan to Spain. Then came the Ottoman Turks, who achieved their maximum domain in the sixteenth century. Southwest Asia has experienced no unity in recent decades, but the Arab League offers a possible basis for future cooperation.

All the world is central to somewhere, and there is no need to overemphasize the location of Southwest Asia, but to understand its role in Asia one needs to see it in its tricontinental location.

To some Europeans this realm has been known as the Near or Middle East, but such a point of view reflects the egocentricity of the West. Thus people in London or Paris viewed distant China and Japan as the Far East, while the Levant or even Greece was seen as the Near East; India thus became the Middle East. Americans might with equal justification look across the Pacific and speak of China as the Near West, or of Southwest Asia as the Far West.

Important places should be named from where they are, per se, not merely in relation to somewhere else where the viewer may be. The realm we are considering is a part of Asia, but if the name Southwest Asia appears too long, the title may be shortened to Swasia. Certainly the term Middle East is too vague; for under some usages it takes in everything from Gibraltar to the Indus, and even to East Pakistan.

As here considered, the Swasian realm includes the area from Turkey to Afghanistan, inclusive, and south through the Arabian Peninsula. In size it covers 2½ million square miles; in population it counts nearly 100 million. This roughly matches in latitude, area, and population arid Mexico and the dry southwestern third of the United States.

Surrounding the realm are seven seas: the Black and Caspian on the north, the Mediterranean and Aegean on the west, and the Red, Arabian, and Persian Seas to the south.

Both where bordered by these arms of the ocean as well as elsewhere, Swasia is fringed by high mountains; only in a few places is it easily accessible from the outside world. In fact, these penetrating seas and divisive mountains make the realm anything but a homogeneous unit. In place of one unified culture there have been many ways of life and thought: Persian, Arab, and Turkish, plus numerous minority groups. It is only in terms of the overall environment and the contrast with bordering realms that Swasia is coherent.

MEDITERRANEAN CLIMATE

One of the features which make the southwestern part of the continent unique is the pattern of winter rain and summer drought, typically *Cs* in Koeppen terms. This is a char-

acteristic of mid-latitude lands on the western sides of continents, intermediate between the zone of variable westerlies farther north and the high-pressure deserts with their descending air to the south. The Mediterranean basin supplies the typical example, but similar conditions prevail in southern California, central Chile, and southernmost Africa.

Southwest Asia has a modified Mediterranean climate, best developed near that sea but with increasing continentality and aridity eastward. Since Afghanistan represents the easternmost extent of winter-maximum precipitation and West Pakistan is characterized by summer monsoon rain, this change marks the eastern limit of the Swasian realm.

During much of the year Swasia is overlain by an area of high pressure, with gradients decreasing to the south. Air is typically descending from aloft and blowing outward from the interior of Eurasia to the tropical seas. Since this air is initially dry and moves into warmer areas where its moisture-holding capacity increases, little rain is to be expected.

This simple pattern is interrupted by the seasonal tilt of the earth's axis. When the overhead sun shifts to the Southern Hemisphere, the earth's circulation pattern moves with it. As a result, the normal path of variable westerlies or cyclonic storms shifts southward from central Europe, and an occasional low-pressure area invades northern Swasia.

Cyclonic storms or migrating low-pressure whirls involve a frontal interplay of different air masses; where moist air is sufficiently cooled, precipitation results. Weak fronts, moving across the realm roughly once a week in winter, account for the rainy periods. The beginning and end of the rainy season is thus related to the southward or northward shift of storm paths, and perhaps in turn to high-level jet streams.

The usual climate of the area is one of long, hot, dry summers with little variation from day to day, and short, cool, wet, variable winters. Areas which are brown and lifeless in summer suddenly turn to green after the rains.

While lowland rainfall is related to frontal conditions within the migrating lows and to distance from maritime sources of moisture, mountains introduce an orographic element. Where moisture-bearing winds are forced to rise over barrier ranges, the cooling action which results may bring heavy rain or snow. This is true of much of Swasia's precipitation.

Lowland areas with but 5 to 10 inches of rainfall are bordered by highlands with 50 inches. The traveler across parched desert basins is often within sight of snow-crowned peaks. Just as windward slopes are humid, so lee slopes where descending air is warmed by adiabatic compression are usually arid. The map of precipitation thus reflects winds and mountain alignments.

In so large a realm variations are inevitable. Even though central Arabia has a winter rainfall maximum, the annual total is so low that the area is a desert. Coastal Beirut averages 35 inches, but Baghdad, 500 miles due east of the mountains, receives only 6 inches. The wettest location appears to be the mountain slopes near Rize in northeastern Turkey, where the annual amount exceeds 100 inches. In contrast, southern Arabia may average but 2 inches.

Conditions depart from normal Mediterranean situations in the extreme north and south. The Black Sea coast of Turkey receives rain the year round because of its location on the lee side of the sea and its proximity to the storm paths of Europe. The highlands of Yemen are far enough south to catch occasional summer monsoon rains. So do the mountains of Afghanistan.

Deserts, *BW*, cover at least half of Swasia, and steppe climates, *BS*, account for about one-fifth of the area. While these areas are both too dry to fit typical Mediterranean conditions, they do have a winter-rainfall maximum. Many months may pass with scarcely a drop of rain; then a sudden shower brings up the average.

In terms of effective moisture or the balance between precipitation and potential evapotranspiration, most of the lowland has a large deficit.

Over vast areas the unsatisfied evaporation potential amounts to tens of inches, and exceeds 30 inches in all the desert and steppe. This suggests the extensive amount of irrigation water which must be added for crops.

If Swasia had no mountains, very few areas would have enough rainfall for agriculture, and if the highland moisture were not stored up in the form of snow, few rivers would flow the year round, so that summer irrigation would be out of the question. Snow is thus one of the realm's greatest resources.

For the most part, Southwest Asia has a delightful year-round climate, rarely uncomfortable in winter and with bright sunny skies throughout the year. Lowland temperatures may become excessively hot for several months, but highland cities enjoy some of the world's best weather, with Koeppen categories of *Ds* rather than *Cs*.

Istanbul has an annual average of 57°F, while Aden, 2,000 miles to the south, averages 85°F: a change of 1 degree F per degree of latitude. Temperatures at Jerusalem, 2,500 feet in elevation, average 63°F, while the Dead Sea, 1,286 feet below sea level, appears to average 76°F and nearby Mount Hermon, 9,232 feet in elevation, has 40°F on the basis of the normal change of 3.3 degrees F per 1,000 feet.

The lowest recorded temperature is −35°F at Sivas in central Turkey; Khuzistan in southwestern Iran has reached 129°F. Perhaps the world's most uncomfortable climate is found along the shores of the Red Sea and the Persian Gulf, where there are long periods with temperatures of 120°F and humidities in excess of 70 per cent.

The problem of climatic variation has received much attention, but without conclusive evidence. The precipitation-evaporation balance has fluctuated within cyclic limits, but it seems probable that the average has not changed for several thousand years. Many ruined cities lie in presently inhospitable areas, but all of them contain aqueducts and cisterns, indicating that water was a problem then as now. Traces of abandoned fields may reflect changes in run-

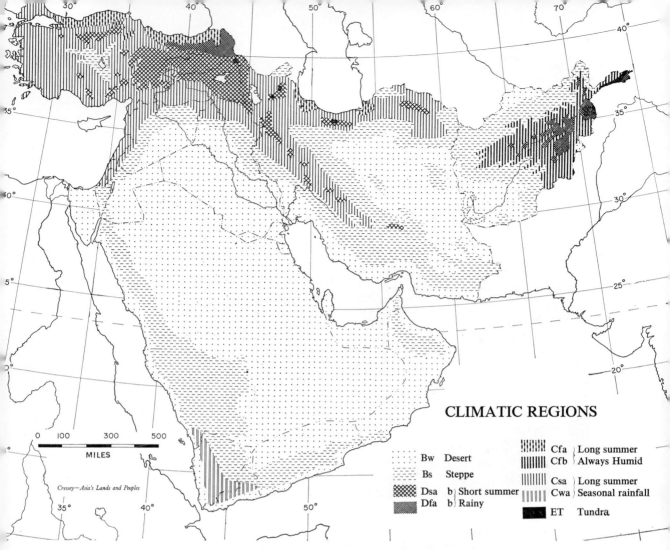

CLIMATIC REGIONS

⋮⋮⋮ Bw	Desert
Bs	Steppe
Dsa b⟩ Short summer	
Dfa b⟩ Rainy	

Cfa ⟩	Long summer	
Cfb ⟩	Always Humid	
Csa ⟩	Long summer	
Cwa ⟩	Seasonal rainfall	
ET	Tundra	

Elevation and wind systems give Swasia a variety of climates, most of them Mediterranean types, with winter precipitation and summer drought. High mountains receive considerable snow. (*Hassan Al-Khayat*)

off from nearby hills, related to the destruction of forests rather than to an actual decrease in precipitation.

Still earlier climatic changes are clearly indicated by variations in the size of salt lakes such as the Dead Sea, which was formerly fresh when it overflowed to the Mediterranean.

MOUNTAIN PATTERN

Young mountains, for the most part rugged and barren, cover a million square miles in Southwest Asia. In the north two great systems cross the realm from east to west; other mountains fringe Swasia in the southwest. Only in a few places can one penetrate very far into Southwest Asia without crossing mountains, and once within the realm, one is encircled by highlands.

Eastern Afghanistan extends into the rugged complex known as the Pamir highlands. From this "roof of the world" two ranges radiate westward, the Hindu Kush on the north and the Sulaiman and its continuations on the south; each continues irregularly and under various names to the Aegean Sea. The Hindu Kush

Nomadic life in the desert would be almost impossible without the camel, for he is a converter of sparse desert vegetation into products useful to man: food, clothing, shelter, and wealth, as well as transport. (*Courtesy Standard Oil Company of New Jersey*)

merges into the Koh-i-Baba and then the Paropamisus; in Iran the ranges are known as the Kopet Dagh and Elburz; in northern Turkey the chain is called the Pontus or North Anatolian Mountains. In general, this sequence forms the northern fringe of Swasia.

The Sulaiman and Kirthar Ranges extend southwestward from the Pamirs to mark the border between Afghanistan and Pakistan, and then continue westward through the Makran region of Iran. Where the sequence turns to the northwest along the Persian Gulf it is known as the Zagros Mountains. In southern Turkey the continuation forms the Taurus system. These two great festoons which radiate from the

Pamirs nearly join in a similar mountain knot or nucleus, the Armenian highlands, near the border of Turkey and Iran.

The northern sequence forms part of the "alpide" fold system, which extends from the Alps to the Kunlun and Chin Ling of China. The southern succession belongs to the "dinaride" system which has its continuation westward into Yugoslavia and eastward to the Himalaya and beyond. The geologic structures are far from continuous and everywhere tend to be complex; it is the topographic continuity which is important.

The intervening area between the alpide and dinaride systems is occupied by rigid and essentially unfolded masses. In interior Turkey there is the Anatolian Plateau; in central Iran lies the Plateau of Iran which merges into the Seistan Basin of Afghanistan.

To the south of this sequence of folded mountains and interior plateaus, the structure and topography are quite different. Parallel to the eastern Mediterranean coast and continuing south through Arabia along the Red Sea is a line of block-fault mountains, in places divided into a double series by a syncline or graben.

In Syria, Lebanon, and Palestine there are twin ranges, one close to the sea, the other parallel and farther inland. The coastal series includes the Alma Dag, the Lebanon Mountains, and the Hills of Judea. The interior lowland is drained by the north-flowing Orontes River in Syria, the south-flowing Litani in Lebanon, and the Jordan River and Wadi el Araba in Israel and Jordan.

Fault structures continue southward along the Red Sea, with the sea itself occupying the enlarged graben. High, one-sided escarpments form the Hejaz and Asir Mountains in Saudi Arabia and the Yemen Mountains farther south.

To the east of this north–south mountain alignment is a great area of rolling hills and plains which occupies much of Syria, Iraq, and Saudi Arabia. West-central Arabia is underlain by an ancient crystalline block or shield, away from which sedimentary rocks dip gently eastward, in places outcropping in low cuestas. Recent alluvium veneers these sedimentary rocks near the Persian Gulf.

Volcanic outbursts, old and modern, have spread over several hundred thousand square miles in Turkey and southward through Syria and Arabia to Aden. No volcanoes are currently active, but several cones and flows are

no more than a few thousand years old. The Armenian highlands contain several symmetrical lava cones, including Mount Ararat.

Many of the mountains of both systems have recently been uplifted and are thus subject to vigorous erosion. Occasional earthquakes are reminders that uplift is still under way especially in the northern chain across Turkey and Iran. Slopes tend to be steep, and since many are unprotected by vegetation, runoff is rapid. Vigorous erosion in the mountains is reflected in the broad alluvial fans and waste-filled interior basins. Only a small fraction of the sediment washed out of the highlands ever reaches the ocean; in fact little runoff continues to the surrounding seas, for much evaporates en route or ends in playa lakes.

DESERT AREAS

Dry lands occupy 2 million square miles of Southwest Asia, some of them full deserts, others semiarid, but all with inadequate rainfall for normal cultivation. Some of these lands owe their aridity to mountains lying to windward which block inblowing moisture; others are the product of descending air or south-moving air masses which are characterized by evaporation rather than precipitation. Thus, as winds move equatorward over Arabia they are gradually warmed, and since this increases their moisture-holding capacity, precipitation is unlikely.

Deserts may be described in many ways: some criteria are climatic; other definitions are based on ecological, geomorphic, hydrographic, or geographic considerations.

If we consider actual precipitation, no part of Swasia is completely rainless, but there are 200,000 square miles where the total averages only 1 or 2 inches a year, and years may pass

Climatic Deserts of Swasia

(based on the precipitation-evaporation ratio)

Extremely arid	272,000 square miles
Arid	1,525,500 "
Semiarid	302,250 "
Dry land total	2,099,750 square miles

between showers. On the basis of rainfall alone, Swasian deserts might be defined as all lands having less than 10 inches of rain. Such a definition would take in parts of every country except Lebanon. Even if the term, desert, is limited to the area receiving under 5 inches or less it measures 1½ million square miles.

But the effectiveness of precipitation is to be measured by its concentration, and by comparison with potential evapotranspiration. On this basis, four parts of Southwest Asia are characterized by extreme aridity, areas where twelve months may pass without any rain, and the precipitation-evaporation ratio is very high. These are the Rub' al Khali of southern Arabia, the coast near Aden, the southern Sinai peninsula, and possibly the Seistan Desert of eastern Iran and Afghanistan.

Elsewhere, normal aridity characterizes the lowlands of Arabia, the interior of Syria and Jordan, most of Iraq, and the basins of Iran and Afghanistan. Semiarid climates are found over much of the remaining parts of Swasia except for the humid coasts of the Mediterranean, Black, and Caspian Seas and the higher mountain slopes.

As defined by Thornthwaite's evapotranspiration formula and mapped by Meigs, the area of Swasia's deserts amounts to 2,099,750 square miles. When this is compared with the total area of Southwest Asia, namely 2,796,275 square miles, it is obvious that only 13 per cent may be classed as humid. It is well to remember that rainfall in Southwest Asia is limited to the winter months, and that deserts expand and contract with the season. Arid lands may "blossom as the rose" after occasional showers, but the landscape retains a greenish cast for only a few weeks. So dry are large areas that there are many places where one may travel several hundred miles without crossing a permanent stream or finding a spring; ground water may be so far below the surface that even wells are lacking.

Another measure of a desert is not its low rainfall or excessive evapotranspiration, but the character of its plant life. Few parts of Swasia are completely lifeless; but all show unique adjustments to aridity. The areas of lifeless salt flats, bare sand dunes, desert shrub, and short grass are practically as extensive as the climatic deserts just described; certainly they cover upwards of 2 million square miles.

Deserts may also be defined in terms of geomorphic processes and the resulting land forms.

Geographic Deserts of Swasia

Region	Area, in square miles
Afghanistan	81,000
Iran:	
Dasht-i-Kavir	67,000
Dasht-i-Lut	30,000
Jaz Murian Desert	8,000
Persian Gulf-Makran coasts	89,000
Other Iranian deserts	33,000
Arabian Peninsula:	
Syrian-Iraq Desert (to 30°N)	224,000
Rub' al Khali	229,000
Other Arabian deserts	847,000
Turkey	14,000
Total	1,622,000

Shifting sands cover 30 per cent of Arabia, varying from sheet sand to dunes 700 feet high. This is a view near the oasis of Kharj near Riyadh. (*Courtesy Standard Oil Company of New Jersey*)

Southwest Asia has large areas where unique weathering, erosion by intermittent streams, or a dominance of wind work have given the landscape a unique stamp. One clear evidence of a desert is the presence of loose sand, whether developed as dunes or present as an irregular sheet. The total extent of sand is unknown, but in the Rub' al Khali it covers 229,000 square miles, and the volume may exceed 4,000 cubic miles; for all of Swasia the figure may approach ½ million square miles.

Many parts of Southwest Asia contain topographic depressions with fluctuating salt lakes or mud flats. Enclosed basins are present in Turkey, Iran, and Iraq. In most of Arabia, precipitation is so low that there is little, if any, runoff. Even where slopes lead progressively downward to the ocean, so much water may be lost through seepage, evaporation, or diversion for irrigation that nothing remains. A million square miles in Arabia, Iraq and Syria are thus "noncontributary," while Turkey, Iraq, Iran, and Afghanistan have about as much interior drainage. Around the Arabian Peninsula hardly a single stream reaches the sea the year round, and only a few wadis occasionally carry water during the rainy season.

Since geography is concerned with the totality of aridity, the geographic concept centers around land usability. The desert limits of Southwest Asia are difficult to draw, since boundaries are gradational and climate fluctuates over the decades. The fact remains that deserts present a challenge, a place where man enters at his peril and remains through his ingenuity.

The geographic deserts of Southwest Asia, as here defined, cover 1,622,000 square miles; semideserts or steppe lands as in Turkey, which are not included, would bring the total area of dry lands, considered in terms of difficult human usability, to over 2 million square miles.

Whatever criteria are considered, Southwest Asia is dry. Every country has its desert or steppe, and some countries have little else. Parts of the desert are irrigated, as in Iraq, but this is possible only because of waters from melting snow on the mountains. No part of Asia is more critically dependent on limited rainfall.

THE FERTILE CRESCENT

When a nomadic sheik named Abraham migrated from southern Iraq to Palestine some sixteen centuries before Christ, he was not the first traveler to follow the route of the Fertile Crescent. This grassland corridor has tied together the lands of Southwest Asia since the earliest times; in fact, civilization may first have emerged in the central part of the crescent about ten millenniums ago.

The northern extension of the Arabian Desert is surrounded by a crescentic line of mountains. To the northeast rise the Iranian Zagros; on the north are the Taurus and other border folds of Turkey; to the west are the Levantine ranges which border the Mediterranean in Syria, Lebanon, and Palestine. These form a continuous crescentic wall, 1,500 miles long, from the Persian Gulf around to the Sinai peninsula, broken only by two gaps on the west; one is south of Jerusalem, where the mountains change to hills, and the other is situated in the northwest opposite Aleppo, known as the Syrian Saddle.

At the base of the mountains, and facing inward, are a series of alluvial fans which coalesce to form a continuous piedmont slope, 50 to 100 miles wide and 1,000 to 2,000 feet in elevation. There is no topographic break, but the fans rise noticeably above the desert plain.

Four situations combine to change this area from a desert to a steppe, and make it known as the Fertile Crescent. In the first place, the higher elevation brings slightly lower temperatures and thus slightly less evaporation. Second, since the latitude is 35°N, cooler winters are to be expected, and the area is closer to the humid middle latitudes.

Third, and even more important, the gap in the mountains known as the Syrian Saddle permits moisture-bearing winds to penetrate well inland. Elevations in this mountain gap are around 1,000 feet, whereas to the north and south highlands rise to 1 and 2 miles and force the winds to leave their moisture on the windward slopes.

A fourth factor is related to the behavior of the low-pressure cyclonic whirls which cross the northern half of Swasia each winter. While the storm center may move along the Mediterranean and enter Asia along the 35th parallel, the inblowing air follows a circling course which brings it into the interior on a low-level path south of Jerusalem. Moist air thus enters Mesopotamia and Iraq from the southwest. As it advances northward the humid air mass is crowded into a broad funnel between the Zagros and the Levantine mountains, and as it approaches the piedmont areas it is forced to climb. The combination of crowding and elevation causes the air to rise and become cooled. The result is moderate rainfall on the piedmont slopes and rather heavy snowfall in the mountains.

As a further factor in this cyclonic rainfall, not infrequently a warm air mass may move northeastward across Mesopotamia, bounded on its left by a cold front extending roughly north-to-south, parallel to the Euphrates. As the cold air undercuts the warm, frontal action brings rain.

The Fertile Crescent is thus a piedmont zone where topography and air-mass movements combine to produce a little rain. Nowhere can the area be described as moist, and the traveler who has not seen Arabia proper may think of this as practically a desert. The rainfall is from 8 to 15 inches: too much to warrant calling the

Locusts have been a plague throughout Southwest Asia for millenniums. Here they are stripping a grain field in Iran. (*Courtesy International Cooperation Administration*)

area a desert and scarcely enough to describe it as subhumid. In terms of vegetation this is a steppe, with a natural cover of short grass. Potential evapotranspiration ranges from 30 to 40 inches, so that the thirsty air absorbs all available moisture.

Since this region has long been a dry grassland, the soils have accumulated considerable amounts of humus, and since rainfall is low, the soil profile is unleached. Given water, crops grow well. Water for irrigation is available from mountain streams, but only those which rise in snow-storage areas continue to flow through the dry summer. The gentle piedmont slopes provide ideal sites for irrigation canals, while the ground-water situation keeps the water table low and prevents the accumulation of injurious salts.

Unfortunately, there is not enough river water to irrigate the available cropland. Some alluvial fans are too dissected, or too porous to hold irrigation water. Deep wells, modern storage dams, and canal systems are adding to the irrigated acreage, but much of the crescent must remain without water. In the absence of irrigation, dry farming is the only alternative to grazing.

While a rainfall of 8 to 15 inches is normally inadequate for crops, Swasian precipitation is more effective because it is concentrated during the cooler season. Successful dry agriculture depends on conserving soil moisture, chiefly through repeated harrowing, which keeps pore spaces above capillary size and thus reduces losses through evaporation. This calls for large-scale extensive agriculture, preferably with tractors and machinery to handle large acreages of low-yielding crops.

During the mid-decades of the twentieth century, thousands of acres were brought under cultivation, chiefly for wheat and barley but also for cotton, where some supplementary irrigation was available. The area is indeed crescentic, and the soils are rich, but in agricultural terms the fertility is modest.

The Fertile Crescent has long been important. Some of the earliest archaeologic sites on earth are found near its center, and it may be that civilized man first emerged here, several millenniums ago. Since the grasslands offer pasture for nomads, this has been the historic avenue for migrating tribes, for trading caravans, and for conquerors bound from Persia or Mesopotamia to the Levant and Egypt. Here may have been the world's first international highway.

The crescent was initially defined by James H. Breasted, who located its "west end at the southeast corner of the Mediterranean, the center directly north of Arabia, and the east end at the north end of the Persian Gulf." Breasted pointed out that "the history of Western Asia may be described as an age-old struggle between the mountain peoples of the north and the desert wanderers of these grasslands . . . for the possession of the Fertile Crescent."

As here described, the crescent lies entirely within the mountain wall and is the piedmont zone with slightly higher rainfall than the desert which it half surrounds. The coastal Levant is excluded, as are also the dry areas of southern Iraq, even though they are now irrigated. The southeastern horn of the crescent properly ends near Kirkuk in Iraq; in the southwest it extends to Homs in Syria. The widest portion of the crescent lies in the area from Aleppo in northern Syria across southern Turkey to Mosul in northern Iraq. Only in a very broad sense does the crescent link the Persian Gulf with Palestine.

While the Fertile Crescent is the largest continuous region of rain-fed agriculture in the realm, there are extensive areas in Turkey and elsewhere where dry farming is possible. There is also little problem of moisture in the humid coastal areas from Palestine around to the

Land Use in Swasia [1]

(in thousand hectares)

Country	Total area	Arable land incl. fallow and orchards	Irrigated land	Forest land
Aden, incl. protectorates	29,029	120	—	—
Afghanistan	65,000	9,015	—	1,500
Bahrein	60	—	—	—
Iran	163,000	16,760	1,600	19,000
Iraq	44,444	5,457	2,800	1,770
Israel	2,070	401	126	73
Jordan	9,661	6,072	32	525
Kuwait	1,554	—	—	—
Lebanon	1,040	278	71	92
Masqat and Oman	21,238	—	—	80
Qatar	2,201	—	—	—
Saudi Arabia	160,000	210	—	400
Syria	18,448	5,491	476	449
Turkey	77,698	24,972	1,988	10,584
Yemen	19,500	—	—	150
All Swasia	604,943	68,776		34,623

[1] United Nations, Food and Agricultural Organization: *Production Yearbook*, 1960.

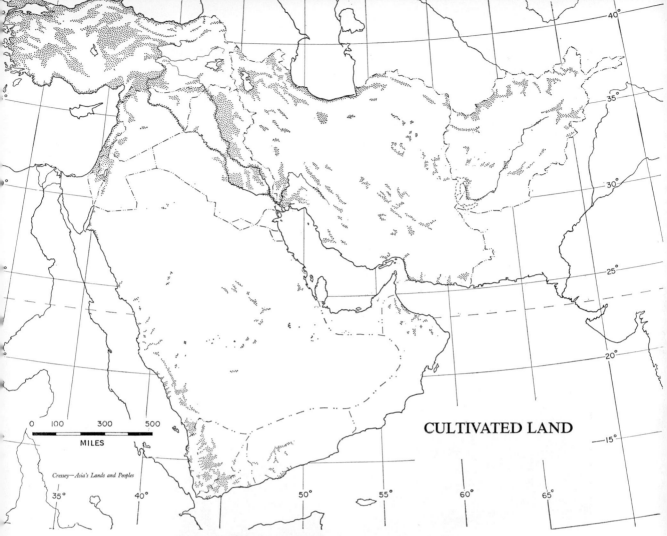

Agricultural land covers about 125,000 square miles out of the 2½ million square miles in the realm. Most cultivation depends on irrigation or on dry-farming techniques; much of the area will long remain unproductive.

Caspian shores of Iran, where rainfall exceeds 25 inches and the original cover of vegetation was a forest, or in a few favored areas of upland Iran or Turkey, where rainfall is adequate or ground water is near the surface. Yemen is a special case; there agriculture is possible only through extensive terracing and special water-conserving schemes.

IRRIGATION AGRICULTURE

Agriculture could scarcely be possible in Arabia, southern Iraq, the bulk of Iran, or in Afghanistan if water were not available for irrigation. Few lowlands have adequate rain or, to state the situation more accurately, most areas outside the mountains have such a high rate of potential evapotranspiration that crops will not grow unless the moisture deficit is made up by supplementary water.

On the basis of incomplete United Nations statistics of "arable land including fallow and orchards," the total for Swasia amounts to 178,150 square miles, or roughly 10 per cent of the realm.

Accurate data are unavailable as to the ex-

Water is the key to agriculture and to life. This irrigation lift is at Qatif in eastern Arabia. (*Courtesy Standard Oil Company of New Jersey*)

tent of irrigated land. The incomplete statistics of the Food and Agricultural Organization indicate that a little over one-tenth of the "arable land, including fallow and orchards" is irrigated, but we must realize that extra water is certainly responsible for a much larger share of Swasia's food.

Afghanistan and Saudi Arabia report no irrigated land, whereas most of their crops are watered; the percentage in Iran is also far higher than recorded. Furthermore, a great deal of the rain-fed land lies fallow every other year.

At least one-fifth of all of Swasia's fields are irrigated, and it may be safe to say that outside of Turkey, the Fertile Crescent, and the humid coasts, irrigation is used on two-thirds of the harvested area.

Irrigation water is secured in several ways. The simplest arrangement is through canals which divert part of a river or lead away from a spring. Several large reservoirs are now available for storage in the uplands. Along the Tigris and Euphrates thousands of modern pumps lift water into canals which lead back several miles from the river. Elsewhere wells supply water for garden areas, either with hand or animal lift or by pumps.

Another device, long used in Iran and Afghanistan, is a gently sloping tunnel which leads up the slope of an alluvial fan until it intersects the water table. These horizontal wells are known as qanats or karez. Many are miles in length, even tens of miles long, and the initial mother well may be hundreds of feet deep.

To dig a qanat, a series of shafts are sunk at intervals of 100 yards so that the excavated earth may be brought to the surface. When seen from the air, this earth, piled around the mouth of the shaft, looks like a line of huge doughnuts. Although expensive and time-consuming to excavate, the qanat flows night and day and provides a year-round supply of water.

Two major problems arise in most irrigated areas—silt and salt; both have brought cultivation to an end over wide areas.

The rivers of Swasia tend to be heavily laden with silt, a by-product of their swift mountain headwaters and the barren hillsides along their middle course. Many streams, such as the Tigris and Euphrates, are so overloaded that they are unable to carry their sediment onward to the sea, and its deposition is building their beds above the general level of the countryside.

When silty river water is diverted into the canals, whose gradient is generally less than that of the rivers, the suspended material is gradually deposited. The coarser sediments are dropped within a few miles, but the finer silt may move on into the various distributary canals. This river silt clogs the canals, and in time may accumulate to such an extent that irrigation water ceases to flow. Vast areas of ancient Mesopotamia show traces of old canal systems, long since abandoned. The canal sediment may of course be cleaned out, but if the accumulation coincides with a period of civil unrest or invasion, abandonment may be necessary.

Salt presents an even greater problem. All river or ground water contains dissolved chemicals. Where they are carried onward to the sea, they present no problem; where they accumulate in the upper few inches of the soil the concentration may become so great that fields must be abandoned.

River waters in Swasia usually contain 200 to 500 parts per million of dissolved material, some of it sodium chloride, some lime, gypsum, and so on. Such water tastes "fresh" to most people. Desert dwellers can tolerate brackish water with a chemical content of 3,000 parts per million, and even up to 5,000 for brief periods. Cattle can drink water with 9,000 parts per million and sheep up to 15,000. On the other hand, the safe maximum chemical content, depending on its composition, for irrigation water is around 740 parts per million, equivalent to 1 ton of salts per year for each acre-foot of water.

The key to safe irrigation practice is to keep the water table lower than 5 feet below the surface, and thus to make certain that the net movement of ground water is downward. When ground water is closer than this, capillary action lifts soil moisture up to the surface; the moisture then evaporates, but its salts are left behind.

Where irrigation water is applied to porous soils on sloping lands few problems result, but where too much water is added to tight soils on nearly flat plains, subsurface drainage is slow, water logging results, and salt accumulates.

It is not enough to bring water to the fields; arrangements must be made for its removal. In flat areas with clay soils it may be necessary to dig deep drainage ditches between each irrigation canal and perhaps to pump the water from the drains into the nearest river. Costs for the removal of surplus irrigation water may equal the original costs of supply.

References on Southwest Asia

An extensive bibliography and much supplementary text may be found in the author's *Crossroads: Land and Life in Southwest Asia*.
See also general references for Asia, Chapter 1.

Air Ministry, Meteorological Office: *Tables of Temperature, Relative Humidity and Precipitation for the World, Part V, Asia,* London: H. M. Stationery Office (1958).

Boesch, Hans: *Der Mittlere Osten,* Bern: Kummerly and Fry (1959).

Bonne, Alfred: *The Economic Development of the Middle East,* London: Routledge & Kegan Paul (1945).

Bonne, Alfred: *State and Economics in the Middle East,* London: Routledge & Kegan Paul (1948).

Bullard, Reader (ed.): *The Middle East: A Political and Economic Survey,* 3d ed., Fair Lawn, N.J.: Oxford University Press (1958).

Caroe, Olaf: *Wells of Power: Oilfields of Southwestern Asia: A Regional and Global Study,* New York: St Martin's Press (1951).

*Coon, Carleton S.: *Caravan: The Story of the Middle East,* New York: Holt, Rinehart and Winston (1958).

Cressey, George B.: "Water in the Desert," *Annals, Assn. Amer. Geogs.,* XLVII (1957), 105–124.

Cressey, George B.: "The Shatt-al-Arab Basin," *Middle East Jour.,* XII (1958), 448–460.

Cressey, George B.: "Qanats, Karez and Foggaras," *Geog. Rev.,* XLVIII (1958), 27–44.

*Cressey, George B.: *Crossroads: Land and Life in Southwest Asia,* Philadelphia: Lippincott (1960).

Douglas, William O.: *West of the Indus,* Garden City, N.Y.: Doubleday (1958).

Finnie, David H.: *Desert Enterprise: The Middle East Oil Industry in Its Local Environment,* Cambridge, Mass.: Harvard University Press (1958).

Fisher, W. B.: "Unity and Diversity in the Middle East," *Geog. Rev.,* XXXVII (1947), 414–435.

*Fisher, W. B.: *The Middle East,* New York: Dutton (1956).

Fisher, W. B.: "South West Asia," in W. G. East and A. E. Moodie (eds.): *The Changing World,* New York: Harcourt, Brace & World (1956).

Hitti, Philip K.: *The Near East in History,* Princeton, N.J.: Van Nostrand (1961).

*Huxley, Julian: *From an Antique Land: Ancient and Modern in the Middle East,* London: Parrish (1954).

Law, J.: "Reasons for Persian Gulf Oil Abundance," *Bul. Amer. Assn. Petroleum Geologists,* XLI (1957), 51–69.

Longrigg, Stephen Hemsley: *Oil in the Middle East: Its Discovery and Development,* 2d ed., Fair Lawn, N.J.: Oxford University Press (1961).

*Oxford Regional Economic Atlas: *The Middle East and North Africa,* Fair Lawn, N.J.: Oxford University Press (1960).

*Randall, John, and others: "Southwest Asia," in Norton Ginsburg (ed.): *The Pattern of Asia,* Englewood Cliffs, N.J.: Prentice-Hall (1958).

Richardson, F. L. W., Jr., and James Batal: "The Near East," in Ralph Linton (ed.): *Most of the World,* New York: Columbia University Press (1949), 461–547.

Smith, C. G.: "Arab Nationalism: A Study in Political Geography," *Geog.,* XLIII (1958), 229–242.

Warriner, Doreen: *Land and Poverty in the Middle East,* London and New York: Royal Institute of International Affairs (1948).

34 People and Land in Southwest Asia

Historical Backgrounds / Population Patterns / Political Problems /
Swasian Regions

HISTORICAL BACKGROUNDS

In his philosophic survey of world history, Arnold Toynbee describes twenty-one great civilizations which have appeared on the earth. Seven of these had their cradle in Southwest Asia. Few other parts of the world have witnessed such a surge of peoples; this has indeed been an historic crossroads.

We know little about the beginnings of civilization. Many of the earliest recorded events took place in towns along the Fertile Crescent. Thus Jericho appears to be the oldest inhabited settlement in the world, with carbon-14 dating which goes back to 6800 B.C. Even then it had a well-developed culture. Kathleen Kenyon writes: "It has already been established that a date of *c.* 6000 B.C. was comparatively late in the history of neolithic Jericho."

Much of the early history concerns the contest between nomadic and sedentary peoples; the struggle between the grassland pastoralist seeking better land and the settled agriculturist in the well-watered areas. This is the ancient struggle between the brown and the green; between the Bedouin and the farmer. Time after time, desert people have surged into the bordering agricultural lands, possibly under the impetus of arid cycles which reduced the vegetation in their usual grazing areas.

Southwest Asia has provided the stage for a great array of peoples, some apparently originating here, others arriving from outside. One of these were the Semites, who developed in Arabia. Of the many Semitic peoples, only the Arabs and Hebrews are important today. Another were the Indo-Europeans or Aryans, known here as the Persians, who arrived from the north. Whereas Semites used camels, the Aryans were horsemen. A third people were the Turks, who appeared from central Asia.

In addition to these major ethnic groups, Swasia has received contributions from many sources. The Mongol hordes brought widespread devastation but left little ethnic trace. Even the Crusaders left a heritage, for their kingdoms lasted two centuries.

No discussion of Swasia's present racial complexity would be complete without reference to the scores of minority peoples, some of them refugees or otherwise oppressed. Five of these ethnic groups number a million or more each. Five million Pushtuns or Pathans live in eastern Afghanistan, with as many across the border in Pakistan. Three million Kurds occupy the area where Turkey, Iraq, and Iran meet. Two million Jews live in Swasia, not all of them in Israel. Two million Azerbaijanians are in northern Iran. A million Baluchi live in Afghanistan and Iran.

Turkey once had Armenians, Greeks, and Kurds, to the number of a million each. The first have either been liquidated or forced to flee; the second were repatriated to Greece in exchange for Turks living there; only the Kurds remain.

Other minority people are related to groups in Soviet Middle Asia, living on both sides of the Caspian. Nomadic tribes in Iran may number a million people. Religious minorities include the Maronite Christians in Lebanon.

Four areas have provided the homeland for great empires. Babylon and Assyria arose in southern and northern Iraq, respectively, with origins which trace back to the fourth millennium, B.C. The Persian Empire, with its homeland in what is now southwestern Iran, reached its maximum extent in the sixth century B.C., when it extended from the Nile to the Indus. Two great Arab empires, the Ommiad and the Abbasside, centered on Damascus and Baghdad, with a succession of caliphs who lasted from A.D. 661 to 1100. The last of the great empires was that of the Ottomans, who ruled an expanded Turkey from 1299 until 1922. Still earlier, Turkey was the homeland of the Hittite and Byzantine empires.

Each of these faded empires has left its monuments. Some, as at Palmyra or Persepolis, lie in the midst of semiaridity where cities could scarcely exist today. Such ruins have led to speculation about climatic variation. Cycles in rainfall have certainly occurred, some perhaps a century or more in length, but there is no evidence of any overall change in Swasian climate during the past 5,000 years. Each ruined city had its cisterns and aqueducts, indicating that water supply was a problem then as now.

Many avenues of conquest have followed the eastern shores of the Mediterranean along the base of the Lebanon Mountains. Among the earliest invaders were armies from Assyria and Persia, or from Egypt in the reverse direction. Greeks, Romans, and the Crusaders came from Europe. Along this narrow plain moved Arab conquerors or Ottoman Turks pushing south. Here, too, the French and British pushed back the Turks to set up their mandates after the First World War.

On a cliff north of Beirut are nineteen inscriptions in eight languages left by passing conquerors. The sequence begins with Ramses II, and continues through Nebuchadnezzar, Marcus Aurelius, and Napoleon.

All through this historical sequence, it is evident that Southwest Asia as a whole has lacked

Palmyra was the center of a great empire early in the Christian era, when Queen Zenobia ruled the area from the Persian Gulf to the Nile. This is the Temple of Baal. (*Courtesy Iraq Petroleum Company*)

the physical basis for cultural and political coherence. Each empire had a different homeland. Highlands and deserts break the realm into fragments, and no oasis or fertile valley or mountain pass provides a fully logical center of power for the whole.

Iran has had numerous capitals, each focused on an oasis but isolated and off-center for the area as a whole. The various Persian provinces are diverse, so that it has been difficult to develop central authority; loyalty has been to a ruler rather than to the idea of a coherent nation.

Turkey is equally cut into fractions, with mountain barriers which isolate the interior from the few coastal lowlands. The political interests of the dry central basins, traditionally grazing lands, are quite unlike those of the humid deltas.

Palestine has always presented problems of unity. The Old Testament records differences between the coastal Philistines, or later the commercial Phoenicians, and the Hebrews in the hills. Today Israel holds the plain while Jordan has much of the hill land. Present-day Lebanon involves deep-seated differences between coastal Muslims and highland Christians, both Arab in race but with basic suspicions.

Arabian coherence presents a different set of problems. Few mountains are involved, though the west coast is backed by a high escarpment. Rather, political control relates to scattered oases and the loyalty of Bedouin tribes. The Ottoman Empire was never able to police the interior, and the present unity under the Saudis represents the dynamic power of a sheik from a central oasis.

The Fertile Crescent provides some of the best grazing lands, now converted into an area of dry farming, but it has been an international avenue rather than a center of control. There is some political justification for a Fertile Crescent union of Jordan, Syria, and Iraq. But where would one put the capital? Damascus and Baghdad lie near the ends of the crescent, and any midpoint between them would be in the midst of the desert.

Whatever the time or country, human affairs in Swasia have been tied to fertile plains: along the Aegean Sea, in river valleys like the Tigris, in mountain passes such as the Cilician Gates, in isolated oases as at Isfahan, and along narrow seas such as the Bosporus. History does not develop in a vacuum.

Most of the land frontiers are marked by mountains, but present political limits do not fully match topography or culture. Thus the Caucasus lie outside of Turkey and Iran, which once controlled them, and Afghanistan includes lowlands north of the Hindu Kush inhabited by non-Afghan people, but not those areas beyond the Khyber Pass which do contain Afghans.

POPULATION PATTERNS

There are no more revealing maps in the chapters on Southwest Asia than those which show where people live. These not only answer the question of "where," but also raise the problem of "why not elsewhere?"

Upwards of 100 million people live here, but their distribution is far from uniform. The average density for the 2.7 million square miles is nearly 40 per square mile—well below the world average.

Many thousands of square miles are completely empty: areas of desolate dunes, lifeless salt flats, trackless lava flows, or eroded mountain sides. Such areas are almost totally without water or vegetation and may not be visited by a Bedouin looking for a lost camel more than once in several years.

In contrast, irrigated deltas around the shores of Turkey or garden oases fed by mountain streams hold hundreds of people in a single square mile. Measured in terms of agricultural land alone, Swasia has an average of 300 people for each square mile of cropland.

Three coastal areas receive abundant rain: the central shores of the eastern Mediterranean, the southeastern coast of the Black Sea, and the foothills of the Elburz facing the Caspian Sea. Each area stands out strikingly on the map of rural population. Other areas of rain-fed agriculture are evident, as in the highlands of Yemen or in humid sections in Turkey.

For the most part, the population map reflects the availability of irrigation. Ribbons of settlement match the lowland course of each major river. Where population follows the base of mountains it may mark a line of alluvial fans. Clusters of dots in Arabia locate springs or other sources of water. Almost every village in Iran or Afghanistan owes its existence to nearby snow mountains. Terrain also has its place in accounting for settlement. With minor exceptions, mountain slopes are uninhabited; so too are flat areas of sand or salt.

One should look at the present population map as a single frame from a moving picture. If maps of successive centuries could be filmed in sequence, the tides of history would provide a revealing story. Settlement also has its future as well as its past. No major changes should be expected, for the present pattern reflects long experience through trial and error. Large-scale-irrigation programs will add a few dots here and there, and improved farm techniques will push cultivation farther into the desert borderlands.

Population grows, and more food is needed, but most farmers will have to remain about where they are now. A million Palestinian refugees are encamped around the borders of Israel, but even when their resettlement is undertaken it will be difficult to find suitable places for them to live. For centuries to come, large parts of Swasia will remain essentially empty; perhaps as many as a million square miles will continue to average only two or three people in each.

Some of these nearly empty grasslands provide grazing grounds for nomads, but one may need to search many miles by car or by plane to find a nomadic encampment; once located, it may be gone tomorrow. It is hard to map man in motion, or to count nomads in any census enumeration. Swasia's nomads number several million, but many are part-time farmers or spend some of the year looking about for other jobs.

As is true over much of the continent, cities are experiencing an explosive growth. Seven centers exceed 500,000 each in population: Istanbul, Ankara, Beirut, Damascus, Aleppo, Baghdad, and Tehran. Two dozen others range from 100,000 to 500,000 people. Well over 10 million people are city dwellers.

The distribution of these urban centers is of interest. About eighteen are seaports, although only two of them count as many as 500,000 people. A dozen others are near enough to the coast to have ready access. A surprising number are without railway connections; for example, Iran has six cities with over 100,000 people that have neither rail nor water transport.

Lebanon is the only country whose capital is on the sea; no capitals lie on navigable rivers.

Mecca is the shrine which attracts Muslim pilgrims from all the world. Within the sacred area of the Kabah is the Zam Zam well, seen to the right, and the shrine of Abraham, in the center. (*Courtesy Arabian American Oil Company*)

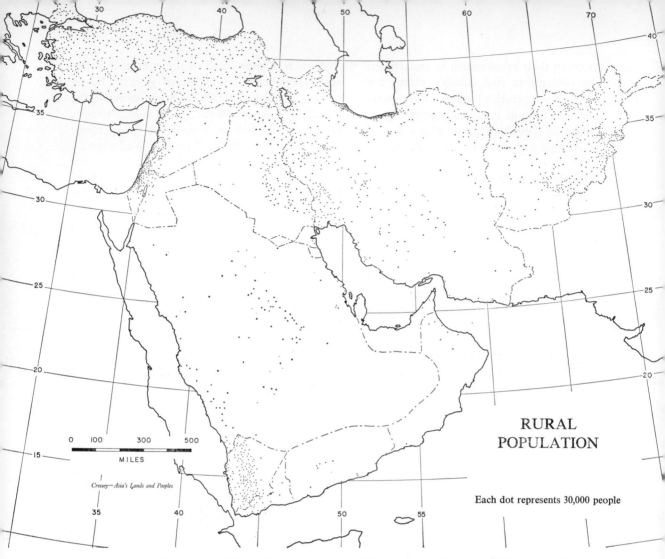

RURAL
POPULATION

0   100   300   500

MILES

Cressey—Asia's Lands and Peoples

35   40   50   55

Each dot represents 30,000 people

Few parts of the realm appear crowded, but everywhere in these ancient lands population presses on means of subsistence. Few maps are more meaningful than those of
areas where people live. The scale of this dot map is the same as those used in other
realms.

Two nations have deliberately moved their
capital cities to the interior—Turkey and Saudi
Arabia.

Two cities owe much of their importance to
religion, Jerusalem and Mecca. To a lesser extent this is true of shrine centers like Meshed.
Petroleum developments account for the growth
of several cities in the area of the Persian Gulf.

Only two countries, Iran and Turkey, have
more than a half dozen cities with over 50,000
people; each also has metropolitan centers of
about 2 million.

Few countries in Southwest Asia have accurate census data; in several cases even the size
of the area is in question. Turkey and Iraq provide good information, but figures that are
available for Saudi Arabia and Afghanistan
are much in doubt.

On the basis of unverified official reports, the
total population for the entire realm exceeds 90
million. Of these, about 65 per cent are farmers;
8 per cent are nomads with various degrees of
pastoral or sedentary life; 12 per cent live in
cities of over 25,000; 1 per cent are displaced

Rapid urbanization characterizes Southwest Asia, as is true throughout the continent. Seven cities exceed ½ million in population. Even remote Kabul and Riyadh have surprisingly modern cores; but here, and generally, parts of each city remain medieval.

Palestinian refugees; and the remaining 14 per cent appear to be village people or of other classifications.

Just as the area is unevenly populated, so wide contrasts exist in social conditions, whether of education or of wealth or government. The cultural landscape throughout Swasia provides many vivid contrasts. Parts of Beirut have an aspect as cosmopolitan and "Western" as Manhattan; towns in northern Afghanistan are about as unchanged and "Inner Asian" as anything on the continent.

POLITICAL PROBLEMS

Southwest Asia is composed of a dozen sovereign states, a dozen or more protectorates, one colony, and two neutral zones. Afghanistan, Iran, Iraq, Saudi Arabia, Masqat, and Turkey are large countries; Israel, Jordan, Lebanon, Syria, Yemen and Kuwait are small. Aden is a British colony.

Along the margins of Arabia are a series of protectorates and ex-protectorates with varying degrees of autonomy. Near Aden are the

Western and Eastern Protectorates, the former partly federated, the latter in part unadministered. At the southern end of the Persian Gulf are seven tiny sheikdoms which make up the Trucial States, none important unless they prove to contain oil.

Along the western side of the Persian Gulf are Bahrein and Qatar, whose legal status has been defined as "independent states, under the protection of Her Majesty's Government." Kuwait was formerly in this category, but in 1961 it was given its sovereignty although with continued British guarantees. Masqat might be included in the category of dependent states, but although it has "treaty relations" with Great Britain, it appears to be fully sovereign; Oman is its interior province.

The two neutral zones along the northern Saudi frontier are administered jointly with Iraq and Kuwait, respectively. Both were empty and unimportant until oil was discovered in the Kuwait–Saudi Arabia neutral zone.

Saudi Arabia, Yemen, and the various sheikdoms have had absolute rulers sans legal restraints. Iran and Afghanistan are constitutional monarchies. The other states are more or less democratic.

In order to understand current political problems in Swasia, it is necessary to examine the changes since the beginning of the century. At that time all the area west of Iran was a part of the Ottoman Empire, although Turkey had little effective control in the interior of Arabia.

At the time of the First World War, Great Britain and France secured the help of the Arabs in driving back the Turks on the basis of specific promises that there would be an all-Arab kingdom. Instead, five mandates were established under the League of Nations. Iraq, Transjordan, and Palestine became British areas; Syria and Lebanon were placed under French control. The last of these mandates were not terminated until 1946.

In order to ensure worldwide Zionist assistance during the First World War, Great Britain issued the Balfour Declaration in 1917. This reads as follows:

His Majesty's Government view with favor the establishment in Palestine of a national home for the Jewish people, and will use their best endeavours to facilitate the achievement of that object, it being clearly understood that nothing shall be done which may prejudice the civil and religious rights of existing non-Jewish communities in Palestine or the rights and political status enjoyed by Jews in any other country.

To Jewish refugees the Balfour Declaration implied the creation of a sovereign state; to the nearly one million Arab residents the reference was to a cultural homeland within British promises "that it is not part of their policy that Palestine should become a Jewish state." Out of this has evolved the state of Israel, created with United Nations approval but still without legal boundaries or treaty agreement with neighboring countries.

Every country has had its periods of greatness when its territory extended over a much larger area. If each nation were to be given all the land which it would like to claim, hopeless confusion would result. The early Jewish states prior to the time of Christ had rather uncertain limits, but these provided the vague excuse for claims from "the Nile to the Euphrates." Arabia might likewise claim all of Iran, part of Turkey, and Egypt. Iraq contends that it should properly own Kuwait since the two countries were united during Ottoman days.

In any consideration of international politics it is well to realize that the Soviet frontier next to Turkey, Iran, and Afghanistan is the only section of the Russian border from Finland to Korea which is not protected by a cushion of satellite or buffer states. Insofar as the Kremlin's policy is motivated by security, the obvious objective of the Soviet Union would be to bring these three states, and all of Southwest Asia, inside the Communist orbit.

Scarcely a boundary in the whole realm is fully stable. Twice in this century the Soviet Union has pushed into Turkey, and Russian pressures for partial control over the Bosporus are recurrent. Still earlier, Turkey owned parts of Soviet Middle Asia, as, for example, the port of Batum. While Turkey's maritime frontier might appear easy to define, most of the off-shore islands in the Aegean are currently Greek territory.

Afghanistan's border with Pakistan along the Durand line is much in dispute, for the presence of several million Pushtuns who live across the frontier outside Afghanistan leads to serious Afghan-Pakistan border problems, especially near the Khyber Pass. Along the northern border, the steady advance of czarist territory during the nineteenth century laid the base for continuing Afghan-Soviet suspicions.

Saudi Arabia is a new creation, and few of its southern boundaries have been defined, much less surveyed; the limit next to Jordan is also in doubt. A century ago the eastern fringes of the Arabian Peninsula, including Kuwait and Bahrein, were under Iranian control, and the western shores of the Persian Gulf are still claimed by that country.

The former northwestern corner of Syria is now part of Turkey, but is still shown as occupied territory on Syrian maps. Many Arabs dream of a Greater Syria to take in the entire Fertile Crescent, including Iraq.

Iran has also had its troubles with the Soviet Union, particularly in the northwest, where there is an ethnic relation to the Azerbaijan and Armenian Soviet Socialist Republics. Much of the Transcaucasus area was once Persian.

Numerous political problems arise over water rights along international rivers. The Helmand acquires all its water within Afghanistan, but its terminal basin is shared with Iran. What right of protest does the latter enjoy if the flow of the Helmand is diminished through upstream diversion for irrigation? Along the Afghan-Soviet frontier there are difficulties about navigation on the Amu Darya, and about water rights on several small streams which rise in the Afghan mountains and wither in the Soviet deserts.

The Shatt-al-Arab River lies entirely within Iraq, whose legal control extends to the high-water line on the east. Thus Iran must pay toll for the shipment of oil from its Abadan refinery and is concerned if Iraq does not dredge the bar adequately.

The Euphrates provides lifeblood for Iraqi agriculture, but almost all the water originates in Turkey, where reservoirs have changed the normal flow pattern. Halfway downriver the Euphrates crosses Syria, which has such extensive plans for dams and irrigation diversion that the volume of water remaining may be considerably reduced when the river reaches Iraq.

The Orontes, Litani, and Jordan are each international rivers, so that any development of hydroelectricity or irrigation schemes requires the consent of downstream nations. In any case, all three rivers are relatively so small that their potentials are limited.

Not only frontier problems, but internal situations also involve geography. Every country has experienced revolution, and further changes are surely in prospect. Dramatic change, which is apparently a basic fact of life in every part of Swasia, calls for an overturn of the previous social, economic, and political structure.

Should Communism take over, airline routes of the Free World might have to be shifted, trade relations would be altered, and export products such as oil might be diverted to other markets. Soviet pressure on Turkey might result in restricted passage through the Bosporus. So long as Israel and the Arab states fail to sign a peace treaty, the Suez Canal agreements give Egypt the right to bar certain traffic.

SWASIAN REGIONS

Southwest Asia as a whole forms a major subdivision of the continent, one of the five great realms. Within this realm are two geographic provinces, and twenty-three regions. These in turn may be further subdivided, for the face of nature provides infinite variety. Any scheme of geographic regionalization is merely a device of convenience to impose understandable coherence on gradational change.

The unity of the realm as a whole is in part

climatic, for this is Mediterranean Asia, a dry land with winter-rainfall maxima. Although cultural unity is lacking, the regions have in common certain facts of historical development and problems of adjustment to aridity. Although surrounded on most sides by penetrating seas, the people of Swasia have never been maritime-minded.

In physical terms, the two geographic provinces might be defined as the Anatolian–Hindu Kush Mountains and the Arabian Peninsula. In geological terms the former is part of the young Tethys foldland which extends from the Alps to the Himalaya and on to the Southeast Asian island arc, while the latter is a part of the old Gondwana stable block underlain by ancient hard formations. In racial terms, the northern province is the home of Turkish and Persian peoples, largely sedentary; the peninsula is the homeland of the Arabs, traditionally nomadic.

Within each province there is wide variety in the landscape. In the absence of detailed field studies, few precise boundaries or definitions are possible. The following paragraphs suggest the highlights of the several regions; in some localities the dominant feature is topography; elsewhere it may be climate, or land use, or culture.

The Anatolian-Persian complex includes a series of linear mountains and intervening basins, roughly grouped into the political sub-provinces of Turkey, Iran, and Afghanistan, with thirteen geographic regions in all. The subdivisions within Turkey are well defined, and include six regions. A part of southeastern Turkey lies in the Arabian province.

The region around the Sea of Marmara forms a small but significant area since it includes Istanbul and the key waterways of the Dardanelles and Bosporus. Here live half of Turkey's total urban population, and here is half of its light industry.

The Aegean region is an embayed coastal area formed by the end of east–west fault-block structures. The adequate rainfall is due to winds from the Mediterranean. Izmir is the chief city.

The Black Sea region takes in the Pontus Mountains, generally well forested because of abundant precipitation. Only small sections of coastal plain are present.

Inner Anatolia includes a series of basins, originally a steppe grassland for the Ottoman nomads but now an area of dry farming, as around Ankara. Salt lakes reflect the excessive evaporation.

The Mediterranean region in the south roughly coincides with the Taurus and Anti-Taurus Mountains; only in a few places is there much agriculture, chiefly present in two deltas.

The Armenian highlands lie in eastern Turkey, northwestern Iran, and the Soviet Union; they are a complex knot of rugged mountains, faulted plateaus, and great volcanic peaks. Several large lakes occupy interior basins. The population of these borderlands includes Turks, Persians, Armenians, Kurds, Azerbaijanians, and others.

Within Iran the geography is more complex than in Turkey. Four large geographic regions may be identified, or five, if we include the Armenian highlands which Iran shares with Turkey.

The Caspian borderlands are made up of the coastal plain, in part below sea level, the high Elburz Mountains which culminate in volcanic Mount Demavend at 18,934 feet, and the lower ranges of Khurasan to the east. While much of the area is dry, as befits its distance from the ocean, the Caspian shore receives heavy rainfall and has luxurious vegetation. The Elburz thus form an important climatic divide.

The Zagros Mountains form a 1,000-mile arc next to Iraq and the Persian Gulf; their extension to the east are the 400-mile-long Makran Mountains. These ranges also mark the climatic boundary for the interior basins of Iran. The higher Zagros are made up of linear ranges, closely folded and overthrust, and cut by deep transverse canyons. The lower Zagros, on the west, have broader folds, some of which contain oil pools as in Iran and Iraq.

The Inner Persian basins are arid and entirely without drainage to the sea. Where

Istanbul was the center of the Christian church under the Byzantine Empire and later the seat of the Islamic caliph. The Blue Mosque appears at the right; St. Sophia, now a national monument, is at the left. (*Courtesy Pan American World Airways*)

streams descend from the surrounding snow-clad mountains they create oases, as at Tehran or Isfahan. Local ranges divide the region into many separate basins, most of them with a central salt flat called a *kavir*. Flat gravel plains, termed *dasht* are interspersed with areas of sand dunes known as *rig*. By analogy, the Inner Persian basins somewhat resemble the basin and range area of the Western United States.

The East Persian highlands are made up of a series of north–south mountains which extend some 800 miles from the Soviet frontier to the border of westernmost Pakistan. Conditions are generally inhospitable, although a few highland oases occur at considerable elevation.

Afghanistan is even more remote from moisture-bearing winds than its neighbors to the west, but since the maximum elevations are

higher, the crests receive considerable snowfall. Three broad regions may be listed, none of them defined with as much detail as in Turkey.

The Hindu Kush Mountains extend westward across Afghanistan from the Pamir highlands of Tibet to the edge of Iran. While the term Hindu Kush may properly be limited to eastern Afghanistan, the topography continues through the Koh-i-Baba and Paropamisus Ranges. The Hindu Kush form a massive barrier between the two halves of Afghanistan. In one of the few basins lies the city of Kabul.

Afghan Turkestan is the name sometimes given to the north slopes of the Hindu Kush and the southern margins of the Turan lowland, the rest of which lies in Soviet Middle Asia. Most of this region drains toward the valley of the Amu Darya, although many mountain-fed streams wither before reaching the river. The several oases were steppingstones along the ancient trans-Asian caravan route which linked China with Europe.

The Registan-Seistan region is a desert basin along the south slope of the Hindu Kush, dry and excessively hot. The Helmand is the main river, ending in the swamps of Seistan along the Iranian border. The Registan is a sand-choked desert next to Baluchistan.

The Arabian Peninsula makes up the second great geographic province, covering more than the political name might imply. The area is largely a broad lowland, bordered on the west and south by escarpment mountains. As here considered, the geographic province takes in a corner of Turkey, most of Iraq, and all of Syria, Lebanon, Jordan, Israel, Saudi Arabia, Yemen, Masqat, and the smaller Arabian areas. There are ten geographic regions.

Now devoted to rain-fed agriculture, the Fertile Crescent is a thin arc of subhumid grassland which swings from northern Syria across southeastern Turkey into northern Iraq. On the outer side are mountains; on the inside is the desert. By extension, the region in some cases includes the irrigated delta of the Tigris and Euphrates Rivers and the steppe areas of Jordan. In these terms the crescent extends from the Persian Gulf to Palestine.

The Syrian Desert lies within the arms of the crescent, extending south to approximately 30°N. On this basis the area is 224,000 square miles. The rainfall is under 5 inches, agriculture is entirely lacking, and pastoral attractions are limited.

Along the eastern Mediterranean is a double line of mountains, with an intervening structural lowland and a discontinuous strip of fertile lowland on either side of the highlands. This is the Levant, one of the most prosperous and literate areas in all Swasia. The Levant, as a geographic region, includes all of Lebanon, most of Israel, and the western parts of Syria and Jordan.

The western border of Saudi Arabia is marked by a series of faults. The downthrow side is responsible for the Red Sea; the upthrow side forms the Hejaz escarpment. This one-sided highland, much dissected, defines the major geographic region of the western peninsula. Elevations in several areas exceed 8,000 feet, high enough to moderate the heat but not enough to yield much rain. One subregion may be mentioned, the coastal lowland or Tihama.

On the south, the Hejaz continues into the Asir and Yemen highlands, a mountain complex which occupies the southern corner of the peninsula. Elevations reach 13,000 feet so that there is enough rainfall to supply the remarkable terrace agriculture.

Southern Arabia is also bordered by eroded uplands, formed by escarpments parallel to the coast. No one name is applicable, but the name of the principal wadi may be used, and the region called the Hadhramaut upland.

The southeastern corner of Arabia is a little-known mountain area, the Masqat upland. In structural terms it may be related to the Zagros folds of Iran.

The arid eastern coast of the peninsula next to the Red Sea is known as the Hasa region, long noted for a series of spring-fed oases and now important for its vast accumulations of oil. While the term Hasa is properly limited to a part of Saudi Arabia, the region may be broadened to include Kuwait and Bahrein Island.

The Rub' al Khali covers a quarter of a million square miles in the empty area of southern Arabia. Much of the region is a sea of remarkable sand dunes, so desolate that few Bedouins ever enter and very few outsiders have seen it.

No clear geographic divisions mark the interior of Arabia. Even the Syrian Desert has no southern limit. As a term of convenience for a broad geographic region, the central area may be called the Nejd plains. Since the region covers a million square miles there are various landscapes: some volcanic, others low escarpments formed on east-dipping sediments, elsewhere sand wastes. Scattered oases form tiny green spots amid a waste of brown.

35 Resources and Potentials of Southwest Asia

Mineral Wealth / Petroleum / Water Power / Accessibility /
Economic Potentials

MINERAL WEALTH

Several of the common metals have been known in Southwest Asia since earliest times. Gold is found in the ruins of Ur dating from the second millennium B.C.; copper was obtained near the Red Sea in 3700 B.C.; the Hittites used iron in 1250 B.C.; later on, Damascus was famous for its steel. The Old Testament contains many references to trade in the metals. In no case, however, is there any indication of large production.

An evaluation of mineral resources is of considerable importance in assessing Swasia's economic future. The preceding chapters emphasize the inhospitable character of much of the landscape and the limited possibilities of agriculture. If the people of this realm are to enjoy a greatly improved standard of living it may be necessary to turn to industry. Industry, in turn, rests on raw materials.

The overall geology of most countries is reasonably well known, although a great deal of detailed work is still called for. The lava

507

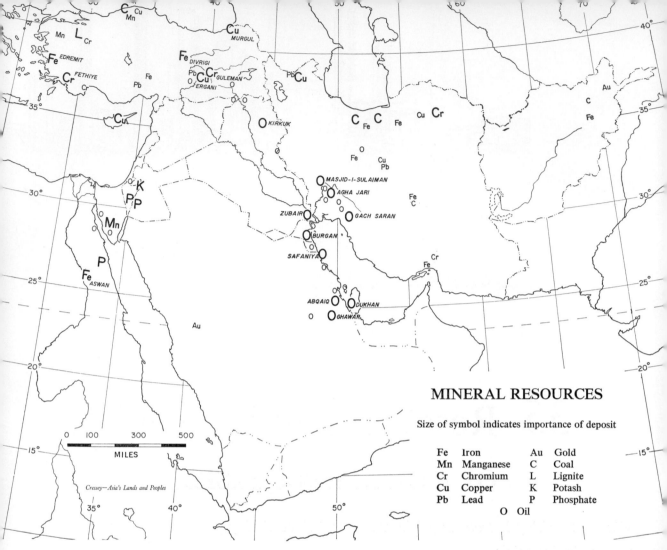

MINERAL RESOURCES

Size of symbol indicates importance of deposit

Fe	Iron	Au	Gold
Mn	Manganese	C	Coal
Cr	Chromium	L	Lignite
Cu	Copper	K	Potash
Pb	Lead	P	Phosphate
		O	Oil

Cressey—Asia's Lands and Peoples

Petroleum is the great resource of the realm, concentrated around the Persian Gulf and up the Mesopotamian geosyncline. Turkey appears to be the only country with important reserves of coal and iron. Chromium is Swasia's unique metal.

flows and igneous areas of Turkey and western Arabia are unlikely to contain coal or oil, and the undisturbed sedimentary basins of Mesopotamia are not apt to have certain metals. On the other hand the folded ranges with their deep-seated intrusions appear to have been a favorable locus for mineralization.

This section deals with coal and the minerals; oil and water power are considered later.

Turkey has been the most thoroughly explored and exploited country, and it may be the richest. There are some reasons to suspect that Iran and possibly Afghanistan may also prove to be well endowed. The Levant States in general are poor; so is Arabia.

Except for phenomenal reserves of oil and gas, and the occurrence of a few unusual minerals such as chromium and phosphate, Swasia appears to have only modest amounts of mineral wealth. Coal is either lacking or poor in quality. If this assessment is wrong, it may require millions of dollars' worth of research as well as several decades of field work to prove otherwise.

Coal is produced in Turkey, and to a much smaller extent in Iran and Afghanistan. The largest output is near the Black Sea port of Zonguldak, where the yield amounts to several million tons a year. About a quarter of the output is used by Turkish railways, and another quarter is consumed by steel mills and copper refineries. Reserves in the Zonguldak area may reach a billion tons, but not all of this can be mined easily.

While Turkish coal is localized in a single area, lignite is widely distributed and is mined in two dozen localities. Reserves may exceed a billion tons. Although lignite is not a first-class fuel, its scattered location reduces transport costs.

Iranian coal is produced on the south slope of the Elburz Mountains near Tehran and in central Iran. The quality is only fair. Afghani-stan also has a small production of coal on the north slope of the mountains. It appears unlikely that any other countries in Swasia contain coal. Fortunately, oil occurs in compensating abundance.

Iron ore does not appear to be plentiful, but Turkey produces a million tons a year. The best deposits are at Divrigi, in the east, where the ore averages 65 per cent iron. Unfortunately, since this deposit is 600 miles from the coal, assembly costs at the steel mill, near the coal, involve high rail charges.

Iran has a small steel center at Azna on the main railway, midway between Tehran and the Persian Gulf, which draws on ore from a number of centers. In addition to ore for blast-furnace use, Iran has long produced finely powdered iron oxide from mines on Hormuz Island at the entrance to the Persian Gulf, exported

Turkey's copper deposits, operated since Roman times, are among the world's richest. This is the Ergani mine in Anatolia. (*Courtesy United States Information Service, Ankara*)

The Dead Sea is a vast storehouse of certain chemicals. This is the potash plant at Sodom in Israel. (*Courtesy Israel Office of Information*)

for use in paint and rouge. Several countries contain low-grade iron deposits which are not commercially valuable because of an inadequate percentage of iron, the presence of undesirable minerals, the absence of nearby coking coal, expensive transport, or the lack of a large enough nearby market.

Chromium is Swasia's unique metal, exported for making refractory brick, for use in the chemical industry or tanning, as an alloy in metallurgy, or for plating purposes. The ore is widely distributed across the northern part of the realm, with Turkey as the leading producer.

Several other metals are in production, but only to a modest extent. These include copper, manganese, lead, zinc, antimony, mercury, and silver. In the production of most of the metals Turkey is in the lead.

Salt leads the nonmetallic field, with a certain amount of production in every country of Southwest Asia. Some salt is obtained from the evaporation of sea water; some is from salt lakes; and rock salt is mined in several areas. Southwestern Iran has over 100 salt domes, roughly cylindrical columns of salt which have punched their way up through the overlying sediments. Phosphate rock is exported from Jordan and Israel, where reserves are large. These nations also share in the dissolved minerals of the Dead Sea, notably potash and bromine. Other nonmetals include asbestos, boracite, magnesite, sulfur, and emery, all produced in Turkey for export when the world price is high enough.

While the list of minerals seems extensive, the reserves appear modest; the requisite coal is poor and scattered; and the domestic market is still too small to justify large-scale development and fabrication. Iron is the chief exception. On the basis of present knowledge, it does not seem likely that Southwest Asia as a whole is richly mineralized or has a conspicuous industrial future.

Each country is ambitious to industrialize. As geological studies proceed, reserves increase, and with a growing economy many developments may be expected in mining and refining. Turkey is clearly the leading mineral country, both in known reserves and in production. Even here the mining industry contributes but 2 or 3 per cent to the gross national product, half of it represented by coal and lignite. Turkey is the only nation with a fully integrated steel industry, or with the rail facilities to take advantage of its mineral potentials.

PETROLEUM

Natural seeps of oil and gas have been known in Iraq and Iran for millenniums, and the bitumen has been used as waterproofing for boats, as a mortar for bricks, as a fiery tip for arrows, and as medicine. Some of the earliest-known agricultural implements are crude sickles for harvesting grain made by using bitumen to cement flints to the jawbones of cattle. The sun-dried bricks of ancient Babylon and Ur were cemented with bitumen. Even Noah's ark is reported to have been coated with pitch, within and without.

Not until the mid-twentieth century was the extent of the buried petroleum fully realized. Iranian oil production began in 1913, but Iraq and Kuwait did not start until 1934, and Saudi

The Abadan refinery is among the largest on earth. Although it lies in Iran, Iraq claims ownership of the entire Shatt-al-Arab. (*Courtesy Hunting Aerial Surveys*)

Arabia began to produce in 1938. What were once thought to be nominal reserves now appear to be the world's largest.

Production has increased spectacularly. The total for Southwest Asia in 1930 amounted to 6 million tons. By 1940 it rose to 12 million, and by 1950 reached 85 million. In 1960 the annual production grew to 265 million tons. This amounted to an average of 5,274,000 barrels per day.

The richness of Persian Gulf oil fields is seen in comparison with those of the United States. Whereas America has nearly 600,000 active wells, with an average yield of some 12 barrels per day, Southwest Asia has fewer than 1,500 wells, and most wells average 5,000 barrels a day. In overall output the United States produces considerably more oil than Swasia, but the latter's share of the world total is rising rapidly.

One advantage of oil production in this area is that the structures are relatively simple, the source rocks exceptionally thick and rich in organic matter, the reservoirs unusually large, and the cap rocks so impervious that gas pressures are high enough to make most wells flow freely. Another asset is that subsurface concession rights are in large blocks, so that drilling may be planned on an efficient scale. Most fields are also near tidewater.

It is now clear that the area around and beneath the Persian Gulf contains the largest reserves of oil on earth, apparently two-thirds of the known total. The quantities are indeed fabulous; the single Burgan dome in Kuwait may hold as much oil as the entire United States.

Unfortunately, this petroleum is highly localized within the realm. Several countries have little or no oil, and even in those which are richly endowed the producing pools are few and far between. Concession areas total some 800,000 square miles out of Swasia's 2,400,000 square miles, a limitation which automatically suggests the area of sedimentary basins where favorable structures may be sought. Within this area, however, perhaps no more than 10,000 square miles are actually underlain by commercial deposits.

Oil companies from several foreign countries are involved in these operations, and those from Great Britain and the United States have each invested more than a billion dollars. The Nether-

Oil in Swasia [1]

(in barrels)

Country	Estimated reserves	Daily production
Bahrein	245,000,000	45,100
Iran	35,000,000,000	1,180,000
Iraq	26,500,000,000	1,000,000
Israel	34,000,000	2,800
Kuwait	62,000,000,000	1,650,000
Neutral zone	6,000,000,000	175,000
Qatar	2,750,000,000	176,000
Saudi Arabia	52,000,000,000	1,392,600
Syria	100,000,000	—
Trucial Coast	3,500,000,000	—
Turkey	75,000,000	7,600
Swasia total	188,204,000,000	5,629,100
United States	35,500,000,000	7,188,000
Soviet bloc	34,252,000,000	3,650,000
World total	309,975,000,000	22,330,800

[1] *Oil and Gas Journal*, Jan. 29, 1962.

Petroleum has brought magic prosperity to the lands around the Persian Gulf with reserves which may include two-thirds of all the oil on earth. This is a well in the Ghawar field in eastern Saudi Arabia. (*Courtesy Arabian American Oil Company*)

lands, France, Italy, and Japan are also represented. In most agreements, profits are divided evenly between the concessionaire and the country. As a result, royalties amounting to several million dollars a day are pouring into the area.

Only a small part of this oil is used within Swasia. More than half moves to Europe, and important shipments supply the rest of Asia, Africa, and even the Americas. Huge supertankers are so economical to operate that they can carry oil around South Africa to Europe or the United States more cheaply than by paying canal tolls through the shorter Suez route. If Western Europe should be deprived of oil from the Persian Gulf, serious economic and political consequences would follow.

The countries bordering the Persian Gulf all have deep-water loading facilities for crude oil.

The shores of the gulf tend to be shallow, so that it is necessary to construct long piers, use submerged pipes, or build offshore artificial islands. In addition, several pipelines cross the desert to ports on the Mediterranean. Several countries have their own refineries.

Iran was the first producer, with major production from seven anticlines in the foothills of the Zagros, inland from the end of the Persian Gulf. The fields are long and narrow, with dimensions up to 5 by 20 miles. These Iranian fields are noted for their large reserves and their great production per well. One field has averaged a million barrels per well per year; in another the average yield has been twice as large. Such output is almost unknown elsewhere. In addition, oil has been developed beneath the gulf, and near Qum in the interior. Some of

Iran's oil is exported in crude form; some is processed in the great refinery at Abadan on the Shatt-al-Arab.

Iraq developments started in the nineteenth century, but without success until oil was discovered in Kirkuk, 140 miles north of Baghdad, where the initial well was a gusher which flowed at the rate of 95,000 barrels per day. As in Iran, oil is found in simple anticlines in outliers of the Zagros Mountains. The main structure is 63 miles long by 2 miles wide, with three separate domes. Kirkuk is unique, for the oil-bearing rocks are phenomenally thick and lie at relatively shallow depths. Since Kirkuk is in the interior, production is limited to the capacity of the pipelines which lead to the Mediterranean. Iraq also has a very large production in the south near Basra, where oil occurs in broad, gently folded Arabian-style domes.

Kuwait is indeed a phenomenon, for oil has transformed a desolate desert coast, where fresh water is entirely lacking, to a boom area of amazing prosperity. The Burgan oil field is a broad dome, covering about 75 square miles. The structure is so simple that there are virtually no dry holes. The wells flow without pumping, and from their hilltop location the oil then moves by gravity to loading piers a few miles distant. The Burgan oil sands are 1,000 feet thick, probably making this the richest field on earth. Other domes in Kuwait hold reserves which may be as large.

The two neutral zones which lie between Saudi Arabia and its northern neighbors were created because of uncertainty over title to areas which were uninhabited and presumably of no value. One is administered jointly with Iraq, the other with Kuwait. Oil has been discovered in the latter, and also offshore beneath the Persian Gulf. As an illustration of the value of oil concessions, even in advance of geological studies, the offshore drilling rights were purchased by Japanese interests for an advance of 3 million dollars a year.

Saudi Arabian oil occurs in several gently folded domes, similar to other structures west of the gulf. Some of these are exceptionally large, notably the Ghawar field, which is 150 miles long and is one of the most extensive in the world, covering at least 1,200 square miles. The first field was that near Dhahran, with dimensions of 4 by 5 miles, and a productive area of 13 square miles. Farther south is the Abqaiq anticline, 12 by 43 miles with a proved oil area of 136 square miles. It may be of interest to compare Abqaiq with East Texas, the largest American pool. Whereas the latter has oil sands 40 feet thick and contains 26,000 wells, the Arabian counterpart has a productive thickness of 210 feet and comparable output requires only 40 wells. Abqaiq had yielded a billion barrels of oil by 1954. Nearby Ghawar produced its billionth barrel in 1956. Saudi Arabia also has the world's largest offshore field, that at Safaniya, where wells are being drilled out of sight of land.

Bahrein Island, the Qatar peninsula, the Trucial Coast, and their offshore areas all contain oil, but production is important only in Qatar where the Dukhan field is a long anticline, 5 by 50 miles in dimensions.

The Levant States appear to be poor in oil, although there is a small production in Syria and Israel.

Turkey has a few oil wells in the southeast, where the continuation of the Persian Gulf–Mesopotamian geosyncline holds modest promise of oil.

WATER POWER

No consideration of the geography of Southwest Asia can proceed far without reference to the role of water, whether stored as snow on the mountains or used for irrigation. This brief section surveys the hydroelectric potential and its relation to economic developments. In the petroleum-rich areas, cheap power is so readily available from oil or gas that the capital costs of installing hydroelectric equipment are scarcely justified.

Within the Taurus, Pontus, Zagros, and Elburz Mountains are numerous swift streams.

But some are too small, and all have a variable flow so that storage reservoirs are needed.

The largest electrical potential lies on the headwaters of the rivers which unite to form the Shatt-al-Arab. On the Euphrates the dam at Keban in Turkey supplies a 1-million-kilowatt plant. The Iraqi dams on the Tigris tributaries at Dokkan and Derbend-i-Khan are constructed so that power plants may be installed at later dates. The 620-foot Diz River dam on a tributary of the Karun in Iran has an ultimate capacity of ½ million kilowatts. These projects are doubtless only the beginning, for the Euphrates, Tigris, and Karun have the largest volume of all Swasian rivers, and their headwaters are swift.

The Helmand in Afghanistan is the second longest river system. In its middle basin are two dams, each with modest electrical potentials.

Since Turkey is the most humid country, it has the most closely spaced river system. It also has made the most progress in utilizing its rivers for power. Five dams completed by 1960 had a total electric capacity of ½ million kilowatts. Proposals look forward to five sites on the Sakarya River, with a combined head of 1,500 feet, and nine sites on the Kizil Irmak, both of them in Northern Turkey.

Iran's rivers have been developed more for irrigation than for power, but plans call for a dozen large installations. Two dams near Tehran have a combined power capacity of 200,000 kilowatts.

The three rivers of the Levant—the Orontes, the Litani, and the Jordan—are each small, but in the absence of local oil their potential electric power is important.

Throughout the realm, seasonal rainfall creates an irregular runoff, so that large reservoirs are needed to maintain a steady year-round flow. Only those streams which rise in snow-fed mountains or which flow through areas of unusually heavy rainfall have important hydroelectric potentials. No estimate is available of the theoretical maximum of electric power, but in some areas the possibilities are considerable.

ACCESSIBILITY

Location and accessibility are too often overlooked as resources in economic development. Swasia as a whole may have a crossroads position, but many areas are isolated and hard to get at. A combined map of railways, roads, seaports, and airports would show large areas tens of miles from any modern means of travel.

Inaccessibility is particularly obvious in the mountains. Only six highways cross the Zagros along the 1,000-mile western frontier of Iran; only one leads through the Armenian highlands to Turkey. Five roads cross the Elburz to the Caspian Sea along a distance of 500 miles. The Iranian-Afghan border has no high mountains but is crossed by only a single road in very poor condition, and only one leads from Iran into Pakistan. Only two or three of these roads are paved. Any other trans-mountain or cross-frontier routes are mere caravan trails, for the most part unusable by a jeep. Fewer than a dozen routes, including four into the Soviet Union, provide overland roads into Iran.

When the railway from Tabriz into Turkey is finished, only three rail lines will cross the entire Iranian border, and only two others lead to the surrounding seas. The southeastern half of Iran has no rail service at all.

Iran's deserts are almost as impenetrable by car; in fact there are areas in the Dasht-i-Kavir and the Dasht-i-Lut where the nearest road is 100 miles away. Even caravan trails avoid these waterless and empty areas.

Turkey's situation is considerably better, although the northern and southern mountains form a barrier. Only a half dozen highways from the Mediterranean cross the Taurus Mountains in 400 miles, and only nine roads cross the Pontus or North Anatolian Mountains to reach the Black Sea. However, most of the country is within 25 miles of a road, and many roadways are improved even though unpaved. All parts of the country are within 50 miles of a railway except the extreme southeast.

Two roads lead west from Iraq, one from

Baghdad, the other from Mosul; three cross eastward to Iran; none lead north to Turkey, and only desert trails extend southward into Arabia.

Even trade-conscious Lebanon has only limited accessibility to its neighbors. The coastal road to Israel is closed for political reasons, but that northward to Syria is open. A major highway connects Baghdad with Damascus, but the Lebanese mountains are so high that only three other roads cross them.

Prewar Palestine had a good road system, but the Israeli borders are now closed.

Saudi Arabia presents a different problem. Not a single improved road crosses its borders although heavy-duty trucks travel freely across the gravel plains which lie along the country's frontier with Jordan, Iraq, and Kuwait. Petroleum operations have led to a series of paved roads in the oil areas, but elsewhere most roads are merely desert trails, often $\frac{1}{2}$ mile wide where one set of ruts has been abandoned in favor of another.

While cross-country travel is possible in the level areas of Arabia, sand dunes and dissected terrain bar access to half of the peninsula. One of the most inaccessible lands on earth is the Rub' al Khali or empty quarter of southern Arabia, rarely penetrated even by Bedouins. Millions of dollars have been invested in the search for oil, but when exploration ends, the area will revert to inaccessibility.

Nearly 100 airports in Swasia have scheduled services, and regular air travel has brought a revolutionary change in accessibility. Pilgrims to Mecca now travel by plane whereas they once crossed the desert by camel caravan. Journeys which formerly required days of uncomfortable travel may now be taken in hours.

Southwest Asia is surrounded and penetrated by seven seas, so that except in Afghanistan, one is always within 400 miles of tidewater. The sea-land relation for the realm as a whole is suggested by the ratio of 1 mile of coast to 300 square miles of land area. Outside contacts are provided by three dozen more or less modern seaports. No river is navigable for more than a few miles above its mouth.

As one travels eastward from Istanbul or Beirut to Kabul, one sees a marked gradation from maritime consciousness to continental isolation. Thousands of Turks and Lebanese have traveled abroad but not many Afghans. The shops of Beirut are filled with every type of overseas merchandise, from American frozen food to Japanese crab meat; in Kabul one finds cheap bazaar goods from abroad but not much more.

ECONOMIC POTENTIALS

The Swasian realm is one of wide contrasts, both physical and cultural. The environments range from very wet, as along the Black Sea, to extremely dry; from the subarctic cold of mountain peaks to tropical heat around the Dead Sea. In most places water is in short supply, and rural livelihood depends on elaborate irrigation schemes.

The social contrasts are as great. Impoverished tenant farmers have little in common with their wealthy landlords who live in luxurious apartment houses and spend the summers in Switzerland. Hundreds of Bedouin shepherds have suddenly been displaced when their ruling sheik has sold the tribe's traditional grasslands to prospective farmers.

Some areas are crowded, others completely empty. Many places appear to be overpopulated in terms of available technology; nowhere is there good idle land ready for the pioneer. Accessibility everywhere presents a problem.

Political organization ranges from autocratic and feudal to constitutional and democratic. Revolution is in the air, usually with international repercussions. Change is as characteristic as contrast. In some countries tenancy is disappearing; elsewhere new crops have introduced a money economy in place of local self-sufficiency. Few areas retain even their early-twentieth-century appearance.

The future of the area rests on its many resources, some quite apart from geographic con-

Cement plants are present in several countries of Southwest Asia. These four rotary kilns are in Lebanon. (*Courtesy United States Operations Mission, Lebanon*)

siderations. Here is an unused reservoir of manpower, as is witnessed by the large numbers of men in every town who spend most of the day sitting in their favorite coffee house. The same villages and cities have new schools, and when these educated children grow up they will have new wants, and new skills.

Location, which must be included in an inventory of assets, is not a constant. During the early nineteenth century Europeans wanted to create an overland route to India, based on a caravan route through Aleppo and navigation down the Euphrates. Then came German dreams of a Berlin-to-Baghdad railway. When the Suez Canal became the main avenue to the East, seaports such as Beirut or Basra lay off the usual steamer tracks and received few boats. Aden was important only because of its transit location. In the days of air travel, Beirut

and Basra are on the direct line between Europe and Asia. Interior cities such as Ankara, Damascus, Baghdad, and Tehran, previously accessible only by long and difficult overland travel, are now served by the great intercontinental airlines. So long as the great-circle route across Soviet air space remains closed, Southwest Asia holds the prime location in East–West travel. This strategic location brings monetary benefits.

Soil is another neglected resource, obvious but seldom added up in any systematic inventory. Although only the beginnings of soil surveys are available, the general picture is one of unused assets. Low rainfall results in unleached soils, high in soluble plant foods; but low rainfall also means limited vegetation and a low accumulation of humus. Some of the best soils occur in the Fertile Crescent where cultivation has already taken over the more attractive areas.

The key to soil usability is water, and it is here that Swasia has the largest opportunities for future development. Yet even if all the precipitation might be conserved, evaporation checked, and the water applied at the proper time, vast areas would remain a desert.

The average precipitation for the lowland part of the basin drained by the Shatt-al-Arab amounts to less than 8 inches. In contrast, potential evapotranspiration averages 50 inches. If the entire runoff received from the headwaters in Turkey and Iran could be evenly distributed across this area, it would add an additional 8 inches. Since in this hot region the combined total of 16 inches is inadequate to meet losses from evaporation, only a small part of Mesopotamia can ever be irrigated.

In an ideal regime, all river water would be used to the full, and little runoff would be left over at the mouth. Such a complete diversion for irrigation would also presume a dependable flow, which is far from the case. No surveys are available of the maximum extent of irrigation possibilities throughout Swasia, but it is possible that the present area might be doubled.

The magic resources of the realm are oil and gas, and royalties are already fabulous. If the world demand continues to grow, and if other sources such as Soviet oil are not too competitive, the income may well double and more. Since most of this petroleum will be used abroad, the foreign exchange will enable the oil-producing countries to purchase goods elsewhere.

So far as now known, mineral resources in Swasia cannot match oil reserves, but the export of chromium, lead, copper, manganese, salt, phosphate, and a few other resources will help the export-import balance.

Among agricultural potentials are the development for export of relatively new crops, such as cotton, sugar, and tobacco, and the increase in the export of such nuts as filberts, almonds, walnuts, and pistachios. Dates and figs have long been important. The production of wheat and barley is growing, and in most years the realm as a whole is more than able to feed itself.

Along with the increase in irrigated and rain-fed fields will come a decrease in pastoral activities. This is related to the marked contraction in good grazing land as it is put under the plow, and to the low income which nomadism provides. Another century may almost see an end to Bedouin life, and incidentally to the camel.

Modest but striking economic changes will occur in the industrial field. Heavy industry is now concentrated in a few areas: the Karabuk steel mills in Turkey, the Iranian steel plant at Azna, and the modest Israeli mill near Haifa. Until transport and local markets develop, no large increase is to be expected. Because of the distance from European or American supplies, each oil field is an industrial oasis, with self-contained machine shops. Light industry, such as textiles, is widespread.

Several countries are in the midst of integrated development programs. The basic problem is to raise the general standard of living, and to reduce some of the differences between rich and poor countries.

A further resource lies in grants and loans from foreign sources. Great Britain and France have traditionally provided help. More recently, American assistance has reached a billion dollars, especially to Israel. Soviet aid is growing. United Nations technical assistance projects and loans from the World Bank have aided several countries.

Additional development moncy might be made available through the creation of a regional bank or development-loan fund, to be financed largely from oil royalties. In some oil-rich countries, revenues are outrunning the opportunities for investment, while elsewhere new capital is inadequate.

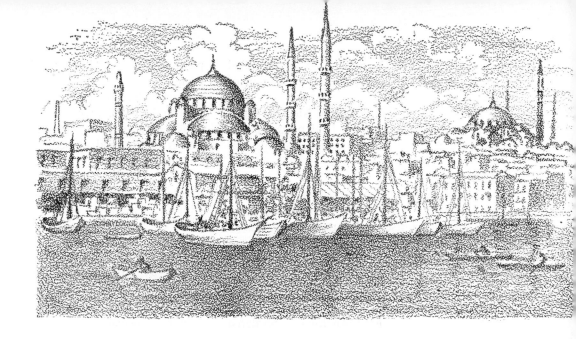

36 Turkey

The Physical Landscape / Land Use / Population Patterns / Turkish Villages / Industrial Prospects / References on Turkey

THE PHYSICAL LANDSCAPE

Turkey is like a miniature continent. On three sides the country is bounded by seas, within which it is still further enclosed by mountains. Continentality is emphasized by seasonal pressure changes which tend to produce, alternately, inward winds in summer and outward winds in winter. Coastal accessibility with maritime orientation and interior inaccessibility are as true of Asia Minor as of Asia as a whole.

For thousands of years Anatolia has been a link between Europe and Asia, while at right angles to it the Dardanelles and the Bosporus have served as an avenue from the Aegean to the Black Sea. Rugged topography and arid climate make overland travel difficult, but movement has ever been characteristic of the people. The bordering mountains have kept out migrants from Europe and maintained the Asiatic character of the country; only along the Aegean did Greek culture secure a foothold.

Six major physical divisions characterize Turkey in Asia: the block-faulted Pontus Mountains along the Black Sea in the north, the high central basins of Anatolia, the mountain complex of the Armenian highlands, the folded Taurus Mountains along the Mediterranean to the south, the ragged Aegean coast

519

where irregular embayments are partly filled with delta plains, and the Marmara region of the Straits.

Neither the Black Sea nor Mediterranean shores provide much level land or good harbors. Fully half of Turkey is mountainous; unfavorable relief makes perhaps as much as two-thirds of the country unusable.

A cross section from north to south shows a narrow fringe of coastal plain along the Black Sea, an abrupt rise to the rugged 2-mile-high Pontus Mountains, a slight descent to the broad undulating Anatolian plateau with its playa lakes, another rise to the equally high Taurus, and a steep descent to the Mediterranean, with little room for a coastal plain.

The plateau basin of Anatolia is bordered on the north and south by a complex series of ranges; neither the Pontus nor Taurus are simple mountains. Heights reach 10,000 feet in each system. The northern area is a continuation of alpine folding, traceable from Switzerland to the Pacific, whereas the southern mountains are a part of the dinaric system. Both ranges are formed of sediments laid down in an ancient geosyncline known as Tethys.

Toward the east, the Pontus and Taurus systems meet in the Armenian knot or nucleus, with an elevation of a mile in the plateau and twice to three times that level in the mountains.

Turkey has many volcanic areas, such as Mount Ararat in the extreme east, an active volcano which rises to 16,946 feet. Severe earthquakes have occurred in many parts of the country, especially in the Pontus Mountains.

Within this mountain enclosure lies the basin of Anatolia, covering more than a third of

Turkey Data [1]

Area:		
Thrace (in Europe)	9,121	square miles
Anatolia (in Asia)	292,159	"
Total area	301,380	"
Population	27,809,831	(1960 census)
Istanbul	1,459,528	
Ankara (capital)	646,151	
Izmir	370,923	
Adana	230,024	
Primary and secondary pupils	2,795,338	(1960)
University (6) students	44,368	
Wheat	8,590,000	metric tons (1960)
Barley	3,700,000	"
Corn	1,000,000	"
Tobacco	130,200	"
Cotton lint	195,000	"
Cottonseed	316,000	"
Beet sugar, raw	696,000	"
Coal (incomplete)	5,304,000	"
Crude oil	362,400	"
Steel	266,400	"
Cement	2,040,000	"
Chromite	206,500	metric tons (1959)
Electricity	2,668,000,000	kilowatthours (1960)

[1] *Britannica Book of the Year*, 1962.

Parts of interior and southeastern Turkey are an arid steppe, too dry for safe cultivation and normally the home of pastoral nomads, whose wanderings are tied to supplies of water. (*Courtesy Turkish Press, Broadcasting, and Tourist Department*)

Turkey. This is a rolling steppeland of withering rivers and semiarid plains. Salt lakes and playa flats are interrupted by low ranges a few hundred or a thousand feet above the plain. The general altitude is 2,000 feet in the west and 4,000 feet in the east.

Most of the usable coastal areas are on the shores of the Aegean Sea and the Sea of Marmara, where alluvium has filled in the heads of submerged bays. The Black Sea coast has more level land than along the Mediterranean; on both coasts are isolated deltas backed by mountains.

Climatic conditions divide Turkey into two parts: the coastal sections, which have a Mediterranean type of climate with 20 or more inches of winter rain, and the semiarid plateau, also with winter precipitation but with less than 10 inches a year. In most areas there is such a deficiency of moisture that unirrigated agriculture in summer is possible only where the soil has stored moisture during the previous winter. Unfortunately, winter precipitation fluctuates, so that many summers witness partial crop failures.

Along the Aegean and Mediterranean coasts conditions resemble those in Greece, with warm, dry summers and cool, rainy winters. During the latter season occasional cold winds sweep out of the interior through gaps in the mountains. The Black Sea coast has much more rainfall than elsewhere, even 100 inches toward the east, and it occurs during the fall as well as in winter.

Coastal vegetation follows altitude, with dry maqui brush on the lower slopes followed by splendid deciduous and then coniferous forests up to the tree line at 6,000 to 8,000 feet, above which are alpine meadows.

Conditions within Anatolia are more extreme. Bitterly cold winds blow from the northeast during winter and spring. Occasional cyclonic storms bring a little rain. High summer temperatures help to develop a semipermanent low-pressure area over interior Turkey, with inblowing winds and severe dust storms. The precipitation is under 10 inches, since moisture from the surrounding seas is precipitated on the intervening mountain slopes. Snow may lie on the ground for three months. Summers are entirely dry. This is a treeless steppe with many saline wastes.

The mountains of eastern Turkey are even colder than central Anatolia. This region, sometimes known as the Siberia of Turkey, has six months of winter.

Two major rivers drain northward to the Black Sea, the Sakarya and the Kizil Irmak; two others flow south, the Tigris and the Euphrates. Much of the interior is too dry to support rivers which ever reach the sea; if Anatolia were more humid it would contain a number of large freshwater lakes. Several of Turkey's rivers hold hydroelectric possibilities.

LAND USE

Much of Turkey has no agricultural use; fully 100 million acres are too steep, too infertile, or too dry for crops. Even so, agriculture and grazing are the predominant occupations, usually accounting for 70 per cent of the national income and 90 per cent of the exports. Thirty per cent of the total area is optimistically classed as arable, though only 25 per cent is actually used and a third of this lies fallow each year. Turkey has made conspicuous progress in agriculture, for the cultivated area has been increased fivefold since 1927. Tree and vine crops occupy 2 per cent of the country. Grazing areas and meadows cover 45 per cent, and forests account for 13 per cent, leaving the balance of 15 per cent for mountains and wasteland.

Wheat, by far the most important crop, occupies 50 per cent of the cultivated land. Barley occupies 25 per cent; corn, rye, and oats are minor cereals. These are all fall-planted. Cotton has risen to 4 per cent, and tobacco utilizes 1 per cent. Olives, filberts, and grapes are the chief tree and vine crops.

As a result of government efforts, wheat production has increased so much that Turkey has changed from a wheat-importing to a wheat-exporting country. Wheat is grown in all but a few districts, and tends to be more important in the drier interior.

Tobacco is a distinctive Turkish export, but the plant is an American variety introduced in 1602 which has acquired unique properties in its new environment. Most of the tobacco is grown in two humid coastal districts along the Aegean and Black Seas. It is usually raised on the southern side of hills, protected from high winds; where raised in flat country, straw mats are erected for its shelter. Two-thirds of the crop is exported.

Cotton is grown in the west and south, and supplies the raw material for a growing textile industry. As with wheat, there has been extensive government research and support. Production has increased severalfold, and the area in cotton amounts to 2 million acres. Much of the export comes to the United States.

Various other crops are important. Sugar beets are extensively grown, and the country is now self-sufficient in sugar. Turkey is the world's leading producer of hazelnuts, or filberts, shipped largely to Europe. Grapes are widespread, and sultana raisins rank second or third in the export trade, so that in their export the country ranks with the United States. Figs apparently originated here and are a major export from Izmir, formerly known as Smyrna. Turkey is by far the world's largest exporter of dried figs.

Olive trees are more numerous than elsewhere in Southwest Asia, with most production located within 50 miles of the Aegean or Mediterranean coasts. Irrigation is unnecessary, since olives will grow with as little as 8 inches of rain. Since summer rain is a disadvantage, olives are not found along the Black Sea. Most of the olive oil is used within Turkey.

Mohair is a distinctive product of the interior, and the raising of angora goats is an important occupation in central Anatolia. The wool combines softness and durability. Turkish mohair is the finest in the world.

Turkey's export trade is predominantly made up of agricultural products. Only through the sale of these items is the country able to import the industrial materials that she needs. The chief agricultural exports are tobacco, filberts, raisins, cotton, mohair, wheat, wool, figs, hides and skins, and barley.

Interior Anatolia leads in total crop acreage and output. Some sections are rather dry, but no other part of Turkey has so much level land or good soil. The most intensively used farm land is found in the coastal deltas, none of them more than a few miles in extent.

Irrigation is practiced wherever water is available, but only 10 per cent of the farm area is so supplied. Turkey has numerous snow-fed rivers, and with proper engineering the irrigated area might be doubled. Elsewhere, water-conserving dry-farming techniques are used to check evaporation and store up moisture in the soil. Many fields raise a crop only in alternate years.

Most of Turkey has been so long settled that the farming conditions in the older areas represent many generations of occupancy. The widespread availability of tractors has enabled cultivation to push into former grazing lands, and the development of irrigation has changed the crop patterns in many areas, so that there are now three agricultural landscapes: the old and traditional, the new and extensive in dry areas,

Wheat is Turkey's main crop, and mechanization has brought a large increase in the production, especially in the interior areas of marginal rainfall. This scene is on the Anatolian Plateau near Ankara. (*Courtesy Turkish Information Office*)

and the new, intensive cultivation in irrigated areas.

One of the major changes in Turkish agriculture has been the decrease in tenancy. Land redistribution between 1950 and 1960 brought the number of farmers who were full owners to 75 per cent.

Pastoral activities increase in relative importance eastward, although nomadism as a whole is in decline. Thousands of Kurdish people move up and down the slopes of eastern Turkey each year.

POPULATION PATTERNS

Turkey is an old part of the world. Innumerable wars have occurred here. Almost every important country in Europe and in western Asia has fought in this area, either for control of the Straits, for command of the through route by land, or for the small patches of fertile soil. Here are many province and city names which were famous in Greek and Roman history and in the New Testament—Troy, Ephesus, Miletus, and Tarsus.

Some of the earliest history goes back to the Hittites, who were dominant from 2000 to 1200 B.C. At one time they were the chief cultural force in western Asia, frequently at war with both Syrians and Egyptians. Much later came the empire of Alexander the Great.

Turkey dates from the thirteenth century, when the Ottoman Turks were nomads in the Anatolian uplands. During the period of its greatest extent in 1566, the Ottoman Empire reached from Hungary to southern Arabia and from Egypt to the Sea of Azov, covering 1,-700,000 square miles and ruling 40 million people. Successive losses of land followed until the end of the First World War, when the country was deprived of all its territory except that in Asia Minor and a small area around Istanbul.

In 1922 the Turkish Revolution occurred under the leadership of Mustafa Kemal, or Kemal Atatürk, and the capital was removed to Ankara in the interior in order to make in-dependence more secure. No part of Turkish history is more dramatic than the events that followed. The old Oriental Turkey became modernized at a rate which has been described as a century in a decade. Some midcentury events seem like aftershocks following the earthquake.

Location is of vital concern to Turkey, for her position in two continents is of great importance. Czarist Russia repeatedly sought an outlet through the Straits. During the First World War, Germany brought Turkey to her side in order to secure a route from Berlin to Baghdad. In the Second World War, the Allies bargained with Turkey and succeeded in keeping her neutral by agreeing to purchase the bulk of her exports.

This is a long-settled land and the cultural landscape is the result of successive human occupancy. Since agriculture is the occupation for most of the people, population patterns match land use. This is true elsewhere in Southwest Asia, but the Turkish landscape is farther along on the road to modernization. So too are settlement features.

As he flies over Turkey, a geographer may examine the physical environment and compare the past with the future; he may identify the ruins of antiquity, the landscape of the present, and the potentials which are evolving.

Sparse populations characterize inner Anatolia, the dry Syrian borderlands, and the cold mountains of the east; densities are below 25 people per square mile in this sixth of the country. Some areas are almost completely empty. In contrast, two other areas show densities in excess of 250 per square mile: the eastern coast of the Black Sea and the Aegean complex of deltas, flood plains, alluvial basins, and low hill lands. Many linear population patterns match narrow valleys in the Pontus or Taurus Ranges. Almost everywhere rural settlement is discontinuous.

Few countries have such ethnic homogeneity. There are $1\frac{1}{2}$ million Kurds in the east, but the former Armenian, Greek, and Bulgar groups have either been liquidated or repatriated.

The Galata Bridge in Istanbul spans the Golden Horn, an arm of the Bosporus, which appears at the right. Few cities in the world have a more commanding site or a richer history. (*Courtesy Pan American World Airways*)

Cities have developed where snow-fed rivers supply oases, or near critical passes, or on isolated deltas. Other and newer centers are related to mines or to political administration. Four cities call for attention: Istanbul with about 2 million people, Ankara, with 750,000, Izmir with nearly 500,000, and Adana with 250,000. Some 15 others count at least 50,000 people. Everywhere urban growth is spectacular, as shown in modern buildings, urban redevelopment, street widening, and new and growing suburbs.

Istanbul commands the Straits and thus the 180-mile passage from the Mediterranean to the Black Sea. The Bosporus is a sea river, 16 miles long and in places only ½ mile wide. For three thousand years Istanbul has been an important center, long known as Byzantium, later

renamed Constantinople. Across the Bosporus is the suburb of Üsküdar (Scutari).

Here two continents and two seas meet. Few cities have a more striking location, or a more spectacular skyline. Hundreds of minarets rise above the several hills. The rich cultural heritage of Istanbul make it one of the most fascinating cities in the world, along with Jerusalem, Peking, Moscow, and New York.

Istanbul enjoys a pleasant climate, although winters may be snowy and damp. July temperatures never exceed 100°F, while winters do not drop below 17°F. Every month has at least an inch of rain, with an average total of 29 inches.

Ankara is different. Although it was an ancient Hittite center, the city was of no importance until the capital was moved to the interior in 1923. Whereas Istanbul has a maze of winding streets, crowded among the hills which border the Bosporus, much of Ankara is a new development with broad avenues and fine modern buildings. In some ways it might be described as one of the most European cities in Asia; in fact some Turks resent any classification of their country as Asiatic.

The city lies amid steppelands at an elevation of 3,000 feet. It is a day's train ride from Istanbul, but only an hour and a quarter by airplane. Because of its interior location, Ankara has a greater temperature range than Istanbul. Summers do not exceed 100°F, but in winter the thermometer may drop to −13°F. One reason for the semiarid landscape is shown by the precipitation, which averages but 14 inches a year.

Izmir is Turkey's second port, with a magnificent harbor at the head of a drowned embayment on the Aegean. Adana is the fourth-largest city, located on the fertile Cilician Plain, which is the delta of the Seyhan River at the northeast corner of the Mediterranean.

TURKISH VILLAGES

Turkey is predominantly rural, with two out of every three people living in a village or *koy*. There are no less than 35,000 villages, and 3 million farm families. These settlements derive much of their personality from the surrounding countryside. Many of them lie in the Anatolian Plateau—dry, brown, treeless, and sparsely settled. Much of the surrounding landscape is a grazing land for sheep and goats,

Ankara has been the capital of Turkey since 1923 and has grown from a village to a city with a population of nearly a million. Fine boulevards make it one of the most Europeanized cities of Asia. (*Courtesy Turkish Press, Broadcasting, and Tourist Department*)

and where cultivated, the fields tend to be large, although not all the land is planted each year. People prefer to cluster in villages rather than to be dispersed through the countryside.

The typical village has a mosque with its slender minaret, a few shops, and one or more coffeehouses although when foreign exchange is limited the latter may provide only tea. Here men sit by the hour. Larger towns have a restaurant, a municipal building for the police, and a school. Most villages have a statue of Atatürk, and every public room contains his portrait. Every village is equipped with a headman or *Muktar,* who has the final word on almost every question. This is an inherited office, dating from the early acquisition of land.

Villages show surprising uniformity. Most houses have but one story, and are built of mud or stone and thatched with straw or covered with slabs of stone. The headman and a few others may live in two-story houses, often with balconies. Streets are unpaved, and only those villages which are fortunate enough to lie near a modern highway have ready access to the rest of the country. Where bus transport is available, people can reach urban centers, and new merchandise becomes available.

Whereas animals and men once provided the only source of energy on the farm, thousands of tractors are now available. In fact, Turkey averages one tractor for every 750 acres of cultivated land. Wooden plows, ill-fed livestock, and poor harvests still characterize most villages. Cattle dung is the principal domestic fuel.

The people of rural Turkey are essentially uniform in racial stock, for most foreign elements have been eliminated. Exceptions are the traditional woodcutters, or Alaouites, who form a special religious sect, and the seminomadic Yuruks, who migrate up and down the Taurus Mountains with their flocks of camels.

INDUSTRIAL PROSPECTS

Turkey leads all Swasia in industry, and apparently in mineral resources as well. The country has only limited oil, all in the border folds next to Iraq, but is well supplied with coal, lignite, chrome, iron, copper, and several other metals. Turkish meerschaum and emery are world-famous.

Coal is mined in only one area, that around Eregli and Zonguldak near the Black Sea. The coal is Carboniferous in age, and of good coking quality. Production began early in the nineteenth century, and by the mid-twentieth century the mine capacity had reached 5 million tons a year. Reserves amount to 1 billion tons of coal. The Zonguldak area contains fifty seams, ranging from 2 to 20 feet in thickness, but unfortunately many beds dip steeply.

Lignite, of Tertiary age, is widespread, especially in the west. Reserves exceed 1 billion tons, and there are two dozen mining districts. While lignite is inferior to bituminous coal in heat value, it is fortunately available in those areas where coal shipments might prove too costly.

The ferroalloys in production include manganese, molybdenum, and tungsten. Nonferrous minerals are antimony, aluminum, copper, gold, lead, mercury, and zinc—none are important. Salt, sulfur, and boron are in the nonmetallic-export list, along with distinctive commodities such as meerschaum, which is a weathered serpentine, and emery, an aluminum oxide.

While this list is relatively impressive and may promise a bright industrial future, several limitations must be noted, such as quality, amounts, accessibility, and competition with better deposits abroad. Capital and technology present other problems.

The steel business leads in the field of heavy industry. While high-grade ore is available at Divrigi, and Zonguldak coal makes good coke, the raw materials are 600 miles apart, and the expense of rail transport raises the cost of the pig iron.

The Karabuk steel mill, 50 miles south of Zonguldak, is the largest plant between Hungary and India. The three blast furnaces have a capacity of 600,000 tons of pig iron a year, and there are also five open-hearth steel furnaces, coke ovens, rolling mills, a foundry,

Turkish heavy industry, based on the country's resources of coal and the metals, is by far the most important in the realm. These ingots are being poured at the Karabuk steel mill in the northwest. (*Courtesy Turkish Information Office*)

and a sulfuric acid plant. A new plant, at the port of Eregli, will be almost as large.

Oil must be imported, since the available production supplies but one-fifth of Turkey's needs. The principal field is near Diyarbekir in the southeast, and occurs in a series of anticlines along the margin of the Anatolian–Hindu Kush folded mountains and the Arabian shield. Most of the country appears to have unfavorable geology for oil occurrences.

Although hydroelectricity is not a mineral resource, its availability should be listed here. Plants already in operation generate over 500,-000 kilowatts, and plans call for at least three times this amount. Since several of these installations are in areas otherwise without power, their development opens new industrial possibilities.

Iron ore occurs in several areas, but the best deposits are found in the Divrigi area near Sivas in the east. Here the ore is a high-grade magnetite containing 65 per cent of iron; reserves amount to 40 million metric tons, and production exceeds 1 million tons a year. Iron ore is also produced around Edremit near the Aegean, but the quality is inferior since there are undesirable amounts of arsenic.

Chromium is Turkey's unique metal, produced since 1860. Reserves are extensive, and at one time the country was the world's chief source of supply, but the highest-grade deposits are nearly exhausted. Two areas are important, Fethiye in the southwest and Guleman in the east. Most of the ore is exported.

Except for steel, heavy industry has limited development. There are a number of cement mills, railway and ship yards, small chemical plants, and arsenals, but the great bulk of the country is nonindustrialized. Even light industry is overly concentrated, with half the production around Istanbul.

Turkey's overall potentials are good, provided that the country has the wisdom and skill to realize them. The domestic market for minerals and manufactured goods is still too small to warrant much local fabrication; in the meantime the country can export raw materials and use the foreign exchange to purchase needed manufactured goods.

In measuring Turkey's assets and economic prospects one should not overlook the value of location. So long as Turkey commands the Straits she is inescapably one of the key powers of western Asia. With the improvement of overland transport from the Black Sea to Iran, Turkey may become an important back door for that country, and an outlet for its interior oil fields.

References on Turkey

See also general references under Southwest Asia, Chapter 33.

Erinc, Sirri: "The Climate of Turkey according to Thornthwaite's Classification," *Annals, Assn. Amer. Geogs.*, XXXIX (1949), 26–46.

Erinc, Sirri: "Climatic Types and the Variation of Moisture Regions in Turkey," *Geog. Rev.*, XL (1950), 224–235.

Erinc, Sirri, and Necdet Tuncdilek: "The Agricultural Regions of Turkey," *Geog. Rev.*, XLII (1952), 179–203.

Helburn, Nicholas: "A Stereotype of Agriculture in Semiarid Turkey," *Geog. Rev.*, XLV (1955), 375–384.

International Bank for Reconstruction and Development: *The Economy of Turkey*, Washington (1951).

Nowland, John L.: "The Port of Istanbul," *Scottish Geog. Mag.*, LXXVII (1961), 67–74.

Russell, Richard J.: "Alluvial Morphology of Anatolian Rivers," *Annals, Assn. Amer. Geogs.*, XLIV (1954), 363–391.

Thornburg, Max W., Graham Spry, and George Soule: *Turkey: An Economic Appraisal*, New York: Twentieth Century Fund (1949).

Tumertekin, E.: "The Iron and Steel Industry of Turkey," *Econ. Geog.*, XXXI (1955), 179–184.

Wright, Iona, and Densi Wright: "The Black Sea Coast of Turkey," *Geog. Mag.*, XVIII (1945), 118–125.

37 The Arabian Peninsula

The Political Areas / The Arabs / Desert Landscapes / Highland Landscapes / Arabian Regions / References on Arabia

THE POLITICAL AREAS

The peninsula of Arabia is as large as the United States east of the Mississippi, covering an area of about a million square miles. Most of it is included in the relatively new kingdom of Saudi Arabia, put together after the collapse of the Ottoman Empire by military conquest under ibn-Saud, and guided by the conservative Muslim group known as the Wahabis.

Saudi Arabia is ruled from the ancestral tribal center at Riyadh, and is composed of five main politico-geographical areas; the Nejd in the center, the Hejaz and Asir in the west, the Eastern Province, and the Northern Province.

One of the great assets of Saudi Arabia is that the kingdom includes the holy places of Islam: Mecca and Medina. Since all faithful Muslims should make the pilgrimage at least once during their lifetime, this gives Saudi Arabia a unique cultural and political advantage. Of equal importance is the revenue from oil. What was an illiterate and underdeveloped area of rival tribes is becoming an educated and modernized state, although in comparison with other Arab states conditions are still backward.

The country of Yemen, formerly ruled by an imam (one who leads in prayer) occupies the southwestern highlands. Only a small part of its frontier next to Saudi Arabia has been defined,

530

and there is continual dispute concerning its border next to the Western Aden Protectorates, some of which once gave nominal allegiance to Yemen. The traditional capital is Sana, but the last imam ruled from Taiz.

Yemen dates from the tenth century B.C., and may well be the oldest country in Arabia. It is the traditional home of the Queen of Sheba. Because of its elevation, Yemen is a subhumid country, and this corner of the peninsula was once known as Arabia Felix, the happy Arabia, in contrast to the term Arabia Deserta which applied to most of the peninsula.

In the southeastern highlands lies Masqat, an independent sultanate with which the United States has had treaty relations since 1833. Masqat borders the Indian Ocean and the Gulf of Oman for a thousand miles. The narrow coastal plain contains a few oases, as do the interior mountains, but most of the country is barren. The capital city of Masqat has one of the world's most uncomfortable climates, where temperatures frequently reach 120°F.

Western Masqat includes the slightly more humid Dhufar coast, home of frankincense and myrrh; in the interior is little-known Oman, ruled by a semi-independent imam.

A series of states line the western shores of the Persian Gulf, several of them at one time under nominal Persian control. The area was once a center for piracy and the slave trade. The trade was suppressed by Great Britain early in the nineteenth century, and each local sheik agreed to cease such operations. He also agreed not to enter into treaty relations with foreign states without British consent, a stipulation which precludes membership of the western Persian-Gulf states such as Bahrein in the United Nations or in the Arab League. In return Great Britain guaranteed their independence and has assisted in their development.

Until the discovery of oil, the states were unimportant coastal bits of desert, almost waterless and kept alive by the pearl industry and by trade with India or Zanzibar. Three of these sheikdoms contain oil and now enjoy boom prosperity; the others live in hopes and on advance payments based on concessions for prospecting.

Kuwait lies between Iraq and Saudi Arabia, and is the most prosperous of the group. In addition to its own oil, the country receives half the royalties from the adjoining neutral zone. In 1961 it reduced its ties with Great Britain and began to handle its own foreign affairs. Bahrein is an island, with a history of settlement which dates back to the third millennium B.C. Artesian springs make possible some cultivation. The peninsula of Qatar is especially desolate, scarcely fit for grazing, since the rainfall averages but 4 inches per year. Thanks to oil, the per capita income is among the highest in the world.

Farther south the Trucial Coast extends for

Saudi Arabia Data [1]

Area	872,722 square miles
Population	6,036,000 (1956 est.)
Mecca	200,000
Jidda	160,000
Riyadh (capital)	150,000
Primary and secondary pupils	85,847 (1960)
Higher education students	2,116 (1960)
Wheat	37,000 metric tons (1956)
Sorghum	69,000 " "
Dates	200,300 metric tons (1957)
Crude-oil exports	51,420,000 metric tons (1959)

[1] *Britannica Book of the Year*, 1962.

Arabian Bedouins live in black goat-hair tents, moving every few weeks as grazing conditions change. This scene from northern Arabia is near Badanah along the Trans-Arabian pipeline. (*Courtesy Arabian American Oil Company*)

400 miles and includes seven petty sheikdoms. The two most important are Dibai and Sharjah. Since boundaries are nowhere surveyed, there are disputes as to the extent of oil rights in the interior.

The southern coast of Arabia presents further problems. Aden has been a center of dispute since it was captured by the Romans in A.D. 24. Marco Polo visited the city in 1285, and the city was long a traditional base for pirates, including Captain Kidd. Great Britain took possession in 1839, and later entered into treaty relations with several dozen rulers inland; sheiks, emirs, and sultans. The Western Protectorate includes eighteen states, partly federated; the Eastern Protectorate is even more complex and in part is "unadministered," mean-ing that the tribes are too warlike to be policed. Here is the Hadhramaut, the remarkable box-walled wadi with its skyscraper apartments.

While the eastern peninsula is fabulously rich in oil and gas, Arabia appears to have little else in the way of mineral wealth. Gold mining ended in 1954. Iron deposits occur in the extreme northwest, but the quality is poor. Salt is present in many interior playas, but there is nowhere enough for export.

THE ARABS

Interior Arabia is the only area in Southwest Asia never settled or conquered by an outside culture. Its people are thus a relatively pure ethnic group, although around the western side of the peninsula there is an African mixture. Much of the early history awaits archaeological research.

The population of the peninsula as a whole is uncertain, but apparently exceeds 12 million, half of whom may live in the highlands of Yemen, Asir, and Masqat. The number of Bedouins is unknown but is probably less than 3 million; possibly 2 million people live in cities; the rest are farmers scattered through the many oases.

The Arabs divide themselves into two groups; the *hadar* are those who live in permanent houses in towns, while the *badia* are the dwellers in black haircloth tents; from the latter comes our term Bedouin.

While nomads may spend most of their life in the desert, they all have some attachment to a fixed settlement. Many tribes own date groves, or a patch of cultivated land, or are related to some village where they call for supplies which cannot be procured in the desert and where they sell their pastoral products.

Within the Bedouin tribes is a hierarchy of prestige. The most aristocratic groups keep camels and look down on the herders of sheep and goats; they likewise control the better grazing lands. Tribal alliances and feuds may be of long standing.

All of this is changing. Trucks are making camel caravans obsolete; pilgrims travel to Mecca by plane; deep wells open up grazing lands which may have adequate grass but lack water; many Bedouins have found employment

Arab hospitality is proverbial; every guest is offered coffee, freshly prepared and served from copper pots in small porcelain cups, followed by sweetened tea served in small glasses from enameled kettles. (*Courtesy Trans Arabian Pipe Line Company*)

in the oil industry or in the new cities; and tribes which were once confined to one corner of Arabia are now found elsewhere. Many of the fine qualities of life developed in the desert seem to be disappearing with the drastic changes in the way of life.

Oasis life revolves around the availability of water. It may come from transient highland streams, from flood spreading in wadis where the occasional runoff is diverted and encouraged to sink into the ground, from wells in areas where ground water lies within a few feet of the surface, or from springs which provide a dependable flow. Several semiartesian areas are present in the Hofuf and Qatif oases along the Hasa coast, and on Bahrein Island. In some oases, diesel pumps draw on water hundreds of feet below the surface, but such supplies may have required millenniums to accumulate and should not be overtapped.

In every oasis, temperatures are so high that evaporation is excessive and crops may require 4 to 5 acre-feet of irrigation water. This suggests that losses from reservoirs may be so large as to make them impractical, even in the valleys of the Hejaz where water runs to waste.

Where adequate water is available, rice is a preferred crop. In drier areas, as in Yemen, millet is widespread.

Dates are the chief crop in the oases and supply the principal food for many townsmen and nomads. Date palms occupy nine-tenths of the irrigated area, and a small grove of trees may provide the chief income of a family. Fortunately palms require little moisture and are tolerant of brackish water. The Hasa oasis con-

tains 2 million date trees, and the harvest weighs 125 million pounds.

Several towns call for attention. On the west coast the main seaport is Jidda, 700 miles south of Suez. Parts of the city are old, with narrow fly-infested lanes and carved purdah balcony screens; other sections have wide streets with dozens of modern buildings, some nine stories in height. Jidda has come to be the home of a new prosperous middle class, made up of government employees, contractors, dealers in the import-and-export trade, and skilled mechanics.

The two leading cities in the western interior are Mecca and Medina, with elevations of 2,000 and 2,100 feet, respectively, both sacred to Islam as the birth and burial places of Mohammed. The central attraction in Mecca is the nearly cubical structure of the Kaba, draped in black cloth and containing in one corner the venerable "Black Stone," possibly a meteorite, which was once a pagan idol. The city is closed to non-Muslims but is the spiritual capital for the 200 million followers of Mohammed. As many as 250,000 pilgrims visit the city during the annual hadj, or pilgrimage.

The capital of Saudi Arabia is at Riyadh, near the center of the peninsula. What was once a sleepy, mud-walled town has become a dramatic city with splendid government office buildings and a university. The city lies along the wadi Hanifah, which has occasional runoff and formerly had near-surface saturated gravels, although these have been nearly pumped dry for urban needs.

On the east coast three neighboring cities form a triangle: the oil-company settlement at

Bahrein Data [1]

Area	231 square miles
Population	143,135 (1959 census)
Manama (capital)	61,837
Crude oil	2,256,000 metric tons (1960)

[1] *Britannica Book of the Year*, 1962.

Kuwait Data [1]

Area	6,000 square miles
Population	206,473 (1957 census)
Kuwait (capital)	104,551
Crude oil	81,744,000 metric tons (1960)

[1] *Britannica Book of the Year*, 1962.

The new prosperity based on oil royalties has created modern cities, semiwestern oases quite out of tune with traditional Bedouin life. This is Dammam, capital of the Eastern Province of Saudi Arabia. (*Courtesy Arabian American Oil Company*)

Dhahran, which is a direct copy of a prosperous American residential area; the administrative and port city of Dammam; and the commercial center at Khobar. All are new and booming.

Two other cities lie along the Persian Gulf:

Qatar Data [1]

Area	8,500 square miles
Population	45,000 (1960 est.)
Doha (capital)	30,000

[1] *Britannica Book of the Year*, 1962.

the oil-rich town of Kuwait and the city of Manama on Bahrein Island. Both are old trading and pearling ports; both now share in the prosperity from oil.

Aden is the one remaining British city in Swasia. So long as ships pass through the Suez Canal, the free port of Aden will retain its importance as the southern gateway to the Red Sea. Whereas vessels formerly stopped for bunker coal, they now take on bunker fuel oil. Each year 5,000 ships and 500,000 passengers pause for a few hours at Aden.

While race, language, and isolation unify Arabia, one of the greatest cohesive factors is Islam. Mohammed was born in Mecca about

A.D. 570, and his flight to Medina in 622 marks the beginning of the year 1 in the Muslim calendar. Many of his teachings in the Koran are based on Jewish and Christian traditions, and his initial appeal was to them as God's latest prophet.

DESERT LANDSCAPES

The aridity of the Arabian Peninsula is suggested by the fact that scarcely a single stream reaches the surrounding seas throughout the year. A few wadis carry water after the rains, at times with torrential flow, but much of this soaks into the ground, is lost by evaporation, or is diverted for irrigation. Even in the more humid highlands there are few streams which flow the year round.

This hydrographic concept of a desert reflects the limited amount of precipitation, its seasonal character, and the very high rate of potential evapotranspiration, which in turn reflects intense solar energy. In the south, evapotranspiration reaches 72 inches a year. No section is completely rainless, but the amount may be only 2 or 3 inches, and this is merely a statistical average based on scattered showers followed by several years without a drop.

Such rain as falls either comes from the southern edge of cyclonic storms which migrate across areas farther north during the winter or is due to local convectional showers. Occasional monsoon winds bring a bit of summer moisture to the southern highlands, but in general the circulation is from the north.

Enveloped in aridity, the Arabian landscape reflects the unique geological processes which have formed it and the scanty cover of vegetation on the surface. Large areas are covered by shifting sand dunes; when rain falls it quickly sinks into the ground and leaves no trace of erosion. Other areas, underlain by lava, may be so porous that there is no surface erosion.

Even where sand or lava are absent, months or years may elapse between times of effective runoff. Nevertheless, most of Arabia bears the mark of erosion and deposition by running water, often with vertical walled wadis, poorly graded slopes, broad alluvial fans, and wastefilled depressions. Saline playas occupy the centers of enclosed basins, fed by transitory streams which usually wither before reaching their terminal basin.

At least 325,000 square miles of Saudi Arabia are covered by active sand dunes. In a few places these are isolated crescentic or barchan types; elsewhere there are long *uruq* dunes or the remarkable isolated sand mountains; more commonly there is a complex sea of sand without individual dune forms.

In the north the largest sand area is the Great Nafud, 300 miles from west to east and 150 miles from north to south. From this area streamers of sand extend in an arc 700 miles to the south. The easternmost of these linear dune areas is the Dahna. Another sand complex southwest of Riyadh is almost as large as the Great Nafud.

By far the largest of the dune areas is the Rub' al Khali, covering much of the area between the highlands of Yemen and Oman. The area amounts to 229,000 square miles, including its northward extension in the Jafura. The eastern section is dominated by isolated sand mountains or pyramid dunes, steep on all sides and up to 700 feet in height. In the west are the equally remarkable uruq linear dunes, some of which extend some 100 miles in an unbroken line.

The total volume of this loose sand in the Rub' al Khali may amount to 4,000 cubic miles, and one may well ask where it came from. Merely to say that Arabia has had sand for at least a geologic period does not solve the question of its origin. Some sand has been derived from the weathering of underlying formations; much represents stream load from transitory wadis which have never been able to carry their load to the sea; a good deal has been washed in from distant highlands in the east and south; and some of the sand may date back to glacial times, when so much water was locked up in continental ice sheets that sea level was low-

Falconry is a favorite sport of Arab sheiks. (*Courtesy Arabian American Oil Company*)

ered, thus exposing unconsolidated materials on the floor of the Persian Gulf.

Although aridity dominates, a number of places support vegetation which is adequate for grazing. These include areas with sufficient elevation to receive extra rain, areas where ground water is high enough to make wells feasible, and locations where flowing springs change the brown of the desert to the green of an oasis.

Pastoral activities represent the principal use of the land, and there are few areas apart from the sandy deserts and lava fields where animals do not graze from time to time. Only rarely is there a continuous carpet of grasses, never tall enough to cut as hay; more commonly, animals find widely scattered tufts of vegetation which provide a passable livelihood. Camels, sheep, and goats serve as converters of this desert growth into food and products useful to man. Eastern Saudi Arabia contains several dozen

natural flowing wells, artesian in character, which supply a copious flow for the country's largest gardens and palm groves. The gardens around Hofuf cover 30,000 acres, making it one of the world's largest natural oases. Scattered through the interior are hundreds of cultivated areas, mere pinpoints on most maps. In total, no more than 1 per cent of the desert has any agricultural use.

The statement that much of Arabia is lifeless must be considered relative. Even desolate areas of shifting dunes have scattered vegetation, and what appear to be barren plains suddenly take on a touch of green after the rains. Desert plants represent a specialized adjustment to aridity, with xerophytic forms which can remain dormant for years if need be. Once in a decade or so, many surfaces are carpeted with flowers.

From the earliest times, clouds of locusts

have swept across Arabia, devouring all vege- tation as they advance. Swarms of these grass- hoppers appear to originate in Africa, cross the Red Sea, advance through Arabia, and finally reach Iraq. International anti-locust campaigns have slightly reduced the damage.

HIGHLAND LANDSCAPES

The desert character of Arabian climate is modified in a few places by altitude, which brings somewhat cooler conditions and also slightly more rainfall. Whereas the lowlands receive less than 5 inches a year, the highlands may have 10 to 20 inches, and even 30 inches on the highest slopes. Unlike the lowlands where rainfall is a winter phenomenon, the southern highlands re- ceive a little summer rain from the monsoon. Though the highest areas occasionally experi- ence frost, they rarely have snow.

Four highland oases are formed where ele- vations exceed a mile: the Hejaz escarpment facing the Red Sea and its southern continu- ation in the Asir, in both of which maximum elevations exceed 8,000 feet; the Yemen high- lands, where the highest peak is 12,336 feet; and the Masqat highlands in the southeast which also rise above 9,000 feet. The maximum elevations in interior Arabia do not exceed 3,000 feet.

In total area these oases may measure 75,000 square miles. Taken together they account for half of the population of the peninsula. Their span of recorded history goes back to at least 1000 B.C.

Irrigation is generally impractical, but rain- fed agriculture is practiced wherever conditions permit. In Yemen this has involved extensive terracing, often on very steep slopes. The nar- row strips of cultivated land are leveled to hold the rain before it runs off rather than for irri- gation. Many mountain slopes have hundreds of terraces, one above the other, each labori- ously faced with stone to check erosion. In the perfection of this terracing the Yemenese rank with the Ifugao in Luzon and the Chinese of Szechwan.

The form of millet known as durra is the chief highland crop, along with wheat, barley, corn, and a wide variety of fruit. In most cases, an elevation of 8,000 feet represents the upper limit of cultivation. Date palms and cotton are found below 2,500 feet. One of the major cash crops in Yemen and Asir is coffee, grown under shade trees on the more humid slopes between 4,500 and 7,000 feet. The latter is probably the highest elevation for coffee anywhere in the world.

Agricultural statistics are completely lack- ing, but field observations in Yemen suggest that there may be an acre of cropland per per- son, and a total of some 6,000 square miles under cultivation.

Most of the highland cultivation and popula- tion lies in Yemen and Asir, since neither the Hejaz nor Masqat has adequate areas at suffi- cient elevation. Unlike other parts of Swasia, the highlands have only a limited amount of seasonal nomadism or transhumance.

Masqat Data [1]

Area	82,000 square miles
Population	560,000 (1960 est.)
Masqat (capital)	5,500

[1] *Britannica Book of the Year*, 1962.

Yemen Data [1]

Area	75,290 square miles
Population	5,000,000 (1960 est.)
Sana (capital)	60,000
Hodeida	30,000
Taiz	12,000
Primary and secondary pupils	2,155
Coffee	5,700 metric tons (1959)

[1] *Britannica Book of the Year*, 1962.

Oil wells around the Persian Gulf are phenomenally productive. This derrick is in the Dukhan field in Qatar. (*Courtesy Iraq Petroleum Company*)

ARABIAN REGIONS

If much of Arabia appears monotonous, it is because the regional differences are on a broad scale. There is variety, but it is of macro- rather than of micro-proportions. The interior has no mountains to create differences in topography or climate; one sand area is much like another. Most oases are too small to stand out, and the character of nomadism is essentially uniform throughout.

A cross section from west to east, say from Jidda to Dhahran, would begin with the narrow coastal plain along the Red Sea, very arid and uninhabitable except where wadis come out from the bordering highlands. This is the Tihama alluvial coast. Next to the plain is the fault escarpment known as the Hejaz. The elevation rises to a mile, and the resulting slightly higher rainfall has led to deep dissection. Since the western side of the Hejaz is a fault zone rather than a single dislocation, the mountain zone is some tens of miles in width. Much of the Hejaz is underlain by ancient crystalline rocks and young lava flows, both of which give their stamp to the surface features.

From the Hejaz watershed, the eastern two-thirds of Arabia slopes gently to the Persian Gulf. The surface is underlain by sedimentary rocks which have a regional dip slightly greater than that of the surface. As a result, here and there the eastward slope is interrupted by the outcrop of sedimentary formations which create low west-facing cuestas or escarpments a few hundred feet high. Along the line of this east–west traverse there are a half dozen such outcrops, of which the most prominent is the Tuwaiq escarpment. Some of these east-dipping sediments are aquifers whose outcrops form recharge areas, supplying artesian wells or natural springs farther east and down the dip. The city of Riyadh lies on the back slope of the Tuwaiq escarpment.

The great sand areas of Arabia lie either north or south of this cross section, but in places along this traverse are dune belts 10 miles or more in width, the largest of which forms a part of the Dahna.

Most of the eastern peninsula lies near sea level, and has a rolling surface, veneered here and there with loose sand, and interrupted by saline playas known as *sabkhas*. The area carries the regional name of Hasa. Here are the spring-fed oases of Qatif and Hofuf, and the broad structural domes which account for the oilfields around Dhahran.

This west-to-east cross section presents the main structural features of the peninsula.

In regional terms, eight major geographic areas stand out. The first is the Hejaz, a highland region parallel to the Red Sea, which ex-

The southern Arabian highlands hold half of the population of the peninsula and have an ancient and distinctive civilization. These elaborate Yemenese homes are in Sana. (*Courtesy Bruce Conde*)

tends from near the Gulf of Aqaba, where it is locally known by its Biblical name of Midian, southward to beyond Mecca. The area extends some 700 miles from north to south and reaches inland for 100 to 200 miles. The word Hejaz means "barrier," and refers to the isolating effect on the interior.

Volcanic tracts, known as *harra,* form either tablelands or rough and nearly impassable areas of lava flows; elsewhere ancient igneous and metamorphic rocks have been dissected into desolate landscapes. Slopes tend to be barren except at elevations above a mile. Numerous summits exceed 8,000 feet. Small areas of cultivation follow a number of the valleys, fed by springs or from wells which tap wadi gravels. Palm trees are found at the lower elevations; millet represents the principal upland crop.

Along the Red Sea is the Tihama coastal plain, very hot, very dusty, very dry, yet at times with insufferable humidity. The result is one of the worst climates in the world.

The Asir and Yemen highlands, which constitute Arabia's second major geographic area, form the southern and higher continuation of the Hejaz, with elevations of 2 miles and more. The northern half of the region lies in Saudi Arabia, while the south (and at one time both sections) makes up the country of Yemen. In contrast to the relatively narrow mountains to the north, the Asir-Yemen highlands extend inland for more than 100 miles. The Tihama coastal plain continues to the southern end of the Red Sea.

The higher elevations bring cooler temperatures and 20 to 30 inches of rain, so that millet may be raised with little or no irrigation. This is one of the traditional homes of coffee, especially on the upper slopes behind the ancient port of Mocha.

Yemen has long been isolated, for roads are few and outsiders have not been welcomed. The country's history goes back for several thousand years. In the absence of a census, the population is estimated as 5,000,000.

Southern Arabia forms a third highland area, for the most part a rolling upland, less than a mile in elevation, which slopes gently northward from a faulted escarpment facing the Arabian Sea. Here and there the plateau is cut by vertical walled canyons which drain southward although they rarely carry water. The chief of these is the Hadhramaut, famous for its tall modernistic houses and spring-fed gardens. By extension, the term Hadhramaut may be used for the entire area. The coast from Aden eastward is as desolate as the Tihama, and as harborless. In political terms, this is the area of the various Aden Protectorates, whose total area of 112,000 square miles is credited with approximately 650,000 people.

Masqat makes up the fourth of the Arabian geographic regions, much of it also a highland but drier than Yemen. On the east is the Batina coast, with date palms, while in the southwest is the coastal area of Dhufar, once famous for its resins such as frankincense and myrrh. In the center, arid mountains rise to 9,900 feet, but there is insufficient rain to permit unirrigated crops. The term Oman is applied to the interior, including a rolling desert plain. While presumably under the sultan of Masqat, it is ruled by a semi-independent imam.

The fifth region is the Rub' al Khali, the most empty part of Arabia, seldom penetrated by Bedouins and uncrossed by outsiders until the early twentieth century. The possibility of oil has led to extensive geological exploration but only at great expense. Should oil be found, its development would pose major problems of logistics. There are no towns, and very few sources of water.

The Syrian Desert, the sixth region, occupies the eastern half of Syria, the western part of Iraq, much of Jordan, the Negeb of southern Israel, and the northern part of Saudi Arabia. For the most part it has a gravel surface which forms a desert pavement, known to the Arabs as a *hamad*. Here and there are widespread lava flows; dunes are uncommon. No single name is applicable to the Saudi portion, but it may be termed the "tapline plain," so named from the Trans-Arabian pipeline which crosses it.

The average rainfall is under 5 inches, and since there are no rivers, agriculture is impossible apart from the few areas with springs or where wadi gravels have "upside-down streams." Local basins such as the wadi Sirhan contain central playas which yield a little salt. From time to time and from place to place a sparse cover of short grass or desert brush appears; this provides nourishment for camels. Some areas with fair vegetation may be unusable since they are too far from any source of water for grazing animals.

The area along the tapline plain formerly had no indigenous population, but the mobility of the nomad is shown by the number of tribesmen who arrived when wells were dug. The concession provided that the Trans-Arabian Pipe Line Company should supply water from its deep wells to any passing Arab and his flocks. In its second summer one of the pump stations was called on to furnish water for 12,000 Bedouins, 20,000 camels, and 40,000 sheep. Some tribes came from as far as 500 miles.

The seventh region lies in the eastern margin of Arabia, which is flat and much more monotonous than the west. The best regional name is Hasa. The absence of interior highlands means that there is no opportunity for higher rainfall or wadi gravels which might contain underground water. Artesian springs fortunately provide copious supplies in a few places, each the center of a date-palm oasis and a few rice fields. Until oil was developed most of the area was nearly empty.

The Persian Gulf carries much less shipping than the Red Sea, but there has long been a considerable dhow traffic and pearl trade, as at Bahrein and Kuwait. With the development of petroleum, the economy of the Hasa area has changed from misery to prosperity.

The last of the eight geographic regions is

much the largest. Within the Nejd or central interior are large dune areas such as the Nafud in the north or the Dahna sand streamers in the east, and crescentic escarpments dissected into wadi country toward the west. This is the heart of classic Arabia Deserta, desolate except for a few oases, but the home of a virile people.

Several thousand acres of cropland lie near Riyadh, watered either by wells, now nearly drained dry, or from large springs. The principal crops are dates, alfalfa, wheat, millet, and vegetables.

References on Arabia

See also general references on Southwest Asia, Chapter 33.

Crary, Douglas D.: "Recent Agricultural Developments in Saudi Arabia," *Geog. Rev.,* XLI (1951), 366–400.

Cressey, George B.: "Land Use in Yemen," *Annals, Assn. Amer. Geogs.,* XLVII (1958), 257–258.

*Dickson, H. R. P.: *The Arab of the Desert,* London: Allen & Unwin (1949).

Dickson, H. R. P.: *Kuwait and Her Neighbors,* London: Allen & Unwin (1956).

Fayein, Claudie: *A French Doctor in the Yemen,* London: Hale (1957).

Hay, Rupert: "The Persian Gulf States and Their Boundary Problems," *Geog. Rev.,* CXX (1954), 433–445.

Hay, Rupert: *The Persian Gulf States,* Washington: Middle East Institute (1959).

Johnstone, T. M., and J. C. Wilkinson: "Some Geographical Aspects of Qatar," *Geog. Jour.,* CXXVI (1960), 442–450.

Lipsky, George A., and others: *Saudi Arabia,* New Haven, Conn.: Human Relations Area Files (1959).

Melamid, Alexander: "Political Geography of Trucial Oman and Qatar," *Geog. Rev.,* XLIII (1953), 194–206.

Morris, James: *Sultan in Oman,* London: Faber (1957).

Pike, Ruthven W.: "Land and Peoples of the Hadhramaut, Aden Protectorate," *Geog. Rev.,* XXX (1940), 627–648.

*Sanger, Richard H.: *The Arabian Peninsula,* Ithaca, N.Y.: Cornell University Press (1954).

Scott, Hugh: *In the High Yemen,* London: John Murray (1947).

Thesiger, Wilfred: "A New Journey in Southern Arabia," *Geog. Jour.,* CVIII (1946), 129–145.

Thesiger, Wilfred: "Across the Empty Quarter," *Geog. Jour.,* CXI (1948), 1–21.

Thesiger, Wilfred: "A Further Journey across the Empty Quarter," *Geog. Jour.,* CXIII (1949), 20–46.

Thesiger, Wilfred: "Desert Borderlands of Oman," *Geog. Jour.,* CXVI (1950), 137–171.

*Thesiger, Wilfred: *Arabian Sands,* New York: Dutton (1959).

Thomas, Bertram: "A Camel Journey across the Rub' Al Khali," *Geog. Jour.,* LXXVIII (1931), 1–57.

Thomas, Bertram: *Arabia Felix: Across the "Empty Quarter" of Arabia,* New York: Scribner's (1932).

Twitchell, K. S.: "Water Resources of Saudi Arabia," *Geog. Rev.,* XXXIV (1944), 365–386.

*Twitchell, K. S.: *Saudi Arabia,* 3d ed., Princeton, N.J.: Princeton University Press (1958).

Vesey-Fitzgerald, Desmond: "From Hasa to Oman by Car," *Geog. Rev.,* XLI (1951), 544–560.

38　The Levant States

Crossroads Location / The Physical Setting / Lebanon / Syria /
Jordan / Israel / References on the Levant States

CROSSROADS LOCATION

Few parts of Asia have witnessed more history than the lands east of the Mediterranean. Recorded settlement stretches far back in time, and many tides of conquest have swept across the area. Along the narrow corridors, coastal and interior, which link Egypt with Mesopotamia or Turkey have moved Abraham, Ramses II, Darius I, Alexander, and Napoleon.

The term Levant includes the Republic of Syria, Lebanon (or the Lebanese Republic), the kingdom of Jordan, and the state of Israel. The area is small but the historic importance is great. Long-forgotten countries have arisen in

the Levant, many of them short-lived, some with memories which persist, as they do still in Biblical Palestine. Other groups were the Phoenicians, the Amorites, and the Aramaeans. Scores of outside nations have ruled here. Even the Crusaders' kingdoms lasted for two centuries. The last of the conquerors were Great Britain and France.

One cannot appreciate the second half of the twentieth century without an understanding of what has gone before. Arab hopes for freedom at the end of the First World War were met by a series of mandates, and after these ended the foreign powers still claimed various special privileges. Just as the several countries were

543

Only a few hundred of the magnificent cedars of Lebanon remain, many of them several thousand years old. (*Courtesy United States Operations Mission in Lebanon*)

Eastern Asia, and Beirut is one of the world's major airports.

Not the least of the Levant's assets is the fact that it is a focal point for the world's three great monotheistic religions. Christians recognize their heritage in Judaism but too often overlook the fact that Islam is the product of both. In his earlier years, Mohammed faced Jerusalem when he prayed, rather than Mecca. Half the world stands in cultural debt to the Levant. Each of these three faiths finds political expression here. Israel is Jewish; Lebanon always has a Christian president; Syria and Jordan are definitely Muslim states.

THE PHYSICAL SETTING

The Levant is the most maritime of the several areas of Southwest Asia; at the same time it is among the most mountainous. For 300 miles from north to south the area looks west to the blue Mediterranean, while on the east it faces the brown desert. In between lie 100 miles made up of two parallel mountain systems and an intervening lowland.

The eastern Mediterranean shore has a succession of bold headlands and broad half-moon bays. Nowhere is there a good natural harbor, and all ports depend on a sheltering breakwater. The Mediterranean seldom experiences storms, and the coastal people have long been sea-oriented.

The coastal plain is discontinuous, seldom extending for more than a few miles along the shore until interrupted by cliffs, and rarely reaching more than 10 miles inland. This coastal avenue has provided a route for caravans since the earliest days.

Mountains parallel the shore from Turkey to Sinai, in some places so near that one may look up through palm trees to snow-crowned peaks. This is an area of limestones and other

securing full nationalism, outside penetration reappeared in the form of political Zionism. Arab resentment of Israel is not related merely to territorial encroachment or to the refugee problem, although these are serious; it exists partly because Israel is regarded as another form of European imperialism.

Few of the area's historic events have been related to local resources or productivity, for the countries themselves have little to offer. The Levant takes in the western end of the Fertile Crescent, which once supplied grain to Rome, but the area as a whole produced little for export until the introduction of modern machine agriculture. The cedars of Lebanon were shipped to Egypt, and the purple dye derived from mollusk shells was highly valued, but there were few other treasures.

Instead, the Levant has always been prized as a transit zone; its ports provide gateways to the interior, and the coastal plain forms a corridor from north to south. Iraq and Iran, both nearly landlocked, find in the Levant a direct avenue to the Mediterranean and Europe. Here is one of the major crossroad locations in Southwest Asia. In the air age this has become the principal avenue from Europe to India and

sediments folded into linear ranges. In Syria the coastal mountains are the mile-high Amanus and Jebel Ansariya. Farther south is the 10,000-foot Lebanon Range; this then merges into the hills of Galilee, below 2,000 feet, which join the hills of Judea around Jerusalem. The coastal mountains are not continuous. There are several gaps such as the Syrian Gate opposite Aleppo and the Plain of Esdraelon in Israel. Both openings permit moisture-bearing winds to reach the interior.

To the east of this mountain series is a more or less continuous lowland, in part a syncline, in part a down-faulted trench or graben; in most places it is from 10 to 20 miles wide. Across Syria the lowland is known as El Ghab and is occupied by the north-flowing Orontes River.

In Lebanon the valley, here known as the Bekaa, is drained by the south-flowing Litani. Across Israel and Jordan flows the Jordan River, and the depression continues to the Red Sea through the Wadi el 'Araba. The first two streams break through to the Mediterranean; the Jordan ends in the Dead Sea.

A second line of mountains lies inland, somewhat lower than those along the coast. In Syria these are the Kurd Dagh and the Jebel Zawiyeh, which are matched farther south by the Anti-Lebanon with Mount Hermon and the uplands of Moab in Jordan.

Still farther east and parallel to the mountain alignment, is a steppe zone with several oases where alluvial fans have been built at the eastern base of the ranges. The Levant thus has

Elaborate terracing has been necessary to hold the remaining hillside soil in the western Levant. Fruits and olives are widely raised, as in this view from Lebanon. (*Courtesy United States Operations Mission in Lebanon*)

five parallel topographic forms: the coastal plain, a line of mountains, a structural valley, another mountain chain, and an interior upland. In most areas the mountain chains are from 10 to 40 miles wide.

The highlands, deeply dissected and divided into plateaulike compartments, have provided a haven of refuge for many persecuted people. When the Philistines occupied the lowlands, the Hebrews held the Judean hills. In present-day Lebanon the uplands are the home of the fanatical Druses and of a half dozen Christian groups, both Arab and non-Arab, while Muslim Arabs occupy the coast.

Location and topography combine to give most of the Levant abundant rainfall. Coastal lowlands receive 25 to 35 inches; windward mountain slopes may have twice this figure with much of the precipitation falling as snow, while rain-shadow lowlands receive 10 to 20 inches. All of this comes in winter; the weather is dry and hot from May through October.

In climate and latitude the Levant finds some analogy with California between San Francisco and San Diego, and inland to Nevada. While all Southwest Asia has a continental version of Mediterranean-style climate with winter precipitation, it is best developed in the Levant.

Coastal Beirut has recorded all-time minimum and maximum temperatures of 30°F and 107°F; upland Jerusalem has had 26°F and 107°F; and interior Damascus has an extreme range from 21°F to 113°F. The average rainfall for the three cities amounts to 35, 21, and 9 inches, respectively.

The Litani, Orontes, and Jordan are each small rivers, fed by winter runoff or summer melting snow, and from springs which derive their water from storage in cavernous limestones. Each river crosses international boundaries, with resulting political problems.

The Jordan, with its tributaries, is only 110 miles long, but its basin varies in elevation from 9,232 feet on Mount Hermon to 1,286 below sea level at the Dead Sea. The Jordan flows through a double valley. The upper floor, from 2 to 14 miles wide and bounded by fault lines,

is the Ghor, now much dissected. Within it is the inner valley, or Zor through which the river flows in intricate meanders. Elaborate development schemes for utilizing the river have been proposed by both Jordan and Israel, but only limited amounts of water are available. Evaporation rates are high. Thus Lake Tiberius, erroneously called the Sea of Galilee, loses 5 feet a year, and over the Dead Sea, evaporation rates may reach ½ inch a day in summer.

The Dead Sea is remarkable: it covers 370 square miles and has a maximum depth of 1,310 feet, so that its floor is ½ mile below sea level. The salinity is 24 per cent, seven times that of the ocean; much of it is made up of magnesium and sodium chlorides along with potash and bromine. The last two are extracted in evaporation works at either end of the sea. The reserves form a resource of considerable potential, for the amounts total 2 billion and 900 million tons of potash and bromine respectively.

Few other minerals are produced in the Levant. Large tonnages of phosphate are mined in Jordan and Israel. Syria, Jordan, and Israel each have modest amounts of oil, but investigation gives no indication of large reserves. Although Damascus steel was famous in antiquity, there is no current iron production. Copper is present in Israel, but neither this nor any other resource holds out much industrial promise in that country. Salt is obtained from interior playas and by evaporation of sea water.

Coal is lacking, but the various rivers yield modest amounts of hydroelectricity. Fortunately the Arab states may draw oil from the pipelines which cross their territory.

LEBANON

Lebanon serves as a gateway, one of the principal avenues to Arab Asia. Airlines and truck routes fan out from Beirut. In commerce, the country is an entrepôt and an entrepreneur. Its warehouses stock merchandise and spare parts from all Europe and the Americas. Lebanese banks are a depository for some of the new wealth pouring out from the Persian Gulf, and these funds are financing hundreds of new industries or tall apartment buildings. The country's currency is sound.

Lebanon has the coolest mountains in the Arab world; skiing is possible well into the spring. When summer brings temperatures above 110°F to Iraq, Arabia, and Egypt, Lebanese mountain resorts attract tens of thousands of vacationers. Winter months offer Western-style entertainment and luxury not readily available in stricter Muslim lands.

By analogy these assets find some parallel in the Netherlands and in Switzerland. The former is a gateway to Europe; the latter is banker and resort center for much of the world. Lebanon's financial function is of regional importance only, and its mountains have none of the scenic qualities of the Alps, but the country likes to think of itself as the Switzerland of Swasia.

The comparison with the Netherlands is less obvious, but both countries act as a gateway between sea and land. Their hinterlands are quite different, for traffic up the Rhine to Germany has little similarity to overland traffic inland from Beirut to Syria and Iraq. Both countries have a shortage of cropland; in one it has been reclaimed from the sea; in the other it has been obtained from painstaking terracing.

In area and in population Lebanon is one of the smallest of the states in Swasia; in general prosperity it ranks near the top. There is poverty, but the average person lives well, literacy is high, and there are three universities.

No other country presents so much cultural variation. While the bulk of the people are Arab in nationality, only half are Muslims, and these are divided between the orthodox Sunni, the Persian-style Shia, and the followers of a fanatical variation, known as the Druses. Christian Arabs include a wide spectrum of Eastern and Roman Catholicism, and of Protestant and Eastern Orthodox groups. In addition to Arab Christians there are refugee members of Armenian, Assyrian, and Chaldean churches.

Many of these minority groups have their separate political status, with traditional areas of residence, whether in isolated mountain plateaus or in recognized quarters of Beirut. In general, Christian monasteries, convents, and churches are perched on the hilltops; mosques and minarets are more numerous on the plain.

Hundreds of thousands of Lebanese have gone abroad, among them many who have traveled to the United States and Brazil and have sent back both money and ideas. Planes fly directly to both South and North America.

Beirut dominates the country, for its population of a half million amounts to a quarter of the national total. Its airport and seaport are the busiest in Southwest Asia; the latter handles

Lebanon Data [1]

Area	4,015 square miles
Population	1,783,000 (1960 est.)
Beirut (capital)	400,000
Tripoli	115,000
Primary and secondary pupils	279,194 (1959)
University (3) students	5,184 (1959)
Wheat	48,000 metric tons (1960)
Citrus fruits	155,000 "
Apples	50,000 "
Cement	852,300 "
Electricity	297,000,000 kilowatthours (1957)

[1] *Britannica Book of the Year,* 1962.

Beirut is a crowded city of apartment houses, with the blue, blue Mediterranean on one side and the snow-covered Lebanon Mountains on the other. The campus of the American University of Beirut appears in the foreground. (*Courtesy United States Operations Mission in Lebanon*)

more tonnage than the port of Istanbul—as much as 3,000 ships and 2 million tons of imports a year. Nearby at Sidon and Tripoli are the terminals of the pipelines which bring oil from Saudi Arabia and Iraq, respectively. Three dozen airlines, operating out of Beirut, reach every continent.

The city of Beirut has a west-coast location and a climate somewhat similar to that of Los Angeles. Both are boom towns, but whereas the California city is one of separate homes, its Lebanese counterpart has developed apartment houses. Sound currency enables Beirut merchants to stock goods from all the world. Few cities in all Asia are more Westernized.

SYRIA

Syria, over the centuries, has varied in its extent. Until 1920 it included Lebanon, and during Ottoman days it took in what is now Jordan. Greater Syria at times has comprised much of Iraq, Palestine, as well as northern Arabia.

The history of the country includes early contacts with Egypt and Babylon; the name may even come from ancient Assyria. The area was conquered by Alexander in 332 B.C. and later became a Roman province. One of the brief but brilliant periods was when Palmyra, under Queen Zenobia, ruled an area from the

Nile to the Persian Gulf. Under the Ommiad caliphs, Damascus was the center of the Arab empire. The country fell to the Ottoman Turks in 1516, and became a French mandate in 1918. The Republic of Syria was established in 1946, and in 1958 it joined briefly with Egypt to form the United Arab Republic.

While Syria has a seacoast, its port of Latakia is of limited importance. At one time Syria used the port of Iskenderun, the former Alexandretta, but this is now part of Turkey. Instead, the country looks eastward toward the desert.

The major economic development of recent decades has been the increase of mechanized agriculture in the Fertile Crescent, notably wheat and cotton for export. Elsewhere irrigation is important. Water is now drawn from the Euphrates or the Orontes Rivers to irrigate a million acres; ambitious projects look forward to doubling this area.

Among the earliest inhabitants were the Amorites, traces of whose language still persist. To a remarkable degree these sedentary people were able to absorb wave after wave of nomadic invaders who shed their wandering customs and became farmers. Among the latest arrivals were 100,000 Armenian refugees from Turkey. Today, Bedouins number but 5 per cent of the population; farm and village people account for 60 per cent; and the urban population numbers 35 per cent.

Two rival cities dominate Syrian life, Damascus in the south and Aleppo in the north, each with a population of nearly a half million. Both are old, but parts of each are remarkably Westernized.

Within a century following the death of Mohammed, Damascus became the capital of an Arab empire larger than that of Rome at its zenith, one which extended from the Bay of Biscay to the borders of China. Long before that Damascus had been a great center of trade.

Damascus lies within a remarkable oasis, the Ghuta, which owes its life to the spring-fed Baroda River as it flows eastward from the Anti-Lebanon Mountains. The water of the Baroda is divided among seven famous canals, and these in turn supply a complex network which irrigates 150 square miles on the alluvial fan. Damascus has been described as a "great and splendid Arab city set in a girdle of fruit trees and filled with the murmur of running water."

Aleppo, like Damascus, dates back to at least the second millennium B.C. Whereas Damascus lies in the rain shadow of the mountains and receives but 9 inches of rain, Aleppo is opposite the Syrian Saddle, so that moisture-bearing winds bring 16 inches. Damascus looks

Syria Data [1]

Area	71,227 square miles
Population	4,821,929 (1960 census)
Damascus (capital)	232,960
Aleppo	231,557
Primary and secondary pupils	487,318 (1959)
University of Damascus students	8,695 (1959)
Wheat	553,000 metric tons (1960)
Barley	157,000 "
Cottonseed	177,000 "
Cotton, fiber	105,000 "
Cement	440,400 "
Electricity (incomplete)	220,800,000 kilowatthours (1960)

[1] *Britannica Book of the Year,* 1962.

eastward to the desert, while Aleppo faces the Fertile Crescent and secures its water supply through a pipeline from the Euphrates.

Through Aleppo passed one of the great caravan routes of antiquity, the shortest avenue from the Mediterranean to Mesopotamia. The city is now Syria's chief industrial center, with textile mills, food-processing plants, flour mills, and cement plants.

Syria has the assets for a good future. It has additional cropland, if irrigated, and phosphate rock is available for fertilizer. Petroleum reserves appear modest but may be adequate for local needs. Salt is the only mineral in significant production.

JORDAN

The kingdom of Jordan is a new creation, established by Great Britain with arbitrary boundaries following the First World War. As originally defined, it lay entirely east of the river and was known as Transjordan, with a population of some 375,000, in part Bedouin. With the partition of Palestine, Jordan took over west-bank areas with a population of 460,000, largely prosperous farmers and townspeople. To these were added nearly 500,000 refugees from Israeli-occupied Palestine. This combination has given the present state a diverse cultural situation, and has raised serious questions of economic viability.

Jordan's only contact with the sea is through the off-center port of 'Aqaba on the Red Sea. Most trade moves through Beirut, but its passage involves shipment across Syria. Access to Haifa, the traditional port, was closed following the partition.

The country is dry, stony, and largely unattractive for agriculture. Long-continued careless use, including overgrazing, has led to serious soil erosion. Several areas in the hot Jordan valley specialize in early vegetables. Irrigation projects involve the diversion of water from the Jordan and its tributary, the Yarmuk, into a canal system along the east bank.

In addition to agriculture, Jordan derives an income from the export of its rich phosphate deposits and from potash and bromine extracted from the Dead Sea.

The two cities of importance are Amman, the capital, and the old city of Jerusalem.

Whereas hilltop Jerusalem receives 21 inches of rain a year, Amman in its rain shadow has but 11 inches; both have about the same temperature regime.

Jerusalem is "a city which cannot be hid," for it occupies a ridge top a half mile above sea level at a point where trade routes cross. That the city was occupied long before Abraham is proved by Egyptian records of 2000 B.C., which refer to "Urusalem, city of peace." Much Jewish, Christian, and Muslim history centers here. The stone beneath the Dome of the Rock is supposed to mark the spot where Abraham prepared to sacrifice Isaac, where Christ ascended, and where Mohammed paused on his way to heaven. Following the Arab-Israeli war of 1948, the city was tragically divided, with the old city, containing all the

Jordan Data [1]		
	Area	37,297 square miles
	Population	1,724,868 (1960 est.)
	Amman (capital)	133,201 (1959 est.)
	Jerusalem	57,450
	Primary and secondary pupils	332,035 (1959)
	Wheat	103,500 metric tons (1959)
[1] *Britannica Book of the Year,* 1962.	Phosphate rock	337,624 "

The old walled city of Jerusalem, currently in Jordan, has many covered bazaars, known as suqs, where one may experience the sights and smells of the ancient East. This is David Street. (*Ewing Galloway*)

shrines, on the Jordanian side and the new city in Israeli hands.

In Greek and Roman days this was the area of the Decapolis, or ten cities, formed after Pompey's campaign of 64 to 63 B.C. Amman was the ancient Philadelphia; nearby are the magnificent ruins of Jerash.

ISRAEL

The state of Israel dates from 1948, but the history of Palestine predates the earliest Biblical times.

Palestine and Israel are not synonymous, for only the western part of Palestine is now in Israel, and the boundary between the Zionist and Arab states is a *de facto* armistice line rather than a *de jure* treaty line.

In its physical geography, Israel is a lower and drier version of Lebanon. Snow mountains are lacking, the precipitation is less, and cultivation somewhat more difficult. Both countries have been seriously deforested and eroded, but with the elimination or drastic control of sheep and especially goats, many Israeli hillsides are becoming green. Haifa once had trade connections similar to those of Beirut.

Present-day Israel is a small country, especially when one omits the southern desert in the Negeb. One may drive by car from Dan in the north, to Beersheba in the south, in a few hours, and at the narrowest point, where Israel holds only the coastal plain, the country is but 15 miles wide. Even from near Jordanian Jerusalem one may look west to the Mediterranean and almost see the waves along the shore.

Before evaluating the dramatic developments of recent years, we should recognize that predivision Arab Palestine was prosperous and relatively advanced. Great credit must be given to the present Jewish inhabitants, whose accomplishments are indeed remarkable, but it is also true that the results are related to the several billion dollars of investment capital which have poured into the country.

Whether Israel can become a viable state with a high standard of living when outside aid ceases remains an open question. Foreign trade has been highly unbalanced, and the country's ambition to become merchant and manufacturer to the Middle East waits on peace with the Arab world.

Although Jews have lived in Palestine for many centuries, the periods of any effective kingdom of their own ended before the time of Christ. Anything like continuous residence includes periods when the Jewish population dropped to very low figures. During the mid-twentieth century 2 million Jews have returned to this homeland. Nearly two thousand years

of separation have introduced ethnic and cultural differences, and the reassimilation of these scattered people creates internal political problems.

The basic problem of agriculture in Palestine is one of water. The hills of Galilee in the north, where elevations reach 3,962 feet, receive as much as 40 inches, and cultivation is quite feasible where land forms permit. The coastal plain near Haifa receives 25 inches, which is hardly enough, although fortunately it all occurs during the cool season; irrigation is generally necessary. The hills of Judea around Jerusalem receive only 20 inches, in part because the elevation is lower than to the north, in part because they lie farther from the rain-bearing storm tracks.

The southern half of Israel merges into the desert, with 8 inches of rain in Beersheba, and 1 inch at Elath on the Gulf of 'Aqaba. Irrigation is thus essential if any crops are to be grown, but there are no permanent streams and no nearby mountains to supply water. Of the available ground water, the supply, if shallow, is quickly exhausted, and if deep-seated, it may have required millenniums to accumulate and will take as long to recharge.

This is the area where engineers hope to

Israel Data [1]

Area		7,993 square miles
Population		2,173,923 (1961 census)
Tel Aviv–Jaffa		386,612
Haifa		182,007
Jerusalem (capital)		166,301
Primary and secondary pupils		401,158
University (4) students		11,050
Wheat		73,700 metric tons (1959)
Barley		65,000 "
Citrus fruits		512,000 "
Cement		805,200 metric tons (1960)
Superphosphate		94,000 metric tons (1959)
Potash		73,000 metric tons (1958)
Electricity		2,316,000,000 kilowatthours (1960)

[1] *Britannica Book of the Year*, 1962.

Southern Israel is too dry for dependable cultivation. This pipeline brings water from the Yarkon River to the Negeb. (*Courtesy United Nations*)

Southern Israel is too dry for dependable cultivation. This pipeline brings water from the Yarkon River to the Negeb. (*Courtesy United Nations*)

bring Jordan River water. Aqueducts already divert part of the small Yarkon River, but any large-scale use of Jordan water must wait on political agreements. In any event the supply is limited, and evapotranspiration is so high that excessive amounts will be required.

Cheap methods for the desalinization of sea water may provide a solution, but it must be remembered that most of the Negeb lies at elevations above 1,000 feet. Even if the Mediterranean were fresh to begin with, the cost of lifting irrigation water to such heights might prove prohibitive. In areas elsewhere in the world with very cheap electricity, as at Grand Coulee on the Columbia River, the maximum economic lift is 300 feet.

The central coastal plain has long been famous for its oranges, especially around Jaffa, and these form the country's major agricultural export. Wheat is the principal grain, grown largely without irrigation. Cotton and sugar beets represent recent developments.

Israel as a whole covers 5 million acres. About 2 million acres are desert and rough

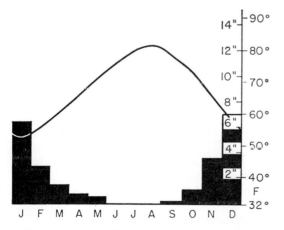

HAIFA. Elevation 33 feet, average temperature 71°F, annual precipitation 26 inches. Israel has a Mediterranean-type climate, with winter rain.

slopes; land fit only for poor pasture covers 1 million acres; areas which may be suitable for dry farming may amount to 1 million acres; and land now in cultivation covers about 1 million acres, of which one-third receives some irrigation.

When the Old Testament describes Palestine as "a good land of brooks and water, fountains and depths, springing forth in valleys and hills, a land of wheat and barley, vines and fig trees, and pomegranates; a land of olive trees and honey . . ." (Deut. 8:7–9), the description was doubtless in comparison with the deserts from which the people had come. There is no evidence that there has been any major change in climate. If pastures were greener, as suggested by the Twenty third Psalm, their grassy cover may have been due to less overgrazing and erosion, or to minor cyclic fluctuations.

Mineral resources are limited. The chemicals of the Dead Sea have already been mentioned. Phosphate, copper, iron, and oil are produced to a limited extent, all in the south. Because of the lack of a mineral base and the necessity both to import raw materials and to export manufactured goods, Israel has concentrated on the production of items for which the value added by manufacture is high. This includes cut diamonds, steel fabrication, textiles and clothing, food products, and drugs. As a result, industry contributes one-fifth of the national income, a figure much larger than in any other part of Southwest Asia.

Three cities account for one-third of the total population. Modern Tel Aviv has grown up alongside ancient Jaffa, and is a metropolis with a population of about 400,000. Haifa is an older city, built on the slopes of Mount Carmel, and has the country's chief seaport. Israel controls the newer part of Jerusalem and has made it the capital, but since the United Nations agreed that Jerusalem was to be an internationalized city, most of its members do not recognize it as the capital and keep their embassies in Tel Aviv. The populations of Haifa and Israeli Jerusalem are each approaching 250,000.

References on the Levant States

See also general references on Southwest Asia, Chapter 33.

Amiran, S. H. K., and A. Shahar: "The Towns of Israel: The Principles of Their Urban Geography," *Geog. Rev.,* LI (1961), 348–369.

Boxer, Baruch: *Israeli Shipping and Foreign Trade,* Chicago: The University of Chicago Press (1957).

Cohen, Saul B.: "Israel's Fishing Industry," *Geog. Rev.,* XLVII (1957), 66–85.

Crowfoot, J. W.: "Syria and Lebanon: The Prospect," *Geog. Jour.,* XCIX (1942), 130–141.

Davies, H. R. J.: "Irrigation in Jordan," *Econ. Geog.,* XXXIV (1958), 264–271.

Dening, B. H.: "Greater Syria: A Study in Political Geography," *Geog.,* XXXV (1950), 110–123.

Fenwick, Peter: "The Lebanon Today," *Geog. Mag.,* XXXIII (1960), 369–383.

Fish, W. B.: "The Lebanon," *Geog. Rev.,* XXXIV (1944), 235–258.

Garrett, Jean: "The Site of Damascus," *Geog.,* XXI (1936), 283–296.

*Glueck, Nelson: *The River Jordan,* Philadelphia: Westminster Press (1946).

Grant, Catherine P.: *The Syrian Desert,* London: Black (1937).

Harris, George L.: *Jordan,* New Haven, Conn.: Human Relations Area Files (1958).

Highwood, R. W.: "Baalbek," *Geog. Mag.,* XXX (1957), 84–93.

Hoyningen-Huene, and David M. Robinson: *Baalbek, Palmyra,* Locust Valley, N.Y.: J. J. Augustin (1946).

International Bank for Reconstruction and Development: *The Economic Development of Syria,* Baltimore: The Johns Hopkins Press (1955).

International Bank for Reconstruction and Development: *The Economic Development of Jordan,* Baltimore: The Johns Hopkins Press (1957).

Karmon, Yehuda: "The Drainage of the Huleh Swamps," *Geog. Rev.,* L (1960), 169–193.

Kedar, Yehuda: "Water and Soil from the Desert: Some Ancient Agricultural Achievements in the Central Negev," *Geog. Jour.,* CXXIII (1957), 179–187.

Kennedy, Alexander: "The Rocks and Monuments of Petra," *Geog. Jour.,* LXIII (1924), 273–301.

*Kenyon, Kathleen M.: *Digging Up Jericho,* London: Benn (1957).

Lewis, Norman N.: "Lebanon: The Mountain and Its Terraces," *Geog. Rev.,* XLIII (1953), 1–14.

Lewis, Norman N.: "Malaria, Irrigation, and Soil Erosion in Central Syria," *Geog. Rev.,* XXXIX (1949), 278–290.

*Lowdermilk, W. C.: *Palestine, Land of Promise,* New York: Harper & Row (1944).

Lowdermilk, Walter C.: "The Reclamation of Land-made Desert," *Scientific American,* CCII (1960), 55–63.

Nuttonson, M. Y.: "Agroclimatology and Crop Ecology of Palestine and Transjordan, and Climatic Analogues in the United States," *Geog. Rev.,* XXXVII (1947), 436–456.

Patai, Raphael: *Jordan, Lebanon, and Syria,* New Haven, Conn.: Human Relations Area Files (1957).

Rumbold, Constantia: "Baalbck, City of Ruined Temples," *Geog. Mag.,* XIII (1941), 270–279.

Runciman, Steven: "The Holy Land: Centre of the World," *Geog. Mag.,* XXIX (1956), 363–373.

Smith, S. G.: "The Boundaries and Population Problems of Israel," *Geog.,* XXXVII (1952), 152–165.

Van Valkenburg, S.: "The Hashemite Kingdom of Jordan," *Econ. Geog.,* XXX (1954), 102–116.

White, R. O.: "The Phytogeographical Zones of Palestine," *Geog. Rev.,* XL (1950), 600–614.

*Willatts, E. C.: "Some Geographical Factors in the Palestine Problem," *Geog. Jour.,* CVIII (1946), 146–179.

*Wooley, Leonard: "Syria as the Gateway between East and West," *Geog. Jour.,* CVII (1946), 179–190.

39 Iraq

Twin Rivers / The People of Iraq / Climate and Land Use / Development Potentials / References on Iraq

TWIN RIVERS

Just as Egypt is the gift of the Nile, so Iraq is the product of the Tigris and the Euphrates. Both rivers transform parts of a desert into a garden; without water Iraq would be an empty land peopled by a few Bedouins whose flocks would find scanty pasture.

Unlike the Nile, whose flood waters cross Egypt in late summer and fall, the Tigris and Euphrates reach their peak flow in late winter and spring, just in time for planting. The Nile loses much of its sediment when it passes through the Sudanese swamps, but the Tigris and Euphrates reach their delta as very silty and overloaded rivers.

Whereas irrigation in Egypt formerly involved the flooding of large basins whose water drained out when river levels dropped, irrigation in Iraq has always involved canals. Under the Egyptian system, any surface salts which accumulate during the growing season are dissolved out during the period of inundation. With canal irrigation in Iraq and no period of flooding, the water table remains high, capillary action lifts ground water to the surface where it evaporates, and a saline crust may form.

The history of the Mesopotamian area since

ancient Sumerian times, about 3400 B.C., may be written in terms of water. Great dynasties dug canals and extended cultivation into the desert. When these canals became clogged with silt or the land developed an excess of salt or alkali, large areas were abandoned. New areas were successively reclaimed, so that there probably never was a time when all Mesopotamia was in cultivation.

The traveler by plane may look down on vast areas of desert country where there are traces of old irrigation works, but this is presumably a record of settlement and abandonment. It is one thing to supply irrigation water; it is another problem to drain away the surplus and keep the water table below 4 or 5 feet from the surface.

The accumulation of salt is a critical problem in present-day Iraq agriculture, as it has been in the past. Each year some 30 cubic kilometers of water are evaporated from the irrigated areas. This leaves behind 22 million metric tons of dissolved chemicals, some lime or gypsum, some common salt. Since this process has continued for centuries, there may well be a billion tons of salts which have accumulated through careless irrigation methods and which must be flushed out of Iraq's potential farm lands before they can be restored to full fertility.

The Tigris and Euphrates rise in the humid mountains of Turkey and Iran where much of the precipitation falls as snow. When this melts rapidly, or when there is concentrated rainfall on the bare lower slopes, floods follow. Both rivers are subject to wide seasonal fluctuations; on the Euphrates the range between the lowest and highest water may have a ratio of 1 to 28; on the Tigris it may reach 1 to 80. Small wonder that floods like the Deluge that Noah weathered are still to be expected.

Northern Iraq, the ancient Assyria, is a rolling plain which forms a part of the Fertile Crescent. Here the rivers flow in well-defined valleys so that irrigation is normally limited to their flood plains.

Southern Iraq, once the site of Babylonia, begins where the Tigris and Euphrates enter their depositional deltas in the vicinity of Baghdad. Below these points the current is unable to move the sediment brought down from the hills, deposition follows, and natural levees develop; above them man has built dikes; when these dikes are overtopped widespread inundation may follow.

The city of Baghdad is especially vulnerable,

Iraq Data [1]

Area	171,599 square miles
Population	7,085,000 (1960 est.)
Baghdad (capital)	355,958 (1957 census)
Metropolitan area	1,306,604
Mosul	179,646
Basra	164,623
Primary and secondary pupils	651,433 (1958–1959)
Higher education students	8,431
Barley	697,000 metric tons (1960)
Wheat	591,000 "
Rice	118,000 "
Dates	324,300 metric tons (1958)
Crude oil	47,280,000 metric tons (1960)
Electricity	736,000,000 kilowatthours (1959)

[1] *Britannica Book of the Year*, 1962.

for there is no high land nearby and the central city is entirely surrounded by dikes; at flood times the enclosed area may be an island below river level.

Fortunately both rivers have natural flood retention basins alongside, each a playa below sea level with large storage capacity. Engineering works now divert surplus flow into these reservoirs and reduce the likelihood of serious flood. Upstream dams on the tributaries also hold back water for irrigation.

Toward the Persian Gulf both rivers enter a vast swamp area which fluctuates widely in size, ranging from 3,200 square miles at low water in the fall to 10,900 square miles in spring. During the 1946 flood the total inundated area amounted to 35,000 square miles, equal to the area of Iowa. Evaporation amounts to 6 feet a year.

Since this inland delta absorbs most of the river-borne silt, only clear water reaches the Persian Gulf. If it were not for the sediment of the Karun, which flows from Iran, the head of the Gulf might remain stationary. There is no evidence that the sea has extended very far inland during historical time.

Rivers in humid lands grow progressively larger toward their mouths, but in arid regions they lose water by seepage, evaporation, and diversion for irrigation. This is notably true with the Tigris and the Euphrates. The low-water discharge past Baghdad amounts to 158 cubic meters per second. The mean flow is 1,236; in flood it has risen to 13,000. So much

This aerial view looks south along the Tigris, with the old crowded city of Baghdad to the left and newer suburbs to the right. Groves of date palms appear in the foreground. (*Courtesy United States Air Force*)

water is lost downriver that near the junction with the Euphrates the corresponding figures are 11, 78, and 179 cubic meters. Few other rivers anywhere shrink so amazingly. Water passing Baghdad has but one chance in 35 of flowing to the Persian Gulf.

The Euphrates has an overall length of 2,100 miles; the Tigris measures 1,270 miles. To these must be added 113 miles for the Shatt-al-Arab, formed by their junction. This is enough to place the Shatt-al-Arab system among the 16 longest rivers in the world.

THE PEOPLE OF IRAQ

Most of the people of Iraq are Arabs, but five millenniums of invasion from Turkey, Arabia, Iran, and beyond have introduced diverse elements. Despite this, there is remarkable present-day homogeneity. Some Iraqi Arabs are Bedouin tribesmen, either still nomadic or part-time farmers or townsmen; others are city dwellers, more or less in tune with the world; still others are the marsh Arabs who live an aquatic life quite unlike that of their desert cousins.

Several minority peoples deserve mention. These include about a million Kurds, apparently descendants of the ancient Medes, and their relatives, the Yezidi or devil-placators; both live in the north, as do a few Turkmen. In the south, and near the Tigris, are the Sabaeans, who speak of themselves as followers of John the Baptist and stress frequent ceremonial ablutions.

Jews have lived in Babylonia since the days of the captivity; there are Jewish colonies in Baghdad and Basra. Groups of Eastern Orthodox Christians date from Byzantine times, augmented by refugee Armenians and Assyrians. Among the Christians are Chaldeans, Nestorians, Jacobites, Syrian Catholics, and Armenian Gregorians.

The Arabs and Kurds are all Muslims, with Shias outnumbering Sunnis by eight to five. Since the former sect is a Persian variant of Islam it is natural that the Shias are most numerous south of Baghdad and east of the Euphrates. Although in the minority, Sunni Muslims hold the political power.

Two famous gold-domed Shia shrines are at An Najaf and Karbala, within which are the tombs of Ali, son-in-law of Mohammed, and of Husain. Other important mosques are at Kadhimain and at Samarra, also with golden domes. Many pilgrims come from Iran and other Shia areas.

Tribal ties are strong, in part economic where indebtedness to the sheik may create virtual slavery. Both nomad and farmer are bound to the tribe, and the individual may find it difficult to break away and seek employment in a city. Many of these people are very poor.

Stock breeding or agriculture, the principal occupations outside the towns, label the people as Bedouins or fellahin, respectively. In many situations people are alternately one or the other, perhaps also camping on the outskirts of some city for a few months each year in search of temporary employment. Here as elsewhere in the Arab world, nomads who keep camels look down on those who tend sheep.

A detailed map of the distribution of people reveals a great deal as to the population-supporting capacity of the land. The western desert is nearly empty, and its population, if any, is on the move. Ribbons of dense settlement follow the rivers and major canals, spreading across the irrigated areas. Where productivity rises, there population is more dense.

Several areas of relative concentration stand out. Irrigated lands along the Shatt-al-Arab have densities which exceed 500 per square mile; the same is true in small areas near Baghdad. Where rain-fed agriculture is the rule, the highest densities are below 100 per square mile, as around Mosul or Erbil. Sharp contrasts exist in all canal areas, for the desert begins a few feet beyond the outermost irrigation ditch.

The future extent of settlement and of cultivation depends in part on technology. Mechanized agriculture has already enabled farming to advance into semiarid lands. Upstream reservoirs provide dependable supplies of water, so

Modern Iraq has many reminders of ancient Mesopotamia and the later Arab empires. Present-day Samarra, with its golden-domed mosque, is surrounded by ruins of ancient cities. (*Courtesy Iraq Petroleum Company*)

that areas which once produced but one crop a season now grow two. Improved drainage has reclaimed land formerly waterlogged or salinized. Better seeds or fertilizers bring prosperity and change the carrying capacity of the land.

With her presently known resources and techniques, Iraq may produce more food through the wise investment of her oil royalties. So long as a million of the present inhabitants are desperately poor, it seems wise to use these new possibilities for their benefit rather than to look forward to a large population increase or to the possibilities of resettling Palestinian refugees. The population map for the year 2000 should show a new pattern of settlement, partly in response to an expansion of rain-fed dry agriculture but primarily through the development of new irrigated land.

Four cities call for attention: the metropolitan center of Baghdad, the port of Basra, the historic northern city of Mosul, and the oil center at Kirkuk.

Baghdad has lost whatever glamour it had in the days of Harun al-Rashid and the *Arabian Nights*. In the absence of any nearby stone or lumber, the successive centers in and around Baghdad have all been mud cities. Since fuel is very expensive, they were built of sun-dried or poorly burned bricks. As buildings collapsed, or were destroyed by flood, new mud structures were built on the slumped ruins of the old. Little remains for the archaeologist except foundations.

While parts of Baghdad are modern, especially around the old north and south gates and on the west bank of the Tigris, the old center is one of the most unattractive large cities of Swasia. About the only unique attraction for the tourist are the craftsmen in the suq or covered bazaar, where copper vessels are still pounded out of flat sheets, and artisans make shoes and other everyday items. Gold and silversmiths work in tiny shops.

Baghdad has five bridges across the Tigris, and modern homes are replacing the old. Industry is still largely in the artisan stage, although there is the beginning of complex production. Metropolitan Baghdad, with its suburbs outside the old wall, numbers more than 1 million people, out of the national total of 7 million.

Basra is Iraq's one sea gateway, with excellent port facilities for freight and, nearby, for shipping oil. The bar at the mouth of the Shatt-al-Arab is dredged to a depth of 25 feet. The Tigris and Euphrates themselves are seldom used for navigation, but two railways lead north to Baghdad and beyond.

Mosul lies on the Tigris not far from the edge of the mountains; across the river is ancient Nineveh. The city is the supply center for Iraq's portion of the Fertile Crescent.

Kirkuk is a new center, developed in response to the nearby oil fields. In contrast to other parts of Iraq where old family ties and traditions persist, many of the people of Kirkuk have come from elsewhere and are setting new social patterns, not always in strict conformity with strict Islamic teachings.

CLIMATE AND LAND USE

Lowland Iraq is a hot desert, grading into a dry steppe on the north and east where elevations are slightly higher. This is an area of high thermal energy, even greater than that of the Sahara. With clear air in summer, solar insolation becomes intense. Through this dry air the sun warms the earth, and the earth in turn regularly raises air temperatures to 120°F. As a result, potential evapotranspiration reaches 45 to 60 inches, dropping to 35 inches in the northern steppe lands. Every month has a high figure, with 9 inches in July.

Partly offsetting this dryness, rainfall amounts to 5 inches in the south, or three times this figure in the north. Every month experiences a deficit, and even during concentrated rainy periods most soil is unable to store up enough moisture to enable crops to grow.

The numerical difference between the demand and supply of water suggests the amount which must be added through irrigation. Even if all the water of the Tigris and Euphrates might be diverted onto the fields, large desert areas would remain. Most of Iraq must remain unproductive.

During much of the year Iraq is in a high-pressure area, with northerly winds which have descended from aloft and are thus dry and increasingly warmed by adiabatic compression and by their southward passage. This steady air movement in summer, from the north and northwest, forms the *shamal,* a hot, dry wind which often blows for nine days out of ten.

This normal sequence is occasionally interrupted in winter by passing cyclonic storms, a part of the irregular westerly circulation of middle latitudes which, because of the tilt of

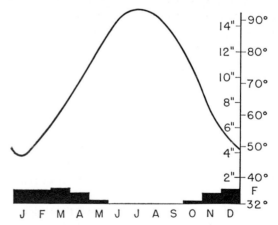

BAGHDAD. Elevation 111 feet, average temperature 73°F, annual precipitation 6 inches. Fortunately for agriculture, the limited rainfall occurs during the growing season.

the earth's axis, dips southward across northern Swasia. The center of these migrating low-pressure areas crosses northern Iraq several times a month in winter. Rain does not always follow, but the passing storms do bring variable weather, with a strong inflow of hot, dusty Arabian air on their southeast quadrant, often forming a sirocco wind, and an accompanying inflow of cooler air to undercut it from the northwest.

Most precipitation is associated with these weak cyclonic storms, spread through two or three days as gentle rain. Where frontal action is pronounced, rainfall may amount to several inches a day. Occasionally, a well-developed depression may remain stationary over Iraq for several days, with a front extending roughly north to south somewhat west of the Euphrates. This draws in large amounts of air from the south, originally of Atlantic and Mediterranean origin but reaching Iraq from the direction of the Red Sea and Persian Gulf. This air mass enters a funnel with the cold front on its left, the Zagros on its right, and the Turkish mountains ahead. It is thus forced to rise, yielding flood-producing rain in the lowland and heavy snowfall in the mountains.

Aridity has its bearing on vegetation, soil, and land-use potentials. Only specialized xerophytic plants can survive during the long periods without moisture. Even in northern Iraq the so-called Fertile Crescent lacks a continuous grass sod. On the other hand the swamps of southern Iraq have a luxurious growth of tall reeds. Few parts of the central desert are entirely lifeless, but vegetation is limited to low and widely spaced dry shrubs and sparse grass.

In irrigated areas or in valleys where ground water is near the surface, date palms are the principal trees, along with poplar, willow, and tamarisk. The only forests lie in inaccessible mountains along the Turkish border.

Desert soils are unleached and thus high in mineral nutrients, but are low in humus; many tend to be reddish. Much of the delta has immature alluvial soils, productive if water is available. Thousands of square miles of once-irrigated land have been abandoned because of the accumulation of injurious salts, and in other areas crop yields have been reduced from the same cause.

Four distinct landscapes are present within Iraq. Northern Iraq extends into the high folded mountains along the Turkish and Iranian border. Climatic conditions are more humid than in the rest of the country, but the topography is so rugged that little agriculture is possible. Oil occurs in the foothills near Kirkuk and Mosul.

The Western Desert is a monotonous plain, strewn with small pebbles and irregularly covered with scanty vegetation. In appearance the area resembles a peneplain. Western Iraq forms a part of the large Syrian Desert.

Mesopotamia, the land between the rivers, has two divisions, the rolling Fertile Crescent country of the north known as the Jazira or island, and the delta of the south sometimes known as Iraq proper. The north, somewhat more humid but without much possibility for easy irrigation, is ancient Assyria; the south, flat, dry, and dependent on canals is traditional Babylonia.

The Jazira is a dissected upland across which the rivers flow in well-defined valleys. Any large-scale development of irrigation will require pumping or long canals to bring water to the uplands. Fortunately rain-fed agriculture is generally possible. Mosul and Erbil are the traditional urban centers, with Kirkuk as the new oil city.

Most of the delta appears to be dead flat. In areas away from the rivers or cultivated land, one may look to the full circle of the horizon without seeing any perceptible slope, a single tree, or any sign of human occupancy. In the canal areas the landscape is quite different; trees, houses, and fields give the country a very human stamp.

Rivers flow with a gentle gradient and are unable to carry all their load of sediment; for this reason natural levees capped with dikes border the Tigris and Euphrates. Irrigation canals easily lead away from the rivers, but drainage ditches do not readily reenter the main streams. Many parts of the delta have poor drainage, especially north of Basra, where marshlands cover many thousands of square miles.

During one flood near Baghdad a lake formed with an area of 27 square miles and depths up to 75 feet, and required seven months to drain away. When the water was gone it left mud deposits 12 inches thick.

Where temperatures are favorable and water is available, crops grow well. Since the days of Herodotus, Mesopotamia has been noted for its productivity. It may be that agriculture has been carried on here longer than anywhere else on earth. One farming community has been unearthed at Jarmo, near Kirkuk, which dates from 5000 B.C.

The total agricultural area amounts to about one-seventh of the country, but much of the cultivated land lies fallow in alternate years, or raises only one crop a year because of lack of water. As a result the harvested area amounts to about an acre per capita. More food will be available when upstream reservoirs store flood waters for release during the low-river period, and when additional land can be reclaimed from the desert or swamps or from salinized areas.

Barley is the main grain, with wheat a close second; both are winter crops. Rice is grown around the marshlands in summer. Cotton and tobacco are minor crops. Livestock form the chief source of income for the nomads, with sheep far in the lead.

Iraq grows most of the world's dates. Eighteen million of its 30 million trees grow along the Shatt-al-Arab, where the tidal rise and fall of the lower river sends a surge of fresh water into the canals which properly irrigate the date groves.

Natural bitumen is available from numerous oil seeps. These sun-dried bricks of ancient Babylon were cemented with bitumen. (*Courtesy Iraq Petroleum Company*)

DEVELOPMENT POTENTIALS

Until the discovery of oil near Kirkuk in 1927, the economy of Iraq rested on its crops and animals. Almost no mineral wealth was available.

Petroleum royalties have brought a new era. By 1960 the Iraq Petroleum Company and its subsidiaries were producing 1 million barrels a day. Profits are divided equally between the company, which assumes all expenses and risks, and the country, the owner of the land. In contrast to most fields around the Persian Gulf, much of Iraq's oil lies well inland and must move by pipeline to the Mediterranean. Although transportation expenses somewhat reduce the profit, the country receives an annual income of many hundred million dollars.

The oil will someday be gone, though reserves are adequate for many decades. Iraq's problem today is so to invest the momentary royalties that new sources of income may be available in the future. While the oil industry employs thousands of people, it directly affects only a small fraction of the total population.

Camels and oil wells suggest the contrasts in culture which are transforming South-west Asia. These soldiers are members of the Iraq Border Police near Basra. (*Courtesy Iraq Petroleum Company*)

A series of development programs have devoted more than a billion dollars of oil money to water, agriculture, communications, housing, schools, and other public works.

Iraq's greatest resource and its largest unrealized potential is its water, primarily that of its rivers. This in turn represents the gradual melting of snowfall in Turkey and Iran. In an ideal situation all this runoff should do something useful on its way to the sea. Two high dams on Tigris tributaries generate electric power, and others are in prospect. Flood damage has been serious, but storage facilities have reduced its likelihood.

Much water has gone to waste in high-water periods, whereas there is barely enough flow at other seasons. Yet enough unused water passes through Iraq to double the crop area and also to ensure dependable supplies for areas now spasmodically irrigated. It is not enough to bring water; it must also be removed. In the slope lands with coarse-textured soils in the north, subsurface drainage is usually adequate, but in the flat delta with tight clay soils, many irrigated areas tend to become so waterlogged that deep drainage ditches are necessary. The cost of removing surplus water may equal the original irrigation expense.

River projects have involved high-storage dams, low-diversion barrages, flood-detention basins, dikes, and port improvements. New canals have been dug and old ones improved. One traditional problem has been the accumulation of silt in the main canals, but to the present time no desilting works have been constructed.

Communications have always presented a problem. Navigation was once important but has largely ceased and may not be redeveloped. In the absence of crushed rock, most railways are ballasted with local sand, so that trains must operate slowly. Modern paved highways, raised above the wet ground, make it possible to drive in comfort from Baghdad to Mosul or Basra in a few hours, whereas previously each journey was an arduous two-day experience.

New textile factories, cement plants, oil refineries, electric power plants, sugar mills, and machine shops enable the country to produce more of its own needs. Experiments in crops and animal breeding are beginning to show results.

One of the most widespread evidences of the new prosperity is to be seen in schools, hospitals, housing, and urban reconstruction. Baghdad shows the beginnings of metropolitan development.

If Iraq is to become a prosperous and advanced nation, she must recognize that her long-range future lies in the proper management of her water. This for the moment rests on the wise use of her oil income.

References on Iraq

See also general references on Southwest Asia, Chapter 33.

*Cressey, George B.: "The Shatt-al-Arab Basin," *Middle East Jour.*, XII (1958), 448–460.

Davies, D. Hywel: "Observations on Land Use in Iraq," *Econ. Geog.*, XXXIII (1957), 122–134.

Fisk, B.: "Dujaila: Iraq's Pilot Project for Land Settlement," *Econ. Geog.*, XXVIII (1952), 343–354.

Harris, George L.: *Iraq,* New Haven, Conn.: Human Relations Area Files (1959).

International Bank for Reconstruction and Development: *The Economic Development of Iraq,* Baltimore: The Johns Hopkins Press (1952).

*Jacobson, Thorkild, and Robert M. Adams: "Salt and Silt in Ancient Mesopotamian Agriculture," *Science,* CXXVIII (1958), 1251–1258.

Lebon, J. H. G.: "Population Distribution and the Agricultural Regions of Iraq," *Geog. Rev.*, XLIII (1953), 223–228.

Lebon, J. H. G.: "The New Irrigation Era in Iraq," *Econ. Geog.*, XXXI (1955), 47–59.

*Lees, G. M.: "The Geographical History of the Mesopotamian Plains," *Geog. Jour.*, CXVIII (1952), 24–39.

Lloyd, Seton: *Foundations in the Dust,* Fair Lawn, N.J.: Oxford University Press (1947); Baltimore: Penguin (1955),

Longrigg, Stephen H.: "Prospects for Iraq," *Geog. Mag.*, XXVI (1953), 276–290.

Maxwell, Gavin: *People of the Reeds,* New York: Harper & Row (1957).

Mitchell, C. W.: "Investigations into the Soils and Agriculture of the Lower Diyāla Area of Eastern Iraq," *Geog. Jour.*, XLIII (1959), 390–397.

Mitchell, C. W., and P. E. Naylor: "Investigations into the Soils and Agriculture of the Middle Diyāla Region of Eastern Iraq," *Geog. Jour.*, CXXVI (1960), 469–475.

Thesiger, Wilfred: "The Marshmen of Southern Iraq," *Geog. Jour.*, CXX (1954), 272–281.

40 Iran

History and Forecast / Geographic Regions / Water and Crops /
Economic Potentials / References on Iran

HISTORY AND FORECAST

Ancient Persia had a rich and proud history. Though the beginnings are lost, we find traces of a Caspian culture of 5000 B.C. From 2850 to 635 B.C. we read of the Elamites, with their capital at Susa near the Persian Gulf. They were followed by the Kassites, an Indo-European group who brought in the horse.

The Medes flourished around 675 to 550 B.C., with their base near Hamadan, but were conquered by the great Persian Empire under the Achaemid dynasty which ruled from around 700 to 331 B.C. with its capitals at Persepolis and Susa. These were the days of Cyrus II,

Darius I, and Xerxes I, when the empire spread to and beyond the Bosporus, the Nile, the Indus, and the Syr Darya. The ruins of Persepolis, destroyed by Alexander in 325 B.C., remain among the most impressive monuments of antiquity.

During the Achaemid Empire came the development of Zoroastrianism, an ethical monotheistic religion which states: "There is only one God, and no other is to be compared to him. The Creator is invisible, just, and worthy of admiration." Under Zoroastrianism it is man's duty to choose the light, speak the truth, and combat evil; by his free choice man determines his fate. The creed is summarized by the injunction to "perform good actions, and refrain from evil ones."

Following the days of Cyrus II, Darius I, and Xerxes I came the Parthian and Sassanian empires. Under Shapur I the Persians captured the Roman emperor Valerian. Then followed the Arab invasion of A.D. 641, and later a period of Mongol rule. Persia again reached great heights during the Safawid dynasty, especially under Shah Abbas I, who ruled from 1587 to 1629.

Iran's ethnic composition is as complex as its history. Two-thirds of its 20 million people are classed as Persians and speak that language, which belongs to the Indo-European or Aryan family. Three main streams of Aryans moved south from central Asia during the first millennium B.C.: the Medes, who may be represented by the present Kurds; the Persians; and the Sanskrit-speaking people who went to India.

Besides the Persians proper, other Indo-European groups include the Kurds, Baluchi, and Armenians, of whom there are 2 million. Tribal groups such as the Lurs and Bakhtiari also speak Persian but with dialect differences.

Two million Arabs live in the plains near the Persian Gulf. Variations of Turkish, a Ural-Altaic language, are spoken in the northwest and in the Zagros Mountains. These include Azerbaijanians, Turkmen, and Qashqai. Still other groups are the Assyrians who speak Aramaic; the Brahui, who are related to the Dravidians; and the Jews, who number 75,000.

In addition to racial and linguistic variation there are religious differences. Most of the people are Muslims, and nine-tenths of them belong to the Shia sect. On the other hand, many minority groups are Sunni Muslims, among them the Kurds, Turkmen, and Arabs. Rivalries at times have become fanatical.

Poor tenancy situations, absentee landlords, great differences in wealth, and too striking urban-rural contrasts all create explosive political situations.

Like all Asia, Iran is in cultural and political transition. Outside pressures, once between the czarist bear and the British lion, are continued between the Soviet Union and the United States. Iran is becoming stronger in its own right, but internal pressures increase.

Iran Data [1]

Area	636,293 square miles
Population	20,678,000 (1961 est.)
Tehran (capital)	1,512,082 (1956 census)
Tabriz	289,996
Isfahan	254,708
Meshed	241,989
Abadan	226,103
Shiraz	169,088
Primary and secondary pupils	1,400,000 (1959)
University students	18,085 (1959)
Wheat	2,500,000 metric tons (1960)
Barley	904,000 "
Rice	499,000 "
Dates	127,000 metric tons (1958)
Crude oil	51,204,000 metric tons (1960)
Coal (govt. mines only)	190,000 metric tons (1959)
Cement	532,800 "
Electricity	442,000,000 kilowatthours (1959)

[1] *Britannica Book of the Year*, 1962.

Iran looks back on her days of glory, and there is no geographic reason why she may not look forward to a new prosperity. The fact remains, however, that much of central Iran is a desert waste and that the country is ringed by highlands on all sides. The attractive areas lie on either side of the mountains and around the edge of the desert.

GEOGRAPHIC REGIONS

Iran is one of the most diverse countries in Southwest Asia. Like Turkey, it is surrounded by mountains, but the Elburz and Zagros are higher and more rugged than the Pontus and Taurus. Inner Iran is much drier and hotter than Anatolia and is a desert rather than a steppe. Few parts of Iran have dependable rain-fed agriculture, whereas only a part of Turkish crops require irrigation. Settlement is spotty in both countries but more so in Iran where most population concentrations represent oases fed by streams from snow mountains. Both Iran and Turkey have one very humid area, quite distinct from the situations just described. In Iran it is found along the Caspian Sea at the base of the Elburz Mountains, and in Turkey toward the eastern end of the Black Sea.

The patterns of topography, climate, and land usability break Iran into a series of fractions, isolated and lacking in central focus. Most of the capitals have been off-center and not easily accessible to the rest of the country. It is thus surprising that any entity called Persia has persisted for so many thousand years.

Five major geographic regions may be identified: northwest Persia, which forms a part of the Armenian highlands already described under Turkey; the Caspian borderlands, which take in both the coast and the adjoining mountains; the Zagros highlands; the Inner Persian basins, several in number; and the Eastern Persian highlands. In addition there is the Persian Gulf coast, which is a continuation of the Shatt-al-Arab delta plain described under Iraq.

Northwest Persia has much in common with eastern Anatolia and the adjoining areas of the Soviet Union. Armenians once lived in all three areas, and Azerbaijanians are present in both Iran and the U.S.S.R. Kurds live near the borders of Iran, Turkey, and Iraq.

This is an area of faulted and dissected plateaus, lava flows and volcanic peaks such as Mount Ararat, 16,946 feet in height, deep canyons, and enclosed basins as around Lake Urmia. Much of the area is rather dry, so that most cultivation is restricted to irrigated alluvial slopes. Winters are bitterly cold.

The Urmia Basin provides the best agricultural land in northwestern Iran. The lake measures 30 by 90 miles, and is salty since there is no outlet. Around its shores are several thousand square miles of old lake bed which provide good cropland. This is the traditional home of the ancient Nestorian or Assyrian Christians, whose conversion dates from the fifth century.

Tabriz is the metropolis of the northwest and the railroad gateway into Turkey and the Soviet Union. This was once a great center for trade between China and the West, but many of the splendid buildings which once marked Tabriz have been destroyed by war or earthquake.

The Caspian borderland includes in part a humid lowland below sea level, in part glacier-clad peaks which rise to heights of 3 miles. Whereas the former is the most densely inhabited part of Iran, parts of the latter are nearly empty.

Moist northerly winds from the Caspian Sea bring clouds, fog, and heavy rain. Poets speak of the area as enjoying perpetual spring. Rice, sugar cane, oranges, tobacco, and tea reflect the warm and moist climate.

The Elburz Mountains, 500 miles long, form a major climatic boundary, wet on the north slopes and dry on the south. This is a folded structure with two or three main ranges, cut by deep gorges. Severe earthquakes occur frequently. The one railway across the Elburz involves 104 bridges and 96 tunnels, including one beneath a pass at 6,924 feet. The few

Northwestern Iran is somewhat more humid than much of the country, with possibilities for rain-fed agriculture. These fields are in Azerbaijan near the Soviet frontier. (*Courtesy International Cooperation Administration*)

transverse highways reach elevations of 6,600 to 8,700 feet. Rising above the main range is the volcanic cone of Mount Demavend, which reaches an elevation of 18,934 feet. Vegetation matches altitude and exposure; forests were once extensive but have been cut over in all accessible areas. Only a few valleys have enough level land for cultivation.

Two cities dominate the north, the capital at Tehran and the Shia shrine city of Meshed. Tehran occupies a broad alluvial fan on the south face of the Elburz at an elevation of 4,000 feet. The old bazaar city lies downslope, the modern city above, with the newer residential suburbs at the base of the mountains, 1,000 feet higher. The situation finds some parallel in Salt Lake City at the base of the Wasatch; irrigation ditches run down the sides of many streets in Tehran as they once did in Salt Lake

City. Tehran became the capital in 1788, following the development of the Qajar dynasty. The city is the political, commercial, and cultural center of the country, and about equal in population to the total of all other Iranian cities put together.

The Zagros Mountains and their continuation in the Makran form a 1,400-mile rampart which extends from the Turkish border to the frontiers of Pakistan. This is a folded, faulted, and overthrust arc, made up of a series of ridges and valleys 100 to 200 miles wide in all. Only one railway and a half dozen roads cross them. Anticlines in the western foothills are the locus of Iranian oil near the Persian Gulf and of Iraq oil at Kirkuk.

A major earthquake in 1962 shook the area between Kazvin and Hamadan. The quake occurred at night, and since many of the mud and stone buildings collapsed, some 6,000 people perished.

While the Zagros Mountains form less of a climatic barrier than the Elburz, they do shut in the very dry interior. Unlike the Elburz, both flanks tend to be barren. Most cultivation is related to streams which depend on melting snow in the higher peaks; a few favored basins are moist enough for dry farming.

This is an area of seasonal nomadism or transhumance, where several hundred thousand tribesmen move up and down the slopes in quest of grass, shifting from alpine meadows in summer to lowland valleys in winter. Among the many tribes are the Kurds, Bakhtiari, and Qashqai. Within the Zagros lie the cities of Kermanshah and Hamadan.

Inner Persia includes a half dozen major basins, each with a terminal salt lake, or *kavir*. Some of these basins are among the hottest, driest, and most lifeless parts of Asia. Such streams as enter them soon wither. Even camel caravans avoid crossing them.

Less than one-fifth of Iran drains to the ocean; the rest slopes toward the Caspian, Urmia, or Seistan basins, or to the many saline playas which characterize the interior. Bordering these kavir flats are gravel-strewn plains called *dasht*. Except on higher slopes, this area is a desert where rainfall averages 5 inches. If the climate were more humid, all these topographic depressions would be filled to overflowing by great fresh-water lakes.

Two basins next to the Zagros are some-

The city of Tehran lies on an alluvial fan at the base of the Elburz Mountains. Many streets have small canals, or *jubes,* which carry water on specified days for gardens and even domestic use. The road cut was opened for the installation of new water pipes. (*Courtesy International Cooperation Administration*)

Most Iranian cities lie within sight of snow-crowned mountains; otherwise they would be without water. This is near Kermanshah in the Zagros Mountains. (*Raymond Wilson, courtesy Iranian Oil Participants*)

what different because of their higher elevation and larger streams. The most famous is that around the oasis of Isfahan; the other centers on Shiraz.

Few cities in Southwest Asia have the charm of Isfahan. The city became the capital of Persia about 1063 but owes its splendor to the work of Shah Abbas, who ruled from 1587 to 1629. This was the glory which led to the statement that "Isfahan is half the world." Here Persian culture found its full flower, with magnificent carpets, ceramic and metal work, and miniature painting. Several mosques with their blue-tiled domes remain.

The Eastern Persian highlands are of limited importance. The area includes mountains and lowlands along the Afghan border. Most of the sparse population are nomads, or

are concentrated in a few unpromising oases.

The Persian Gulf coast is very hot, and although the rainfall is low, the humidity is very high. The refinery city of Abadan is reputed to have one of the worst climates on earth. This area is known as Khuzistan. It is the site of a major development project, where water from behind a 620-foot dam on a tributary of the Karun irrigates a large area.

WATER AND CROPS

The four landscape colors which characterize Southwest Asia are all present in Iran: the brown of the desert, the white of the snow-capped mountains, the green of the oases, and the black of the oil. The first three relate to climate.

An analysis of the water balance for Isfahan shows a moisture deficit in the soil during every month except January and February, for a total of 30 inches during the year. This may be compared with an annual rainfall of 4 inches; only 15 days receive as much as 0.1 inch. In other words there is rarely enough rainfall properly to moisten the soil.

Isfahan's elevation is 5,817 feet, but temperatures have reached 110°F, and the July day-and-night monthly averages are 98°F and 67°F; the absolute winter low is −3°F, while December has maximum and minimum daily averages of 47°F and 24°F.

Since evaporation greatly exceeds precipitation, crops will not grow unless moisture is conserved or added, or the soil is moistened by a high water table. Three sources are available to supplement rainfall: from rivers and springs either directly or through storage reservoirs, from wells, or from the infiltration galleries or horizontal wells known as qanats. Each requires canals for distribution.

Water requirements vary but commonly amount to several acre-feet a year. A stream or a qanat with a flow of 1 cubic foot per second is usually necessary for 100 acres of winter crops, or for 50 acres in summer. Most streams are small, averaging only a few hundred cubic feet per second, with much less during the dry season when irrigation water is especially needed. Storage reservoirs to hold back flood waters conserve the water but evaporation may remove as much as 5 feet a year. Since few canals are lined, seepage losses may be high. The common practice of planting trees along the canals leads to further losses by increased transpiration. The accumulation of silt in canals is a problem as in Iraq.

Well water is often lifted by an endless chain of buckets, made of earthenware or old gasoline tins, which are turned by a draft animal through a simple gear arrangement. These devices are known as Persian water wheels, and dip into a well 20 or 30 feet deep. These and other animal-powered arrangements can irrigate ½ acre a day. Diesel pumps and deep wells are rapidly coming into use.

Qanats, often known as karez, are a widespread device for obtaining water in Iran and adjoining areas. These tunnels tap ground water beneath the upper part of alluvial fans and close to the base of the mountains where runoff recharges the gravels. The gradient of the qanat is just enough for water to flow, and since it is less than the slope of the ground, the tunnel with its flowing stream emerges on the surface downslope.

The construction of a qanat involves sinking a mother well upslope and then digging a small tunnel, perhaps 1 yard in diameter. To bring the excavated earth to the surface or to clean out accumulated sediment, successive shafts are dug every 100 yards. The traveler by plane thus looks down on a series of openings, extending sometimes for miles; around each is a circular pile of excavated earth.

Many Iranian qanats are centuries old, and the mother well may be several hundred feet deep. Once dug, and occasionally cleaned, they supply water day and night for years. Half of the irrigated land in Iran depends on qanats; when a tunnel caves in, the fields and village which it supplies may have to be abandoned.

Large-scale irrigation programs involving dams and a network of canals have been under consideration for decades, but many projects were not feasible until oil royalties became available. Emphasis is now placed on large

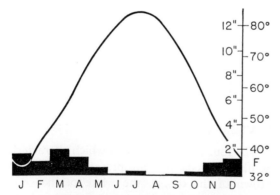

TEHRAN. Elevation 4,002 feet, average temperature 72°F, annual precipitation 10 inches. Iran is high, but its climate resembles that of Iraq.

Iranian farmers are here receiving improved seed, contributed from the United States under a Point Four technical assistance program. The allocation was determined by a village committee. (*Courtesy International Cooperation Administration*)

reservoirs and canal systems. These are located near the Caspian Sea, around Tehran, and in the Karun system along the Persian Gulf. Detailed surveys are lacking, but estimates look forward to supplying water to 500,-000 additional acres. This compares with about 5 million acres under irrigation during the mid-century.

Despite the historic attention to water, two-thirds of Iran's agricultural land is without irrigation and thus depends on the scanty and variable rainfall. Government figures suggest a total of 40 million acres under occasional cultivation, of which the area cropped in any one year averages 15 million acres. The difference represents land which lies fallow so that it may accumulate enough moisture in the soil during

two or three seasons to enable crops to grow. Because of the lack of water, little of this dry-farming land is susceptible to irrigation.

Fortunately, such rain as falls occurs in the cool season so that less is lost by evaporation. Where rainfall averages less than 12 inches, harvests are uncertain, with only one fair crop in two or three years. On the other hand, while irrigated crops are more dependable, they require much more labor.

Most of Iran is unproductive desert or mountain land. A little over 10 per cent is listed as forest, but for the most part this represents useless scrub; 6 per cent is called grazing land, but much of this is too dry for good pasture; the actual food-producing cropland in any one year amounts to under 4 per cent. This is less than 1 acre per capita and is too low for adequate income.

In most years Iran feeds itself. Sugar and tea must be imported, but there is usually a surplus of grain, fruits, and nuts.

Four crops lead. Wheat is the chief grain and is raised wherever possible, planted in the fall and grown with or without irrigation. In some mountain areas wheat is planted in the spring and thus must have irrigation. Barley is the second crop, covering an area about one-third as large as wheat, often in the drier areas. Rice is raised wherever adequate water is available, as along the Caspian coast. Since rice requires high temperatures, it is a summer crop. Dates have an important role in the diet along the dry southern coast; most of the interior is too cool for palm trees. There are said to be 10 million trees, as compared with 30 million in Iraq.

Nuts constitute an important export, especially almonds and pistachios.

ECONOMIC POTENTIALS

Iran may have an important industrial future, perhaps comparable to that of Turkey, to which there are some geological parallels. Much field work remains to be done, but the known assets appear promising. Industry will be of importance since agriculture alone does not hold out much hope of future development.

Oil and gas seeps have been known in Iran since ancient times. The early modern wells, however, were unsuccessful. The first oil was struck in 1908 at Masjid-i-Sulaiman opposite the head of the Persian Gulf, but production had to wait until 1913 for the development of roads, towns, and pipelines. Within the first four decades the output of this one field totaled 1 billion barrels. There are now several producing areas in the Zagros foothills, some of which average nearly 20,000 barrels of oil per well per day.

Iranian reserves and yields in the Persian Gulf area are very large, both on land and offshore. A large field is also present in the interior around Qum, south of Tehran. By 1960, the national production had passed 1 million barrels a day. There are domestic pipelines for the distribution of gasoline, but most oil is exported, either in refined form from Abadan on the Shatt-al-Arab, or as crude from Bandar Mashur in the delta and the deepwater terminal on Kharg Island.

Profits have been shared by a complex formula, but roughly divided equally between the Oil Consortium and the government. Here, as in Iraq, most of the royalties have been used for development projects, including irrigation and industry. Should the oil business continue to be profitable, it can pour billions of dollars into social and economic welfare.

Water power offers another significant source of energy, although the seasonal precipitation requires large storage facilities if power is to be available the year round. Hydroelectric developments and potentials are located in the Elburz and Zagros Mountains; elsewhere lower elevations bring inadequate rainfall and limited storage in the form of snow.

Large reserves of fair-quality coal are present in the Elburz and in central Iran, with an annual production of several hundred thousand tons. Eight mines lie within 50 miles of Tehran; twice that number are located elsewhere.

Iron ore of acceptable quality is available in several localities and provides the base for a steel mill at Azna on the railway midway between Tehran and the Persian Gulf. Powdery iron oxide has long been exported from Hormuz Island for use as a pigment in paint and for rouge.

Numerous mineral occurrences are known, but production is small. Chromium is widespread, as in Turkey. There is also a small output of lead, copper, manganese, and salt. Cement is an important product.

If Iran is to become modernized, better transport is essential. Gravel roads connect the major cities, but many small streams are unbridged. Travel may be difficult in the rainy season, and mountain passes are apt to be closed by snow. Only a few highways are paved.

The railway network is incomplete, and a half dozen cities with populations of 100,000 or more have no rail connections. The main trans-Iranian line leads from Bandar Shapur at the head of the Persian Gulf across the Zagros to Tehran and thence across the Elburz to Bandar Shah on the Caspian Sea. From Tehran railways extend east to Meshed and west to Tabriz, where there is a connection north to the Soviet Union and plans for a link with Turkey. The only other railway is in the far southeast, where a Pakistani line ends just inside the border. Early dreams of a Europe-to-India railroad line have been made less necessary by the development of aviation. Overland distances are also too great to warrant freight charges for most commodities in competition with ocean rates.

Since Iranian ports on the Persian Gulf are rather remote from Europe, some trade moves overland to the Turkish port of Trabzon on the Black Sea, now linked only by highway.

Iran started its second Seven-Year Plan in 1958. Among its objectives were "increased production, developing exports, . . . agriculture and industry, discovering and exploiting mines and natural resources, improving and completing means of communications, improving public health, . . . raising educational standards . . . and living conditions." Costs of over a billion dollars were involved.

Iran is anxious to become modernized. It is important to recognize, however, that material progress cannot safely outrun the needed social changes such as the tenant-landlord relations.

Many of the problems of twentieth-century Iran resemble those of ancient Persia, such as the management of water, economic and cul-

The foothills of the Zagros are the site of numerous narrow but elongated oil fields, some of them so productive that wells average 10,000 barrels a day. This is well number 19 in the Agha Jari field. (*Courtesy Socony Mobil Oil Company*)

tural coherence in the face of physical disunity, poor communications across high mountains and desolate deserts, wide contrasts between the very rich and very poor, the presence of unassimilated ethnic groups, and political pressures from the outside world.

References on Iran

See also general references on Southwest Asia, Chapter 33.

Beckett, P. H. T.: "Waters of Persia," *Geog. Mag.,* XXIV (1951), 230–240.

Clapp, Gordon R.: "Iran: A TVA for the Khuzistan Region," *Middle East Jour.,* XI (1957), 1–11.

*Costa, A., and L. Lockhart: *Persia,* London: Thames & Hudson (1957).

Elwell-Sutton, L. P.: *Persian Oil,* London: Lawrence and Wishart (1955).

Haas, William S.: *Iran,* New York: Columbia University Press (1946).

*Melamid, Alexander: "The Geographical Pattern of Iranian Oil Development," *Econ. Geog.,* XXXV (1959), 199–218.

Ullens de Schooten, M. T.: "Among the Kashkai: A Tribal Migration in Persia," *Geog. Mag.,* XXVII (1954), 68–78.

Ullens de Schooten, M. T.: *Lords of the Mountain: Southern Persia and the Kashkai Tribe,* London: Chatto & Windus (1956).

Smith, Anthony: *Blind White Fish in Persia,* New York: Dutton (1953).

Vreeland, Herbert H., and others: *Iran,* New Haven, Conn.: Human Relations Area Files (1957).

Wilbur, Donald N.: *Iran,* Princeton, N.J.: Princeton University Press (1955).

41 Afghanistan

Three Landscapes / Livelihood / Political Problems / References
on Afghanistan

THREE LANDSCAPES

Towering mountains extend westward across Afghanistan and divide the country into three quite different geographic regions: a central highland core, and two arid plains, one on either side of the highlands. This is the easternmost country of Southwest Asia, and also the driest and most mountainous; its similarity to the rest of the realm lies in the winter concentration of rainfall, as contrasted with summer monsoon rain in India, and in the general character of life and landscape.

A double series of mountain ranges form a festoon across Swasia from the Aegean Sea to Tibet. In Turkey these are the Pontus and Taurus Ranges; in Iran they continue as the Elburz-Kopet Dagh and Zagros-Makran Mountains respectively; in Afghanistan the northern sequence forms the Paropamisus, Koh-i-Baba, and Hindu Kush Ranges; to the south and east, largely within Pakistan, are the Kirthar and Sulaiman Mountains (in each case reading eastward). These all belong to the Anatolian-Persian highland province, geologically known as the Tethys foldland.

In place of the Arabian geographic province, or, in geological terms, the Gondwana stable block which occupies the southwestern third of Swasia, northern Afghanistan extends into another stable block, that of the Turanian lowland, largely within the Soviet Union.

Afghanistan has a range in elevation from 24,000 feet in the east to 1,526 feet near the end of the Helmand River, and less than 1,000 feet where the Amu Darya River leaves the country. Despite these differences, most of the country is dry, and few of the higher elevations receive as much as 20 inches of rainfall. Forests are rare, and pasture lands continue to the snow line.

Although winter precipitation predominates, the south occasionally receives summer rain from the edge of the Indian monsoon. The only rivers whose flow persists throughout the year are those which rise in snow-clad peaks; many disappear after they leave the mountains.

Afghanistan somewhat resembles the roof of a house, with the irregular crest of the Hindu Kush and its continuations as the central ridge line. Since there are several offshoots and elevations are lower in the west, one may add that the roof has numerous gables.

The Hindu Kush form one of the several mountain ranges which radiate from the Pamir highlands. As a whole, the system measures 700 miles from east to west. Properly speaking, the term Hindu Kush applies only to the eastern half; then follows the Koh-i-Baba, or "Father of Mountains" Range, with the Paropamisus in the west. Near Tibet several peaks exceed 20,000 feet; toward Iran summits reach 10,000 feet. The origin of the term Hindu Kush is in doubt, but may refer to "Hindu Killer," since so many Indian slaves died while crossing the mountains in the severe cold and deep snow.

Mountains dominate the east-west core of Afghanistan and form the first of three geographic regions. Within the Afghan mountains three subdivisions may be recognized. The very rugged northeast is Badakhshan, where majestic snow-crowned peaks feed torrential streams. The area includes the long projection of Afghanistan which extends up the Wakhan corridor to the border of China. The projection was created to isolate czarist Russia from British India. Badakhshan is famed for its lapis lazuli, specimens of which even reached Crete in days of antiquity. The few people are limited to ribbons of irrigated flood plains or small bits of terrace land. Many of the people are Tajiks.

The central mountain area, from Kabul to Herat, is known as the Hazarajat, the home of the Hazara Mongols. Two different people oc-

Afghanistan Data [1]

Area	ca. 250,000 square miles
Population	13,799,037 (1961)
Kabul (capital)	310,000
Kandahar	195,000
Herat	150,000
Mazar-i-Sharif	100,000
Primary and secondary pupils	141,319 (1959)
University of Kabul, students	1,104
Wheat	2,100,000 metric tons (1958)
Wool	6,000 metric tons (1957)
Barley	280,000 metric tons (1955–1956)
Rice	316,000 metric tons (1958)
Coal	34,000 metric tons (1958–1959)
Salt	25,600 metric tons (1958)
Electricity	49,200,000 kilowatt hours (1957)

[1] *Britannica Book of the Year*, 1962.

This is the magnificent Tangigaru Gorge which is situated twenty miles to the east of Kabul, capital city of Afghanistan. (*Courtesy James Cudney, American Embassy, Kabul*)

cupy these mountains: the sedentary Hazaras, whose villages are strung along steep hillsides where farmers irrigate ribbons of wheat, barley, peas, and beans; and the migratory Pushtun tribesmen known as *kuchi,* meaning "the marchers," who graze their flocks in the mountains and then migrate 200 to 300 miles to the Indus lowlands in winter. While the Hazarajat is largely roadless, here and there are a few fertile valleys with small towns.

Eastern Afghanistan is the most important part of the country, with the capital city of Kabul and several other towns, each in an irrigated basin. Aside from these basins, cultivated land amounts to no more than a fraction of 1 per cent. The area lies south of the main Hindu Kush proper and forms part of the mountain complex where the Hindu Kush and Sulaiman Ranges converge. The Khyber Pass forms the eastern gateway.

Kabul, at an elevation of 6,000 feet, is the metropolis of modern Afghanistan, with paved streets and modern buildings. Since the basin commands passes to the north and east, the area has long been important and was visited by Darius and Alexander. The population, numbering about 300,000, includes proper Afghans (otherwise termed Pushtuns or Pathans), Tajiks, Hazaras, and representatives of the twenty different groups who make up Afghanistan. Many of the people speak Persian rather than Pushtu.

To the north of the Hindu Kush system lie the plains of Turan, extending into Soviet Middle Asia. This is the second main geographic region, with two subdivisions. In the east, and tributary to the Amu Darya (or Oxus) lies Bactria; farther west is Afghan Khurasan, a continuation of Iranian Khurasan. This northern area has roughly twice the agricultural land of the south.

The Hindu Kush, Koh-i-Baba, and Paropamisus Mountains supply a number of north-flowing streams such as the Kunduz and the Hari Rud. The former is a tributary of the Amu Darya; the latter, along with many others, withers on entering the plains and never reaches an ongoing river. At the point where each stream leaves the mountains is a city. Many of these towns are old and famous as stepping-stones along the ancient caravan routes which linked China and Europe.

Bactria is a land with rich history. Greek rule lasted for two centuries following the conquests of Alexander. Other times have brought Mongol, Arab, Persian, Indian, and Chinese

Central Afghanistan is the home of several hundred thousand nomads who spend their summers in highland pastures and then migrate with all their animals to the Indus lowland in Pakistan for the winter. (*Courtesy James Cudney*)

Southern Afghanistan is a desert plain, dotted with ruins of ancient settlements and oases fed by lines of qanats. Parts of this area are to receive water from the new dams in the Helmand valley. (*Courtesy Morrison-Kundson-Afghanistan*)

cultures. The area is now Muslim in religion, but old Christian churches, Buddhist temples, and Zoroastrian buildings reveal the complex history. Cities such as Balkh were the center of a civilization which rivaled Babylon.

North of the Hindu Kush one enters central Asia: two-humped bactrian camels replace one-humped dromedaries; round, white, felt-covered tents or yurts take the place of the black cloth tents which characterize Swasia. Until 1933 no road crossed the mountains, and since that involved a pass at 9,800 feet, isolation from the rest of Afghanistan is inevitable.

Afghan Khurasan includes the broad valley of the Hari Rud and several nearby basins. If Bactria somewhat resembles Arizona, the greater elevation of Khurasan gives it a landscape comparable to Wyoming. Across most of the area one may travel for miles without seeing a trace of human habitation. The chief city

is Herat, where 200,000 acres of cultivation stand out as a green island in a lifeless sea. The old city wall with its 150 ruined towers is a reminder that Herat commands a north–south avenue across the mountains and that there has seldom been a war within a thousand miles which did not involve Herat.

Southern Afghanistan, the third of the major regions, has one major river system, the Helmand. Where it and its tributaries enter the Registan-Seistan plain there are irrigated oases and towns similar to those of the north. Chief among them is Kandahar, the principal entrepôt for trade with Pakistan and gateway to the port of Karachi.

The Helmand Valley Authority represents the country's largest development project, built by American engineers but paid for by Afghanistan. Two reservoirs store up spring floods for later diversion through several hundred miles of modern irrigation canals, providing dependable supplies for 500,000 acres. If all the flow of the Helmand could be conserved, this irrigated area might be doubled. Owing to the high rate of evaporation, it may be necessary to apply 5 or 6 acre-feet of water in order to raise crops. Problems of salinized soils are met by deep drainage ways interspersed between the irrigation ditches. Some of the land which the project proposes to reclaim contains 3 to 5 per cent of salt in the upper 6 inches of the soil.

Most of southern Afghanistan is occupied by the sand-choked Registan Desert in the east and the terminal basin of the Helmand farther west known as Seistan, extending into Iran. Both are arid lands with few settlements and few nomads. The Helmand ends in a series of lakes and marshes which reach a maximum area of about 7,000 square miles but which in dry seasons shrink to a very small fraction of that extent.

Seistan is one of the most inhospitable parts of Asia. Summer temperatures exceed 120°F, while winters approach zero. This is the area of the "wind of 120 days" in summer. In one March, winds averaged 88 miles an hour for 16 hours and reached a maximum velocity of 120 miles per hour. Despite the poor climate, and the low state of present development, Seistan was once an area of prosperous cities and well-developed irrigation, possibly a second Mesopotamia.

LIVELIHOOD

Afghanistan is a fascinating country for geographic study, but it does not appear to offer much income for its inhabitants. All statistics are in doubt, including the reported population of 13 million. If the cultivated land is correctly estimated at 7 million acres, the man-land ratio is unfavorable; elsewhere in Swasia it takes an acre to feed one person.

Eighty-five per cent of the population are engaged in agriculture; the others are pastoralists or city dwellers. About 1 million acres are irrigated, roughly one-seventh of the total cultivated area. Since most lowlands receive less than 10 inches of rain per year, dry-farming methods must be used, conserving the soil moisture with crops in alternate years. Wheat is the main grain; cotton and sugar beets are expanding crops.

The livestock population includes 12 to 14 million sheep, 6 to 8 million goats, 3 million cattle, and ½ million camels. The country's most valuable income is from karakul lambskins, with an export of 1 to 3 million skins a year.

Agriculture is restricted by the limited water and by the decreasing length of the growing season at higher elevations. Barley is found up to 11,200 feet, whereas spring wheat does not ripen above 10,900 feet or winter wheat over 9,250 feet. The limit for rice is 7,000 feet. Apricots are found at 9,600 feet and apples at 8,250; melons are limited to 7,900 feet. The maximum height for cotton is 6,950 feet. Figs, sugar cane, date palms, and bamboo are all warm-weather crops, with height limits of 3,500, 3,400, 2,800, and 2,200 feet, respectively.

Melons and grapes are exceptionally sweet, especially in the north, and are normally exported to Pakistan and India along with raisins, apricots, and nuts. Mulberry trees are raised for their leaves which are fed to silkworms. The country has a small silk industry.

Plans for agricultural improvement involve irrigation, better seeds, food processing, and community development.

The Afghan landscape is one of abrupt contrasts. For the most part, the two lowlands, north and south, are a desolate waste, in winter a cold desert covered with a trace of grass after the scanty winter rains, but for much of the summer a dusty furnace. In many areas the water table may lie 200 feet below the surface.

In the midst of this lifeless brown land the traveler abruptly enters verdant gardens with fruit and flowers. Poplars line the canals or surround the houses. This is the miracle of

Interior Afghanistan is a land of barren mountains and irrigated valley bottoms, fed from distant snow peaks. Camels cover 20 miles a day. (*Courtesy International Co-operation Administration*)

water in the desert, made possible by gradually melting snow in distant mountains.

Where streams or springs are not available, many areas draw their water from qanats, the long horizontal wells which tap deep-seated ground water upslope, often near the base of the mountains, and carry it through an underground aqueduct. Thousands of qanats are used in Afghanistan, as in Iran.

Industry is only beginning, but there appears to be a modest raw-material base. Coal is produced on the north slope of the mountains. Hydroelectricity is available on several rivers. Though there are suggestions of oil on both sides of the mountains, all the country's needs are imported, chiefly from the Soviet Union. Cement is produced in two plants. Mineral pro-

duction is handicapped by poor roads and distance, for the country has few paved highways. Textile mills for either cotton or wool operate in a half dozen centers.

POLITICAL PROBLEMS

Afghanistan has long been a contest area. Here Greek troops clashed with people of inner Asia, and Hellenic culture met Buddhism. Here flowed the westward tides of Mongol conquest under Genghiz Khan and Tamerlane. Persia conquered the country during the sixth century B.C., and has ruled western Afghanistan off and on until recent times; nearly half the people still speak Persian.

Repeated invasions from what is now Soviet

Middle Asia brought in Tajiks, Turkmen, Uzbek, Kirghiz, and other people. Chinese pilgrims crossed the Hindu Kush in the seventh century, bringing Buddhism from India to China.

More than 5 million Afghan people, of Aryan stock and commonly known as Pushtuns or Pathans, live across the border in Pakistan, a reminder of the time when the Mogul dynasty ruled from Delhi. This leads to agitation for the annexation of frontier areas known as Pushtunistan, for the present boundary, called the Durand line, represents the limit of British control rather than any sound geographic boundary. It is equally true that India has several times controlled eastern Afghanistan. Most cities have frequently changed hands.

Only seldom has a single state occupied the present territory of Afghanistan, and never has there been anything like ethnic or cultural unity. Loyalty and coherence are still tribal rather than national.

The nineteenth century witnessed the gradual approach of the czarist bear and the British lion. Russian penetration into Middle Asia did not reach the Aral Sea until the middle of the nineteenth century or the borders of Afghanistan until the 1880s. Alarmed by this advance toward India, Great Britain sought to bring Afghanistan into her orbit, fighting three wars on its territory.

After Great Britain ceased to control India, Afghanistan was no longer a frontier of empire. The Kremlin continues to look southward for an avenue to India, and Afghanistan's willingness to accept American aid may represent a desire to find a new counterinfluence.

Afghanistan faces many problems, domestic and external. The first category concerns the lack of topographic unity and the difficulty of welding together such diverse cultural groups. Equally serious is the transition from a former feudal monarchy to a modern state. The country needs economic assistance, but to pay for such outside help she relies largely on the export of karakul skins.

On the international side, the country finds herself without access to the ocean and surrounded by none too friendly neighbors. Four railways touch the frontier, but none cross it: two are next to the U.S.S.R.; two are along the edge of Pakistan through the Khyber and Bolan Passes. The only connection with Iran is by one very poor road. Karachi is the logical seaport, but the boundary may be closed in times of disagreement, as might happen over a possible Pushtunistan. Since the country depends on the Soviet Union for its gasoline, any embargo along that border produces serious results.

This is a significant frontier, one where the totalitarian and democratic worlds contend for the loyalty of an undeveloped area; one of little importance in itself but an area whose location is of strategic significance.

Americans who think of Afghanistan as far away and unimportant would do well to read the words of Justice William O. Douglas of the Supreme Court.[1]

We of the west have all the rudiments of civilization, all the dividends of a mounting standard of living. But the Afghans—one thousand years behind us in many respects—have a warmth of human relations that is often missing all the way from New York City to San Francisco.

[1] William O. Douglas: *Beyond the High Himalaya,* Garden City, N.Y.: Doubleday (1952), 265. Quoted by permission.

References on Afghanistan   See also general references on Southwest Asia, Chapter 33.

Clarac-Schwarzenbach, Annemarie: "Afghanistan in Transition," *Geog. Mag.,* XI (1904), 326–341.

Fox, Ernest F.: *Travels in Afghanistan, 1937–1938,* New York: Macmillan (1943).

Fraser-Tytler, W. Kerr: *Afghanistan: A Study of Political Development in Central Asia,* Fair Lawn, N.J.: Oxford University Press (1950).

Keffel, Joseph: *Afghanistan,* London: Thames & Hudson (1959).

*Michel, Aloys Arthur: *The Kabul, Kunduz, and Helmand Valleys,* Washington: National Academy of Sciences (Office of Naval Research) (1959).

Thesiger, Wilfred: "The Hazaras of Central Afghanistan," *Geog. Jour.,* CXXI (1955), 312–319.

Thesiger, Wilfred: "The Hazarajat of Afghanistan," *Geog. Mag.,* XXIX (1956), 87–95.

Wilber, Donald W.: *Afghanistan,* New Haven, Conn.: Human Relations Area Files (1956).

THE SOVIET REALM

The key word in Soviet geography is continentality, not merely in its vast size or remoteness from the ocean or seasonal extremes in temperature, but in its isolation from world commerce and from the ideas which cross the seas. Soviet potentials represent a balance between rich mineral resources and a limiting climatic environment, modified by a dynamic idea.

"In the current decade (1961–1970), the Soviet Union . . . will surpass the strongest and richest capitalist country, the U.S.A., in production per head of population; the people's standard of living and their cultural and technical standards will improve substantially; everyone will live in easy circumstances; all collective and state farms will become highly productive and profitable enterprises; the demand of the Soviet people for well-appointed housing will, in the main, be satisfied; hard physical work will disappear; the U.S.S.R. will become the country with the shortest working day." (Twenty-second Congress of the Communist Party, 1961)

Novo Lipetsk Rolling Mill. (*L. Polikashin, courtesy Soviet Embassy, Washington*)

42 Soviet Potentials

A Geographic Preface / Historical Geography / Socialist Economy / Political Structure / Soviet Nationalities / References on the Soviet Union

A GEOGRAPHIC PREFACE

One-seventh of all the land on earth lies within the Union of Soviet Socialist Republics. From the Baltic Sea to Bering Strait the country spreads across 170 degrees of longitude, nearly halfway around the globe. From the Carpathians to Kamchatka is as far as from San Francisco to London. The Trans-Siberian Express requires 9½ days for the journey from the Polish frontier to Vladivostok. Within the Union's 8,649,489 square miles is room for all of the United States and Canada, plus Mexico. This is a very large country.

The most significant factors in Soviet geography are the unique political, social, and economic features which have made the U.S.S.R. such a dynamic country. These human elements differentiate and distinguish the realm even more than do its climate or topography. Geography normally deals with the physical and cultural environment, but it must also consider the Communist ethos which makes this land a distinct part of Eurasia. Regardless of whether one favors or opposes Marxian socialism, he must admit that the Soviet Union is one of the most challenging phenomena of our time. It stands apart in its government and equally in its transformation of nature.

The key word in the physical geography of the Soviet Union is continentality. Here is a land mass of vast proportions, lacking in many of the benefits which come from contact with the ocean. Even though the country borders the Arctic for thousands of miles, this coast is of little value since it is frozen for much of the year. Few of the seas which surround the U.S.S.R. are important as sources of moisture. On the Union's landward side, except toward the west, a continuous line of mountains and deserts bars ameliorating winds or cultural intercourse.

This continentality means low rainfall, pronounced seasonal contrasts in temperature, inadequate access to the commerce of the high seas and the ideas which come with international contacts, and an outlook on both domestic and world problems which is in contrast to that which characterizes lands in maritime surroundings. Continental isolation is a geographical constant, made even more pronounced by political decisions.

Too much of the Union is too mountainous or too hilly, too cold or too hot, too dry or too wet, or too infertile, or too inaccessible, or too something else to be of much value as a home for man. Potential agricultural land covers no more than one-eighth of the country, largely within a narrow triangle or wedge bounded on the north by Leningrad and on the south by Odessa, and tapering eastward toward Irkutsk. In other words, the agricultural core of the U.S.S.R. is limited by the Gulf of Finland, the Black Sea, and Lake Baikal. Within these million square miles only one-half of the area is actually cultivated. Outside the fertile triangle may be the attraction of minerals or timber or local oases, but climatic barriers restrict normal settlement over vast areas. Despite a population nearly one-fourth greater than that of the United States, the Union of Soviet Socialist Republics has about the same area in agricultural use.

Although landlocked continentality is obvious, the Soviet Union at the same time has the longest coastline of any country. Unfortunately, much of this coast is almost useless. Arctic seas are frozen for nine or ten months. Even the rivers flow in the wrong direction. The Volga ends in the isolated Caspian, and the Ob, Yenisei, and Lena point to the Arctic Ocean. Even the Amur bends north before joining the Pacific. The Don and the Dnieper enter the Black Sea, but it, too, is enclosed. Nowhere does the country border open ice-free water except at Murmansk in the extreme northwest, or at Kaliningrad on the Baltic. How different might have been the country's history if her continental position had been modified by easy access to the ocean!

Russian geographers have long lamented these frozen seas. The czarist regime made some effort to navigate the Arctic, but active development of the northern sea route had to wait on weather information, scouting planes, and the construction of powerful ice breakers. Scores of steamers now call at Siberian ports during the brief summer period of open water, and a few dozen make the complete transit from Murmansk to Vladivostok. If Arctic navigation proves dependable in linking the Atlantic and Pacific coasts of the Union, it may

POPULATION-DISTRIBUTION MAP

Most people in the Soviet Union live in a roughly triangular area bounded by the Gulf of Finland, the Black Sea, and Lake Baikal, in other words a wedge-shaped area between Leningrad, Odessa, and Irkutsk.

This settled area corresponds to the distribution of cultivated land, and to the penetration of moisture from the Atlantic Ocean. Population patterns elsewhere in Siberia and Middle Asia reflect accessibility along rivers and railways.

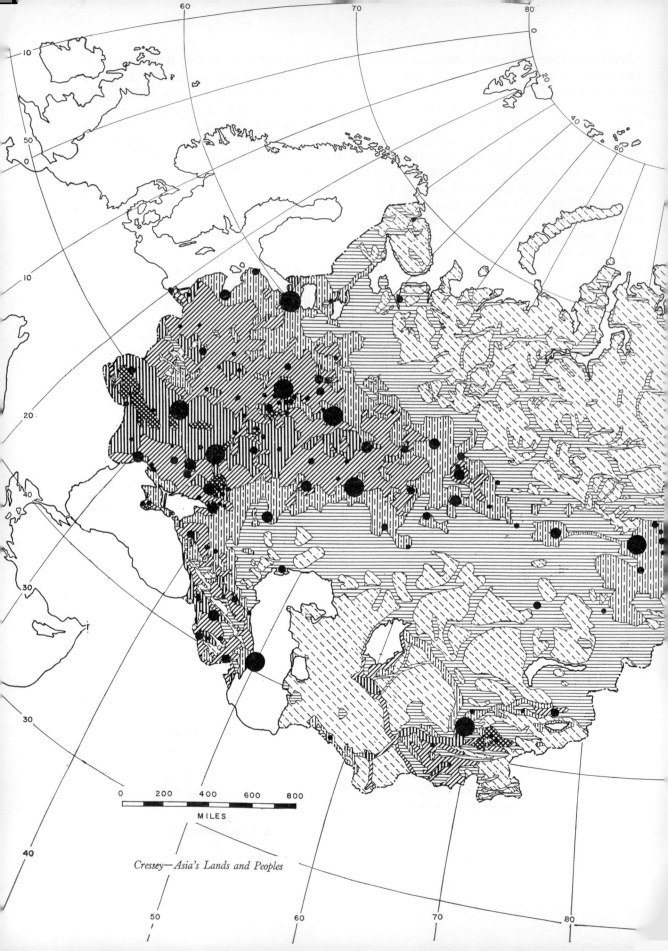

MILES

Cressey—Asia's Lands and Peoples

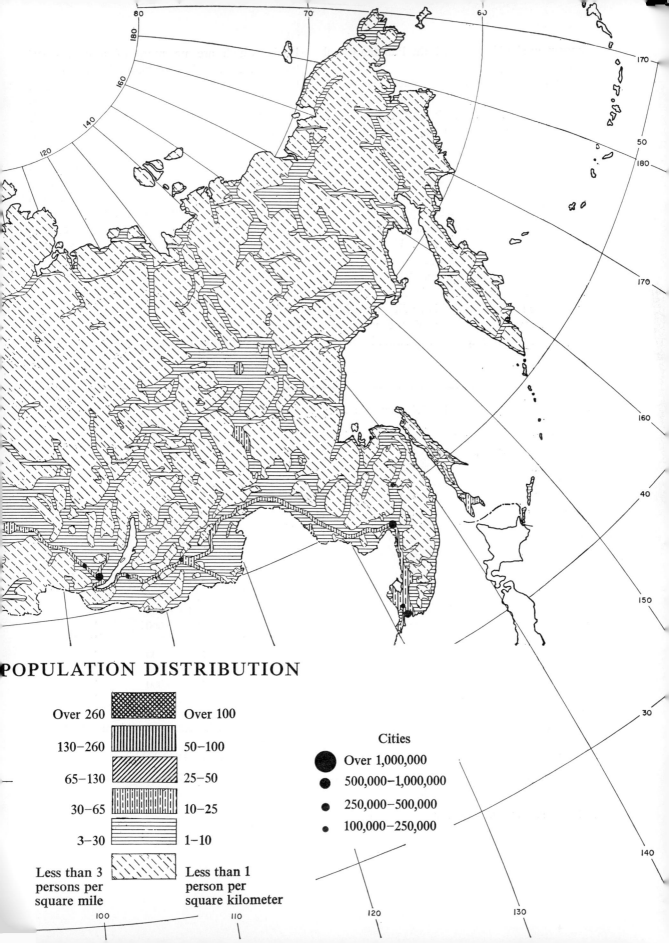

POPULATION DISTRIBUTION

	Persons per sq. mile	Persons per sq. km
	Over 260	Over 100
	130–260	50–100
	65–130	25–50
	30–65	10–25
	3–30	1–10
	Less than 3 persons per square mile	Less than 1 person per square kilometer

Cities

Over 1,000,000

500,000–1,000,000

250,000–500,000

100,000–250,000

compare in significance with the Panama Canal for the United States.

Like the U.S., the U.S.S.R. faces two ways. Both are two-ocean countries, and both have interests in Europe and Asia. But whereas most of America's allies lie across the seas, the neighbors of the Soviet Union, on all frontiers except the west, lie across deserts and mountains. The country is influenced by its position in an isolated part of Asia and the climatically least desirable portion of Europe, remote from the Atlantic. This position would be even more of a disadvantage were not the Union's economy largely self-sufficient because of the abundant resources within the country.

Custom has divided Russia into European and Asiatic sections, but this tradition has little geographic validity. Many of the presumed limits do not even follow the summit of the Urals, which are no more of a continental barrier than the Appalachians, for the mountains do not mark any conspicuous change in climate, crops, nationalities, or economic activities. Ancient Greek geographers drew their dividing line at the Don River, and with reason, since for centuries Asiatic nomads roamed across the plains northwest of the Caspian. Soviet geographers now place the limit of "Europe" at the eastern base of the Urals and along the northern slopes of the Caucasus.

It may be convenient to separate the eastern and western parts of the Union, but any use of the terms Europe or Asia in this connection is apt to be misleading. What we conventionally mean by European culture lies in the peninsular areas of western Eurasia, not in the vast plains of the Volga. The Soviet Union is a single geographic realm; in some ways she is

Soviet Union Data [1]

Area	8,649,489 square miles	Population (continued)	
		Ufa	546,000
Population	208,826,500 (1959 census)	Minsk	515,975
Moscow (capital)	5,045,905	Yerevan	509,340
Leningrad	2,899,955	Primary and	
Kiev	1,104,334	secondary pupils	36,200,000
Gorki	942,000	University students	2,396,000
Kharkov	930,000		
Tashkent	911,930	Cattle	75,800,000 (1961)
Novosibirsk	887,000	Collective farms	45,100
Kuibyshev	806,000	State farms	7,400
Sverdlovsk	777,000		
Donets (Stalino)	701,000	Grain	133,228,000 metric tons (1960)
Tbilisi	694,507	Sugar beets	56,900,000 "
Chelyabinsk	688,000	Cotton	4,400,000 "
Odessa	667,000	Potatoes	84,000,000 "
Dvepropetrovsk	658,000	Sunflower seed	3,800,000 "
Kazan	643,000	Coal	513,600,000 "
Baku	642,507	Petroleum	147,600,000 "
Perm	628,000	Iron ore	106,800,000 "
Rostov-on-Don	597,000	Steel	65,280,000 "
Volgograd (Stalingrad)	591,000	Cement	45,480,000 "
Saratov	581,000	Natural gas	35,386,000,000 cubic meters (1960)
Riga	580,423		
Omsk	579,000	Electricity	291,600,000,000 kilowatthours (1960)

[1] *Britannica Book of the Year*, 1962.

Tundra landscapes range from barren lands with almost no vegetation on the Arctic islands southward through mosses and brush to wooded areas, such as this winter scene on the Kola Peninsula. (*E. Yasinov, courtesy Soviet Embassy, Washington*)

knit to Europe, but by nature she stands between two worlds, the Orient and the Occident. In his *Diary of a Writer* Dostoyevsky has pointed out that Europeans consider the Russians Asiatics, whereas Asiatics have always regarded the Russians as Europeans. Herein lies a profound truth; when rebuffed in the West the Russian finds recognition by the peoples of the East.

The factors that give the Soviet Union its geographic coherence are its homogeneous expanse of level land; its isolation by oceans, deserts, and mountains; the general sameness of its continental climate; the distinctive achievements in agriculture and industry which are transforming the landscape; and its unique political structure. These all make it a phenomenon as well as a place. This tendency to-

ward unity is offset by the diversity of nationalities, by the wide contrasts in natural vegetation and usability, and by the difficulty of communications.

We should remember that the geography of the Soviet Union is more nearly comparable with that of Canada than with the United States. Climatic conditions in both countries place severe limitations on agricultural possibilities. Almost all Soviet territory lies north of the 49th parallel; the Black and Caspian Seas are in the latitude of the Great Lakes. Fortunately there is no Soviet equivalent to the Rocky Mountains to keep moderating Atlantic influences from penetrating interior Eurasia, but the Himalaya block moisture from the Indian Ocean. Where the Union extends farthest south in Middle Asia, conditions resemble Wyoming and Utah. The Ukraine has analogies in Minnesota, the Dakotas, and Montana. Southern Siberia resembles the Canadian prairie provinces. The exceptions to these comparisons with North America are the cotton and fig country of the southern oases, the citrus and tea regions east of the Black Sea, and the rice land around Vladivostok.

HISTORICAL GEOGRAPHY

Russian history has its beginnings in the vast forests and rolling steppes which characterize the area west of the Urals. Travel was aided by the many navigable rivers. Internal conflicts between grassland nomads and woodland hunters were matched by external pressures from the west and southeast.

The beginnings of Russia as a political unit go back to a series of independent Slavic principalities in the ninth century. The chief of these centered around Kiev. Later on, some of the petty states were united by adventurers from Sweden, one of whom was Rurik the Rus. Conflicts between these principalities were interrupted by the Mongol invasions that occurred from 1238 to 1462, when the Golden Horde established its capital on the lower Volga.

With the creation of the czardom of Muscovy in the fifteenth century came a succession of autocratic rulers who enlarged the territory to its present limits. Notable among them was Ivan the Terrible (1533–1584), who pushed the Tatars eastward and also pressed westward into Lithuania and Poland. Under subsequent rulers, the Ukraine was frequently a battleground with Poland.

In 1580 the Cossack bandit Yermak crossed the Urals and captured the town of Sibir on the Irtysh. This started the conquest of Siberia which brought Russia to the Pacific by 1639. Following Bering's discovery of Alaska in 1741, colonists pushed south to within 40 miles of San Francisco in 1812, and Russia retained a foothold in North America until the sale of Alaska in 1867.

Peter the Great (1689–1725) was the unifier of the country. So great was his contribution to the expansion and Westernization of Russia that the Soviets accept him as a great national hero.

Free access to the ocean is an indispensable requisite for modern nations, and the quest for an ice-free port has been an inevitable part of Russia's foreign policy. Since the days of Peter the Great, Russia has sought to break her landlocked limitations and reach the open sea. The Russian bear's quest for warm water explains much of the country's evolution. Fur trading at times motivated exploration and expansion in Siberia; elsewhere trade in other commodities prompted infiltration, as in Middle Asia. Territorial security was also involved in aggressive and defensive moves.

After Peter gave Russia a "window to Europe" on the Baltic, there were successive outward thrusts to the Black Sea under Catherine II (1762–1796), toward the Persian Gulf by Nicholas I (1825–1855), across Siberia to Vladivostok under Alexander II (1855–1881), and on to Port Arthur under Nicholas II (1894–1917). Intrigue in Iran, Afghanistan, Tibet, Mongolia, and China are parts of the same story. Elsewhere, this expansionist tendency brought Russia into conflict with Great Britain in the Crimean War and along the northwestern approaches to India. Completion of the Chinese Eastern Railway to Vladivostok and to Port Arthur in China resulted in the Russo-Japanese War of 1904–1905. Southward expansion was marked by the conquest of Bessarabia in 1812, the Caucasus in 1864, and Turkestan in 1881.

Russia did not share in the intellectual stimulus of the Renaissance, nor was she influenced by the Reformation. Nevertheless, revolutionary movements are of long standing. In 1825 came the Decembrist outbreak. The revolution of 1905 was premature, but resulted in the formation of a parliamentary Duma. After the reverses of the First World War, the Russian Soviet Socialist Republic was established on November 7, 1917, followed in 1923 by the creation of the Union of Soviet Socialist Republics.

Just as Russia has grown externally, so population has shifted internally. In the middle of the nineteenth century the center of population was near Kaluga, 36°E, while today it has shifted southeast to Saratov on the Volga, 46°E. The progressive eastward shift reflects the settlement of Siberia, while the southward component is due to the growth of population in Middle Asia. With the development of Siberia, the center of population should gradually approach the southern Urals. The center of area is near Tomsk. It may be of interest to add that the center of population for the entire world lies 500 miles northeast of the Aral Sea, near 62°45′E and 53°52′N.

Through the course of Russian history, settlement has pushed into Asia as an advancing wedge. At present this triangle of population is roughly limited by the Gulf of Finland and the Black Sea, and extends eastward to Lake Baikal, an area roughly comparable to the agricultural triangle.

To the north of the occupied land lies the great coniferous forest with a short summer and acid podsol soils; to the south is the grassland or steppe, fertile but precariously dry. Yet each eastward thrust of the wedge of settlement brings a corresponding expansion to the north and to the south. Population pressure and the lure of pioneering combine to push cultivation eastward, and at the same time north and south. The northward course of

The Soviet taiga is the world's largest forest, some of it providing excellent commercial timber. Reserves are so large that there is little interest in conservation. (*Tass*)

agriculture has already moved the frontier into lands of precariously short growing season, while southward expansion encounters drought. Both movements involve the hazard of famine. The southward thrust is more attractive, since there are no forests to be cleared and the soils are exceptionally fertile; in good years, rainfall may be adequate, but too often a limited amount or poor distribution results in widespread starvation. Drought is especially hazardous in the newly tilled virgin lands of Siberia.

Siberia has been Russia's pioneer east, just as Anglo-Saxon settlement pressed westward into the New World. The dates are comparable: Tomsk was founded in 1604 and Plymouth in 1620; Siberia was occupied rapidly but thinly, with Yakutsk on the Lena dating from 1632, whereas Hartford was not founded until 1638;

on the other hand, the Trans-Siberian Railway was not completed until thirty years after the Union Pacific.

The extent of Russian explorations in the Pacific is not usually known or appreciated. They include not only voyages in the vicinity of Alaska, but also exploration along the northern coasts of Japan. In early days the supplies for colonists in Russian-occupied America had to be carried across Siberia to Okhotsk. Since overland travel was expensive, this led (in 1803–1805) to a round-the-world voyage via Cape Horn, which brought the discovery of numerous islands in the mid-Pacific. Subsequent trips led to extensive explorations in the central and north Pacific and included Bellingshausen's notable discoveries in the Antarctic.

With the defeat of the Russian navy by Japan in 1905, her influence almost disappeared from

Broad steppes spread across a million square miles in the Soviet Union from the Ukraine to the Yenisei. While rainfall is scanty, soils may be excellent. This is a farm in the Kazakh Soviet Socialist Republic. (*Tass*)

Eastern Asia, gradually to return after the Second World War. The U.S.S.R. borders the Pacific for 5,000 miles and cannot be ignored in East Asiatic affairs. Many of the developments in Siberian railways, industries, agricultural colonization, and city expansion are designed to strengthen the Soviets' place in the East.

SOCIALIST ECONOMY

Dialectical logic, as developed by Marx, conceives of society as in constant process of modification according to fixed materialistic principles. Nature, likewise, is not a constant but can be altered by man. This implies change, but Leninism asserts that the power to accomplish this change adequately is within man's control only under a socialist system. Geography becomes a tool in the reshaping of nature and the redistribution of productive forces, all in accordance with state planning. This includes the alteration of any existing environmental restrictions on crop production, and the wholesale modifications of nature.

When the Soviet Union emerged from the disorder of the First World War and the revolution, her industrial structure was chaotic. Railway equipment was in disrepair, factories had been destroyed, and mines lay in disuse. Consumer goods were seriously inadequate. A severe drought had brought widespread agricultural suffering.

In order to rebuild and expand the economic structure, the first Five-Year Plan was inaugurated in 1928, followed by a series of others. The first Seven-Year Plan began in 1959. Each plan envisaged specific objectives in industrial and agricultural output, usually involving a doubling of production within the period. In the initial programs of reconstruction, heavy industry came first. Not until the late 1950s was much attention given to the consumer.

Soviet geography is utilitarian. To Russian geographers, the function of the subject is to develop the productive resources of the state. This calls for an evaluation of soil, minerals,

and the entire environment. The first step in planning is an inventory of available resources, and it is here that geography has a large role. But to plan, the government must both evaluate and predict, and to predict it must control. Hence it is desirable to understand and if necessary to modify climate and all nature's variables; in human terms, this requires a police state.

Both the Union as a whole and the constituent republics have planning bureaus which include numerous geographers. These organizations not only deal with the development of industries and transport but allocate raw materials to factories and manufactured products to retail outlets. Thus the quota for clothing or nails is mapped out in advance and correlated into the national scheme.

With pressing needs of many types, the procedure has been to select a few for thorough attention and let the others drift. Thus the Moscow, Leningrad, and Kiev subways are unquestionably the most beautiful in the world; the Kuznets and Magnitogorsk steel plants were built with the most modern techniques; the Northern Sea Route Administration was given unlimited resources; and the various Soviet atlases are without a rival.

The goal of the Soviet Union is nothing short of overtaking and surpassing all other nations. As a result, millions of people have been moved from farms into factories. Illiterate peasants, whose mechanical experience was limited to a plow and a hoe, now operate complex machinery. Thousands of miles of new railways have been laid down and thousands of new locomotives built; factory cities of 200,000 people replace tiny villages; and large areas of virgin steppe have been plowed for the first time in history.

If continentality is the basic note in Soviet physical geography, pioneering developments characterize the economic life. No one can travel across the country without being impressed by the material results of planned economy. The pioneering spirit that typifies all parts of the Union is obvious. While Siberia is rather

Shifting sands and sparse xerophytic vegetation characterize parts of Soviet Middle Asia, as in this desert scene from the Turkmen Soviet Socialist Republic. Desert areas in the Soviet Union measure 316,000 square miles. (*Tass*)

cool for many crops, nowhere else in temperate lands is there so much newly developed farm land. Climate, soil, and topography impose permanent restrictions in some respects, but in other ways it is evident that the land of the Soviets has become one of the major world powers.

All this must be viewed in relative terms. In comparison with czarist times, the current changes are stupendous; yet in comparison with Western Europe, the country still has a long way to go. Following the Second World War, the Union boasted that it had become the second largest producer in the world of coal, oil, steel, and many other products. This did not mean that there were as many automobiles on the streets, or that people lived as well as in Paris or London.

It is now clear that the Union of Soviet Socialist Republics is one of the richest countries in the world. Soviet geologists credit their country with vast reserves of coal and oil. Hydroelectric possibilities are great. Iron-ore deposits are huge, and within the country are manganese, copper, lead, zinc, gold, platinum, aluminum, and nickel. Commercial timber covers 2 million square miles, and there is four times as much rich chernozem soil as in the United States. Here is one land where a self-sufficient national economy is feasible.

Any analysis of Soviet economic development must first consider the reliability of Soviet statistics. Unfortunately, a complete check is out of the question, for the only figures available are those of the government. Actual production figures are often confused with planned production or are given as percentages of increase without stating the actual quantity involved.

This use of percentages once reached a humorous climax in the annual statistics from an Arctic station where it was reported that 2 per cent of the men had married 50 per cent of the women; yet only one wedding was involved.

In any comparison with the Western world, it is important to distinguish between the output of heavy machinery and that of consumers' items, and between national totals and production per capita. Decades may elapse before the cumulative results of manufacturing give the Soviet landscape an appearance of material abundance resembling Western Europe.

POLITICAL STRUCTURE

The term "Russia" should be used only historically or in a very loose sense. Russian people live in most of the country, but alongside them are Ukrainians, Georgians, and many other national groups, each in its separate republic.

The Union of Soviet Socialist Republics is a federation of republics, primarily based on na-

tionalities. The secondary basis of political regionalization is economic. On these two criteria, sometimes conflicting, the local *okrugs* (districts), *oblasts* (regions), *rayons* (subdistricts), and *autonomous areas* are grouped into larger *krais* (territories) and republics, and these in turn into union republics. One of the latter is very large and complex; others are small and with few subdivisions. Boundaries are fluid, so that changes in economic developments or political policy may be quickly reflected in the administrative structure.

The highest governing body is the Supreme Soviet. One chamber is called the Soviet of the Union, with one deputy elected directly for every 300,000 citizens, and the other is the Soviet of Nationalities, apportioned among the various republics and national areas. Each local area has considerable responsibility in its internal affairs.

Only four census enumerations have ever been made. In 1897 the total was found to be 129,200,200; in 1926 it was 146,989,460.

The Political Divisions of the Soviet Union [1]	Republic	Capital city	Area, square miles	Population, 1959 census
	Russian Soviet Federated Socialist Republic	Moscow	6,592,812	117,534,315
	Ukrainian Soviet Socialist Republic	Kiev	232,046	41,869,046
	Byelorussian S.S.R.	Minsk	80,154	8,954,648
	Estonian S.S.R.	Tallin	17,413	1,196,791
	Latvian S.S.R.	Riga	24,594	2,193,458
	Lithuanian S.S.R.	Vilnius	25,174	2,711,445
	Moldavian S.S.R.	Kishinev	13,012	2,884,477
	Georgian S.S.R.	Tbilisi	26,911	4,044,045
	Azerbaidzhanian S.S.R.	Baku	33,436	3,697,717
	Armenian S.S.R.	Yerevan	11,506	1,763,048
	Kazakh S.S.R.	Alma-Ata	1,064,092	9,309,847
	Turkmen S.S.R.	Ashkhabad	188,417	1,516,375
	Uzbek S.S.R.	Tashkent	157,876	8,105,572
	Tadzhik S.S.R.	Dushanbe (Stalinabad)	55,212	1,980,029
	Kirghiz S.S.R.	Frunze	76,641	2,065,837
	Soviet Union	Moscow	8,649,489	208,826,650

[1] Data from the *Statesman's Yearbook*, 1961.

These figures are not comparable as to area, for after the revolution of 1917 the country lost 27 million people in Finland, Poland, and other frontiers. The 1939 total was 170,467,186. The census of 1959 gave a total of 208,826,650, and by 1961 the estimated total reached 238 million. In 1940 portions of Poland allocated to Russia by the Treaty of Brest-Litovsk but seized by Poland during the troubled years of the civil war were reoccupied and added to the Ukrainian and Byelorussian Republics. Additional areas were acquired at the end of the Second World War in the Baltic States, southern Sakhalin, the Kurile Islands, and parts of Finland and eastern Prussia. Tannu Tuva was annexed in 1946.

Between 1926 and 1959, striking changes took place in the proportion of people living in rural and urban areas. In these three decades the urban population increased from 26,314,114 to 99,728,000, and the urban ratio rose from 18 to 48 per cent. Such figures reflect the increasing efficiency of agriculture and the ability of the farmer to feed more and more city dwellers.

The first of the Union republics, the Russian Soviet Federated Socialist Republic, is by far the largest and most powerful. Within it are five krais and more than eighty oblasts, autonomous oblasts, national okrugs, and autonomous soviet socialist republics. It occupies three-quarters of the area and dominates the political life of the U.S.S.R. This is the only part of the Union to which the term "Russia" might properly be applied.

Moscow, or more correctly Moskva, is the capital of both the U.S.S.R. and the R.S.F.S.R. It lies at the center of the old industrial area and is the focus of eleven railway lines. Four hundred miles to the northwest is the port of Leningrad. Within the European portion of the R.S.F.S.R. are a score of roughly equal-sized oblasts, each dominated by a city such as Moscow, Gorki, Rostov-on-Don, or Volgograd. There are also a dozen autonomous soviet socialist republics set up because of their non-Russian population. East of the Urals the po-

litical units are larger and more complicated. They include oblasts with capital cities such as Sverdlovsk and Novosibirsk; large krais such as the Krasnoyarsk and Far Eastern krai, and the huge Yakut Autonomous Soviet Social Republic.

The Ukrainian Soviet Socialist Republic includes two large cities, the capital at Kiev and industrial Kharkov. There are a score of oblasts, some reaching into former Polish territory around Lvov. Within the republic are the great coal and iron areas of Donets and Krivoi Rog.

The Byelorussian S.S.R. occupies an area in the west, extending into former eastern Poland. The capital is Minsk. The republic is sometimes known as White Russia, a name which apparently results from the white clothing formerly worn by the peasants.

Three small republics border the Baltic, each of them a part of czarist Russia before the First World War but independent during the inter-war years. From north to south these are the Estonian, Latvian, and Lithuanian Soviet Socialist Republics. In the southwest, adjoining Romania and in part covering Bessarabia, which was once a part of czarist Russia, is the Moldavian S.S.R.

The Caucasus is a region of diverse nationalities, now divided into three union republics, the Georgian or Gruzian S.S.R. with its capital at Tbilisi, the Azerbaidzhanian S.S.R. with its capital at Baku, and the Armenian S.S.R. with the capital at Yerevan.

The large area east of the Caspian and south of Siberia was once known as Turkestan, but the name is no longer correct since the Turkmen Soviet Socialist Republic occupies only a small part of the area. Its capital is Ashkhabad. East of it is the Uzbek S.S.R., centered at Tashkent; farther on is the Tadzhik S.S.R. whose capital is Dushanbe (Stalinabad). The short-grass area next to Siberia was once known as the Kirghiz Steppe, but the name is no longer applicable since the Kirghiz S.S.R. is located in the southeastern corner of Soviet Middle Asia, with its capital at Frunze. Covering the so-called Kirghiz Steppe is now the

High mountains border the U.S.S.R. on the south and east. Melting snow brings moisture to lowland valleys, as in this scene from the Kazakh Soviet Socialist Republic. (*Sovfoto*)

huge Kazakh Soviet Socialist Republic, whose center is Alma-Ata.

SOVIET NATIONALITIES

The original home of the Slavic peoples appears to lie northeast of the Carpathians, from whence they began to migrate during the first century. The present Bulgars and Serbs represent a southern group, the Poles and Czechs a northwestern division; and the eastern group is divided among the Great Russians, White Russians, and Little Russians, or Ukrainians.

Although the Russians are clearly of European origin, two centuries of Mongol domination and the later Siberian expansion brought in an Asiatic element. The plains of Russia have been a melting pot akin to those of North America. The genealogical register of the sixteenth century shows that 17 per cent of the noble families were of Tatar and Oriental origin, while 25 per cent were of German and Western European extraction. To speak of the Russians as Asiatics with a European veneer is incorrect; one cannot "scratch a Russian and find a Tatar," but in their midcontinental environment they have acquired a mixed culture. The Russians are at the same time the most eastern of European peoples and the most western of Asiatic.

Nearly 200 ethnic groups are recognized within the Union, although only 80 number more than 10,000 representatives. Slavs account for three-quarters of the population; most of the remainder are of Mongol, Persian, or Turkic extraction.

Slavs occupy the bulk of eastern Europe and have spread across Siberia along railways and rivers. Turkic peoples are concentrated in Middle Asia with extensions into the Tatar Republic and Bashkiria in the Volga valley, and in Yakutia. Mongol peoples live around Lake Baikal, and along the lower Volga. In the extreme north and northwest are relic races such as the Finns and Nentsi, while the northeast has Paleo-Asiatics and Tungus.

Anthropologically, the peoples of the Soviet Union are more or less mixed and present many grades and variations of stature, head form, and other features. The most homogeneous are the Great Russians. Their characteristics are well marked and include blond hair, bluish or gray eyes, rounded head, and medium-featured face. Their stature is not so high, their blondness so pronounced, or their eyes so blue as those the Scandinavians, but they are generally lighter than the Germans.

Since the revolution, cities have grown enormously. In fact, it is hard to find a center which has not doubled or tripled in size. Moscow and Leningrad are each multimillion cities; Kiev, Baku, Gorki, Kharkov, and Tashkent are in the million class. A dozen others have populations of a half million or more. In 1959, the Union had 149 cities in excess of 100,000 population, as against 82 in 1939, 33 in 1926, and 14 in 1897.

The uneven distribution of people is clearly shown in the population map on pp. 590–91. As the features of climate, soil, and agriculture are developed in subsequent chapters, the reasons for this concentration will be apparent,

Semi-subtropical conditions are found along the Black Sea in the lee of the Crimean Mountains. These sanitaria are at one of the many resort areas. (*A. Bushkin, courtesy Soviet Embassy, Washington*)

for most settlement rests on natural factors. The triangular or wedge shape of settlement has scattered extensions east of Lake Baikal and outliers in the fertile valleys of the Caucasus and Soviet Middle Asia.

With increasing emphasis on industry, new concentrations of population have arisen in the mining districts of the Ukraine, the Urals, the Kuznetsk Basin, and Siberia. Improved irrigation has added to the population in the oases of Central Asia and along the lower Volga. Old industrial areas such as the Donets Basin and the Moscow area have grown. Everywhere urban expansion is conspicuous. Agricultural colonization is especially important in the development of the Soviet Far East.

Although population is shifting eastward, it is probable that the general pattern of occupancy is well defined. The center of population lies near the Volga, but with the growth of Siberia it should gradually reach the Urals.

Settlement patterns conform to types of land use. Hunting, fishing, and lumbering predominate in the north. Many people in these areas live in compact clearings along navigable rivers, for the watersheds tend to be swampy and overland travel is difficult. In the cleared coniferous forest lands devoted to cereals and flax, villages are apt to be on morainic hills away from the damp valleys. In the fertile black-soil lands of the south, settlements are larger and typically on high stream banks. Russian villages often extend for a mile or more along a single street. Scattered farmsteads are uncommon.

References on the Soviet Union

A bibliography and much supplementary text may be found in the author's *Soviet Potentials: A Geographic Appraisal.*
See also general references for Asia, Chapter 1.

Atlas C.C.C.P. (ATLAS OF THE U.S.S.R.), Moscow (1955).
Bolshoi Sovietska Atlas Mira (*Great Soviet World Atlas*), with English translation for legends by George B. Cressey, Moscow, vol. I (1937); vol. II (1943).

Armstrong, Terence: *The Northern Sea Route,* New York: Cambridge University Press (1952).
Balzak, S. S., V. F. Vasyutin, and Y. G. Feigin: *Economic Geography of the U.S.S.R.,* New York: Macmillan (1949).
*Baransky, N. N.: *Economic Geography of the U.S.S.R.,* Moscow: Foreign Languages Publishing House (1956).
*Berg, L. S.: *Natural Regions of the U.S.S.R.,* New York: Macmillan (1950).
Clark, M. Gardner: "Soviet Iron and Steel Industry: Recent Developments and Prospects," *Annals, American Academy of Political and Social Sciences,* CCCIII (1956), 50–61.
Cole, J. P., and F. C. German: *A Geography of the U.S.S.R.,* London: Butterworth & Co. (1961).
Cressey, George B.: "Pioneering in Yeniseiland," *Jour. of the Scientific Laboratories,* Denison University, XXXIV (1939), 103–169.
Cressey, George B.: *How Strong Is Russia?* Syracuse, N.Y.: Syracuse University Press (1954).
*Cressey, George B.: *Soviet Potentials: A Geographic Appraisal,* Syracuse, N.Y.: Syracuse University Press (1962).
Erroll, F. J.: "Industrial Life in Russia Today," *Geog. Mag.,* XXVII (1955), 585–598.
Field, Weil C.: "The Amu Darya: A Study in Resource Geography," *Geog. Rev.,* XLIV (1954), 528–542.

Fitzsimmons, Thomas (ed.): *Russian Soviet Federated Soviet Republic,* 2 vols., New Haven, Conn.: Human Relations Area Files (1957),

Fitzsimmons, Thomas, Peter Malof, and John C. Fiske: *U.S.S.R.. Its People, Its Society, Its Culture,* New Haven, Conn.: Human Relations Area Files (1960).

Fullard, Harold: *Soviet Union in Maps,* Chicago: Denoyer Geppert (1961).

Gerasimov, I. P.: "The Geographical Study of Agricultural Land Use," *Geog. Jour.,* CXXIV (1958), 452–463.

Gregory, James, and D. W. Shave: *The U.S.S.R.,* New York: John Wiley (1944).

Grigoryev, A. A.: "Soviet Plans for Irrigation and Power: A Geographical Assessment," *Geog. Jour.,* CXVIII (1952), 168–179.

Harris, Chauncy D.: "Ethnic Groups in Cities of the Soviet Union," *Geog. Rev.,* XXXV (1945), 466–473.

Harris, Chauncy D.: "The Cities of the Soviet Union," *Geog. Rev.,* XXXV (1945), 107–121.

*Harris, Chauncy D.: "Soviet Agricultural Resources Reappraised," *Journal of Farm Economics,* XXXVIII (1956), 258–273.

Hassmann, Heinrich: *Oil in the Soviet Union: History, Geography, Problems,* Princeton, N.J.: Princeton University Press (1953).

*Hodgkins, Jordan A.: *Soviet Power: Energy Resources, Production and Potentials,* Englewood Cliffs, N.J.: Prentice-Hall (1961).

Hooson, David J. M.: "The Middle Volga—An Emerging Focal Region in the Soviet Union," *Geog. Jour.,* CXXVI (1960), 180–190.

Hooson, David J. M.: "A New Soviet Heartland," *Geog. Jour.,* CXXVIII (1962), 19–29.

Jackson, W. A. Douglas: "The Virgin and Idle Lands of Western Siberia and Northern Kazakhstan: A Geographic Appraisal," *Geog. Rev.,* XLVI (1956), 1–19.

Jackson, W. A. Douglas: "The Russian Non-chernozem Wheat Base," *Annals, Assn. Amer. Geogs.,* XLIX (1959), 97–109.

Jackson, W. A. Douglas: "The Problem of Soviet Agricultural Regionalization," *Slavic Rev.,* XX (1961), 656–678.

*Jackson, W. A. Douglas: "The Virgin and Idle Lands Program Reappraised," *Annals, Assn. Amer. Geogs.,* LII (1962), 69–79.

Jackson, W. A. Douglas: *Russo-Chinese Borderlands,* Princeton, N.J.: Van Nostrand (1962).

Jackson, W. A. Douglas: *Soviet Union,* Grand Rapids, Mich.: Fideler (1962).

Jorré, Georges: *The Soviet Union: The Land and Its People,* 2d ed., New York: David McKay (1961).

Kish, George: "Soviet Air Transport," *Geog. Rev.,* XLVIII (1958), 309–320.

*Kish, George: *Economic Atlas of the Soviet Union,* Ann Arbor, Mich.: University of Michigan Press (1960).

Krypton, Constantine: *The Northern Sea Route and the Economy of the Soviet North,* New York: Praeger (1956).

Lydolph, Paul E., and Theodore Shabad: "The Oil and Gas Industries in the U.S.S.R.," *Annals, Assn. Amer. Geogs.,* I (1960), 461–486.

Mikhailov, Nikolai: *Across the Map of the U.S.S.R.,* Moscow: Foreign Languages Publishing House (1960).

Mikhailov, Nikolai: *Glimpses of the U.S.S.R.,* Moscow: Foreign Languages Publishing House (1960).

Mills, Dennis R.: "The U.S.S.R.: A Re-appraisal of Mackinder's Heartland Concept," *Scottish Geog. Mag.,* LXXII (1956), 144–153.

Nalivkin, D. V.: *The Geology of the U.S.S.R.,* New York: Pergamon (1960).

Nuttonson, M. Y.: "Agroclimatology and Crop Ecology of the Ukraine and Climatic Analogues in North America," *Geog. Rev.,* XXXVII (1947), 216–238.

Nuttonson, M. Y.: *Ecological Crop Geography of the Ukraine,* Washington: Amer. Inst. of Crop Ecology (1947).

Nuttonson, M. Y.: *Agricultural Climatology of Siberia,* Washington: Amer. Inst. of Crop Ecology (1950).

*Oxford Regional Economic Atlas: *The U.S.S.R. and Eastern Europe,* Fair Lawn, N.J.: Oxford University Press (1956).

Roof, Michael K., and Frederick A. Leedy: "Population Redistribution in the Soviet Union, 1939–1956," *Geog. Rev.,* XLIX (1959), 208–221.

Saushkin, Julian S., "Economic Geography in the U.S.S.R.," *Econ. Geog.,* XXXVIII (1962), 28–37.

Schloss, Milton: "Cloud Cover of the Soviet Union," *Geog. Rev.,* LII (1962), 389–399.

*Shabad, Theodore: *Geography of the U.S.S.R.,* New York: Columbia University Press (1951).

Shabad, Theodore: "The Soviet Concept of Economic Regionalization," *Geog. Rev.,* XLIII (1953), 214–222.

Shabad, Theodore: "Soviet Union," in George Hoffman: *A Geography of Europe,* 2d ed., New York: Ronald (1961).

*Shabad, Theodore: *Soviet Geography: Review and Translation,* New York: American Geographical Society (monthly).

Shimkin, Demitri B.: "Economic Regionalization in the Soviet Union," *Geog. Rev.,* XLII (1952), 591–614.

*Shimkin, Demitri B.: *Minerals: A Key to Soviet Power,* Cambridge, Mass.: Harvard University Press (1953).

*Suslov, S. P.: *Physical Geography of Asiatic Russia,* San Francisco: Freeman (1961).

Taafe, Robert: *Rail Transportation and the Economic Development of Soviet Central Asia,* Chicago: University of Chicago, Dept. of Geog., Research Paper no. 64 (1960).

Taaffe, Robert N.: "Transportation and Regional Specialization: The Example of Soviet Central Asia," *Annals, Assn. Amer. Geogs.,* LII (1962), 80–98.

Taskin, George A.: "The Falling Level of the Caspian Sea in Relation to Soviet Economy," *Geog. Rev.,* XLIV (1954), 508–527.

Thiel, Erich: *The Soviet Far East,* New York: Praeger (1957).

Volin, Lazar: *A Survey of Soviet Russian Agriculture,* Washington: U.S. Dept. of Agriculture, Monograph no. 5 (1951).

43 Soviet Landscapes

Geological Foundations / Land Forms / Climatic Problems / Natural Vegetation / Soils

GEOLOGICAL FOUNDATIONS

The geography of the Soviet Union begins with its most ancient geology. In four corners of the country are areas of ancient crystalline rocks around which younger mountains have been folded and between which lie protected and undisturbed horizontal sedimentary basins. Each buttress or shield has tended to remain above sea level and thus has been deeply eroded. In their geology and topography the buttresses somewhat resemble the Canadian Shield.

The best known of these shields is in the northwest where much of Scandinavia is occu-

pied by a complex of granite, gneiss, and metamorphic rocks. This is termed the Fenno-Scandian Shield, but the only part within the U.S.S.R. lies in Karelia and the Kola Peninsula.

In the Ukraine are scattered exposures of a crystalline area which extends from the Sea of Azov northwest to the Carpathian foothills. Its central portions are thinly buried beneath sediments. This is the Azov-Podolian Shield. Whereas Karelia and Kola rise 3,000 feet above sea level, the surface of the Ukrainian crystalline block lies below 900 feet.

The eastern corners of the quadrilateral are in central Siberia; one near the Arctic, the other near Lake Baikal. Between the mouths of the Yenisei and Lena is an area of schist and gneiss along the Anabar River, from which the shield derives its name. Farther south is a larger and more irregular area situated mainly to the east of Lake Baikal near the Aldan River.

Three of these crystalline areas are mining regions of significance. The Kola Peninsula has very large deposits of apatite; the Ukrainian area has iron and manganese; and the Aldan Shield is rich in gold. Too little is known of the Anabar Shield to measure its potential.

Four basins of sedimentary rocks lie within these shields. Soviet Europe is largely underlain by a great platform of essentially undisturbed old formations. East of the folded Urals, the western Siberian lowland is floored with young marine deposits and glacial sands. Beyond the Yenisei are the central Siberian uplands, underlain by old sediments and considerably more hilly than the platform in Europe. Except for the narrow Urals, there is no major folding or faulting in the 3,000 miles from the Baltic to the Lena. East of the Caspian Sea is the fourth basin; here recent sands mask young sedimentary formations.

Surrounding these four basins are a continuous series of high, rugged mountains, except in the west. The outermost of these are the youngest, such as those in Crimea, the Caucasus, the Hindu Kush, and Kamchatka. Older mountains occupy the area from the Sea of Okhotsk to the Lena. The Urals and the structures of Kazakhstan are still more ancient.

Earthquakes and volcanoes are limited to the borders of the Union. Except for two small quakes in the central Urals, no centers have ever been recorded outside the limits of the young mountains. The areas of greatest intensity are the Caucasus, the mountains of Middle Asia, Lake Baikal, and southeastern Kamchatka. Vulcanism is currently restricted to the Caucasus and Kamchatka.

The last chapter in geology is often more important than the first. During the ice age, the northwestern quarter of the Union was glaciated, while the eastern third acquired permanently frozen ground.

At least three continental ice sheets invaded the area. The earliest stage was the Mindel, corresponding to the Kansan in North America. The most widespread was the Riis, equivalent to the Illinoian, when a lobe of ice followed the valley of the Dnieper to latitude 48°N, its southernmost limit in Europe, as compared with 37°N in North America. The uplands south of Moscow blocked this ice and formed a reentrant, but a second lobe occupied the Don valley, limited on the east by hills along the Volga. The ice front crossed the Urals near latitude 60°N, and the boundary continued irregularly to the Yenisei, east of which it swung sharply to the north and reached the Arctic Ocean east of the Taimyr Peninsula.

The last stage was the Wurm or Wisconsin, but the advance did not reach Moscow, and the Asiatic portion was limited to the Ob estuary and the Taimyr Peninsula. Eurasian ice radiated from three centers, Scandinavia, Novaya Zemlya, and the Taimyr Peninsula, each ice mass smaller and farther north with increasing distance from the source of moisture in the Atlantic.

Local glaciers spread out from the mountains in the Caucasus, Pamirs, Tien Shan, Altai-Sayan, Baikal, and Verkhoyansk areas, but it is certain that there were no continental ice sheets in eastern Siberia. Much of the Union now has an average annual temperature below freezing; only the absence of an adequate snowfall prevents continental glaciers today.

These glacial invasions left a record of morainic deposits, swamps, and deranged drainage, but the effects were not confined to the ice limits. Increased precipitation and decreased evaporation greatly enlarged the Caspian and Aral Seas, so that they overflowed westward into the Black Sea. Ice blocked the mouths of the north-flowing Ob and Yenisei, and a vast lake developed in southwestern Siberia, which in turn found its outlet south across the Turgai lowland to the enlarged Caspian. This proglacial lake was evidently the largest fresh-

Active volcanoes are present in the Kamchatka Peninsula and the Kurile Islands; this photo is from the latter area. Several peaks rise to heights of three miles. (*S. Fridland, courtesy Soviet Embassy, Washington*)

water lake ever known. The amazing flatness of western Siberia is partly due to the silt deposited by this huge lake.

During the rigorous climate of glacial times, the absence of blanketing snow or ice in northern and eastern Siberia permitted excessive radiation so that the ground became permanently frozen to great depths. Despite summer thaw extending to depths of several feet, temperatures at depth continue below freezing. Thus any water present remains as ice; where dry, the rocks merely have negative temperatures. This condition is known as permafrost.

Extensive research has traced the characteristics of this frozen ground. In many areas its base extends to depths of 100 feet, with a maximum of 2,000 feet. Around the southern margins of the frozen area are local pockets of complete summer thaw. Elsewhere within this area are buried zones which never thaw. The total area underlain by permanently frozen earth amounts to 3,728,900 square miles, larger than the United States.

Frozen ground presents special engineering problems for buildings, railroads, and airports. Foundations must either go down to solid rock or gravel, or be deep enough to reach ground which does not thaw and soften during the summer. Most Siberian log houses are heated by a large brick stove. Winter warmth from these stoves often thaws the soil underneath one end of the building, causing it to settle into the resulting mud. Much of the permafrost area has too brief a summer for agriculture, but in favored localities spring thaw may melt the upper 10 feet or so, and enable cultivation to proceed. Within the tundra, summer melting penetrates no more than 1 foot.

LAND FORMS

Within the Soviet Union are land forms of wide variety, ranging from alpine peaks to featureless plains. The detailed picture of surface configuration shows 18 land-form provinces, 8 of them in Soviet Europe, 4 in Soviet Middle Asia, and 6 in Siberia. These may be divided into 85 land-form regions. Provincial names reflect elevation, such as lowland, upland or highland, while regional names indicate land form, such as plain, plateau, hill, or mountain. If the following listing seems long it is because the country is complex.

The Fenno-Scandian Uplands are a land of low hills developed on a Pre-Cambrian shield of great complexity. Glacial erosion has scoured and smoothed the surface, disrupted drainage, and produced innumerable lakes. The Karelian Hills resemble Finland. The Kola Hills are nearly detached and more mountainous. Along the eastern and southern margins are a series of lowlands between the crystallines and bordering sedimentaries, partly due to glacial scour. These are represented by the Gulf of Finland and the White Sea at either ends, and Lakes Ladoga and Onega in the center.

The Central European Lowlands extend into Germany and France, but within the Union are three separate regions. The Baltic Glacial Plain is the result of glacial deposition in a region of early Paleozoic sedimentaries. This region roughly coincides with the limits of Baltic drainage and the extent of the latest glacial invasion, the Wurm. It is crossed by a series of recessional moraines. The Upper Dnieper Plain was also glaciated but is a southward sloping surface without lakes. The Pripet or Polesian Marshes spread over western Byelorussia into former Poland. The large extent of uncultivable land is reflected in the map of population density.

The Central Russian Upland is an elongated province of low hills reaching from Lake Onega south into the Ukraine. In the north the Valdai Hills are formed by a west-facing Devonian escarpment. The transverse Smolensk-Moscow Hills, which die out just north of Moscow, are in part a morainic belt. The southern and largest region is the Kursk Hills, well known for extensive iron-ore deposits in the buried Voronezh crystalline block.

Beneath the sediments of the Ukrainian Uplands is a partly exposed Pre-Cambrian shield, but the topography is related to the outcrop of southward-dipping formations of the late Paleozoic. These form a series of northwest–southeast cuestas arranged *en échelon*. Several Ukrainian rivers flow southeast, parallel to these escarpments, then turn and cut through them in antecedent valleys. Hence, reading from the east, the regions may be termed the Don Hills, the Donets Hills famous for their coal, the Dnieper Hills, and the Bug Hills. Farther west are the Podolian Hills along the base of the Carpathians; these also have a north-facing escarpment overlooking the Pripet Marshes. Bessarabia might be included as the Dniester Hills, though the structural parallel does not hold.

The Central Russian Lowlands spread from the Arctic tundra to the black-soil steppes. The most representative region is the rolling hill and valley country south of Moscow, termed the Oka-Don Plain, drained by the headwaters of these rivers. The Upper Volga

---

Within the 8½ million square miles of the Soviet Union is a wide variety of land forms. Plains and low hills characterize the west, with mountains in the east. This map locates eighteen major geographic regions and a total of eighty-five subdivisions.

Soviet Europe extends to the eastern base of the Ural Uplands and the northern foothills of the Caucasian Highlands. Soviet Middle Asia lies between the Black Sea and the borders of China, and includes the Turan Lowlands and Kazakh Upland. Siberia occupies two-thirds of the Union but accounts for only one-seventh of its population.

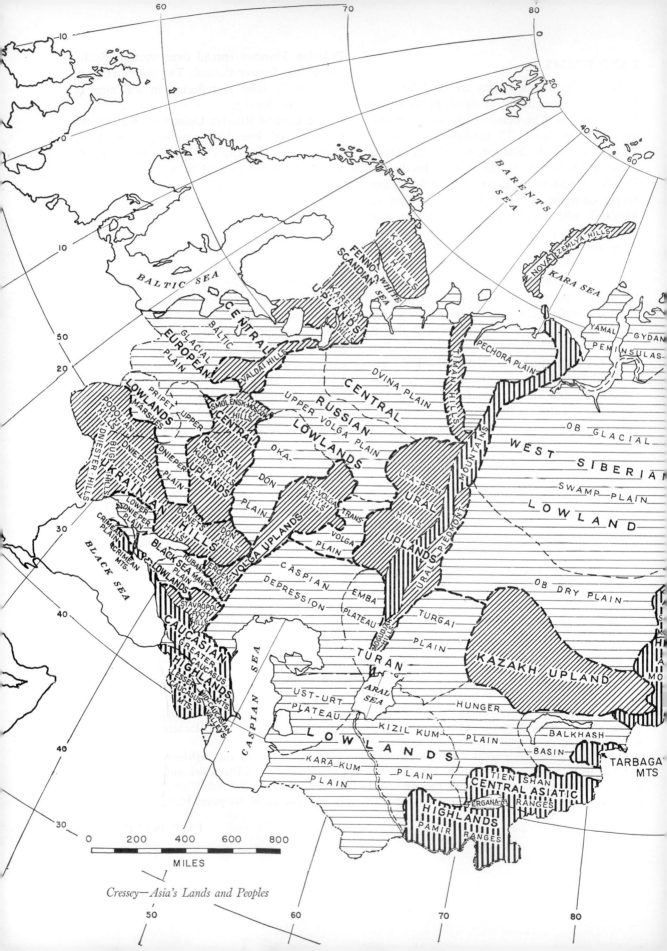

BARENTS SEA

KOLA HILLS

NOVAYA ZEMLYA HILLS

KARA SEA

BALTIC SEA

FENNO-SCANDIAN UPLANDS

KARELIAN HILLS

WHITE SEA

YAMAL

GYDAN PENINSULAS

CENTRAL

GLACIAL

EUROPEAN

PLAIN

BALTIC

VALDAI HILLS

PRIPET UPPER MARSHES

SMOLENSK-MOSCOW HILLS

CENTRAL RUSSIAN UPLANDS

KURSK HILLS

DVINA PLAIN

UPPER VOLGA PLAIN

CENTRAL

RUSSIAN

LOWLANDS

PECHORA PLAIN

TIMAN HILLS

OB GLACIAL

WEST SIBERIAN

LOWLAND

SWAMP PLAIN

LOWLANDS

PODOLIAN HILLS

BUG HILLS

DNIEPER HILLS

DNIESTER HILLS

UKRAINIAN

HILLS

DNIEPER PLAIN

OKA

DON

PLAIN

PRE-VOLGA HILLS

VOLGA UPLANDS

UFA-PERM HILLS

URAL MOUNTAINS

URAL UPLANDS

URALS-PEDMONT

TRANS-VOLGA PLAIN

DONETS HILLS

LOWER DNIEPER PLAIN

CRIMEAN PLAIN

CRIMEAN MTS

BLACK SEA

BLACK SEA LOWLANDS

MANICH PLAIN

KUBAN PLAIN

ERGENI HILLS

CASPIAN

DEPRESSION

VOLGA PLAIN

EMBA PLATEAU

OB DRY PLAIN

TURGAI PLAIN

MUGODJAR

KAZAKH UPLAND

STAVROPOL FOOT HILLS

CAUCASIAN

HIGHLANDS

GREATER CAUCASUS MTS

LESSER CAUCASUS MTS

CAUCASUS VALLEYS

CASPIAN SEA

TURAN

ARAL SEA

LOWLANDS

HUNGER

BALKHASH BASIN

TARBAGA MTS

UST-URT PLATEAU

KIZIL KUM PLAIN

KARA-KUM PLAIN

PLAIN

CENTRAL ASIATIC HIGHLANDS

TIEN SHAN RANGES

FERGANA BA

PAMIR RANGES

0   200   400   600   800

MILES

Cressey—Asia's Lands and Peoples

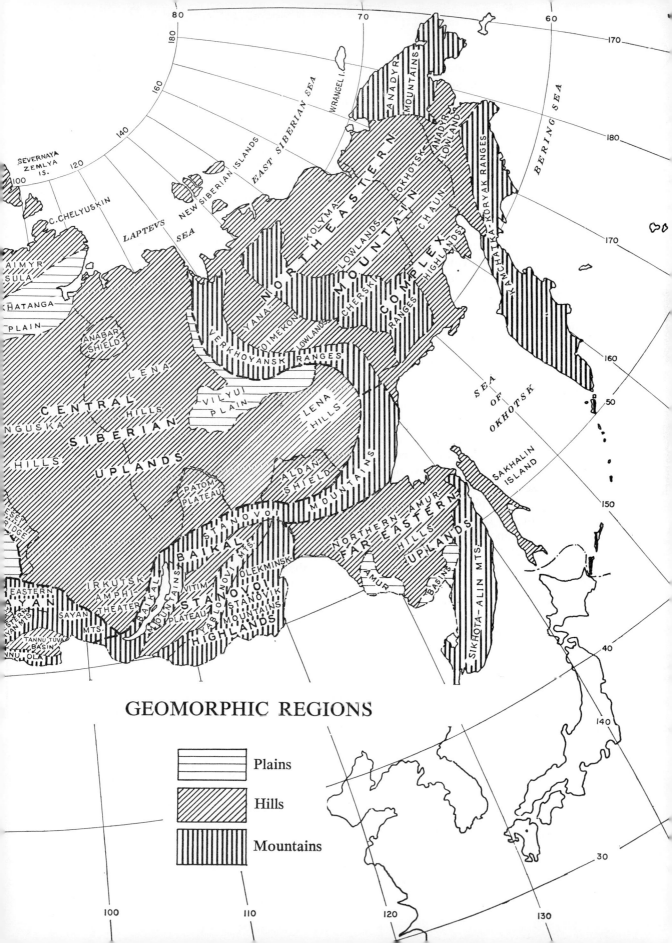

GEOMORPHIC REGIONS

Plains

Hills

Mountains

Plain is slightly more hilly, but in its gross aspects it is a nearly featureless plain. Russians have long named various areas Pre- or Trans- with relation to their position as regards Moscow, as for example the Trans-Volga Plain on the left blank below the junction of the Kama. This is a dry steppe which gradually rises to the Urals. Two regions of Arctic drainage complete the division, the Dvina Plain and the Pechora Plain. Both have a veneer of glacial deposits and postglacial marine sands. The Pechora area is underlain by coal and oil.

The Volga Uplands comprise the Pre-Volga Hills along the right bank, including the low Jiguli Mountains in the Samara Bend. The Ergeni Hills form the southern end of the area.

The Black Sea Lowlands include the Lower Dnieper Plain extending from the Dniester to the Sea of Azov, the Crimean Plain in the northern two-thirds of the peninsula, and the extensive Kuban and Manych Plain between the Don and the Caucasus. The Manych River was once an outlet for the enlarged Caspian Sea.

The Ural Uplands are an old linear mountain range, largely reduced to rounded hills. In history, structure, and relief they somewhat resemble the Appalachians. On the east is a peneplained crystalline platform termed the Ural Piedmont. In the center are the narrow Ural Mountains, composed of folded geosynclines on either side of a granite core, deformed at the end of the Paleozoic. The southern projection is the Mugudjar Hills and the northern extension is found in the Novaya Zemlya Hills. The Timan Hills to the northwest are a peneplained anticline of late Paleozoic rocks, bordered by Mesozoic synclines. To the west of the Ural Mountains is a broad dissected plateau carved in Permian formations, the Ufa Hills.

Soviet Middle Asia begins with the Caucasus. This land-form province presents such great topographic variety that the divisions here suggested are an oversimplification. On the north the Stavropol Foothills project into the Kuban-Manych Plain. Next is the main range of the Greater Caucasus Mountains with rugged land forms and elevations to 18,468 feet. South of the mountains are valleys draining toward the Black and Caspian Seas, which may be termed the Mid-Caucasus Valleys. Beyond them rise the Lesser Caucasus Mountains followed by portions of the high Armenian Plateau. The structure of the Greater Caucasus is continued westward in the Crimean Mountains.

The Turan or Central Asian Lowland is mostly desert. The Caspian Depression embraces the area north of the sea, partly below ocean level, which was covered when the enlarged Caspian overflowed westward. East of the Caspian is the Emba Plateau and the Ust Urt Plateau. Three desert plains lie between and on either side of the Amu Darya and Syr Darya. Between the former and the Caspian is the Kara Kum Plain, sometimes romanized as Qara Qum; between the rivers is the Kizil Kum Plain, or Qizil Qum, and to the east of the Syr Darya is the Hunger Plain or Bedpak Dala. The Balkhash Basin farther east commands the entrances to China. The Turgai Plain in the northwest is a corridor into Siberia, and once carried drainage from glacial lakes to the north.

The Central Asiatic Highlands mark the structural core of the continent and extend into Afghanistan, India, and China. The Pamir Ranges include numerous other mountains such as the Alai, Turkestan, and Gissar. Here are the highest elevations in the Soviet Union: Peak Communism, formerly Mount Stalin, 24,584 feet, and Mount Lenin, 22,377 feet. North of these ranges is the Fergana Basin in the upper valley of the Syr Darya. Beyond it is the western end of the Tien Shan Range with numerous subregions.

The Kazakh Upland is an ancient mountain range, worn down to rolling hills and plains so that only the roots of the mountains remain. The Kazakh Hills contain coal and copper. This area has sometimes been incorrectly referred to as the Kirghiz Steppe.

Siberia includes six land-form provinces. The southern and eastern borders are fringed with high mountains, from the Altai to the Verkho-

Lake Issyk, in the Kazakh Soviet Socialist Republic, lies in the high Tien Shan where intermediate slopes are covered with splendid forests. (*I. Budnevich, courtesy Soviet Embassy, Washington*)

yansk. The Altai-Sayan Highlands are made up of numerous structures with a general northwest–southeast trend. At the western end are the Tarbagatai Mountains, and next to them lie the Siberian Altai Mountains which continue into Mongolia. The Salair Mountains and Kuznetsk Alatau Mountains extend northward on either side of the Kuznetsk Basin, famous for its coal. East of the Kuznetsk Alatau is the Minusinsk Basin along the upper Yenisei, surrounded on the south side by the Western Sayan Mountains and on the north by the Eastern Sayan Mountains. The latter extend to near Lake Baikal.

The West Siberian Lowland occupies the vast plain of the Ob and Irtysh, one of the largest and flattest lands on earth. Two projections characterize the Arctic portion, the Yamal and Gydan Peninsulas. The Ob Glacial Plain is veneered with glacial and recent marine deposits; south of it is the Vasyugan Swamp. Along the Trans-Siberian Railway is the dry Ob Plain, pitted with innumerable deflation hollows, and drained by the Tobol, Ishim, Irtysh, and Ob Rivers. The Khatanga Plain is a northeast continuation of the Lowland. The Lowland extends a short distance to the east of the Yenisei.

The Central Siberian Uplands reach from the Yenisei to the Lena and are sometimes called Angaraland. The core is the Anabar Hills or Shield, north of the Tunguska Hills, a dissected platform of late Paleozoic formations with extensive coal beds and widespread lava flows. The Taimyr Peninsula projects into the Arctic beyond the Khatanga Plain. In the southwest, the Yenisei Ridge formed by an upfaulted block combines with the Eastern Sayan and Baikal Mountains to enclose the amphitheater of Irkutsk, a southern subdivision of

Massive formations line the Lena River in Yakutia. These are the Stolby cliffs. (*M. Redkin, courtesy Soviet Embassy, Washington*)

the Tunguska platform. The geomorphic characteristics of the Lena valley are less apparent. A large basin in the center may be termed the Vilui Plain, and in the south are the Patom and Aldan plateaus, the latter a shield. The remainder of the valley is grouped as the Lena Hills although part of the region is a plain.

The Baikal-Stanovoi Highlands continue the mountainous relief described in the Altai-Sayan Highlands. The Baikal Mountains rise on either side of the trench or graben that holds the lake. To the east is the Vitim Plateau, part of the ancient shield of southeastern Siberia, and beyond it are the Yablonovi Mountains. The latter have a southwest–northeast trend and extend from the Mongolian border to the Olekma River. East of them is an area of low mountains and basins known as the Olekminsk-Stanovik Mountains. Much uncertainty has surrounded the location of the Stanovoi Mountains but it

is now clear that they embrace a series of mountains from near the upper end of Lake Baikal eastward and northward along the Okhotsk Sea to latitude 60°N.

The Far Eastern Uplands include but one well-defined range, the Sikhota Alin Mountains; the remaining geomorphology is obscure. A series of lowlands along the Amur and its tributaries, notably the Zeya, Bureya, and Ussuri, form the Amur Basins. To their north lie the Amur Hills. The island of Sakhalin and the Kuriles may be included.

The Northeastern Mountain Complex is adequately characterized by its title. The line of the Stanovoi is continued by the curving Verkhoyansk Range along the right bank of the Lena. Between it and the high Cherski Range are the Yana and Oimekon Basins; air drainage into these valleys makes them the coldest inhabited places on earth. The Kolyma Lowlands comprise the swampy Kolyma Plain in the north, the Alazeya Plateau on the west, and the Yukagir Plateau on the south. Farther east and south are a series of uplands, chief of which is the Gydan Range bordering the northern Sea of Okhotsk and continuing through the Anyui Mountains to the Arctic, collectively known as the Okhotsk-Chaun Uplands. The Anadyr Mountains cover the Chukchee or Chukotsk Peninsula opposite Alaska, and the Anadyr Lowlands lie between the Anadyr and Gydan Mountains and the Koryak Mountains. The Kamchatka Peninsula contains volcanoes whose size and activity parallel those of Java.

CLIMATIC PROBLEMS

Despite the vast extent of the Soviet Union, climatic conditions over a large part of the interior have much in common. The situation is different near the Black Sea and in the Far East, but elsewhere long winters, low precipitation, and sharp seasonal contrasts dominate. Continentality is as much a climatic characteristic as it is a locational or cultural phenomenon.

Millions of square miles are eliminated from normal settlement because of their short growing season, inadequate rainfall, or high summer temperatures which lead to the rapid evaporation of the available moisture. In many places occasional frosts that extend into the summer or come early in the fall, the lack of adequate spring rainfall or ground moisture from melting snow, or the occurrence of drying winds introduce crop uncertainties that do not appear in the annual climatic averages.

It has long been a recognized climatic rule that the lower the annual rainfall, the greater the variability from year to year: it appears to be equally true that the lower the annual temperature, the greater the variation in the period between spring and fall frosts. Climatic hazards thus compress the central fertile triangle on both north and south.

Only a few areas in the west and in the higher mountains receive more than 20 inches of rainfall. If it were not for moderate summer temperatures and limited evapotranspiration, little of the country would be safe for agriculture. In the United States 20 inches of rain is the lower limit for dependable crops, but with less evaporation in the Soviet Union, farming can be carried on with only 15 inches of precipitation. Middle Asia and northeastern Siberia each have under 10 inches, but whereas the former is a hot desert, the other is a cold tundra. Fortunately precipitation in the cultivated areas comes during the summer when it is most needed. From time to time the spring rains necessary for planting are seriously delayed. Severe famines have resulted from this cause in the steppes of the Ukraine, Don, and Volga. During dry seasons, the Emba River does not reach the Caspian Sea, and streams in Kazakhstan lose so much water by evaporation that they wither away.

Although surrounded by seas on three sides, the country receives surprisingly little marine

---

MAP OF CLIMATIC REGIONS

Cold and/or drought characterize most Soviet climates. The following Koeppen types are present. *ET,* or polar tundra, climates are present in the Arctic and on mountain summits. *D* types, with short summers and severe winters, cover much of the country; *C* climates, with long hot summers and mild winters, occur in the far south. Both *D* and *C* types have steppe, *BS,* or desert, *BW,* modifications.

These major categories are further modified by *a,* hot summers, with the warmest month averaging over 72°F; *b,* cool summers, with four months above 50°F; *c,* short cool summers, with one to three months above 50°F; *d,* severe winters, with the coldest month below −36°F; *f,* moist throughout the year; *s,* dry summers; and *w,* dry winters.

Cressey—*Asia's Lands and Peoples*

CLIMATIC REGIONS

E	Climates
D	Climates
C	Climates
B	Climates

— — Southern Limit of Permanently Frozen Ground

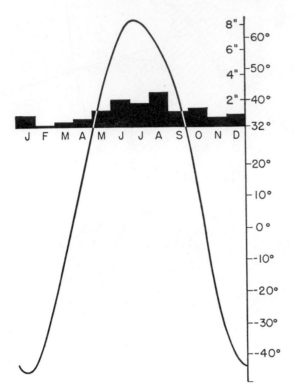

YAKUTSK. Elevation 535 feet, average temperature 12°F, annual precipitation 7 inches. While continentality is obvious in this graph for northern Siberia, a similar curve for Verkhoyansk would require 5½ inches.

benefit. On the south, mountain barriers and great distances effectively bar any influence from the Indian Ocean. The Pacific lies to leeward of most winds, and mountains limit the penetration of its summer monsoon moisture to Lake Baikal. For much of the year the Arctic Ocean is frozen, and the summer area of ice-free water available for evaporation is never large. The low temperatures of the Arctic at all seasons make it an unimportant source of moisture or ameliorating warmth. Only the Atlantic remains, and it lies across the width of peninsular Europe; yet even in central Siberia the bulk of the rain is apparently of Atlantic origin. For the country as a whole, excluding only the immediate shores of the Pacific, Atlantic moisture supplies perhaps 85 per cent of the total precipitation. This is all the more surprising since the only low-altitude path from the Atlantic lies through the 900-mile gap between the Alps and the Scandinavian highlands.

While lowlands are dry, interior mountains such as the Sayan record a yearly precipitation of over 40 inches. Apparently this moisture has come overland 4,000 miles from the Atlantic.

Changes of latitude and altitude do not al-

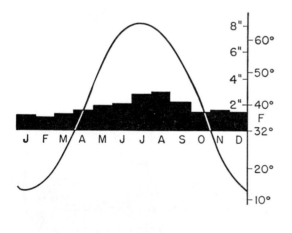

Moscow. Elevation 480 feet, average temperature 39°F, annual precipitation 21 inches. This graph is a fair sample of Soviet Europe.

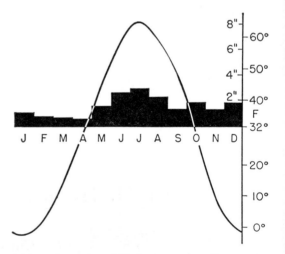

Tomsk. Elevation 399 feet, average temperature 29°F, annual precipitation 20 inches. Central Siberia has a taiga climate.

ways bring the normal results found elsewhere. The yearly average temperature at Moscow is about the same as at Leningrad, though 300 miles to the south. Winters in the deltas of the Volga and Syr Darya are colder than near the Gulf of Finland. Likewise, the New Siberian Islands in the Arctic Ocean are warmer than the coast of Siberia, which in turn is warmer than the interior. The lowest recorded temperatures in the Yenisei valley lie near the Mongolian border, 1,300 miles south of the mouth in the Arctic.

Air drainage in the mountains introduces further inversions. Intense winter radiation, especially in windless northeastern Siberia, causes surface air to become very cold and heavy. It thus flows into the valleys, which are colder than surrounding mountains. The extremely low temperatures at Verkhoyansk are well known, with a January average of −58°F and an extreme minimum of −90°F. Other very low temperatures have been recorded at nearby Oimekon, which reported −108°F in 1938. These are the coldest towns in the world.

Winter is the dominant season throughout the Union. The frost-free period is less than 60 days in the Siberian Arctic and only 90 to 120 days in the northern half of Soviet Europe and central Siberia. In the central European area, the Ukraine, and in southwestern Siberia, the frost-free time is between 120 and 180 days, and exceeds 200 days only in Middle Asia.

Bitterly cold waves sweep southward across the entire country except for sheltered areas in the Crimea and Caucasus. Snowfall is not heavy but, since thaws are rare in winter, it accumulates and may be blown into formidable drifts. Throughout Siberia snow lies on the ground for 160 to 260 days, and in the European part of the Union it persists for 100 to 200 days except in the Ukraine.

The severity and duration of the winter season affect man in many ways. Daylight hours are short. Outdoor farm activities and general construction are obviously restricted. Blizzards block communications and may cause the loss of unprotected cattle. Fresh foods are lacking, and the winter diet is characteristically monotonous and deficient in vitamins.

Seasonal contrasts are intensified toward the eastern interior, and the range from January to July averages increases from 51°F at Moscow to 118°F at Verkhoyansk.

Summers are almost everywhere warm. Along the Arctic coast long hours of sunshine raise the day and night monthly average to 50°F. From Arkhangelsk and Igarka south to Kiev and Irkutsk, July temperatures are 60 to 68°F. In the steppes temperatures increase to 75°F and exceed that in the deserts.

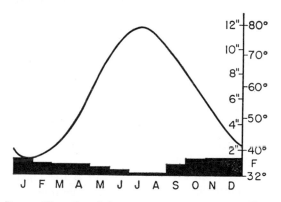

BAKU. Elevation 0 feet, average temperature 58°F, annual precipitation 10 inches. The Caspian area experiences a desert climate, with excessive evapotranspiration.

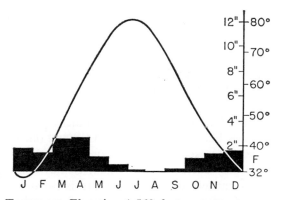

TASHKENT. Elevation 1,569 feet, average temperature 55°F, annual precipitation 15 inches. This part of Soviet Middle Asia has a steppe climate.

January conditions show sharp contrasts. Monthly averages in Soviet Europe range from 25 down to 5°F, while Siberian stations drop to −5°F or even −40°F. Soviet Middle Asia has averages of 32 to 14°F.

During winter, great masses of cold air develop in the vicinity of Lake Baikal and westward along latitude 50°N, with a high averaging 1,033 millibars. This stationary center of subpolar continental air is the dominant factor in winter climate, with outblowing winds over most of Asia. To the north, the circulation tends to be from the west, bringing in cyclonic storms from the Atlantic. Winter winds over southern Siberia thus tend to blow from the north, so that cold air masses push into China.

Summer conditions are somewhat reversed, for high pressures prevail over the surrounding oceans, and the center of low pressure shifts to Mongolia and northwestern India. Summer circulation is irregular, but in general there are inblowing winds from the west and northwest.

NATURAL VEGETATION

The general pattern of natural vegetation is both simple and significant. No other regional picture is so expressive of land usability, for natural vegetation sums up many of the items of temperature, rainfall, surface configuration, drainage, and soils. In the long-settled lands of old Russia, man has so changed the landscape that the original cover of vegetation is largely gone, but in undeveloped areas like Siberia it still dominates.

Most of the Soviet Union is a forest land, one-fifth of the forested area on earth. Many of the trees are conifers such as pine, spruce, or larch; broad-leaved forms are in many places softwoods like birch and aspen. Oak and other hardwood forests were never extensive and are now largely cut over. The Union is thus deficient in hardwoods. Most furniture is perforce made of softwoods. Railroad ties of pine deteriorate within five years unless treated.

From north to south there are four main zones of vegetation. Adjoining the Arctic, and extending southward along the mountain tops, is the treeless tundra. The next major zone is the taiga, a vast coniferous forest unbroken from Europe to the Pacific. To the south, a grassland steppe extends from the Black Sea to northern Mongolia. Deserts cover the Union between the Caspian and the Pamirs. Between the taiga and the steppe in both the extreme west and east are wedges of mixed conifers and hardwoods.

The tundra has a severe winter with frosts even in summer. From north to south are four subzones, each with progressively more vegetation. The northernmost is the Arctic tundra with moss and lichens but without trees or bushes. Second is the typical bush tundra with dwarf birch and willow, and lichens and moss. Next is the south tundra with low fir, birch, and larch trees along river valleys, and well-developed sphagnum peat bogs. The wooded tundra, the fourth subzone, forms a transition to the true forest. Patches of tundra are present almost to the southern limit of the taiga, but in general the tundra zone lies north of the Arctic Circle and within 250 miles of the ocean. The southern limit corresponds with the July isotherm of 50°F. Comparable tundra vegetation is present on the higher mountains as far south as the Caucasus and Pamirs.

Tundra vegetation is exclusively perennial. Many forms spread over the ground to secure the maximum solar insolation. Dwarf growths are typical. Bright flowers and green grass suddenly come to life during the long summer days. Remains of trees in peat bogs more than 100 miles north of the present wooded tundra suggest a warmer and drier postglacial climate. Since frozen subsoil prevents ground-water drainage, widespread swamps develop during the summer and become breeding grounds for swarms of mosquitoes.

Farther from the Arctic Ocean is the taiga, a cool temperate forest, dominantly coniferous. Winters are severe, but summer months have average temperatures between 50 and 68°F. The usual trees are pine, fir, larch, and cedar, with subordinate but locally important areas of birch, aspen, and alder. There are scattered meadows on river-flood plains and open watersheds.

East of Lake Baikal, Daurian larch replaces the Siberian larch which grows to the west. The former is especially adapted to growth above frozen ground. When the forest is burned or cut over, birch and whitewoods precede conifers in order of natural restoration. Peat bogs and marsh, widespread in western Siberia and northern Europe, are rare east of the Yenisei, where relief is greater; the summers have less rainfall, and the air is dry. Much of the northern taiga has no commercial value, but trees are taller and larger in diameter toward the south. Large mammals such as elk, reindeer, bear, and lynx were formerly abundant, but the chief taiga animals are now squirrels, rabbits, and foxes.

The mixed-forest zone of the western Soviet Union lies in a milder climate where fir and oak are found together. The warmest month exceeds 68°F. The distribution of deciduous trees is somewhat conformable with the wedge of population and cultivated land. Scattered oak forests thus spread from Leningrad almost to the Black Sea and east to the Ural and Kama Rivers. Along river valleys such as the Volga, oak extends north to 57°N. Maple has about the same distribution; ash covers a smaller area; linden spreads farther north and east than oak, while hornbeam is confined to the middle Dnieper valley.

In the Far East, another mixed-forest zone reappears in the basin of the Amur with oak, maple, ash, linden, and elm. Considerable areas of splendid timber remain. Bright summer greens and brilliant fall foliage distinguish these mixed forests from the somber taiga. The fauna includes wild boars, reindeer, leopard, and Manchurian tigers.

South of the continuous forest lies a transition zone termed the wooded steppe, where solid stands of trees alternate with open grassland. Local factors of soil, relief, or vegetation history cause islands of steppe to lie within the mixed forest, and forest outliers are present within the continuous steppe to the south. In the European areas, oak is dominant; in Siberia birch is the typical tree. In the west, the boundaries of the wooded steppe are Kiev and Kharkov; along the Volga they are Kazan and Kuibyshev. East of the Urals the center of the wooded steppe follows the railway from Chelyabinsk to Omsk and Novosibirsk.

The true steppe is a treeless expanse with a continuous cover of short grass, in many places developed on loessial soils. Summers are dry and warm, with the July average above 68°F; the yearly rainfall is 12 to 16 inches. Only near the northern and more humid margin is the grass luxuriant enough to be termed a meadow; elsewhere short cereal grass and feather grass are typical. The presence of chernozem soil shows that the absence of trees is not due to deforestation by man. Instead, the prolonged dry period, low summer humidity, and deep ground-water surface make natural forest growth unlikely.

Long hours of high-latitude sunshine, low in photosynthetic ability, produce large cabbage leaves at Kirovsk, near the Arctic Circle. (*Sovfoto*)

The extensive development of shelter belts in the steppe represents an attempt to modify the microclimate and remake nature. (*Sovfoto*)

The steppes of the Ukraine and lower Volga are an area of low, variable rainfall, hot drying winds from the east known as *sukhovey,* and frequent drought with subsequent famine. In order to check wind velocities, hold moisture, and protect soil, thousands of miles of shelter belts have been planted. If tree plantings are adequately cared for, they may grow even with rainfall of 10 or 12 inches, but they do not reproduce themselves.

The steppe zone continues from the Black Sea and northern Caucasus east to the Altai Mountains. These grasslands are the traditional home of the Cossacks, especially in the valleys of the Don and Volga, and were once overrun by the Mongol hordes. The steppe has so stamped its personality on the southern third of the country that one author has facetiously en-titled a volume *Across Russia, Steppe by Steppe.*

The semidesert zone is transition area. Whereas the true steppe has a continuous cover of grass and in the true desert it is nearly absent, the semidesert has spotty vegetation. Rainfall is 5 to 10 inches, and July temperature averages exceed 75°F. Characteristic plant forms are wormwood and cereal grass. Salt marshes are present in places.

The deserts of the U.S.S.R. have hot and nearly rainless summers, with July averages to 85°F, and frosty winters. Annual evaporation from free-water surfaces is ten times the precipitation, but soil moisture is locally maintained by rivers from the snow-clad Pamirs. The deserts from the Caspian Sea to beyond Lake Balkhash have shifting sands and alkaline soils. Vegetation is zoned according to rainfall, ground water, and salinity of the soil. Wormwood or sage is common in the north. All plants are especially adapted to reduce transpiration. Thickets of saxaul bushes have developed locally. During spring rains, ephemeral grasses and flowers rapidly come to life. Poplar and tamarisk grow in some valleys. The marmot is the chief animal, especially adapted to the desert by summer hibernation.

Subtropical Mediterranean forests are confined to the valleys of Transcaucasia. Winters are so mild that vegetation grows throughout the year, and precipitation makes possible a luxuriant growth of broad-leaf trees, with an admixture of conifers. Oak, hornbeam, and beech are typical at the lower elevations. Alder thickets are found in marshy areas.

Mountains have such sharp climatic zones that within a few thousand feet of elevation they may reproduce many of the types of vegetation just described. On some mountains vegetation changes from deserts at their base through meadows, deciduous and then coniferous forests, and finally to alpine tundra at the summits. Thus the vegetation sequence in altitude is a replica of changes with latitude. This is especially noticeable in the Caucasus and Pamirs, which are capped by permanent snow fields.

Mountain flora range from alpine meadows with abundant rainfall on windward slopes to steppe or semidesert conditions in the rain shadow. Forests of the Caucasus are especially rich and varied. In the Altai. steppe vegetation covers the lower slopes to around 3,000 feet, above which is a taiga forest to 6,000 feet, followed by alpine meadows. The snow line

Rich chernozem soils underlie much of the Soviet steppe, high in unleached mineral nutrients and organic matter. This is a view in the Kazakh Soviet Socialist Republic. (*Tass*)

lies at 9,000 feet. In the mountains of northeastern Siberia, Daurian larch is dominant, but east of the Kolyma River mountain tundra covers much of the highlands. Drainage and soils differentiate this mountain tundra from the low-level tundra along the Arctic coast.

SOILS

Russian soil scientists have led the world in recognizing that environmental factors of vegetation, rainfall, and temperature produce soils which have similar characteristics over broad areas, regardless of the underlying geology. These modified soil types are termed mature, in contrast to immature soils where initial features of geologic origin still dominate. Thus the parent material, whether stream alluvium, glacial deposits, or rock weathered *in situ,* acquires a definite profile through the action of ground water and vegetation. Surface horizons usually include considerable humus, while lower zones are variously leached or are zones of mineral accumulation.

In areas of abundant rainfall, soluble minerals are leached and removed in solution, while in arid regions such minerals remain in the soil. Where they are present to excess as in deserts, the soil may become alkaline. Grass roots contribute more organic material to the soil than do the leaves of trees. Coniferous forests produce more acid soils than deciduous forests.

Across the Soviet Union, the major soil types reflect climatic and vegetation zones, as well as recent geologic history. Tundra vegetation is associated with tundra soils; the taiga is roughly coextensive with podsol soils; mixed forests coincide with brown forest soils; the steppe area has produced rich chernozem soils; the semiarid lands have chestnut-brown soils; and the deserts correspond with saline or alkaline soils.

Tundra soils are frozen for so much of the year, and have such limited drainage, that they seldom develop a mature profile. Decaying vegetation overlies the mineral soil and renders it so acid that cultivated crops can be raised only with special treatment. Although the rainfall is low, the frozen subsoil may cause excessive surface moisture.

Podsolic types cover nearly half of the Soviet Union. The typical profile shows a surface organic layer derived from coniferous trees unmixed with the mineral soil because of the absence of earthworms and burrowing animals. Below it is a sandy ash-colored horizon which gives the podsols their name, then a dark brownish clay-enriched zone, and below these the unaltered parent material. In the north, podsol formation is retarded by marshes, in the south by deficient moisture. Despite their rather acid character, these podsols provide the soil for about one-third of the cultivated area.

The most productive soil in the world is the chernozem, more extensively developed in the U.S.S.R. than in any other country. Chernozem is a grassland soil, rich with black organic matter and high in lime and soluble mineral nutrients. Some of it is developed on loessial silt. But the very climatic factors that make this soil so fertile also make its agricultural utilization precarious, for rainfall is low and erratic. Were the rainfall heavier, forests would replace the steppe and there would be no chernozem soil. Chernozems underlie half of the cultivated land; so long as the natural sod is not destroyed, wind erosion is seldom serious, but once the soil is cultivated, extensive deflation may take place. Dust-bowl erosion has long been critical in the Eurasian steppes.

Somewhat less fertile than chernozems are the chestnut-brown soils, which, because they are formed in drier areas, are lower in humus but higher in unleached minerals. With still less rainfall, gray desert soils develop; where these are salty they are termed a *solonchak.*

Irrigation may make dry soils usable, but care must be taken for adequate subsurface drainage so that excess water does not evaporate to form a salty crust.

44 Soviet Mineral Resources

The Mineral Prospect / Power / Metals / Nonmetals

THE MINERAL PROSPECT

The Soviet Union is exceedingly fortunate in the variety and quantity of its mineral wealth. Here is clearly one of the richest nations on earth. If Soviet estimates prove correct, the country may have as much as half of the world's reserves of coal, peat, oil, and iron, along with vast amounts of gold, mineral fertilizers such as potassium and phosphate, and a long array of industrial materials. For the moment, these forecasts should be regarded as uncertain.

Geological studies date from the days of Peter the Great, but much of this mineral wealth has been discovered since the revolu-

tion of 1917. In czarist days the Russian Empire accounted for only 1 per cent of the world's known iron and 3 per cent of the coal. During the period between the First and Second World Wars, the reserves of coal and of petroleum each increased sevenfold, lead went up ninefold, zinc increased tenfold. Known copper deposits rose twenty-eight times and iron ore reserves, thirteen times. Other significant increases have been recorded since the Second World War.

Such impressive generalizations conceal a number of practical problems. Many deposits counted as reserves by Soviet geologists would not be considered economically worthwhile in other countries, either because of low metallic

625

percentage, difficult metallurgical problems, the absence of nearby coking coal, or remoteness from markets.

The term "ore" is usually defined as a rock which contains some valuable constituent which can be extracted at a profit. The definition is thus economic rather than geologic. Under a totalitarian regime, low-grade mineral deposits may be developed irrespective of costs if they are needed in the national economy.

Deeply buried deposits of marginal quality in remote areas are not easily transformed into finished products. Although the overall picture of Soviet mineral wealth is one of exceptional abundance, overoptimistic conclusions should not be drawn from mere statistical totals. A great deal of research and large amounts of capital will be required to bring these resources into production.

Estimates as to mineral reserves are usually divided into several categories, such as proved, probable, and possible. The last tends to include broad inferences in advance of detailed field studies. Statistics should be read with necessary reservations as to their reliability. It is clear that Soviet mineral resources are very great, but it is also true that many deposits are imperfectly surveyed, and that the overall totals include many reserves of uncertain value. The known deposits are unevenly distributed; large areas appear to be without important resources; a few areas have a great concentration.

The bulk of the Union's iron ore, bauxite, and oil lies west of the Urals; four-fifths of the coal lies to the east.

The Ukraine has coal, iron, and manganese. The Moscow area has inferior coal and iron. In the Kola Peninsula are spectacular deposits of potash and uncommon minerals. The Urals are a tremendous storehouse of natural wealth, perhaps the richest mountain range of their size on earth. Here are iron, gold, asbestos, potassium and magnesium salts, aluminum, chromium, nickel, low-grade coal, and oil. The Caucasus has oil, manganese, lead, and zinc. Kazakhstan contains coal, copper, iron, lead, and zinc. The Pamirs, Tien Shan, Altai, and Sayan Mountains are all mineralized, with

Soviet Mineral Sufficiency	Surplus	Adequate	Apparently deficient
	Asbestos	Aluminum	Borax
	Bromine	Antimony	Cobalt
	Clay, china and fire	Chromite	Lead
	Coal	Copper	Molybdenum
	Graphite	Diamonds	Tin
	Gypsum	Mercury	Uranium
	Iron	Natural gas	Zinc
	Magnesite	Nickel	
	Manganese	Platinum	
	Magnesium salts	Sulfur	
	Petroleum		
	Phosphate		
	Potassium salts		
	Salt		
	Titanium		
	Vanadium		

conspicuous coal and iron in the Kuznetsk Basin. Eastern Siberia, still partly unexplored, has coal, gold, iron, and other minerals. Despite this imposing list, large areas are entirely without resources.

The industrial utilization of these resources will be considered in the next chapter, but a mere listing discloses the exceptional natural wealth of this vast area. No other land has so great a variety of minerals, and only the United States may be richer.

At the same time we should note that among these many deposits are some low-grade ores, especially copper and aluminum, which have doubtful value if developed on a basis of strict cost accounting. Moreover, reserves and production need to be considered in terms of a country 8½ million square miles in area inhabited by 250 million people.

In view of Soviet-American relations, it may be well to compare their mineral potential. Demitri B. Shimkin summarizes the situation as follows: [1]

In general, the mineral wealth of the Soviet Union, as presently known or inferred, approximates that of the United States. Both countries have enormous reserves of coal and lignite, magnesium salts, and a series of nonmetallic minerals: bromine, fire clay, gypsum, phosphate rock, and low-grade sulfur basics. The known copper reserves are approximately equal, while neither has measurable resources of diamonds. Soviet reserves are much greater than those of the continental United States and Alaska for antimony, asbestos, possibly china clay, chromite, amorphous graphite, magnesite, manganese ore, mercury,

[1] Demitri B. Shimkin: Minerals: A Key to Soviet Power, Cambridge, Mass.: Harvard University Press (1953), 342–343. Quoted by permission.

mica, nickel, possibly petroleum, platinum, potash, natural sodium salts (mirabilite), and tin. On the other hand, the American potentials considerably exceed those known for the U.S.S.R. in bauxite, borax, cadmium, cobalt, fluorspar, helium, iron ore, lead, dolomite, molybdenum, natural gas, titanium (including titano-magnetites), tungsten, vanadium, and zinc.

The major differences between the Soviet Union and the United States in regard to mineral self-sufficiency are therefore not those of more or less ascertained physical endowment but rather of the probabilities of new discoveries, of the politico-economic orientations. Thus, while the finding of numerous new and rich deposits is very likely in the Soviet Union, comparable radical changes are improbable in the United States, with the notable exception of Alaska. Again, American mineral-consumption requirements between 1950 and 1970 may be anticipated, even by a conservative extrapolation, to be 2.5 to 3 times those of the Soviet Union for the same period. Finally, and above all, the Soviet Union has attempted, and will presumably continue to attempt, to gain self-sufficiency without regard to production costs.

POWER

Coal is the great source of power in the Soviet Union, far ahead of oil, peat, or hydro-electricity.

When the Twelfth International Geological Congress collected data on the coal reserves of the world in 1913, Russia was credited with 230 billion metric tons. At the Seventeenth Congress in 1937, Soviet reserves were placed at 1,654,361,000,000 metric tons. By 1956, Soviet estimates placed the total at 8,669,510,-000,000 metric tons, far ahead of those for any other country. These reserves are distributed through nearly 200 fields, with nine tenths

MAP OF MINERAL RESOURCES

Vast mineral resources are present within the U.S.S.R., second only to the United States and perhaps first; this map is limited to those actually in production. The size of the symbols suggests relative importance in world terms.

Three major areas stand out: the Ukraine, with its coal, iron, and manganese; the Urals, with a long array of metals and nearby oil; and the Kuznetsk Basin in Siberia. with its coal.

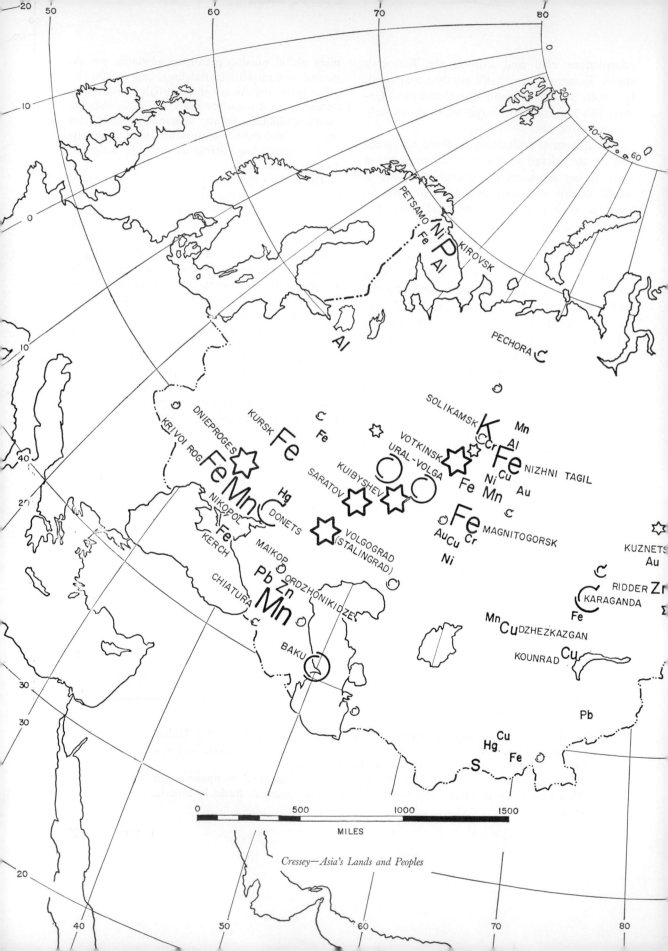

Cressey—*Asia's Lands and Peoples*

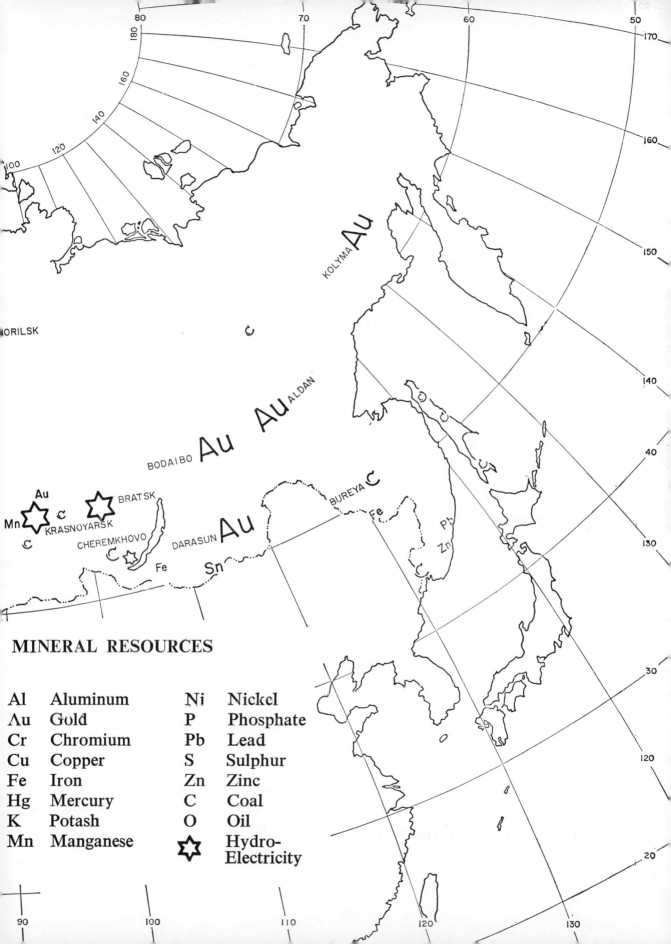

MINERAL RESOURCES

Al	Aluminum	Ni	Nickel
Au	Gold	P	Phosphate
Cr	Chromium	Pb	Lead
Cu	Copper	S	Sulphur
Fe	Iron	Zn	Zinc
Hg	Mercury	C	Coal
K	Potash	O	Oil
Mn	Manganese	✡	Hydro-Electricity

Map labels: ORILSK, KOLYMA Au, ALDAN, BODAIBO Au Au, Au, Mn, KRASNOYARSK, BRATSK, CHEREMKHOVO, DARASUN Au, Fe, Sn, BUREYA, Fe, Pb, Zn

of the total coal tonnage in the Asiatic area.

Before considering these figures we should recognize the criteria involved. In most countries, estimates of reserves are limited to beds at least 30 inches thick, within 3,000 feet of the surface, and containing less than 35 per cent of ash. Current Soviet estimates include deposits with a thickness of 16 inches, to depths of 1 mile, and with up to 50 per cent of ash. Three-fifths of the Soviet coal is also lignite or brown coal. Reserves may further be classified as valid or proved, 3 per cent; probable, 11 per cent; and possible or inferred, 86 per cent. In comparison, coal reserves in the United States, measured on international standards, amount to 2,300 billion metric tons, and include no lignite more than 500 feet below the surface. If Soviet deposits were so measured, the totals in the two countries might be comparable.

Coal production has steadily increased, so that the Union is on a level with the United States. Not only has tonnage increased but its distribution has changed.

The Donets Coal Basin, whose name is often shortened to Donbas, lies north of the Black Sea and has always been the country's leading producer. Despite continued increase in tonnage, its proportion of the national output declined from 87 per cent in 1937 to 36 per cent in 1955, because of the rise of numerous new fields. The Donets coal fields have an area of 10,000 square miles, about three-quarters of which lie within the Ukrainian S.S.R. Nearly half of the coal is anthracite, and there are large amounts of bituminous coal suitable for metallurgical coke, or for chemical uses and gasification. The output supplies the blast furnaces based on iron deposits at Krivoi Rog, 200 miles to the west, as well as at Kerch and Kursk, together with urban and industrial needs west of the Urals.

Both north and south of Moscow are lignite areas which together rank fourth in production. Since lignite is a poor fuel for locomotives or domestic consumption, much of this coal is used in central thermal and electric stations.

Both here and in the Donets area, there is some underground gasification of coal *in situ.*

The Pechora fields lie near the Arctic Circle just west of the Urals. Production in the Vorkuta district supplies coal to Leningrad. Although reserves make this the largest field in Soviet Europe, production is modest. Both Pechora and Donets coals make good metallurgical coke.

Farther east are deposits on both slopes of the Urals. The western coals are high in sulfur and do not make first-class coke for blast furnaces, but are usable for locomotives, electrical power, and for reducing sulfide copper ores. The principal mine is at Kizel. Much of the coal on the eastern side is lignite, such as the deposits near Chelyabinsk.

The development of the Kuznetsk Basin, sometimes called Kuzbas, has transformed a mid-Siberian steppe, south of the Trans-Siberian Railway, into a great industrial center. Reserves are very large and make Kuznetsk comparable to Pennsylvania and Ohio; in production this field holds second place. With a high calorie content, combined with low ash and sulfur, the coals are among the best in the Union. Anthracite is abundant, and some of the bituminous coal is of coking quality. Much of the output is used in the Kuznetsk metallurgical works or shipped to the Urals.

Between Kuznetsk and the Urals lie the very important Karaganda fields, with good coking coal. Their proximity to the Urals has caused them partly to replace Kuznetsk coal in the Magnitogorsk blast furnaces. Some of the coal is near enough to the surface to be mined in open cuts.

East of Kuznetsk are a number of partly developed coal fields. The Minusinsk Basin lies on the Yenisei south of the Trans-Siberian Railway. The Kansk-Achinsk brown-coal field, which extends along the Trans-Siberian Railway on either side of Krasnoyarsk, is largely undeveloped. West of Irkutsk, coal is mined at Cheremkhovo.

Important coal fields are present in the Amur valley, especially along its tributary, the

Karaganda, in the Kazakh Soviet Socialist Republic, is the third-largest coal producer in the Union. There are both open-cut and shaft operations. (*I. Budnevich, courtesy Soviet Embassy, Washington*)

Bureya. Near Vladivostok, coking coal is mined at Artem and at Suchan. Sakhalin also produces coal.

In the Yenisei and Lena valleys lie two vast coal regions, largely undeveloped. Deposits east of the Yenisei, worked at Norilsk, are called the Tunguska coal field, named after the three tributary rivers. Deposits along the Lena are mined on a small scale at Sangar Khai, and appear to be of great extent.

Coal is also mined along the borders of the Caucasus and the Pamirs.

Not only are Soviet reserves exceedingly large, but they are also well distributed. The Urals lack proper metallurgical coke, but new developments at Karaganda make it unnecessary to bring fuel from Kuznetsk. Moscow, once dependent on Donets coal, now produces local lignite. Leningrad once used British or German coal but has developed large central plants for burning nearby peat.

The geology of oil and gas is more complicated than that of coal, and therefore reports of their reserves can be only generalizations. Soviet production has long been a poor second to the American, but her oil reserves are thought to be of large magnitude, apparently to be measured in billions of tons.

The petroleum total may be divided into various categories of probability, of which the larger part is little more than an optimistic geological estimate. Intensive geological and geophysical prospecting has located new fields and spread production widely from the prerevolutionary center at Baku.

In contrast to the widespread distribution of coal, oil deposits are largely in a single zone, extending from the Caspian Sea northward to the Arctic. Sakhalin has important wells, and there is a small output at Nordvyk in the Siberian Arctic, on Kamchatka, near the Pamirs, and east of the Caspian Sea. There is some

The great oil fields of the U.S.S.R. lie between the Volga and the Urals and are known as the "Second Baku." This is the Novo Ufimsk refinery near Ufa. (*Courtesy Soviet Embassy, Washington*)

hope that oil may be present beneath the West Siberian Plain.

Baku in Azerbaidzhan was once far in the lead as a producer, dating from 1869. In 1901 it supplied half of the world's output. Most of the production comes from wells on the Apsheron Peninsula, but there is also offshore production in the Caspian. Pipelines lead west to Batum on the Black Sea, and also north of the Caucasus to the Donets area and beyond.

Oil is produced along the northern slopes of the Caucasus at Grozny and Maikop. Large reserves of natural gas occur in these areas.

Northeast of the Caspian along the Emba River are at least 300 salt domes, many of them with associated oil reserves. Other promising fields lie east of the Caspian in Middle Asia.

The oil fields between the Volga and the southern Urals have been developed since 1928. Reserves are so extensive that the area

is termed a "Second Baku." Proved fields extend from the Caspian Depression north to the Kama River, and the oil possibilities appear to be the largest in the Union. Production in the Ural-Volga area reached first place during the 1950s.

Oil shales in Estonia and elsewhere may some day prove to be important. Natural gas is produced in the Ukraine, the Ural-Volga oil fields, and near the Caspian. Pipelines lead to Moscow.

Hydroelectricity has become a major source of power, although far behind thermal electricity. Soviet plans in this field are very ambitious. Only the Caucasus, Pamirs, Tien Shan, and the eastern Siberian mountains have swift streams fed by melting snow. Elsewhere gradients are gentle and the flow seasonal, but rivers as large as the Volga and Yenisei make the potential power impressive.

Soviet plans look forward to the conversion of every river into a staircase, with a series of dams and reservoirs from source to mouth. On the Volga there are to be nine dams with a total head of 425 feet, generating 8 million kilowatts. Its tributary, the Kama, will have four dams. The Dnieper is scheduled to have more than a dozen installations, with an aggregate production of 3 million kilowatts from a total 300-foot head. The great Siberian rivers have the largest potentials, with ten dams planned for the Ob and another ten on its tributary, the Irtysh, designed to generate 16 million kilowatts. The Yenisei and the Angara together are to have a dozen dams with a combined output of 33 million kilowatts. Equally ambitious projects are designed for the Lena and the Amur.

The proposed program is on a truly gigantic scale. Dams near Kuibyshev and Volgograd on the Volga each generate over 2 million kilowatts. On the Angara River, fed by the constant flow from Lake Baikal, the Bratsk dam generates 4.5 million kilowatts. Three stations on the Yenisei will be even larger. Decades may elapse before these developments are completed, but the availability of this power, plus nearby coal and iron, makes large-scale industry possible.

METALS

Iron-ore reserves are very large, but the impressive totals include numerous deposits which are low in iron and high in undesirable arsenic, sulfur, zinc, or silica, or are too re-

Giant hydroelectric developments are present on every large river. This is the plant at Volgograd (formerly Stalingrad), where the capacity reaches 2,415,000 kilowatts, the largest in the world when constructed. (*S. Kurunin, courtesy Soviet Embassy, Washington*)

mote for present development. The average metallic content of deposits currently in production is only 37 per cent, so that many ores need to be concentrated and sintered before smelting. The mineral composition ranges from inferior limonitic bog ores to high-grade hematite and magnetite. If the totals presented by Soviet geologists are correct, the U.S.S.R. may have as much iron as the rest of the world together; quality and usability are other matters. Only a small part of the reserves are in the actually measured or proved category.

In 1913, reserves of iron ore were thought to total 16 billion metric tons; by 1960 intensive prospecting had raised the overall total to 200 billion metric tons. While low-grade iron ore is almost limitless, high-grade reserves in many of the presently producing areas may be exhausted by the end of the twentieth century. Whereas the bulk of Soviet coal lies in Siberia, most of the iron appears to be in Soviet Europe.

Deposits are grouped in a few localities: the high-grade Krivoi Rog and inferior Kerch areas in the Ukraine and Crimea; the problematical ores of the Kursk magnetic anomaly; the brown ores south and east of Moscow; numerous occurrences in the Urals, notably the

magnetite at Magnitogorsk and Nizhni Tagil; deposits south of the Kuznetsk Basin and in Kazakstan; undeveloped reserves around Lake Baikal; and scattered deposits in the Far East.

Krivoi Rog in the southern Ukraine has long been the leading center of iron mining. The ore is a Pre-Cambrian mixture of hematite, altered martite, and magnetite. In origin and smelting problems it resembles the deposits near Lake Superior. The iron in the martite averages 63 per cent, and in the hematite 51 per cent; the magnetite and brown ores both carry 58 per cent iron. In addition there are large deposits of iron-bearing quartzite.

Near Kerch at the eastern end of Crimea are deposits of brown oolitic, manganiferous, and phosphatic ores. Reserves are large, but the metallic content is only 37 per cent iron.

The Kursk magnetic anomaly lies between Moscow and Kharkov. Compass deviations have been known since 1874, but high-grade hematite and siderite ores were discovered only in 1931; most of the huge reserves are low-grade quartzites, and if all the deposits prove to be workable, this may be one of the largest iron-ore bodies on earth.

South and east of Moscow, notably at Lipetsk and Tula, are sedimentary brown

Giant excavators and conveyor belts remove 500 cubic meters of overburden an hour from the Kursk iron-ore deposits, among the world's largest reserves. (*D. Kozlov, courtesy Soviet Embassy, Washington*)

The Novo Lipetsk steel mills use ore from the Kursk deposits. The plant is a fully integrated operation, with a coke-chemical complex, blast furnaces, and continuous strip-rolling mills. (*Courtesy Soviet Embassy, Washington*)

hematite ores, low in quality but easily worked and close to the market.

Ural iron, which has been known since 1702, is found in scores of localities. The Urals hold second place in ore production. The largest development is at Magnitogorsk in the south, where large-scale operations started in 1931. Much of the ore is magnetite, and the best has a metallic content of 55 to 66 per cent. The oldest and second-most important center is Nizhni Tagil.

When the Kuznetsk coal field was developed, no nearby iron was known, but sizable deposits of magnetite have been developed in the Gornaya Shoria, a mountainous region to the south. The ore is formed by replacement and has an iron content of under 45 per cent. Of

similar importance are the ores found near Karaganda during the Second World War.

East of Lake Baikal, ore is mined near Petrovsk-Zabaikal and in the Amur valley both near the mouth and in the Little Khingan Mountains. Iron is also present in the Angara-Ilim area west of Lake Baikal.

The production of iron ore grew from 9.3 million metric tons in 1913 to 40 million in 1950, and reached 100 million in 1960. Its utilization is considered in the next chapter.

Manganese is one of the most essential of all ferrometals, since it is required as a deoxidizing agent in the manufacture of steel. The Soviet Union leads the world in reserves and usually in production. The largest deposit is at Nikopol in the southern Ukraine, but the ore at Chiatury in Georgia is of higher grade and is largely produced for export. Manganese is also mined in the Urals, in Kazakhstan, and west of Krasnoyarsk. The Nikopol ore is a laterite deposit developed above crystallines, and buried by Quaternary sands. The manganese layer is from 4 to 12 feet thick.

Copper reserves are reported to be very large, but the quality of the ore is so low that the Union is partly dependent on imported supplies. Output has risen since the Second World War but has not kept pace with the demand. Reserves in 1959 were reported to total 35.2 million tons but with no reference to quality. Many deposits contain less than 1 per cent copper. Half of this total lies in the Kazakh S.S.R., 15 per cent each in the Urals and the Uzbek S.S.R., and 10 per cent in the Armenian S.S.R. Most deposits are low-grade oxide ores.

Production is centered north of Lake Balkhash at Kounrad, west of the lake at Djezkazgan, and also to the east; at several locations in the Urals; at Norilak near the lower Yenisei; and in Armenia.

The leading mines are at Kounrad near the north shore of Lake Balkhash, where there are porphyritic deposits with about 1 per cent copper, and farther west at the richer Djezkazgan deposits. The Urals were once the principal copper area, with numerous deposits of varied types, chiefly pyrite. Ore bodies are found over a distance of 500 miles from Krasnouralsk in the north to Orsk in the south.

Lead and zinc reserves are extensive. Important areas are Ordzhonikidze in northern Caucasia, Ridder in the Altai Mountains, Transbaikalia, and the Maritime Province.

Aluminum was once regarded as a deficit metal because the known bauxite deposits were limited and too poor to work. The metal is secured from unsatisfactory ores at Tikhvin east of Leningrad, from large deposits in the northern Urals at Kabakovsk, and in the southern Urals at Kamensk. Huge nepheline deposits in the Kola Peninsula are also worked for aluminum. Despite inferior deposits, the Soviet Union is a major producer.

Nickel is mined in the central and southern Urals, at Norilsk near the lower Yenisei, and in the Kola Peninsula. The output is barely adequate for domestic needs but enables the Union to rank third in world output, following Canada and New Caledonia.

Gold has long been known in Siberia and the Urals, both as placer and lode deposits. Few production figures are available, but estimates place the annual total between 5 and 10 million ounces. The Union appears to hold second place to the Union of South Africa, followed by Canada. The most important areas are along the upper Lena, the Aldan, and upper Kolyma Rivers in northeastern Siberia. Other gold-mining centers are scattered through eastern Siberia, Soviet Middle Asia, the Urals, and the Caucasus.

Platinum production in czarist Russia supplied one-third of the world's supply, largely from ultrabasic rocks near Nizhni Tagil in the Urals, well known for a century; but production has declined.

Chromium is obtained from low-grade ores at Sarany in the Urals and high-grade deposits at Kempirsai in Kazakhstan. The annual production places the U.S.S.R. alongside Turkey and South Africa. Chromium is exported for refractory, chemical, and alloy purposes.

Tin is found east of Lake Baikal and in Kazakhstan, but production is negligible. Tungsten is mined in the same general area.

NONMETALS

In addition to a wide variety of the usual nonmetallic minerals, the Soviet Union has fabulously large deposits of two uncommon substances: apatite and potassium salts. Each has been developed with dramatic rapidity. In both cases resources and production lead the world.

Apatite is a source of phosphate, important as a fertilizer. Phosphate occurs infrequently as mineral apatite but more commonly in phosphatic limestone. Soviet deposits of apatite are located near Kirovsk north of the Arctic Circle in the Khibin Mountains of the Kola Peninsula, and are a magmatic segregation from nepheline syenite. Several million tons are mined yearly. Ore reserves are estimated at 2 billion tons. The mine involves miles of underground galleries, fully electrified, and ordinary freight trains carry out the ore from the heart of the mountain. The high-grade fertilizers obtained from the apatite are of vital importance in Soviet agricultural expansion. From the associated nepheline is produced soda and aluminum.

Potash is secured at Solikamsk on the western slope of the northern Urals. Common salt had been known for three centuries, but potassium and magnesium salts and bromine were not found until 1925. Reserves of potassium salts are estimated at 15 billion tons, and those of magnesium salts at 18 billion tons. There are still larger deposits of common salt, unworked.

Asbestos has been secured from Asbest in the Urals near Sverdlovsk since 1889. The fiber occurs in serpentinized peridotite as in Quebec and Rhodesia. Similar deposits are present in the Altai-Sayan Mountains. Ural reserves are estimated at 20 million tons of fiber longer than 0.7 millimeter, and the production is more than adequate for all domestic needs. Much of the fiber is short, but the percentage of long fiber is reported to be greater than in Canada. The Union is second in world output. Talc and soapstone deposits in the Urals are also large.

Magnesite occurs in large deposits near Sverdlovsk and Chelyabinsk. The output supplies domestic needs and provides a large export to western Europe.

Industrial salt is available in abundance. There are deposits at Solikamsk, along the Emba River, and in the Donets Basin. Salt and other chemicals are extracted from the Caspian Sea water at Kara-Bougaz.

Gems and semiprecious stones have been secured from the Urals for centuries, including emerald, beryl, amethyst, topaz, and massive blocks of malachite. Kaolin production is centered in the Ukraine. Fire clays are present in the Moscow Coal Basin and in the Ukraine. Mercury is available in the Donets Basin and in the Urals. Graphite is abundant, with a large production near the northern Yenisei, in the Urals, and in the Ukraine.

Radioactive minerals are present in the Lake Baikal-Aldan area and in Middle Asia, but information as to reserves and production is limited. As far as is known, Soviet resources of uranium are inferior to those of Africa and North America.

45 Socialist Economy

Manufacturing / Agriculture / Transportation / Soviet Prospects

MANUFACTURING

The Soviet Union aims to be the most powerful industrial nation in the world, and in terms of mineral resources alone this may be a possibility. When one considers the limited progress under czarist Russia, and the fact that post-revolutionary development did not regain this level until 1926, the audacity of such a goal is obvious.

The first Five-Year Plan began in 1928, but the Second World War brought such widespread devastation that the damage was not repaired until 1950. Yet by 1960 the U.S.S.R. led all Europe and held second rank in the world in the production of basic industrial commodities, and had achieved a gross national product approximately half that of the United States. The human cost of development under a totalitarian regime is quite another matter.

Heavy industry holds a high place in Soviet economy. Industrial development calls for a concentration on the mining of many minerals and the production of power from coal, peat, oil, gas, and hydroelectricity. Since producer goods have held priority over consumer products, primary attention has been given to blast furnaces and smelters, the fabrication of steel and other metals into railway equipment and heavy machinery, plants for basic chemicals and fertilizers, and the output of military equipment.

Blast furnaces and steel mills are concentrated in three areas: the eastern Ukraine, the Urals, and central Siberia. Outlying centers of iron production include Tula and Lipetsk south of Moscow, Volgograd on the Volga, Tashkent, Petrovsk-Zabaikal east of Lake Baikal, and Komsomolsk on the Amur. Steel production based on pig iron and scrap also takes place in Leningrad, Moscow, and elsewhere.

Light industry includes a wide variety of processing, from wood products, foods, and processed agricultural items such as rubber and sugar, to textiles and services.

Over 75 per cent of all manufacturing takes place within Soviet Europe, largely around Moscow, in the Ukraine, and in the Urals, while Siberia and Middle Asia each account for about 10 per cent of the national total.[1] These figures for the magnitude of manufacturing operations represent an evaluation of the number of workers and the amount of fixed capital involved.

Moscow leads all other industrial centers, with 8 per cent of the national output. Manufacturing activities cover a wide range, largely in the category of light industry. This includes machine construction, motor vehicles, aircraft, railroad equipment, textiles, foods, chemicals, wood working and publishing. If the area is enlarged to include Gorki and other related cities, such as Yaroslavl, Ivanovo, and Tula, Moscow's place in the national total rises to

[1] Richard E. Lonsdale and John H. Thompson: "A Map of the U.S.S.R.'s Manufacturing," *Economic Geography*, XXXVI (1960), 36–52.

18 per cent, and production includes steel and automobiles.

The central position of the Moscow region with its unsurpassed radial rail pattern has helped to make it the leading manufacturing center for many decades. Local raw materials are limited, but the inferior local coal is supplemented by hydroelectric power cables and oil pipelines from the Volga. Moscow has steel mills without blast furnaces.

The eastern Ukraine ranks close to the Moscow-Gorki manufacturing region, with 14 per cent of the total national output. In place of light industry, this is the great center for basic production of steel, cement, and chemicals. The area includes the Donets Coal Basin with its centers at Donetsk, Makeyevka, and Lugansk, and the iron ore mines at Krivoi Rog, Kursk, and Kerch. Each of these cities has large blast furnaces and steel mills, and mills have also developed at midway locations such as Taganrog and the hydroelectric plant at Zaporozhe on the Dnieper. In addition there is manganese at Nikopol, and important supplies of mercury and natural gas. The Donets coal fields and the iron mines of Krivoi Rog, Kursk, and Kerch, form a quadrilateral, roughly 200 miles on a side.

The cities of Kharkov, Zhdanov, and Rostov-on-Don are other manufacturing centers, the first two specializing in steel, with agricultural products at the third. In addition to the refining and fabrication of steel, the eastern Ukraine is a producer of cement and chemicals. Few industrial areas on earth are more fortunate in

Soviet Production[1]

Commodity	1913	1940	1960	1965 plan
Coal (in million metric tons)	29.2	165.9	514.0	600–612
Petroleum (in million metric tons)	8.3	—	148.0	230–240
Electricity (in billion kilowatt hours)	1.9	48.3	292.0	500–520
Steel (in million metric tons)	4.3	18.3	65.3	86–91
Copper (in thousand metric tons)	31.0	161.0	416.5 (1959)	772
Mineral fertilizers (in million metric tons)	69.0	3,027.0	13,800.0	—

[1] Official Soviet data.

This tube-rolling mill in Azerbaidzhan makes pipe for Soviet oil fields. Soviet steel production ranks second only to that of the United States. (*Y. Yakovlov, courtesy Soviet Embassy, Washington*)

the proximity of high-grade raw materials to power. The Ukraine's proportionate rank in Soviet steel economy is declining because of the growth of new areas to the east, but it should long remain in first place. As the Soviet Union becomes an exporter of heavy machinery, this will probably be the chief producing area since it is near tidewater.

The Ural region ranks third in manufacturing, with 12 per cent of the national total. While the Ukraine is an old industrial area, the Urals have grown rapidly since the Second World War and may come to occupy first place in heavy industry. Great reserves of iron, copper, aluminum, chromium, ferroalloys, and potassium are present, but unfortunately the nearby coal does not make suitable metallur-

gical coke so that it is necessary to transport coal from Karaganda or Kuznetsk many hundreds of miles to the east. The great oil fields between the Volga and the Urals are an additional source of power.

The leading manufacturing cities of the Urals are Sverdlovsk, Chelyabinsk, Perm, Ufa, Magnitogorsk, Zlatoust, and Nizhni Tagil. Iron and steel are produced in scores of localities, led by Magnitogorsk where eight giant blast furnaces enable it to rival Gary, Indiana, as one of the leading steel centers on earth.

The Volga River ties together a number of important manufacturing cities, such as Kuibyshev, Kazan, Volgograd, and Saratov, which among them account for 5 per cent of the Union's output. The importance of the region is due rather to easy transport and nearby markets than to local raw materials. Along the Volga move great amounts of coal, oil, lumber, and grain. Volgograd has steel mills where both coal and ore must come side by side along the same railway from the Ukraine, but scrap and finished products may move along the river. Some of the world's largest hydroelectric plants provide cheap power, as do the nearby oil fields. Machine building, oil refining, food processing, transport equipment, and the manufacture of building materials are important.

Leningrad is an isolated region, which owes some of its present importance to the heritage of czarist days when it was the chief entrepôt for foreign goods and became a center of skilled labor. The city accounts for 5 per cent of the nation's manufacturing, largely for precision machinery, electrical goods, instruments, chemicals, publishing, textiles, and clothing.

These five manufacturing regions: Moscow-Gorki, the eastern Ukraine, the Urals, the Volga, and Leningrad, yield half of Soviet production, and form the core of the industrial belt. In these regions manufacturing has created an industrial landscape comparable to that of similar areas in Western Europe or Eastern North America. Along with scattered centers such as Kiev, Odessa, Minsk, Riga, Voronezh, Lvov, and Arkhangelsk, Soviet Europe accounts for 78 per cent of the Union's output.

Siberian manufacturing is concentrated in three areas: the Kuznetsk Basin with 4 per cent of the overall total, the Far East with 2 per cent, and Lake Baikal with 1 per cent. These percentages will presumably increase with the development of Siberian resources and the needs of local markets. Outlying Siberian cities of importance include Omsk, Krasnoyarsk, and Karaganda.

The Kuznetsk Coal Basin contains excellent metallurgical coal, but the iron ore is of low grade. Novo Kuznetsk is famous for its steel mills as is Novosibirsk for its machine industry. This is entirely a postrevolutionary development, initiated as part of the Magnito-gorsk-Kuznetsk metallurgical combine. Steel and machinery make this the third-most important center of heavy industry in the country.

Most manufacturing in the Far East is related to local raw materials and local markets, chiefly at Khabarovsk, Vladivostok, and Komsomolsk.

Irkutsk is a growing center in the Baikal area, with great amounts of electricity available along the Angara River; in the decades to come this region may become one of the Soviet Union's most important manufacturing areas.

Soviet Middle Asia accounts for 7 per cent of the Union's manufacturing, about evenly divided between the Transcaucasus region and scattered areas east of the Caspian. Industrial operations include the production and processing of oil and mineral resources, as well as textile and food industries related to agricultural products. Baku, Tbilisi, Yerevan, and Tashkent are the major manufacturing cities.

The cities listed in the preceding paragraphs include all those where the magnitude of manufacturing exceeds 0.5 per cent of the national total. When plotted on a map, it is clear that large-scale factory production is strikingly localized in a half dozen regions, one-third of it in the areas around Moscow and in the eastern Ukraine. Vast areas are essentially devoid of manufacturing plants, so that one might fly for hours without seeing a factory. Manufacturing is increasingly being dispersed, and the center of gravity which is somewhere near the Volga is moving eastward.

AGRICULTURE

Agriculture has always presented a problem in Russian economy. Despite the great size of the country, much of the Soviet Union has limited food-producing possibilities. Production has never adequately met the needs of the people; shortages and even famine have been recurrent.

In its environmental setting, the pattern of agriculture is related to factors such as sunshine and temperature, the hydrologic regime, soil fertility, and relief. Crops of some kind may be grown almost anywhere, but the limitations increase as the agricultural frontier advances into areas of short growing season, limited and variable rainfall, unfavorable soil, and steep slopes. The contribution of geography to the evaluation of agriculture is to emphasize the environmental assets and limitations, and to stress the marked regional contrasts. Kamchatka is not the Ukraine, nor is any single area to be regarded as typical of all Russia.

As man's technology develops, new methods are developed for more efficiently utilizing and modifying natural restrictions. Land that was once inhospitable may prove productive under a new economy. Great efforts have been made under the socialist regime to push cultivation into marginal areas, and with some success.

The steady growth of the Soviet population has fortunately been matched by a considerable increase in the total agricultural supply. This has been achieved through additional acreage, new crops, higher yields obtained from better varieties of seed, a wider use of fertilizers, and increased mechanization.

During the period from 1913 to 1960, the sown area nearly doubled, increasing from 118

to 195 million hectares, but some of this additional farm land represents new lands of inferior productivity. During the same decades, population rose by 75 per cent, so that the man-food balance has not been greatly changed. Irrigated lands tripled in the same period.

Crop yields per acre during this period increased slightly in the case of grains, potatoes, flax, and sugar beets, but the yields for each product were less than half of the American averages in 1960. Soviet cotton yields more than doubled, largely because of the widespread use of irrigation.

While the total number of people engaged in agriculture has declined, the widespread use of machinery has increased their efficiency and has raised labor productivity. A major decrease in the number of horses has released considerable land for increased human food.

A further factor in agricultural improvement relates to better yields through the introduction of new crops such as hybrid corn. The total acreage of corn raised for grain quadrupled from 1913 to 1960, and if silage is included, the increase is even greater.

Soviet farming is of two types. The first category is the collective farm or *kolkhoz* where the title and management theoretically rests with the farmers, and the residual profits, if any,

Soviet Crop Area [1]

(in million hectares)

Crop	1913	1930	1940	1950	1960
Wheat	33.0	32.8	40.3	38.5	63.0
Rye	28.2	28.9	23.1	23.6	17.1
Oats	19.1	17.9	20.2	16.2	9.6
Corn	2.2	3.7	3.6	4.8	8.7
All grains	104.6	101.8	110.5	102.9	115.6
Sunflower seeds	1.0	3.4	3.6	3.59	3.9
Sugar beets	0.7	1.0	1.2	1.3	2.8
Cotton	0.7	1.6	2.1	2.3	2.2
Flax for fiber	1.3	1.8	2.1	1.9	1.6
Total sown area	118.2	127.2	150.4	146.3	

[1] United Nations, Food and Agricultural Organization: *Production Yearbooks*.

Short growing seasons and inadequate rainfall handicap Soviet agriculture, as is suggested by this poor crop of wheat in Azerbaidzhan. Mechanization is widespread. (*Tass*)

are shared by each member according to his skill and labor.

Crops are sold to the state in compulsory amounts and at fixed prices which often have little relation to the actual costs of production. Where the farmer's resulting income falls below the proper value of his labor he thus pays an indirect tax to support the state. Much of the cost of rapid industrialization during the early Five-Year Plans was carried by the farmer in this way. So long as incentive remains low, the collectivized peasant remains inefficient.

Whereas there were once 200,000 collective farms, consolidation has reduced the number to less than one-fourth of the former figure.

The second type of agriculture is the state farm or *sovkhoz,* where the government owns and manages everything and pays fixed wages, irrespective of the harvest. State farms have taken over many collectives, and also account for much of the newly cultivated land; as a result they include more than one-fourth of the total crop area. Sovkhoz tend to be large in size, and usually specialize in one or two prod-

MAP OF NATURAL VEGETATION AND CULTIVATED LAND

Five vegetation zones cross the Soviet Union from coast to coast. In the north are two boreal lands with short summers, the tundra and the taiga, or coniferous forest. To the south are two dry lands, the steppe and the desert. Mixed deciduous and hardwood forests occupy an intermediate triangular area in the west.

Agriculture occupies an area carved out of the southern taiga, the mixed forests, and the more humid steppe. Each dot represents 5,000 hectares, or approximately 12,500 acres. (*Data from Great Soviet World Atlas, adjusted for 1960 conditions*)

T U N
CONIFEROUS
MIXED & DECIDUOUS
STEPPE
M&D
M
DESERT
D
M
M
M
M

0   200   400   600   800
MILES

Cressey—Asia's Lands and Peoples

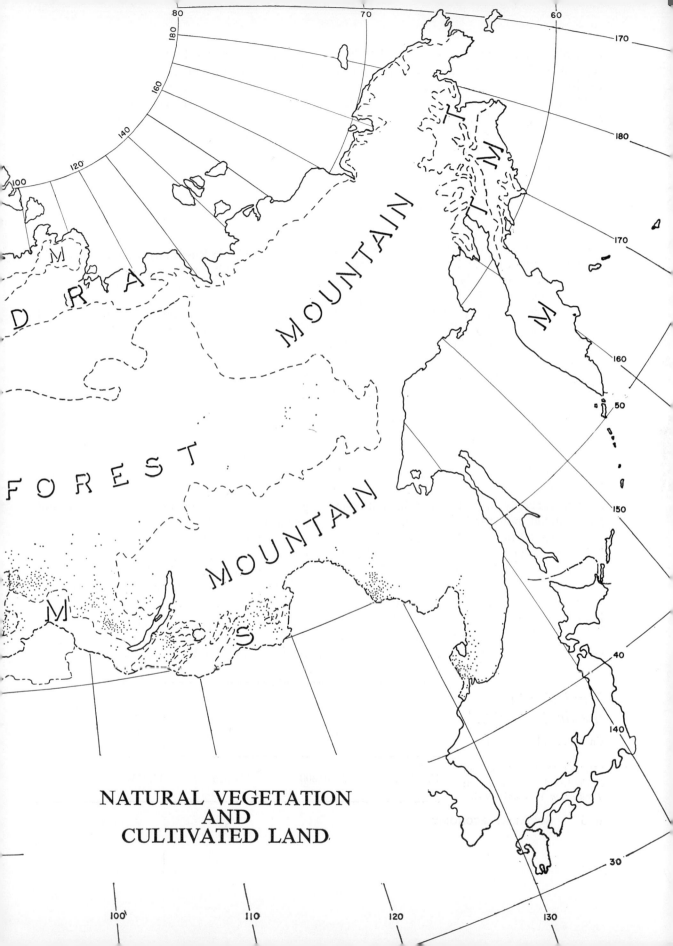

NATURAL VEGETATION
AND
CULTIVATED LAND

ucts. Since state farms are considered to be a superior socialist form of production, they tend to displace the collective farms.

Most farmers in both situations also have a small garden plot of their own, "an acre and a cow," where the produce is their personal property. If there is a surplus beyond their own needs it may be sold on the open market. Private farms have ceased to exist.

In spite of the size of the Soviet Union, much of it is valueless for agriculture. Out of the total area of 8½ million square miles, forests cover 40 per cent, deserts and wastelands occupy 35 per cent, and pastures account for 15 per cent, leaving only 10 per cent as potentially arable. Parts of the latter are unproductive because of poor soils, poor drainage, poor climate, unsatisfactory relief, or the custom of letting dry areas remain fallow in alternate years. Despite the considerable expansion of cropland during recent years, the area actually cultivated or in tree crops covers less than 8 per cent of the entire country.

About a quarter of the harvested land lies in areas which were once forested; they have, for the most part, short summers and rather poor soils devoted to rye, oats, potatoes and dairying. The remaining cropland occurs in the steppe, generally with fertile soils but marginal rainfall, now used for wheat.

Virtually all the good land west of the Urals is in use. Some additional acreage may be obtained through draining swamps, clearing wood lots, and cultivating hillsides, but the prospects are modest. To press cultivation farther north is to invite the prospect of crop failure due to early frost; to advance southward into the dry steppe is at the risk of drought.

Siberia offers the best possibilities for additional cropland, and here was the site of the ambitious virgin-lands program of the 1950s. While large areas of acceptable soils remain untilled, all such areas receive precarious rainfall; rich harvests may be obtained in fortunate years, but repeated failures are inevitable.

In terms of total population and total food supply, the Soviet Union remains a crowded country, overpopulated in terms of its present agricultural productivity. As Jasny has written: [2]

Future gains in Russian agricultural output will have to be largely on the poor soils of central and northern European Russia. With a great deal of manure, made available by the development of a large domestic market for animal products, and with heavy applications of commercial fertilizer, these lands may gradually be made to produce almost twice the yields now obtained in the "rich" Ukraine. But because of the cold climate those lands will always be inferior to similar lands further west, such as in Poland or Germany.

In the area west of the Urals, agricultural land as a whole rises to 45 per cent and, excluding the north of Soviet Europe, the percentage becomes 65, which is even higher than in the settled parts of several Western European countries. Little undeveloped good land remains south of Leningrad. In this area, the rural population ranges from 65 to over 250 per square mile, as against 25 to 65 in the Mississippi valley. Soviet Asia has but 2 per cent under cultivation, or 6 per cent in any agricultural use.

[2] Naum Jasny: *The Socialized Agriculture of the U.S.S.R.*, Stanford, Calif.: Stanford University Press (1949), 132. Quoted by permission.

Land Use in the Soviet Union [1] (in thousand hectares)	Total area	Arable land incl. fallow and orchards	Irrigated land	Forest and woodlands
[1] United Nations, Food and Agricultural Organization: *Production Yearbook*, 1960. U.S.S.R.	2,240,300	221,366	11,223	880,317

Mechanical cotton pickers are used on the Kirov Collective Farm near Tashkent in the Uzbek Soviet Socialist Republic. (*I. Gluberzon, courtesy Soviet Embassy, Washington*)

Tundra covers over 1 million square miles, and the existing taiga forest accounts for nearly 4 million square miles. Neither area offers important agricultural possibilities on account of climate and soil. Desert and semidesert land in the south occupies 2 million square miles where cultivation seems out of the question. Notable developments have occurred in limited areas but are not capable of indefinite expansion.

Optimistic agriculturalists place the limit of feasible cultivation near the Arctic Circle, but restrictions of acid soils and short growing seasons give little expectation that normal agriculture will ever displace the Siberian taiga. Inadequate rainfall and alkaline soils are obstacles in the arid south, and irrigation possibilities are limited.

Climate, natural vegetation, and soil all emphasize the significance of the agricultural wedge from Leningrad and Odessa eastward to Irkutsk, with outliers toward the Pacific. This triangle is far from regular, and there are other farm areas in the Caucasus, Soviet Middle Asia, and the Far East, but its general pattern is obvious. The most important part of the Soviet Union lies toward the Atlantic rather than the Pacific.

During the period from 1913 to 1960, the sown area rose from 262,500,000 acres to 480,000,000 acres. This increase was obtained from virgin steppeland in Siberia, the irrigation of dry lands east of the Volga and in Middle Asia, the drainage of marshes in Byelorussia, and the plowing of pasture or forage land no longer needed because of mechanization. It should be emphasized that most of this added farm land came through the reclamation of poor land within the established agricultural triangle rather than by expansion along its frontier.

Large possibilities for future expansion of cropland seem doubtful except in the steppe. Despite the country's vast size, much of the land must remain agriculturally unproductive. Increased harvests will follow higher crop yields and better utilization rather than added farm acreage. Prior to the revolution of 1917, part of the land always lay idle under the rotating three-crop system of cultivation, pasture, and fallow.

The total of 480 million acres under cultivation (1960) for 208 million people (1959) gives an average of 2.1 acres per person. This compares with 2.5 acres in the United States, or 0.3 in China. The United States and the Union of Soviet Socialist Republics have nearly the same crop area, but the respective rural populations are 54,054,425 (1960) and 109,-098,000 (1959).

Such comparisons need to be understood in terms of soil and climate. The agricultural potentials of the United States are much more attractive. So great is the difference that it seems doubtful whether the people of the Soviet Union can ever be as well fed as those of America.

Famines, largely due to erratic rainfall, have long been the curse of Russia. Drought and the effects of revolutionary Communism in 1921 to 1922 caused the death of 5,250,000 people. Famine occurred again in 1932 to 1933, when inadequate rainfall was combined with excessive government grain collections and peasant sabotage.

New varieties of wheat have steadily pushed the area of cultivation northward to the vicinity of Leningrad, Yaroslavl, and Gorki. Grain crops are even grown near the Arctic Circle. Winter wheat predominates in the Ukraine, and spring wheat is grown east of the Don and in Siberia where the autumn is dry and snowfall light.

Technical crops have received special attention. Cotton production increased fourfold between 1913 and 1960, largely in the irrigated lands of Soviet Middle Asia and the Transcaucasus. Flax has long been important in Byelorussia, as well as around Moscow and Leningrad. Sugar beets are grown in great quantity in the Ukraine, around Kursk, in the Caucasus, Middle Asia, and the Far East.

Subtropical crops such as grapes, tea, oranges, and other citrus fruit are increasing in the Transcaucasus.

The U.S.S.R. appears to lead the world in the total production of rye, barley, oats, potatoes, flax, and sugar beets. Wheat production may also hold first place; uncertainty about the figures is due to the statistics for China.

TRANSPORTATION

The Soviet Union is an enormous country, and the problem of unity is related to transport facilities. Accessibility varies widely from region to region; in the southwest there is a closely spaced network of railways, but in the northeast travel is restricted to rivers many miles apart. Roads are traditionally poor; frequently no more than a slightly improved track

The Trans-Siberian Express covers 6,284 miles from the Polish frontier to Vladivostok. This is the station at Novosibirsk, 2,000 miles east of Moscow. (*Tass*)

which wanders across the country. Air travel has revolutionized accessibility, but in 1960 the Aeroflot timetable listed only 76 cities with regularly scheduled services.

All parts of the Union west of the Volga and south of Leningrad lie within 35 miles of a railway. The most closely spaced rail net centers on the Donets Coal Basin and the related deposits of iron ore. The only other area with a well-developed network is in the central Urals. A coarse grid is developing in southwestern Siberia; elsewhere many areas are hundreds of miles from a railway.

Express trains on the Trans-Siberian Railway cross the continent from the Polish frontier to Vladivostok in 9½ days; or one may travel by rail from Odessa on the Black Sea to Murmansk on the Arctic Ocean in 3½ days. But to cross Siberia from Mongolia northward along the Yenisei by boat requires two weeks. The Union's continental proportions are obvious.

The international isolation of the U.S.S.R. is suggested by the limited number of railways which cross the frontier. East of the Black Sea only six lines lead into Turkey, Iran, Mongolia, and China, none of them offering daily services.

Railways play a larger transport role than in the United States, carrying nearly 90 per cent of the total freight traffic and 75 per cent of all the passengers. Their length grew from 36,350 miles in 1913 to 77,520 miles in 1960. While Soviet railways measure but one-third of the length of those in the United States, the total ton-miles of freight may be the largest in the world. This is due to the intensity with which the rail system is operated and the relative unimportance of traffic by inland waterways, road, and pipeline.

Soviet railways have a gauge of 5 feet in contrast to the standard gauge of 4 feet 8½ inches used in Europe and North America. By 1965 about two-thirds of all railway mileage is to be served by electric or diesel locomotives.

Many rivers are navigable, but most of them are frozen during one-third to one-half of the year; only a few are of more than local importance. Unfortunately most rivers flow in the wrong direction, ending in ice-blocked oceans or landlocked seas. How different the country would be, irrespective of government, if there were a great east–west waterway or a navigable river which reached an open sea!

Regularly operating waterways total 80,000 miles, but they carry less than one-tenth of the commerce moved by rail. Timber in rafts or barges accounts for half of the freight, while minerals and bulk commodities such as grain or fuel make up most of the rest.

The Volga is the leading waterway and forms Russia's Main Street; its traffic accounts for two-thirds of the national waterborne total. Oil and coal move upstream; wood moves downriver. The closest competitor to the Volga is the combined Neva and Svir Rivers which link Lakes Ladoga and Onega with Leningrad and the Gulf of Finland. The great Siberian rivers, the Ob, Yenisei, Lena, and Amur, each account for only 1 or 2 per cent of the total river traffic, a fraction which indicates the sparse population and underdeveloped character of their basins.

A series of canals, generally with 10-foot draft, link the Volga with nearby waterways. The Mariinsk Canal provides a connection from the upper Volga to Lake Ladoga and Leningrad, or ships may proceed northward through the Baltic-White Sea Canal to Arkhangelsk. Moscow lies on a Volga tributary, previously unnavigable, and is now accessible via the Moscow-Volga Canal. The Volga unfortunately ends in the enclosed Caspian Sea, but by means of the Volga-Don Canal, near Volgograd, vessels may reach the Black Sea.

Maritime operations have expanded rapidly but are still of limited extent. The most interesting addition to the Soviet merchant marine during the early 1960s was made by the purchase of several large oil tankers, a reflection of the Union's increasing export of petroleum.

Seagoing vessels operate extensively in the Black and Caspian Seas, and to a lesser extent in the Baltic, Arctic, and Far East. Freight services link Odessa with Vladivostok via Suez and Panama. The distance is 13,264 miles via

The Volga is Russia's major waterway, now linked by canals with the Baltic and Black Seas. This view is at Astrakhan near the mouth. (*M. Redkin, courtesy Soviet Embassy, Washington*)

Suez or 14,177 miles through the Panama Canal. In comparison, the route from Murmansk to Vladivostok by way of the northern sea route measures 6,835 miles but is ice-free for only two months a year.

Highways have never received much attention, and very little intercity traffic moves by truck. Paved roads lead out from the major cities, but there is only the beginning of an integrated network of modern automobile highways. Many country roads are deep in mud or dust in summer and are a line of frozen ruts in winter.

The absence of bedrock in the great plains of Soviet Europe, western Siberia, and Middle Asia means that crushed rock is unavailable and restricts construction materials to sand or river gravel. This lack handicaps both highways and railways.

SOVIET PROSPECTS

How strong is Russia? Is this potentially a great nation or are there major environmental limitations? Chapter 3 on the realms of Asia concludes with a section on geostrategy in Asia, and it might be well to review the ten factors there listed as they apply to the Union of Soviet Socialist Republics. This checklist is in no sense definitive, but it does offer a survey of material assets and limitations. These components of geostrategy involve (1) location, (2) size and shape, (3) land forms, (4) climate, (5) soil, (6) accessibility, (7) boundaries, (8) relation to the ocean, (9) raw materials, and (10) people.

Where is Russia? It is clear that this is a high-latitude country, most of it deep within the largest of the continents. No other nation has so large an area within the Arctic, or is so remote from the ocean. While the map may suggest that the Union occupies a central position in Eurasia, in effective terms it is off-center for both Europe and Asia. This land-locked position is a constant, but its significance may change with developments in transportation and strategy. To appreciate Russia's continentality it is necessary to recognize the confining nature of the bordering mountains, deserts, and frozen seas.

Size and shape have obvious application to the U.S.S.R. One reason why the country survived the invasions of Napoleon, the Kaiser, and Hitler is that there was room into which she might retreat, gradually exchanging space for time. Since the country is as large as all of North America, it is clear that diverse environments and general self-sufficiency are to be expected; here is adequate living room. At the same time, great size imposes problems of domestic coherence. While the country appears compact, the true shape is to be measured in terms of effective settlement; much of Siberia is merely a series of ribbons along railroads and rivers, with vast empty areas in between.

The Soviet Union fortunately has vast areas of level land, so that agriculture proceeds with little topographic restriction in Soviet Europe and western Siberia. Unfortunately, these plains are bordered by rugged mountains on the south and east, so that nearly half of the country is too hilly or too mountainous to provide a good habitat for a dense population.

Climate presents one of Russia's great handicaps. Winters are long and so severe that little out-of-door activity is feasible. On the other hand, the high latitude means that summers have long hours of daylight, even though the sun never climbs very high in the sky. The precipitation is generally low, no more than 20 inches in many of the cultivated areas. The short growing season and the uncertainties as to rainfall and frost place serious limitations on the food supply. Millions of square miles are too cold or too dry for normal agriculture and may always have a sparse population. Other millions are underlain by permanently frozen subsoil.

Soil forms the basis of food supply, and here the story is both good and bad. Within the Union is the world's largest extent of rich chernozem soils, temptingly fertile but marginally dry. Much of the country, however, is underlain by acid podsols of modest productivity, or by unproductive tundra or desert soils. Only 600,000 square miles are cultivated, out of the $8\frac{1}{2}$ million square miles in the country at large. In purely physical terms, Soviet soils are adequate to feed her people but offer no great promise for the future.

Accessibility becomes a critical problem in a country so large as this, as has been explained in the preceding section. At least 4 million square miles are without access to modern transport facilities.

Russia's boundaries have been in flux for centuries, as the frontier has steadily moved outward. Parts of Soviet Middle Asia have been incorporated for only a century, and there are still pressures toward the Mediterranean and the Indian Ocean. The Second World War involved boundary readjustments next to Finland, the reacquisition of Estonia, Latvia, and Lithuania, the conquest of eastern Prussia and one-third of Poland, the addition of Ruthenia from Hungary and northern Bucovina from Romania, along with the annexation of southern Sakhalin and the Kurile Islands from Japan. Tanna Tuva and the Kushka area of Afghanistan were annexed in 1946. During the 1940s, the Union added 262,957 square miles with a population of 23 million. Satellites in Eastern Europe and interests in Mongolia reflect current expansionist pressures.

Maritime contacts are limited by the frozen character of the Arctic and by constricted outlets to the open Atlantic and Pacific. Although the country faces three oceans, access to the

Soviet resources have enabled the U.S.S.R. to achieve high rank in heavy industry. This is the Kirov tractor plant in the Urals. (*Sovfoto*)

high seas is nowhere easy. Only Murmansk is ice-free the year round, and it is off-center for commerce. Kaliningrad and Vladivostok can be kept open most of the winter by the use of ice breakers. Access to the Baltic or Black Seas is of limited wartime value without control of the waters around Denmark or the Bosporus. Nowhere does the Russian bear find warm water.

Mineral resources are one of the Soviets' superb assets. Rich and diversified natural wealth provides a base for expanding industry and international power. Coal, oil, iron, and a long list of basic commodities are abundant. For several the quality or location is poor, but the total reserves of fuels and metals are very impressive. No nation is more nearly self-sufficient; if resources alone could make a nation strong, the Soviet Union has what it takes.

The tenth item in this list is by far the most important. People are a nation's major asset.

Russia's population is approaching 250 million, so that the country has manpower in abundance. No natural resource can match human ingenuity. But numbers are not so important geographically as place—where people live; we thus study the population map to find why some areas are congested, others almost empty.

Soviet assets are impressive, but so too are the limitations to be overcome. Whatever its form of government, a land such as Russia will strive for the development of its domestic resources, additional food supply, freer access to the high seas, enlarged foreign trade, and national security. While the potentials are impressive, the environmental restrictions are also significant. Unless Communism is to be the wave of the future, it does not seem likely that the land of the Soviets can overtake Western Europe or North America in overall material strength or per capita welfare.

INDEX

Numbers in **boldface** type indicate illustrations

653

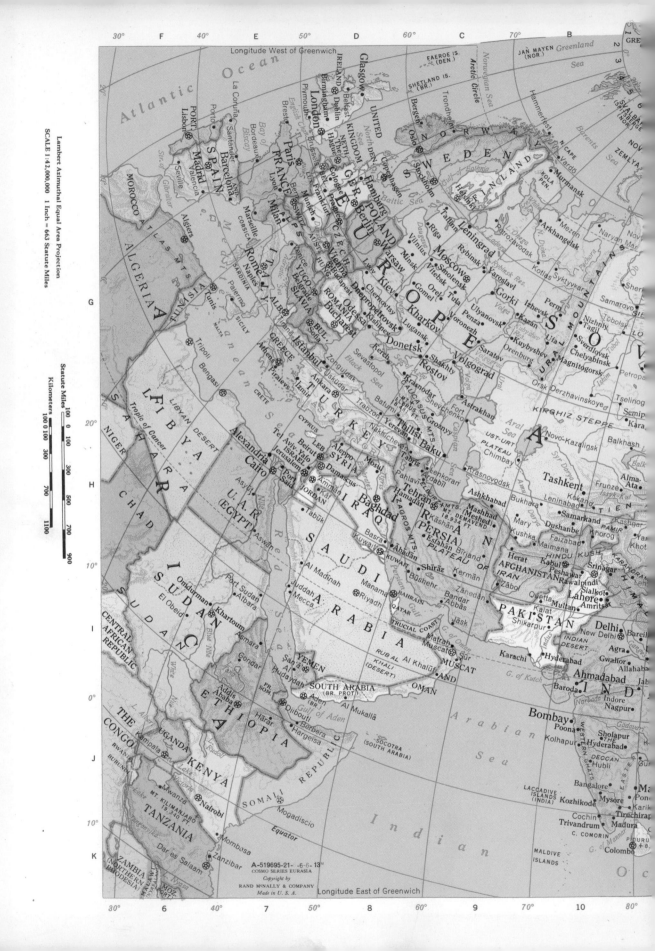